D1226337

PRENTICE HALL

Teacher's SCIENCE EXPLORER Edition

Motion, Forces, and Energy

PRENTICE HALL
Needham, Massachusetts
Upper Saddle River, New Jersey

Copyright © 2000 by Prentice-Hall, Inc., Upper Saddle River, New Jersey 07458. All rights reserved. No part of this book may be reproduced or transmitted in any form or by any means, electronic or mechanical, including photocopying, recording, or by any information storage and retrieval system, without permission in writing from the publisher. Printed in the United States of America.

ISBN 0-13-434573-8
3 4 5 6 7 8 9 10 05 04 03 02 01 00 99

PRENTICE HALL

SCIENCE EXPLORER

GET READY FOR A CONTENT-RICH, HANDS-ON EXPLORATION!

PRENTICE HALL SCIENCE EXPLORER Earth's Waters

PRENTICE HALL SCIENCE EXPLORER Motion, Forces and Energy

PRENTICE HALL SCIENCE EXPLORER Animals

15 Books In All

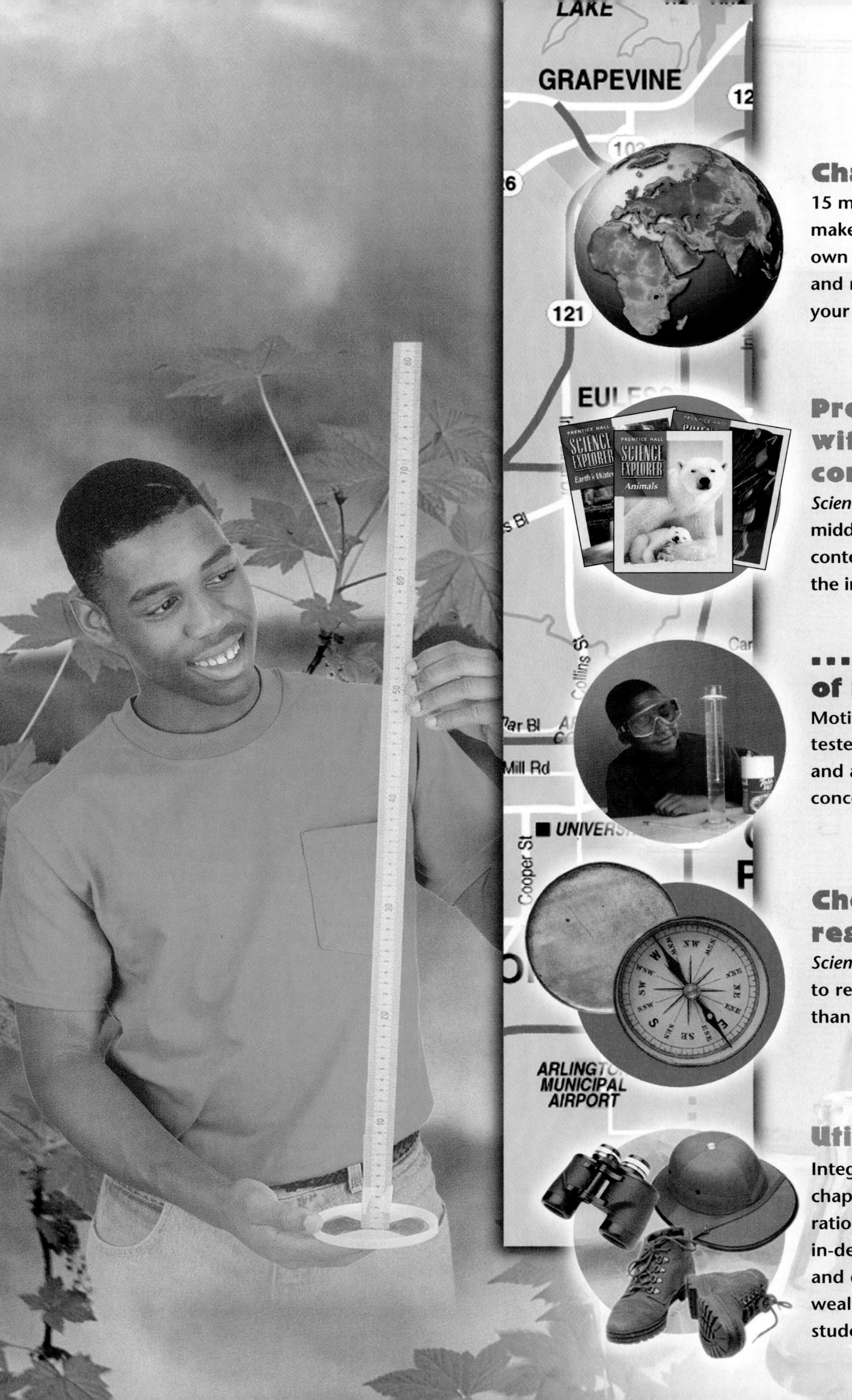

Chart your own course.

15 motivational hardcover books make it easy for you to create your own curriculum; meet local, state, and national guidelines; and teach your favorite topics in depth.

Prepare your students with rich, motivating content . . .

Science Explorer is crafted for today's middle grades student, with accessible content and in-depth coverage of all the important concepts.

. . . and a wide variety of inquiry activities.

Motivational student- and teacher-tested activities reinforce key concepts and allow students to explore science concepts for themselves.

Check your compass regularly.

Science Explorer gives you more ways to regularly check student performance than any other program available.

Utilize a variety of tools.

Integrated science sections in every chapter and Interdisciplinary Explorations in every book allow you to make in-depth connections to other sciences and disciplines. Plus, you will find a wealth of additional tools to set your students on a successful course.

Chart the course you want with 15 motivating books that easily match your curriculum.

Each book in the series contains:
- Integrated Science sections in every chapter
- Interdisciplinary Explorations for team teaching at the end of each book
- Comprehensive skills practice and application—assuring that you meet the National Science Education Standards and your local and state standards

For custom binding options, see your local sales representative.

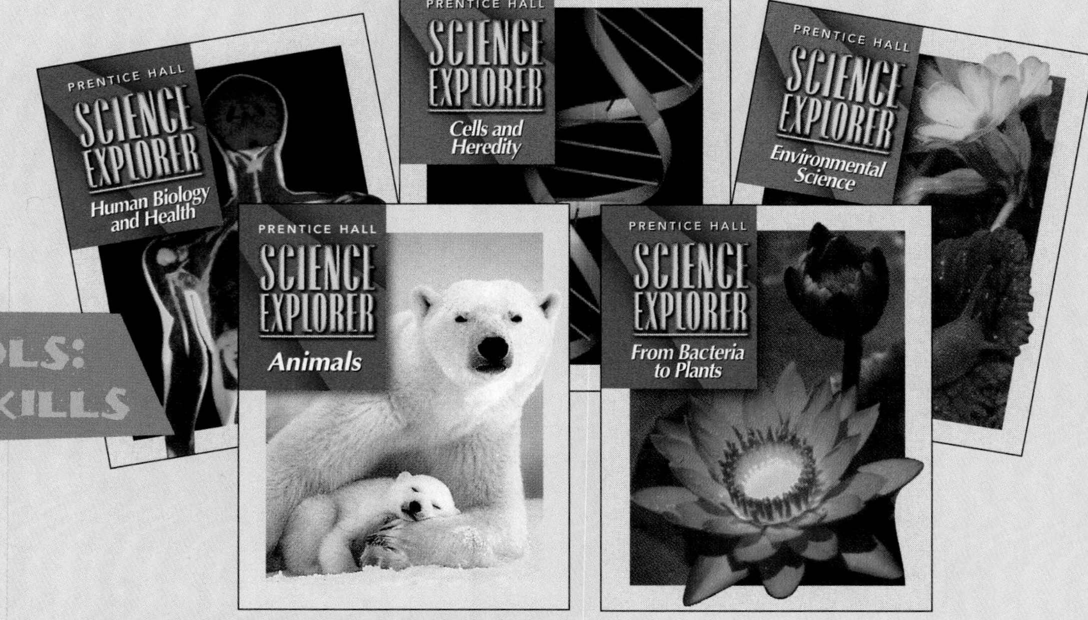

EXPLORATION TOOLS: BASIC PROCESS SKILLS

Observing
Measuring
Calculating
Classifying
Predicting
Inferring
Graphing
Creating data tables
Communicating

LIFE SCIENCE TITLES

From Bacteria to Plants
1. Living Things
2. Viruses and Bacteria
3. Protists and Fungi
4. Introduction to Plants
5. Seed Plants

Animals
1. Sponges, Cnidarians, and Worms
2. Mollusks, Arthropods, and Echinoderms
3. Fishes, Amphibians, and Reptiles
4. Birds and Mammals
5. Animal Behavior

Cells and Heredity
1. Cell Structure and Function
2. Cell Processes and Energy
3. Genetics: The Science of Heredity
4. Modern Genetics
5. Changes Over Time

Human Biology and Health
1. Healthy Body Systems
2. Bones, Muscles, and Skin
3. Food and Digestion
4. Circulation
5. Respiration and Excretion
6. Fighting Disease
7. The Nervous System
8. The Endocrine System and Reproduction

Environmental Science
1. Populations and Communities
2. Ecosystems and Biomes
3. Living Resources
4. Land and Soil Resources
5. Air and Water Resources
6. Energy Resources

 *Integrated Science sections in every chapter*

EXPLORATION TOOLS: ADVANCED PROCESS SKILLS

- **Posing questions**
- **Forming operational definitions**
- **Developing hypotheses**
- **Controlling variables**
- **Interpreting data**
- **Interpreting graphs**
- **Making models**
- **Drawing conclusions**
- **Designing experiments**

EARTH SCIENCE TITLES

Inside Earth
1. Plate Tectonics
2. Earthquakes
3. Volcanoes
4. Minerals
5. Rocks

Earth's Changing Surface
1. Mapping Earth's Surface
2. Weathering and Soil Formation
3. Erosion and Deposition
4. A Trip Through Geologic Time

Earth's Waters
1. Earth: The Water Planet
2. Fresh Water
3. Freshwater Resources
4. Ocean Motions
5. Ocean Zones

Weather and Climate
1. The Atmosphere
2. Weather Factors
3. Weather Patterns
4. Climate and Climate Change

Astronomy
1. Earth, Moon, and Sun
2. The Solar System
3. Stars, Galaxies, and the Universe

PHYSICAL SCIENCE TITLES

Chemical Building Blocks
1. An Introduction to Matter
2. Changes in Matter
3. Elements and the Periodic Table
4. Carbon Chemistry

Chemical Interactions
1. Chemical Reactions
2. Atoms and Bonding
3. Acids, Bases, and Solutions
4. Exploring Materials

Motion, Forces, and Energy
1. Motion
2. Forces
3. Forces in Fluids
4. Work and Machines
5. Energy and Power
6. Thermal Energy and Heat

Electricity and Magnetism
1. Magnetism and Electromagnetism
2. Electric Charges and Current
3. Electricity and Magnetism at Work
4. Electronics

Sound and Light
1. Characteristics of Waves
2. Sound
3. The Electromagnetic Spectrum
4. Light

Integrated Science sections in every chapter

Place your students in the role of science explorer through a variety of inquiry activities.

Motivational student- and teacher-tested activities reinforce key concepts and allow students to explore science concepts for themselves. More than 350 activities are provided for each book in the Student Edition, Teacher's Edition, Teaching Resources, Integrated Science Lab Manual, Inquiry Skills Activity Book, Interactive Student Tutorial CD-ROM, and *Science Explorer* Web Site.

STUDENT EDITION ACTIVITIES

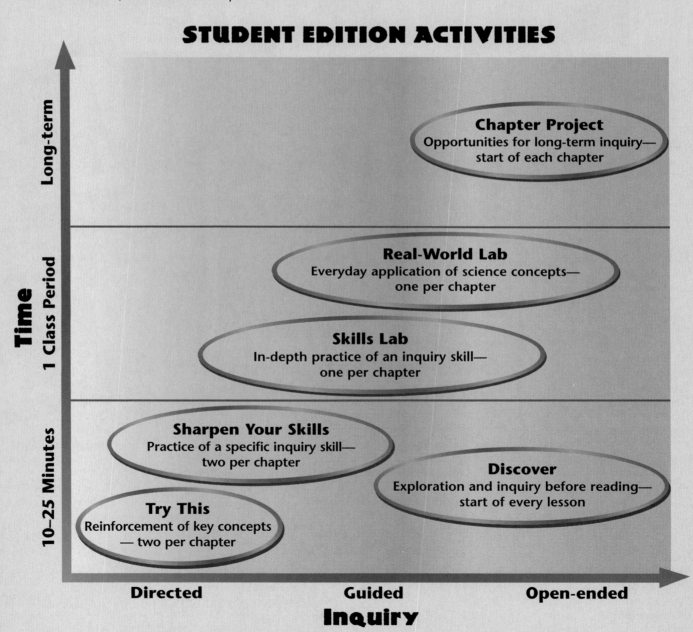

Check your compass regularly with integrated assessment tools.

Prepare for state exams with traditional and performance-based assessment.

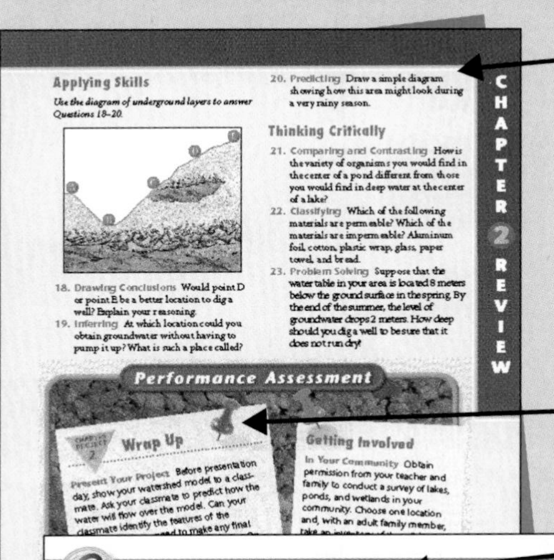

Applying Skills

Use the diagram of underground layers to answer Questions 18–20.

18. Drawing Conclusions Would point D or point E be a better location to dig a well? Explain your reasoning.
19. Inferring At which location could you obtain groundwater without having to pump it up? What is such a place called?
20. Predicting Draw a simple diagram showing how this area might look during a very rainy season.

Thinking Critically

21. Comparing and Contrasting How is the variety of organisms you would find in the center of a pond different from those you would find in deep water at the center of a lake?
22. Classifying Which of the following materials are permeable? Which of the materials are impermeable? Aluminum foil, cotton, plastic wrap, glass, paper towel, and bread.
23. Problem Solving Suppose that the water table in your area is located 8 meters below the ground surface in the spring. By the end of the summer, the level of groundwater drops 2 meters. How deep should you dig a well to be sure that it does not run dry?

CHAPTER 2 REVIEW

Performance Assessment

Wrap Up

Present Your Project Before presentation day, show your watershed model to a classmate. Ask your classmate to predict how the water will flow over the model. Can your classmate identify the features of the ... to make any final

Getting Involved

In Your Community Obtain permission from your teacher and family to conduct a survey of lakes, ponds, and wetlands in your community. Choose one location and, with an adult family member, take ...

Section 3 Review

1. How are wetlands important to wildlife?
2. Explain how wetlands help control floods.
3. How are the Everglades unusual?
4. **Thinking Critically Making Judgments** Some of the plans to restore the Everglades will require millions of dollars and will negatively affect local farmers. What information would you want to have to help decide what plan of action to take to save the Everglades?

Check Your Progress CHAPTER PROJECT 2

At this point, add the body of standing water to your watershed sketch. If your model will include any wetland areas, what materials will you use to model them? (*Hint:* Be sure to consider how water will enter and leave the body of water.)

- **Comprehensive Chapter Reviews** include a wide range of question types that students will encounter on standardized tests. Types include multiple choice, enhanced true/false, concept mastery, visual thinking, skill application, and critical thinking. Also includes Chapter Project "Wrap Up."
- **Chapter Projects** contain rubrics that allow you to easily assess student progress.
- **Section Reviews** provide "Check your Progress" opportunities for the Chapter Project, as well as review questions for the section.

Additional *Science Explorer* assessment resources:

- **Assessment Resources with CD-ROM**
- **Resource Pro® with Planning Express® CD-ROM**
- **Standardized Test Practice Book**
- **On-line review activities** at www.phschool.com

See page T9 for complete product descriptions.

How Waves Affect the Shore

What happens on shore as waves pound the beach? The diagram in Figure 4 shows some of their effects. Since wave direction at sea is determined by the wind, waves usually roll toward shore at an angle. But as they touch bottom, the shallower water slows the shoreward side of the wave first. The rows of waves gradually turn and become more nearly parallel to the shore.

Longshore Drift As the waves come into shore, water washes up the beach. The water then runs off at an angle in the other direction, carrying sand with it. This movement of sand down the beach is called **longshore drift**. As the waves slow down, they deposit the sand they are carrying on the shallow, underwater slope in a long ridge called a **sandbar**.

Rip Currents As a sandbar grows, it can trap the water flowing along the shore. In some places, water breaks through the sandbar and begins to flow back down the sloping ocean bottom. This process creates a **rip current**, a rush of water that flows rapidly back to sea through a narrow opening. Rip currents can carry a swimmer out into deep water. Because rip currents are narrow, a strong swimmer can usually escape by swimming across the current, parallel to the beach.

✓ *Checkpoint In what direction does a rip current pull a swimmer?*

Figure 4 Waves approach the shore at an angle. This results in a gradual movement of sand down the beach. *Interpreting Diagrams In which direction is longshore drift moving the sand along this beach?*

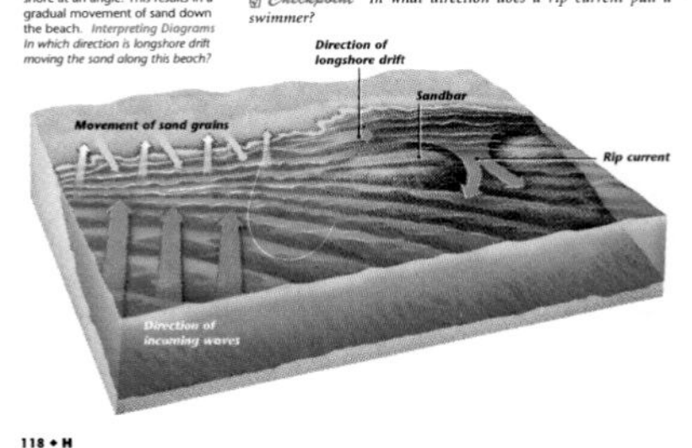

118 • H

Self-assessment opportunities help students keep themselves on course.

- **Caption Questions** throughout the text assess critical thinking skills.
- **Checkpoint Questions** give students an immediate content check as new concepts are presented.
- **Interactive Student Tutorial CD-ROM** provides students with electronic self-tests, review activities, and Exploration activities.
- **Got It! Video Quizzes** motivate and challenge students with engaging animations and interactive questions.
- **www.science-explorer.phschool.com** provides additional support and on-line test prep.

Utilize a wide variety of tools.

Easy-to-manage, book-specific teaching resources

15 Teaching Resource Packages, each containing a Student Edition, Teacher's Edition, Teaching Resources with Color Transparencies, Guided Reading Audiotape, Materials Kit Order form, and Correlation to the National Science Education Standards.

15 Teacher's Editions with a three-step lesson plan—*Engage/Explore, Facilitate,* and *Assess*—that is ideal for reaching all students. Chapter planning charts make it easy to find resources, as well as to plan for block scheduling and team teaching.

15 Teaching Resource Books with Color Transparencies offer complete support organized by chapter to make it easy for you to find what you need—when you need it.

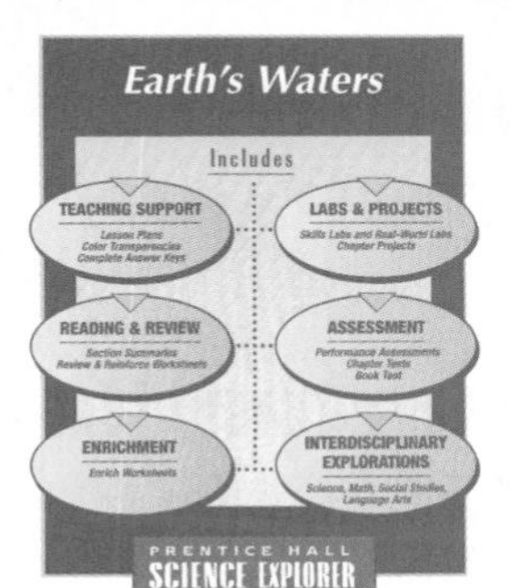

15 Guided Reading Audiotapes (English and Spanish) provide section summaries for students who need additional support.

15 Explorer Videotapes allow students to explore concepts through spectacular short videos containing computer animations. Available in Spanish.

Program-wide print resources

1

2

3

4

5

6

7

1. **Materials Kits**—Prentice Hall and Science Kit, Inc. have collaborated to develop a Consumable Kit and Nonconsumable Kit for each book. Ordering software makes it easy to customize!

2&3. **Integrated Science Laboratory Manual with Teacher's Edition**—74 in-depth labs covering the entire curriculum, with complete teaching support.

4. **Inquiry Skills Activity Book**—additional activities to teach, practice, and assess a wide range of inquiry skills.
5. **Student-Centered Science Activities**—five activity books for the Northeast, Southeast, Midwest, Southwest, and West.
6. **Program Planning Guide**—course outlines, block scheduling pacing charts, correlations, and more.
7. **Product Testing Activities by *Consumer Reports***—19 student-oriented testing activities turn students into real-world explorers.

Additional print resources...

8. **Reading in the Content Area**—with Literature Connections
9. **Standardized Test Practice**—review and self-tests to prepare for statewide exams.
10. **15 Prentice Hall Interdisciplinary Explorations**
11. **How to Assess Student Work**
12. **How to Manage Instruction in the Block**
13. ***Cobblestone, Odyssey, Calliope,* and *Faces* Magazines**

Program-wide technology resources

1. **Resource Pro® CD-ROM**—the ultimate management tool with easy access to blackline masters and lab activities for all 15 books. Planning Express® software lets you customize lesson plans by day, week, month, and year. Also includes Computer Test Bank software.
2. **Assessment Resources with CD-ROM**—*Computer Test Bank* software with Dial-A-Test® provides you with unparalleled flexibility in creating tests.
3. ***Science Explorer* Web Site**—activities and teaching resources for every chapter at www.science-explorer.phschool.com
4. **Interactive Student Tutorial CD-ROMs**—provide students with self-tests, helpful hints, and Explorations. Tests are scored instantly and provide complete explanations to all answers.
5. **An Odyssey of Discovery CD-ROMs**—interactive labs encourage students to hypothesize and experiment. (Life and Earth Science).
6. **Interactive Earth CD-ROM**—explore global trends, search the media library, and zoom in on a 3-D globe.
7. **Mindscape CD-ROMs**—*The Animals!™*, *Oceans Below,* and *How Your Body Works* bring science alive with compelling videoclips, 3-D animations, and interactive databases.
8. **A.D.A.M. The Inside Story**—take an entertaining tour of each body system, designed for middle grades students.
9. **Interactive Physics**—explore physics concepts with computer simulations that encourage what-if questions.
10. **Explorer Videotapes and Videodiscs**—explore and visualize concepts through spectacular short documentaries containing computer animations (Spanish audio track).
11. **Event-Based Science**—series of NSF-funded modules that engage students with inquiry-based projects. Includes video.

Options for Pacing *Motion, Forces and Energy*

The Pacing Chart below suggests one way to schedule your instructional time. The ***Science Explorer*** program offers many other aids to help you plan your instructional time, whether regular class periods or **block scheduling.** Refer to the Chapter Planning Guide before each chapter to view all program resources with suggested times for Student Edition activities.

Pacing Chart

	Days	Blocks
Nature of Science: Understanding Nature's Designs	1	$\frac{1}{2}$
Chapter 1 Motion		
Chapter 1 Project Speeds à la Carte	Ongoing	Ongoing
1 Describing and Measuring Motion	6	3
2 Integrating Earth Science: Slow Motion on Planet Earth	3	1–2
3 Acceleration	2–3	1–2
Chapter 1 Review and Assessment	1	$\frac{1}{2}$
Chapter 2 Forces		
Chapter 2 Project Newton Scooters	Ongoing	Ongoing
1 The Nature of Force	4	2
2 Force, Mass, and Acceleration	1–2	1
3 Friction and Gravity	4–5	$2\frac{1}{2}$
4 Action and Reaction	3	1–2
5 Integrating Space Science: Orbiting Satellites	1–2	1
Chapter 2 Review and Assessment	1	$\frac{1}{2}$
Chapter 3 Forces in Fluids		
Chapter 3 Project Staying Afloat	Ongoing	Ongoing
1 Pressure	4	2
2 Transmitting Pressure in a Fluid	2	1
3 Floating and Sinking	3–4	$1\frac{1}{2}$
4 Integrating Technology: Applying Bernoulli's Principle	2	1
Chapter 3 Review and Assessment	1	$\frac{1}{2}$
Chapter 4 Work and Machines		
Chapter 4 Project The Nifty Lifting Machine	Ongoing	Ongoing
1 What Is Work?	2	1
2 Mechanical Advantage and Efficiency	6–7	$3\frac{1}{2}$
3 Simple Machines	7	3–4
4 Integrating Life Science: Machines in the Human Body	$1\frac{1}{2}$	1
Chapter 4 Review and Assessment	1	$\frac{1}{2}$
Chapter 5 Energy and Power		
Chapter 5 Project Roller Coaster!	Ongoing	Ongoing
1 The Nature of Energy	4	2
2 Energy Conversion and Conservation	3	$1\frac{1}{2}$
3 Integrating Earth Science: Energy Conversion and Fossil Fuels	2	1
4 Power	2–3	1
Chapter 5 Review and Assessment	1	$\frac{1}{2}$
Chapter 6 Thermal Energy and Heat		
Chapter 6 Project In Hot Water	Ongoing	Ongoing
1 Temperature and Thermal Energy	1–2	1
2 The Nature of Heat	5	$2\frac{1}{2}$
3 Integrating Chemistry: Thermal Energy and States of Matter	3	$1\frac{1}{2}$
4 Uses of Heat	2	1
Chapter 6 Review and Assessment	1	$\frac{1}{2}$
Interdisciplinary Exploration: Bridges From Vines to Steel	2-3	$\frac{1}{2}$

RESOURCE PRO®

The Resource Pro® CD-ROM is the ultimate scheduling and lesson planning tool. Resource Pro® allows you to preview all the resources in the *Science Explorer* program, organize your chosen materials, and print out any teaching resource. You can follow the suggested lessons or create your own, using resources from anywhere in the program.

Thematic Overview of *Motion, Forces and Energy*

The chart below lists the major themes of ***Motion, Forces and Energy***. For each theme, the chart supplies a big idea, or concept statement, describing how a particular theme is taught in a chapter.

	Chapter 1	Chapter 2	Chapter 3	Chapter 4	Chapter 5	Chapter 6
Patterns of Change	As an object accelerates, its motion changes as it slows down, speeds up, or changes direction.	Newton's laws determine the nature and magnitude of change in a system.			Energy is converted from one form to another when work is done or energy is transferred.	Matter changes state with loss or gain of thermal energy.
Scale and Structure	Scale is emphasized with SI units and unit conversions. SI units can be used for very large and very small speeds.		Different forms of matter have different densities. The buoyant force on an object is equal to the weight of the fluid displaced by the object.	Simple machines can be found in the human body. Compound machines are made up of more than one simple machine.		Matter is made up of tiny particles.
Unity and Diversity				Although simple machines differ, they all make work easier.	Any form of energy can be converted to another form.	
Systems and Interactions	Earth's tectonic plates comprise a complex system with many different types of interactions.	Interactions between systems of objects are summarized in Newton's three laws of motion and the law of gravity.	The speed of a fluid affects the pressure it exerts on an object.	Compound machines are systems of simple machines that work together to increase mechanical advantage.	An object that has energy can do work which is the transfer of energy.	When a fluid is heated unevenly, convection currents form which are the source of winds and weather systems.
Evolution	Scientists can predict how Earth's plates will change over time.					
Energy				Simple machines convert input force or energy to output force or energy.	Energy conversions occur when work is done or energy is transformed.	The measurement and transfer of thermal energy is analyzed.
Stability		A system is stable and will remain stable as long as there are no unbalanced forces acting on it.				Thermal energy moves from a hotter to a cooler substance until both substances have the same temperature.
Modeling	Students conduct an activity to measure speed. An experiment is designed and conducted to analyze the stopping distance of a basketball player.	Students create models of vehicles.	Students model the effects of the motion of fluids on pressure.	Students model a compound machine by constructing a "lifting machine" consisting of two simple machines that work together.		

Inquiry Skills Chart

The Prentice Hall *Science Explorer* program provides comprehensive teaching, practice, and assessment of science skills, with an emphasis on the process skills necessary for inquiry. The chart lists the skills covered in the program and cites the page numbers where each skill is covered.

Basic Process SKILLS				
	Student Text: Projects and Labs	**Student Text: Activities**	**Student Text: Caption and Review Questions**	**Teacher's Edition: Extensions**
Observing	32–33, 62–63	18, 44, 48, 52, 55, 57, 64, 78, 86, 106, 132, 140, 148, 151, 154, 158, 168, 171, 174, 181, 184, 187, 202	144	21, 56, 59, 98, 108, 112, 120–121, 126–127, 133, 144, 149, 151–152, 155, 159, 173, 175–176, 202
Inferring	32–33	16, 34, 44, 48, 97, 108, 158, 172, 181, 202	57, 59, 75, 80, 109, 134, 137, 143, 165, 172	67, 71, 98, 111, 121, 159, 173, 185, 188, 202
Predicting	41–42, 84–85, 116–177, 130–131, 178–179	29, 44, 55, 68, 70, 90, 97, 113, 118, 140, 148, 151, 188, 202	38, 56, 58, 71, 75, 87, 103, 137, 150, 155	28, 58, 94, 100, 112, 120, 132, 150, 152, 173, 176, 202
Classifying		110, 127, 188, 203	35, 89	120, 122, 142, 203
Making Models	41–42, 76–77, 84–85, 104–105, 130–131, 138–139, 146–147	121, 203		88, 98, 112, 119, 124, 151, 169, 203
Communicating	14–15, 26–27, 32–33, 41–42, 50–51, 104–105, 138–139, 146–147, 160–161, 166–167	20, 34, 46, 48, 87, 108, 118, 122, 125, 127, 129, 152, 180, 183, 203	40, 74, 102, 136, 164–165, 192	16–17, 19, 21, 34–35, 38, 44, 47 49, 52, 54, 57, 59, 61, 64, 69, 78 96, 100, 106, 109, 118, 148–149 158, 171, 203
Measuring	14–15, 26–27, 32–33, 50–51, 62–63, 76–77, 92–93, 116–117, 130–131, 146–147, 160–161, 178–179	16, 28, 34, 60, 91, 151, 154, 188, 204–205	19, 41	17, 19, 25, 112, 124, 126, 174, 204–205
Calculating	14–15, 26–27, 32–33, 50–51, 92–93, 104–105, 130–131, 146–147, 160–161, 178–179	19, 22–23, 28–29, 37, 53, 60, 67, 114, 121, 159	31, 41, 61, 75, 103, 137, 145, 165, 193	19, 21, 25, 29, 31, 36–37, 108, 119, 142
Creating Data Tables	14–15, 26–27, 32–33, 50–51, 62–63, 84–85, 92–93, 116–117, 130–131, 146–147, 160–161, 178–179	212		143, 212
Graphing	26–27, 50–51, 146–147	23, 155, 212–214	25, 137	174, 182, 212–214
Advanced Process SKILLS				
Posing Questions		206–207		206–207
Developing Hypotheses	84–85, 92–93, 116–117	64, 78, 80, 106, 113, 187, 206–207	103	126, 141, 173, 206–207

Advanced Process SKILLS (continued)				
	Student Text: Projects and Labs	**Student Text: Activities**	**Student Text: Caption and Review Questions**	**Teacher's Edition: Extensions**
Designing Experiments	26–27, 50–51, 76–77, 84–85, 92–93, 116–117, 160–161, 166–167, 178–179	55, 206–207	75, 103	56, 112, 119, 126, 141, 159, 173–174, 182, 184, 206–207
Controlling Variables	26–27, 41–42, 50–51, 62–63, 76–77, 84–85, 92–93, 116–117, 138–139, 146–147	28, 34, 206–207		79, 119, 141, 143, 184, 206–207
Forming Operational Definitions	62–63	28, 70, 110, 148, 154, 206–207		206–207
Interpreting Data	50–51, 116–117, 160–161, 166–167, 178–179	20, 206–207	41, 95, 137, 193	206–207
Drawing Conclusions	62–63, 76–77, 84–85, 92–93, 116–117, 130–131	57, 80, 94, 174, 206–207	103, 165, 193	143, 151, 206–207
Critical Thinking SKILLS				
Comparing and Contrasting	116–117, 130–131, 146–147, 160–161	57, 60, 90, 208	17, 21, 61, 69, 75, 83, 89, 94, 115, 162, 169–170, 182, 190	55, 112, 170, 184, 208
Applying Concepts	14–15, 32–33, 62–63, 84–85, 104–105, 130–131, 160–161, 166–167	28, 55, 180, 208	41, 46, 49, 66, 72, 75, 83, 89, 91, 96, 100, 103, 109, 112, 128, 137, 141, 153–154, 165, 168, 170, 177, 184–186, 193	17, 45, 58, 144, 149, 175, 208
Interpreting Diagrams, Graphs Photographs, and Maps	26–27, 50–51, 146–147	155, 208	29–30, 68, 72, 83, 106, 111, 126, 142, 151, 190	30, 65, 82, 111, 126, 208
Relating Cause and Effect	84–85, 92–93, 138–139, 146–147	140, 180, 209	35, 48, 82, 100, 103, 119, 121, 137, 165, 186, 193	80, 119, 141, 174, 209
Making Generalizations		113, 209	36, 41, 45, 98, 128	209
Making Judgments	62–63	129, 180, 209	157	209
Problem Solving	26–27, 32–33, 92–93, 104–105, 130–131, 178–179		29, 25, 31, 38, 41, 54, 61, 75, 79, 145, 162, 165, 177, 193	30, 119, 185
Information Organizing SKILLS				
Concept Maps		210	40, 164, 192	34, 140, 157, 210
Compare/ Contrast Tables		210	74, 136	132, 210
Venn Diagrams		211		55, 211
Flowcharts		211	102	148, 153, 190, 211
Cycle Diagrams		211		211

The *Science Explorer* program provides additional teaching, reinforcement, and assessment of skills in the Inquiry Skills Activities Book and the Integrated Science Laboratory Manual.

Throughout the *Science Explorer* program, every effort has been made to keep the materials and equipment *affordable, reusable,* and *easily accessible.*

The ***Science Explorer*** program offers an abundance of activity options so you can pick and choose those activities that suit your needs. To help you order supplies at the beginning of the year, the Master Materials List cross-references the materials by activity. If you prefer to create your list electronically,use the electronic order forms at:
www.science–explorer.phschool.com

There are two kits available for each book of the ***Science Explorer*** program, a Consumable Kit and a Nonconsumable Kit. These kits are produced by **Science Kit and Boreal Laboratories,** the leader in providing science kits to schools. Prentice Hall and Science Kit collaborated throughout the development of ***Science Explorer*** to ensure that the equipment and supplies in the kits precisely match the requirements of the program activities.

The kits provide an economical and convenient way to get all of the materials needed to teach each book. For each book, Science Kit also offers the opportunity to buy equipment and safety items individually. For a current listing of kit offerings or additional information about materials to accompany ***Science Explorer***, please, contact Science Kit at:
1-800-828-7777
or at their Internet site at:
www.sciencekit.com

Master Materials List

Consumable Materials

*	Description	Quantity per class	Textbook Section(s)
C	Balloons, 13" round, pkg. of 10	1	3-1 (DIS)
SS	Butter, stick	1	6-2 (DIS)
C	Candles, birthday, pkg. of 36	1	6-3 (DIS)
SS	Cardboard	1	1-1 (Lab)
C	Cards, index, blank 3" × 5", pkg. of 100	1	5-2 (DIS)
C	Clay, modeling (cream), 1 lb.	1	3-3 (DIS) 6-3 (DIS)
SS	Cracker	5	4-4 (DIS)
C	Cup, plastic clear, 16 oz.	5	3-3 (DIS)
C	Cup, styrofoam, 14 oz.	20	6-2 (Lab)
C	Forks, plastic, pkg. of 24	1	3-4 (DIS)
SS	Honey	1	1-2 (DIS)
SS	Marker, black, permanent	5	3-1 (Lab) 3-3 (DIS) 4-3 (Lab) 5-1 (Lab)
C	Matches, wooden safety, box of 30	5	6-3 (DIS)
C	Pan, aluminum, 3/4" × 4-3/4" diameter	5	5-3 (DIS) 6-3 (DIS)
SS	Paper	5	4-3 (TT)
SS	Paper towel roll	1	3-3 (Lab)
SS	Pencil	5	4-2 (TT) 4-3 (TT) 6-2 (Lab)
C	Plates, paper, 9", pkg. of 50	1	1-2 (DIS)
C	Rubber band, assorted, 1-1/2 oz. pkg.	1	2-4 (DIS) 4-1 (DIS) 5-1 (Lab) 5-2 (DIS)
C	Salt, non-iodized, 737 g	1	3-3 (Lab)
C	Sand, fine, 2.5 kg (7-1/2 cups)	1	6-4 (TT)
SS	Soda cans, empty, with tabs attached	30	3-1 (Lab)
C	Splints, wooden, 15 cm, pkg. of 25	1	5-3 (DIS)
C	Spoons, plastic, pkg. of 24	1	1-2 (DIS) 3-3 (DIS) 3-4 (DIS) 6-2 (DIS)
C	Straws, plastic (wrapped), pkg. of 50	1	2-4 (DIS) 3-1 (DIS) 3-3 (DIS) 3-3 (TT) 5-1 (Lab)
C	String, cotton, 200 ft.	1	2-1 (Lab) 2-5 (DIS) 4-2 (TT) 5-2 (TT)
C	Sugar, granulated, 454 g	1	3-3 (DIS)
SS	Tape, masking, 3/4" × 60 yd.	1	1-1 (Lab) 1-2 (DIS) 1-3 (DIS) 2-1 (TT) 2-1 (Lab) 2-3 (Lab) 2-4 (TT) 4-2 (Lab) 4-3 (TT) 5-1 (Lab)
C	Thread, white, 200-yd. spool	1	2-1 (TT)
SS	Tube, empty toilet paper	5	5-1 (Lab)

KEY: **DIS**: Discover; **SYS**: Sharpen Your Skills; **TT**: Try This; **Lab**: Lab

Quantities based on 5 lab groups per class.

* Items designated **C** are in the Consumable Kit, **NC** are in the Nonconsumable Kit, and **SS** are School Supplied.

Master Materials List

Nonconsumable Materials

*	Description	Quantity per class	Textbook Section(s)
NC	Ball, ping pong	5	2-1 (TT)
SS	Ball, tennis	5	5-1 (DIS)
SS	Basin, large	5	3-1 (Lab)
SS	Basketball	5	6-4 (DIS)
NC	Beaker, Pyrex, 250 mL	5	3-3 (Lab)
NC	Beaker, Pyrex, 600 mL	5	3-1 (Lab) 3-3 (Lab) 6-2 (DIS) 6-2 (Lab)
SS	Bicycle pump	5	6-4 (DIS)
SS	Blow dryer	5	5-4 (DIS)
SS	Board	5	5-4 (Lab)
SS	Board, at least 10 cm × 50 cm	5	4-3 (Lab)
SS	Board, flat, about 1.5 m long	5	1-1 (Lab)
SS	Book	40	1-1 (Lab) 2-4 (DIS) 4-3 (Lab) 5-4 (Lab)
SS	Bottle, 2-L plastic with cap	5	3-2 (DIS) 3-3 (TT)
NC	Bowl, plastic large, 40 oz.	15	6-1 (DIS)
SS	Brick, or other large mass	10	2-1 (Lab)
SS	Broomstick	10	4-3 (DIS)
NC	Can, metal, 500 mL without lid	5	6-4 (TT)
NC	Car, toy (Matchbox® type)	10	2-1 (DIS) 2-4 (TT)
SS	Container, empty (2-L bottle)	5	3-1 (DIS)
SS	Dime	5	2-3 (DIS)
NC	Dowel, wooden, 8" × 1"	5	4-2 (Lab)
NC	Erlenmeyer flask, Pyrex, 250 mL	5	5-3 (DIS)
NC	Fishing line, 8 lb. test, 100 yd.	1	3-1 (Lab)
NC	Friction block, 7.5 cm × 16 cm × 2 cm	5	4-3 (Lab)
NC	Jar, plastic wide-mouth, 60 mL	5	3-3 (Lab)
SS	Lamp	1	6-2 (TT)
NC	Lid, metal, 53 mm (for 60-mL jar)	5	3-3 (Lab)
NC	Lid, metal, 75 mm (for 500-mL can)	5	6-4 (TT)
NC	Marbles, 5/8", pkg. of 20	5	2-3 (TT) 2-4 (DIS)
NC	Meter stick, half-length, wood	5	1-1 (DIS) 1-1 (Lab) 1-2 (Lab) 1-3 (DIS) 2-1 (Lab) 5-1 (Lab) 5-4 (Lab)
SS	Meter stick, full-length	5	4-2 (Lab) 5-1 (DIS)
SS	Mug	5	4-1 (DIS)
NC	Nails, 20D, pkg. of 15	1	3-1 (Lab)
NC	Nails, 3.75 cm 4D, 500 g	1	3-1 (Lab)
NC	Nails, 7.5 cm 10D, 500 g	1	3-1 (Lab)
SS	Nickel	5	2-3 (DIS)
SS	Object, small, mass about 50 g	5	4-2 (Lab)
SS	Objects, assortment	5	4-2 (DIS)
NC	Pan, aluminum foil, 22.5-cm diameter	10	2-3 (TT)
NC	Paper clips, box of 100	1	3-3 (TT)
NC	Paper clips, jumbo, box of 100	1	2-3 (Lab)
SS	Pennies, post-1982	140	4-2 (Lab)
SS	Pinwheel	5	5-4 (DIS)
SS	Pot, cooking	5	4-2 (TT)
SS	Protractor, 6" plastic, 180 degrees	5	1-1 (Lab)
SS	Quarter	5	2-3 (DIS)
SS	Rocks	30	2-2 (DIS)
NC	Rope, clothesline, 7/32" × 50'	1	4-3 (DIS)
SS	Ruler, plastic, 12"/30 cm	5	1-2 (DIS) 2-3 (DIS) 3-3 (DIS) 4-2 (TT) 4-3 (Lab) 5-1 (Lab) 5-2 (DIS) 5-2 (TT)

KEY: **DIS**: Discover; **SYS**: Sharpen Your Skills; **TT**: Try This; **Lab**: Lab

* Items designated **C** are in the Consumable Kit, **NC** are in the Nonconsumable Kit, and **SS** are School Supplied.

Nonconsumable Materials (cont.)

*	Description	Quantity per class	Textbook Section(s)
SS	Scissors	5	4-3 (TT) 5-1 (Lab) 5-2 (DIS) 6-2 (Lab)
SS	Skateboard	5	1-1 (Lab) 2-1 (Lab)
SS	Sneakers, different types	15	2-3 (Lab)
NC	Spool, plastic, 1-3/8" × 1-3/4" × 1-3/32"	5	2-5 (DIS)
SS	Spoon, metal teaspoon	5	6-2 (DIS)
SS	Spoon, wooden, 10"	5	6-2 (DIS)
NC	Spring scale 2 kg/20 N	5	2-2 (DIS) 2-3 (Lab)
NC	Spring scale 500 g/5 N	5	2-1 (Lab) 2-3 (Lab) 4-2 (TT) 4-3 (Lab)
NC	Stopwatch, electronic LED	10	1-1 (DIS) 1-1 (Lab) 1-2 (DIS) 1-2 (Lab) 1-3 (DIS) 2-1 (Lab) 3-1 (Lab) 5-4 (Lab)
NC	Tape measure, 1.5 m, metric/English	5	1-2 (Lab)
NC	Thermometer, −20 to 110 C	10	5-3 (DIS) 6-2 (Lab) 6-4 (TT)
SS	Truck, toy dump	5	2-2 (DIS)
NC	Washer, flat, 3/16" ID × 7/16" OD, pkg. of 30	2	2-1 (DIS) 5-2 (TT) 6-3 (DIS)
NC	Wire, bare copper, 22 gauge, 125 g	1	6-3 (DIS)

Equipment

*	Description	Quantity per class	Textbook Section(s)
SS	Balance, triple beam, single pan	5	2-3 (Lab) 3-3 (Lab) 5-1 (Lab) 6-2 (Lab)
SS	Calculator, light-powered	5	5-4 (Lab)
SS	Clamp	10	5-2 (TT) 5-3 (DIS) 6-3 (DIS)
SS	Goggles, chemical splash goggles-class set	1	2-5 (DIS) 3-1 (Lab) 5-1 (Lab) 5-2 (DIS) 5-3 (DIS) 6-2 (Lab)
SS	Hot plate	1	6-3 (SYS)
SS	Mass set, gram, brass, 8-piece	5	2-3 (Lab)
SS	Mitten, oven mitt, adult size	5	6-3 (DIS)
SS	Ring stand	5	5-2 (TT) 5-3 (DIS) 6-3 (DIS)
SS	Tea kettle	1	6-3 (SYS)

KEY: **DIS**: Discover; **SYS**: Sharpen Your Skills; **TT**: Try This; **Lab**: Lab
* Items designated **C** are in the Consumable Kit, **NC** are in the Nonconsumable Kit, and **SS** are School Supplied.

Motion, Forces, and Energy

Program Resources
Student Edition
Annotated Teacher's Edition
Teaching Resources Book with Color Transparencies
Motion, Forces, and Energy Materials Kits

Program Components
Integrated Science Laboratory Manual
Integrated Science Laboratory Manual, Teacher's Edition
Inquiry Skills Activity Book
Student-Centered Science Activity Books
Program Planning Guide
Guided Reading English Audiotapes
Guided Reading Spanish Audiotapes and Summaries
Product Testing Activities by Consumer Reports™
Event-Based Science Series (NSF funded)
Prentice Hall Interdisciplinary Explorations
Cobblestone, Odyssey, Calliope, and *Faces* Magazines

Media/Technology
Science Explorer Interactive Student Tutorial CD-ROMs
Odyssey of Discovery CD-ROMs
Resource Pro® (Teaching Resources on CD-ROM)
Assessment Resources CD-ROM with Dial-A-Test®
Internet site at www.science-explorer.phschool.com
Life, Earth, and Physical Science Videodiscs
Life, Earth, and Physical Science Videotapes

Science Explorer Student Editions

From Bacteria to Plants
Animals
Cells and Heredity
Human Biology and Health
Environmental Science
Inside Earth
Earth's Changing Surface
Earth's Waters
Weather and Climate
Astronomy
Chemical Building Blocks
Chemical Interactions
Motion, Forces, and Energy
Electricity and Magnetism
Sound and Light

Staff Credits

The people who made up the *Science Explorer* team—representing editorial, editorial services, design services, field marketing, market research, marketing services, on-line services/multimedia development, product marketing, production services, and publishing processes—are listed below. Bold type denotes core team members.

Kristen E. Ball, **Barbara A. Bertell,** Peter W. Brooks, **Christopher R. Brown, Greg Cantone,** Jonathan Cheney, **Patrick Finbarr Connolly,** Loree Franz, Donald P. Gagnon, Jr., **Paul J. Gagnon, Joel Gendler,** Elizabeth Good, Kerri Hoar, **Linda D. Johnson,** Katherine M. Kotik, Russ Lappa, Marilyn Leitao, David Lippman, **Eve Melnechuk, Natania Mlawer,** Paul W. Murphy, **Cindy A. Noftle,** Julia F. Osborne, Caroline M. Power, Suzanne J. Schineller, **Susan W. Tafler,** Kira Thaler-Marbit, Robin L. Santel, Ronald Schachter, **Mark Tricca,** Diane Walsh, Pearl B. Weinstein, Beth Norman Winickoff

Copyright ©2000 by Prentice-Hall, Inc., Upper Saddle River, New Jersey 07458. All rights reserved. No part of this book may be reproduced or transmitted in any form or by any means, electronic or mechanical, including photocopying, recording, or by any information storage and retrieval system, without permission in writing from the publisher. Printed in the United States of America.

ISBN 0-13-434492-8
3 4 5 6 7 8 9 10 03 02 01 00 99

Cover: Carnival ride at the Del Mar Fair, Del Mar, California

Teacher's Edition ISBN 0-13-434573-8

Program Authors

Michael J. Padilla, Ph.D.
Professor
Department of Science Education
University of Georgia
Athens, Georgia

Michael Padilla is a leader in middle school science education. He has served as an editor and elected officer for the National Science Teachers Association. He has been principal investigator of several National Science Foundation and Eisenhower grants and served as a writer of the National Science Education Standards.

As lead author of *Science Explorer,* Mike has inspired the team in developing a program that meets the needs of middle grades students, promotes science inquiry, and is aligned with the National Science Education Standards.

Ioannis Miaoulis, Ph.D.
Dean of Engineering
College of Engineering
Tufts University
Medford, Massachusetts

Martha Cyr, Ph.D.
Director, Engineering
Educational Outreach
College of Engineering
Tufts University
Medford, Massachusetts

Science Explorer was created in collaboration with the College of Engineering at Tufts University. Tufts has an extensive engineering outreach program that uses engineering design and construction to excite and motivate students and teachers in science and technology education.

Faculty from Tufts University participated in the development of *Science Explorer* chapter projects, reviewed the student books for content accuracy, and helped coordinate field testing.

Book Author

Peter Kahan
Former Science Teacher
Dwight-Englewood School
Englewood, New Jersey

Contributing Writers

Mark Illingworth
Teacher
Hollis Public Schools
Hollis, New Hampshire

Thomas R. Wellnitz
Science Teacher
The Paideia School
Atlanta, Georgia

Reading Consultant

Bonnie B. Armbruster, Ph.D.
Department of Curriculum
and Instruction
University of Illinois
Champaign, Illinois

Interdisciplinary Consultant

Heidi Hayes Jacobs, Ed.D.
Teacher's College
Columbia University
New York, New York

Safety Consultants

W. H. Breazeale, Ph.D.
Department of Chemistry
College of Charleston
Charleston, South Carolina

Ruth Hathaway, Ph.D.
Hathaway Consulting
Cape Girardeau, Missouri

M ◆ 3

Tufts University Program Reviewers

Behrouz Abedian, Ph.D.
Department of Mechanical Engineering

Wayne Chudyk, Ph.D.
Department of Civil and Environmental Engineering

Eliana De Bernardez-Clark, Ph.D.
Department of Chemical Engineering

Anne Marie Desmarais, Ph.D.
Department of Civil and Environmental Engineering

David L. Kaplan, Ph.D.
Department of Chemical Engineering

Paul Kelley, Ph.D.
Department of Electro-Optics

George S. Mumford, Ph.D.
Professor of Astronomy, Emeritus

Jan A. Pechenik, Ph.D.
Department of Biology

Livia Racz, Ph.D.
Department of Mechanical Engineering

Robert Rifkin, M.D.
School of Medicine

Jack Ridge, Ph.D.
Department of Geology

Chris Swan, Ph.D.
Department of Civil and Environmental Engineering

Peter Y. Wong, Ph.D.
Department of Mechanical Engineering

Content Reviewers

Jack W. Beal, Ph.D.
Department of Physics
Fairfield University
Fairfield, Connecticut

W. Russell Blake, Ph.D.
Planetarium Director
Plymouth Community Intermediate School
Plymouth, Massachusetts

Howard E. Buhse, Jr., Ph.D.
Department of Biological Sciences
University of Illinois
Chicago, Illinois

Dawn Smith Burgess, Ph.D.
Department of Geophysics
Stanford University
Stanford, California

A. Malcolm Campbell, Ph.D.
Assistant Professor
Davidson College
Davidson, North Carolina

Elizabeth A. De Stasio, Ph.D.
Associate Professor of Biology
Lawrence University
Appleton, Wisconsin

John M. Fowler, Ph.D.
Former Director of Special Projects
National Science Teacher's Association
Arlington, Virginia

Jonathan Gitlin, M.D.
School of Medicine
Washington University
St. Louis, Missouri

Dawn Graff-Haight, Ph.D., CHES
Department of Health, Human Performance, and Athletics
Linfield College
McMinnville, Oregon

Deborah L. Gumucio, Ph.D.
Associate Professor
Department of Anatomy and Cell Biology
University of Michigan
Ann Arbor, Michigan

William S. Harwood, Ph.D.
Dean of University Division and Associate Professor of Education
Indiana University
Bloomington, Indiana

Cyndy Henzel, Ph.D.
Department of Geography and Regional Development
University of Arizona
Tucson, Arizona

Greg Hutton
Science and Health Curriculum Coordinator
School Board of Sarasota County
Sarasota, Florida

Susan K. Jacobson, Ph.D.
Department of Wildlife Ecology and Conservation
University of Florida
Gainesville, Florida

Judy Jernstedt, Ph.D.
Department of Agronomy and Range Science
University of California, Davis
Davis, California

John L. Kermond, Ph.D.
Office of Global Programs
National Oceanographic and Atmospheric Administration
Silver Spring, Maryland

David E. LaHart, Ph.D.
Institute of Science and Public Affairs
Florida State University
Tallahassee, Florida

Joe Leverich, Ph.D.
Department of Biology
St. Louis University
St. Louis, Missouri

Dennis K. Lieu, Ph.D.
Department of Mechanical Engineering
University of California
Berkeley, California

Cynthia J. Moore, Ph.D.
Science Outreach Coordinator
Washington University
St. Louis, Missouri

Joseph M. Moran, Ph.D.
Department of Earth Science
University of Wisconsin–Green Bay
Green Bay, Wisconsin

Joseph Stukey, Ph.D.
Department of Biology
Hope College
Holland, Michigan

Seetha Subramanian
Lexington Community College
University of Kentucky
Lexington, Kentucky

Carl L. Thurman, Ph.D.
Department of Biology
University of Northern Iowa
Cedar Falls, Iowa

Edward D. Walton, Ph.D.
Department of Chemistry
California State Polytechnic University
Pomona, California

Robert S. Young, Ph.D.
Department of Geosciences and Natural Resource Management
Western Carolina University
Cullowhee, North Carolina

Edward J. Zalisko, Ph.D.
Department of Biology
Blackburn College
Carlinville, Illinois

Teacher Reviewers

Stephanie Anderson
Sierra Vista Junior High School
Canyon Country, California

John W. Anson
Mesa Intermediate School
Palmdale, California

Pamela Arline
Lake Taylor Middle School
Norfolk, Virginia

Lynn Beason
College Station Jr. High School
College Station, Texas

Richard Bothmer
Hollis School District
Hollis, New Hampshire

Jeffrey C. Callister
Newburgh Free Academy
Newburgh, New York

Judy D'Albert
Harvard Day School
Corona Del Mar, California

Betty Scott Dean
Guilford County Schools
McLeansville, North Carolina

Sarah C. Duff
Baltimore City Public Schools
Baltimore, Maryland

Melody Law Ewey
Holmes Junior High School
Davis, California

Sherry L. Fisher
Lake Zurich Middle School North
Lake Zurich, Illinois

Melissa Gibbons
Fort Worth ISD
Fort Worth, Texas

Debra J. Goodding
Kraemer Middle School
Placentia, California

Jack Grande
Weber Middle School
Port Washington, New York

Steve Hills
Riverside Middle School
Grand Rapids, Michigan

Carol Ann Lionello
Kraemer Middle School
Placentia, California

Jaime A. Morales
Henry T. Gage Middle School
Huntington Park, California

Patsy Partin
Cameron Middle School
Nashville, Tennessee

Deedra H. Robinson
Newport News Public Schools
Newport News, Virginia

Bonnie Scott
Clack Middle School
Abilene, Texas

Charles M. Sears
Belzer Middle School
Indianapolis, Indiana

Barbara M. Strange
Ferndale Middle School
High Point, North Carolina

Jackie Louise Ulfig
Ford Middle School
Allen, Texas

Kathy Usina
Belzer Middle School
Indianapolis, Indiana

Heidi M. von Oetinger
L'Anse Creuse Public School
Harrison Township, Michigan

Pam Watson
Hill Country Middle School
Austin, Texas

Activity Field Testers

Nicki Bibbo
Russell Street School
Littleton, Massachusetts

Connie Boone
Fletcher Middle School
Jacksonville Beach, Florida

Rose-Marie Botting
Broward County School District
Fort Lauderdale, Florida

Colleen Campos
Laredo Middle School
Aurora, Colorado

Elizabeth Chait
W. L. Chenery Middle School
Belmont, Massachusetts

Holly Estes
Hale Middle School
Stow, Massachusetts

Laura Hapgood
Plymouth Community Intermediate School
Plymouth, Massachusetts

Sandra M. Harris
Winman Junior High School
Warwick, Rhode Island

Jason Ho
Walter Reed Middle School
Los Angeles, California

Joanne Jackson
Winman Junior High School
Warwick, Rhode Island

Mary F. Lavin
Plymouth Community Intermediate School
Plymouth, Massachusetts

James MacNeil, Ph.D.
Concord Public Schools
Concord, Massachusetts

Lauren Magruder
St. Michael's Country Day School
Newport, Rhode Island

Jeanne Maurand
Glen Urquhart School
Beverly Farms, Massachusetts

Warren Phillips
Plymouth Community Intermediate School
Plymouth, Massachusetts

Carol Pirtle
Hale Middle School
Stow, Massachusetts

Kathleen M. Poe
Kirby-Smith Middle School
Jacksonville, Florida

Cynthia B. Pope
Ruffner Middle School
Norfolk, Virginia

Anne Scammell
Geneva Middle School
Geneva, New York

Karen Riley Sievers
Callanan Middle School
Des Moines, Iowa

David M. Smith
Howard A. Eyer Middle School
Macungie, Pennsylvania

Derek Strohschneider
Plymouth Community Intermediate School
Plymouth, Massachusetts

Sallie Teames
Rosemont Middle School
Fort Worth, Texas

Gene Vitale
Parkland Middle School
McHenry, Illinois

Zenovia Young
Meyer Levin Junior High School (IS 285)
Brooklyn, New York

M ◆ 5

PRENTICE HALL SCIENCE EXPLORER

Contents

Motion, Forces, and Energy

Check your compass— regularly assess student progress.

Self-assessment tools are built right into the student text and **on-going assessment** is woven throughout the Teacher's Edition. You'll find a wealth of **assessment technology** in the Resource Pro®, Interactive Student Tutorial, and Assessment Resources CD-ROMs.

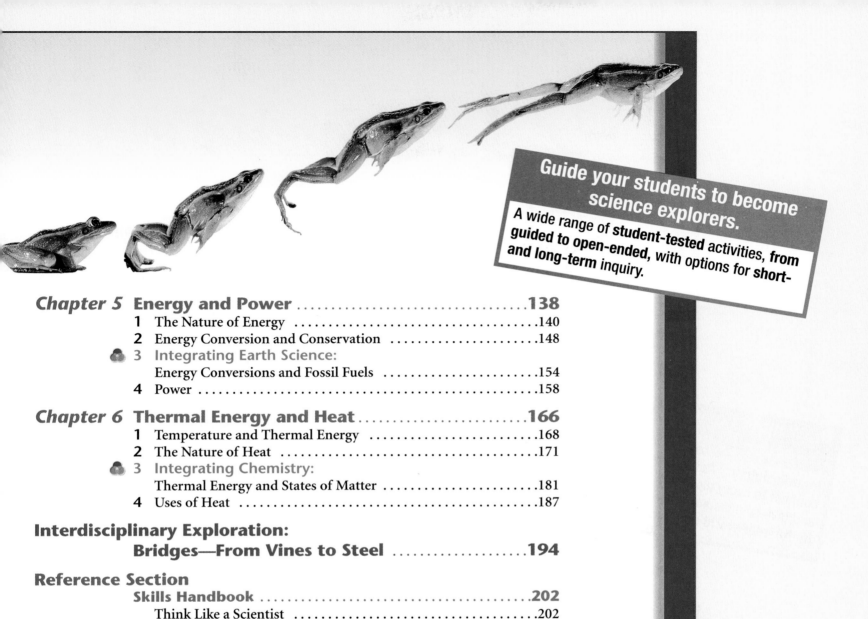

Guide your students to become science explorers.

A wide range of **student-tested activities, from guided to open-ended,** with options for **short- and long-term inquiry.**

Activities

Inquiry Activities

CHAPTER PROJECT

Opportunities for long-term inquiry

DISCOVER

Exploration and inquiry before reading

Draw upon the world around you.

Interdisciplinary Activities connect to every discipline and give science a **meaningful, real-world context.**

Sharpen your Skills

Practice of specific science inquiry skills

TRY THIS

Reinforcement of key concepts

Skills Lab

In-depth practice of inquiry skills

Real-World Lab

Everyday application of science concepts

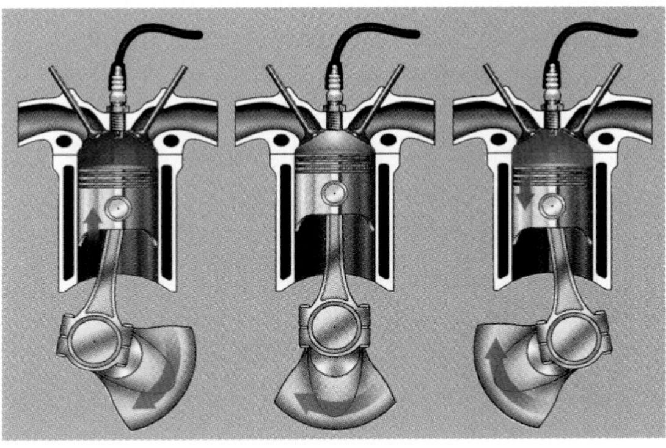

EXPLORING

Visual exploration of concepts

Interdisciplinary Activities

Math Toolbox

Science and History

Science and Society

Connection

Prepare your students with rich, motivating content

Science Explorer is crafted for today's middle grades student, with accessible content and in-depth coverage. **Integrated Science Sections** support every chapter and the **Interdisciplinary Exploration** provides an engaging final unit.

Understanding Nature's Designs

Focus on Engineering

This four-page feature introduces the process of scientific inquiry by involving students in a high-interest, magazine-like feature about a working scientist, engineer Ioannis Miaoulis. By focusing on Dr. Miaoulis's investigation of engineering principles found in nature, the feature highlights making observations and posing questions as key elements of scientific inquiry.

Students do not need any previous knowledge of forces or mechanics to understand and appreciate this feature.

Scientific Inquiry

- Before students read the feature, let them read the title, examine the pictures, and read the captions on their own. Then ask: **What questions came into your mind as you looked at these pictures?** *(Students might suggest questions such as "Why would an engineer study nature?" "How did prairie dogs learn about air currents?" "How do butterfly wings collect heat?" and "Why does a butterfly need heat?")* Point out to students that just as they have questions about what they are seeing, scientists too have questions about what they observe.

Nature of Science

Understanding Nature's Designs

Engineer and Scientist Ioannis Miaoulis
Dr. Miaoulis was born in Greece and grew up there. He then came to the United States to study. He is now a professor of mechanical engineering and Dean of the School of Engineering at Tufts University in Medford, Massachusetts.

Fish in a tank glide under the watchful eye of a video camera. Inside a glass box, spiders spin webs in the wind from a powerful fan. "This is a biomechanics laboratory," says Professor Ioannis Miaoulis (YAHN is my OW lis). "What we study is how animals and plants use energy, motion, and forces."

Miaoulis walks over to a network of earthen tunnels built between two panes of glass. The structure looks like a toy ant farm, but it has a tube for blowing air over the top. Miaoulis explains:

"This is a cross section of a prairie-dog burrow. There are two entrance holes. One hole is flat, while the other one is built up and rounded. Biologists were wondering why. They thought the prairie dogs wanted a good view, but then why not make both holes high and rounded and get a good view from both?"

Background

Engineering is the study of the mathematical and natural sciences and their real-world application. In practice, however, engineering is not a single field. Engineers specialize in various kinds of engineering such as automotive, aerospace, chemical, civil, electronics, industrial, mechanical, textile engineering and many more.

Regardless of which field of engineering a person specializes in, they usually have a basic knowledge of many of the other fields. Real-world engineering involves problems that are complex and involve more than one field of engineering, so a general knowledge is essential.

TALKING WITH IOANNIS MIAOULIS

Miaoulis and his students are learning the likely reason. Wind blowing over a flat surface moves more slowly, because it doesn't have to travel as far as the same breeze going over a rounded surface. "Slow air means high pressure across here" — Miaoulis points to the flat hole. "Fast air going over the rounded hole means low pressure. High pressure here, low pressure there. The holes' shape moves air through the burrow—in the flat hole and out the rounded one. It's prairie-dog air conditioning."

Q *How did you get started in science?*

A I grew up in Athens, Greece. It's a congested and polluted city, but my school was in the woods and I could do things outdoors. I got to love nature. I dug out anthills to see how they were inside. I found the places where turtles laid their eggs. In the summers, we lived near the ocean and every day I'd go fishing and snorkeling. I got to know each rock underwater. I didn't even know what a scientist was then, but I was observing and thinking through things because I wanted to catch more fish. If the flow of water was in this direction, where would be a good place for the fish to hang out? I was observing flow patterns to see where, how, and why fish build their nests. I still do it, in part to catch them, because I still like fishing. But now I do it to observe them, to figure them out. I was always curious.

A prairie dog uses its paws to feed itself grass from the western prairie.

Air moves through a prairie dog hole that can be more than four meters deep. Side pockets are for nesting and food storage.

How Prairie-Dog Air Conditioning Works

1. **Air moves over the flat hole.**
2. **Air moves faster over the rounded hole. Fast-moving air creates a large pressure drop.**

Air flows from an area of high pressure to an area of low pressure. The difference in pressure between the two holes pushes air through the prairie dogs' burrow, creating a breeze.

- Encourage students to tell what they already know about designs in nature that are also practical. To prompt student thinking, have them brainstorm a list of techniques animals use to camouflage themselves. Alternatively, have students brainstorm a list of ways that animals change their body temperature. For examples, when snakes are losing body heat, they coil in order to reduce their surface area. Point out, however, that the snakes do not understand the physics of temperature loss. Their behavior is instinctual, not learned. Similarly, the prairie dogs have not learned that they should round one burrow hole.
- Have a volunteer read the captions on page 11 aloud. Review with students that air moves from higher pressure to lower pressure.
- Encourage interested students to think about what kind of apparatus they would want to design to test the amount of breeze underground. The apparatus would be used to experiment with what effect increasing the amount of rounding has on the amount of breeze.
- Point out that, although curiosity is a useful characteristic to have, interfering with some animals is not only irresponsible but also illegal. For example, on some beaches where endangered sea turtles lay eggs, signs are posted warning people that disturbing the turtles, the nests, or the eggs will result in fines and imprisonment.
- If students seem particularly interested in engineering, share the information in Background on p. 10. Also suggest that they consult library books to learn more about the different types of engineering. (See Further Reading, page 13.)

Background

Dr. Miaoulis is a professor of mechanical engineering. Mechanical engineers design, test, build, and operate machinery. Some mechanical engineers specialize in particular types of machines such as pumps or automobile engines. Mechanical engineers also design and build manufactured goods. Often, an engineer must design not only a product, but also the machine that will make the product. Mechanical engineers who design cars, for example, would also help to design the car assembly process.

Because machinery generates heat, mechanical engineers need to know about heating, ventilation, and energy. Students will be introduced to some of these topics in this book.

- Ask students to name items they have taken apart to see how they worked. Ask students if they ever changed the design of something so that it would work better. Ask students: **What characteristics do you need to be able to take something apart and put it back together again?** *(Student answers will vary. Samples: methodical, careful, organized, tidy)*
- Point out that some people most enjoy studying pure sciences; in other words, studying the laws of science because of their own beauty and logic. Other people enjoy learning how to apply the pure facts of science in practical ways.
- Bring to class a computer chip or a photograph of a chip for students who do not know what they look like. Point out that computer chips do not make any noise. The sound a computer is making when it is turned on is usually the sound of the fan. Most computers have fans to keep the chips from overheating.
- Ask students: **Why did Dr. Miaoulis choose to study butterflies rather than lizards to solve the problem of chips heating unevenly?** *(Butterfly wings are made of thin films. Lizard skin is not.)* **How do we know that butterflies need heat?** *(We see them basking in the sun.)*

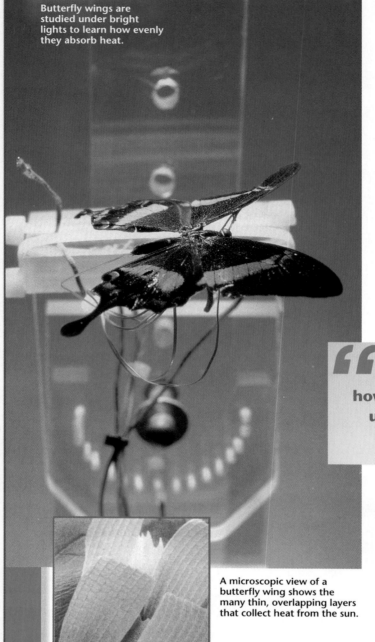

Butterfly wings are studied under bright lights to learn how evenly they absorb heat.

Q *You teach engineering. Is that different from science?*

A Well, I enjoyed doing things with my hands, taking things apart and seeing how they worked, building things and making them work. I found that what I enjoyed about studying was learning science and then doing something with it. And that's engineering. I try to discover something about an animal that nobody ever understood before. Then I'll use that information to design something that will make people's lives easier.

Q *How have you used nature in your engineering designs?*

A Here's an example. I got interested in how heat travels in the chips that make computers work.

> **"What we study is how animals and plants use energy, motion, and forces."**

They're made in very thin layers or films, thinner than one-hundredth the thickness of your hair. Sometimes, if chips don't heat evenly, they fall apart when you try to make them. I wondered if any plants or animals had solved that problem—using thin films to control how heat was absorbed or reflected. We looked for animals that bask or lie in the sun, or for animals and insects that depend on the warmth of the sun.

A microscopic view of a butterfly wing shows the many thin, overlapping layers that collect heat from the sun.

Background

Besides studying butterflies and prairie dog tunnels, Dr. Miaoulis and his students have studied other animals in the Comparative Biomechanics Laboratory. By studying sea anemones in a current, they are learning how the anemone's shape helps it filter food from sea water without being swept away by the current. He has also studied other sea creatures in water currents to see how their shape enables them to survive. Dr. Miaoulis hopes that understanding the design of these creatures will provide solutions to human design problems in the future.

Interested students can access the web page of Dr. Miaoulis's Comparative Biomechanics Laboratory at Tufts University at **www.tufts.edu/as/tampl/cbl/**.

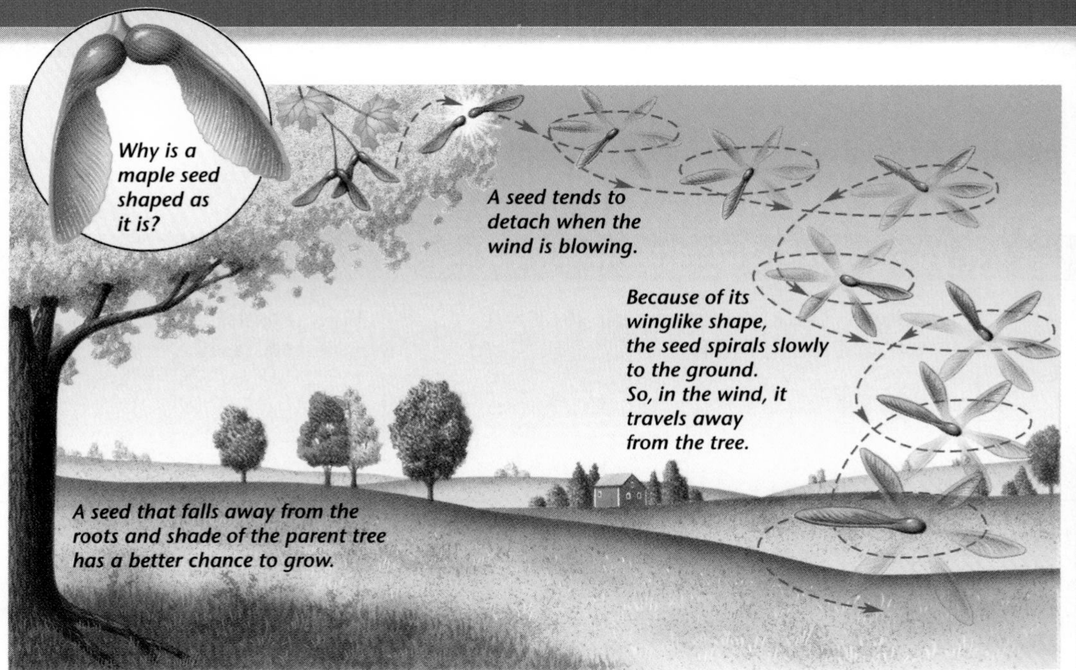

Why is a maple seed shaped as it is?
A seed tends to detach when the wind is blowing.
Because of its winglike shape, the seed spirals slowly to the ground. So, in the wind, it travels away from the tree.
A seed that falls away from the roots and shade of the parent tree has a better chance to grow.

If you touch a butterfly, you get a dust on your fingers. When I was little I used to catch butterflies and didn't really understand what the dust was. If you slice those "dust" particles, you find that they are made of many layers. These thin films are little solar collectors. Butterflies can change the amount of heat they catch. They just change the angle at which they hold the thin films on their wings up to the sun. Large areas of butterfly wings heat evenly. So we're looking at the layers on butterfly wings to learn how to make computer chips that will transfer heat more evenly.

Q *How do you come up with the questions you ask?*

A It depends. Sometimes it's simply by observing things. If you see a maple seed with wings falling in a fancy way, you might not even think twice about it. But if you start observing and appreciating nature, you start asking questions about how things work. Why would it help the tree to have a seed that could be blown by the wind? I can combine my love of nature from when I was small with what I've learned of science and engineering.

Maple seeds can fall to the ground any time from May to early fall.

In Your Journal

Do you, too, have "a questioning eye"? Miaoulis carefully observes plants and animals and asks himself questions about them. Quietly observe some animals in your environment (pets, insects, birds) for 15 or 20 minutes. Then write down four "how" or "why" questions about the movement and speed of the animals. For example, why does a frog have a stop-and-start movement?

- If possible, bring winged maple seeds to class or ask students who live near maple trees to bring seeds to class. Or have students trace the shape of the seeds on paper. Students cut out paper seeds and drop them to compare how they fall. Ask: **Is the shape of the maple seed wing the only factor, or does the seed wing have other features that affect its fall?** *(Accept all reasonable answers.)* Challenge interested students to continue experimenting with different paper seed wings to find how thickness, texture, and size affect the seed's fall.

In Your Journal Point out to students that they can find insects in places that are neither large nor nature-like. They can find insects in a vacant lot, in a garden bed, or around playing fields in the school yard. Provide follow-up in class by giving students a brief opportunity to share the questions they wrote. Extend the discussion by asking: **Where would you begin looking for answers to your questions? Did you observe something about the animal that you had never been aware of before the exercise?**

Introducing Motion, Forces, and Energy

Have students look through the table of contents and the book to find the parts that relate most closely to this feature. *(Chapter 3, Pressure and Applying Bernoulli's Principle; Chapter 6, Thermal Energy and Heat, particularly section 6-1, Temperature and Thermal Energy, and section 6-2, The Nature of Heat.)* Ask: **Besides heat, what else is this book about?** *(motion, forces, and energy)* **What kinds of things do you think you will be learning about?** *(Accept all responses without comments.)*

Reading Strategies

Further Reading

- Hooker, Saralinda, Christopher Ragus, and Mario G. Salvadori, *The Art of Construction: Projects and Principles for Beginning Engineers.* Chicago Review Press, 1990.
- Neill, William, and Pat Murphy. *By Nature's Design (An Exploratorium Book).* Chronicle Books, 1993.
- Willis, Delta. *The Sand Dollar and the Slide Rule: Drawing Blueprints from Nature.* Perseus Press, 1996.
- Freedman, David H. "The Butterfly Solution," *Discover Magazine,* Vol. 18, Number 4, April 1997.
- National Society of Professional Engineers' website for high school students at **www.nspe.org/st-home.htm.**

Motion

Sections	Time	Student Edition Activities	Other Activities
CHAPTER PROJECT 1 **Speeds à la Carte** p. 15	Ongoing (2 weeks)	Check Your Progress, pp. 25, 38 Wrap Up, p. 41	**TE** Chapter 1 Project Notes, pp. 14–15
1 Describing and Measuring Motion pp. 16–27 ◆ Explain when an object is in motion and how motion is relative to a reference point. ◆ Calculate an object's speed and velocity using SI units of distance. ◆ Graph motion showing changes in distance as a function of time.	6 periods/ 3 blocks	**Discover** How Fast and How Far?, p. 16 **Try This** Sunrise, Sunset, p. 18 **Skills Lab** Inclined to Roll, pp. 26–27	**TE** Building Inquiry Skills: Applying Concepts, p. 17 **TE** Integrating Mathematics, p. 19 **TE** Math Toolbox, p. 19 **TE** Inquiry Challenge, p. 21 **TE** Exploring Motion Graphs, p. 24
2 *Integrating Earth Science* **Slow Motion on Planet Earth** pp. 28–33 ◆ Explain the slow movement of Earth's plates and calculate their speed.	3 periods/ 1–2 blocks	**Discover** How Slow Can It Flow?, p. 28 **Sharpen your Skills** Predicting, p. 29 **Real-World Lab: You and Your Community** Stopping on a Dime, pp. 32–33	**TE** Building Inquiry Skills: Problem Solving, p. 30
3 Acceleration pp. 34–38 ◆ Describe what happens to the motion of an object as it accelerates. ◆ Calculate the acceleration of an object and graph changing speed and distance of an accelerating object.	2–3 periods/ 1–2 blocks	**Discover** Will You Hurry Up?, p. 34	**TE** Inquiry Challenge, p. 35 **TE** Integrating Space Science, p. 36 **ISLM** M-1,"Measuring Speed"
Study Guide/Chapter Review pp. 39–41	1 period/ $\frac{1}{2}$ block		**ISAB** Provides teaching and review of all inquiry skills

For Standard or Block Schedule The Resource Pro® CD-ROM gives you maximum flexibility for planning your instruction for any type of schedule. Resource Pro® contains Planning Express®, an advanced scheduling program, as well as the entire contents of the Teaching Resources and the Computer Test Bank.

CHAPTER PLANNING GUIDE

Program Resources	Assessment Strategies	Media and Technology
TR Chapter 1 Project Teacher Notes, pp. 8–9 **TR** Chapter 1 Project Overview and Worksheets, pp. 10–13 **TR** Chapter 1 Project Scoring Rubric, p. 14	**SE** Performance Assessment: Chapter 1 Project Wrap-Up, p. 41 **TR** Chapter 1 Project Scoring Rubric, p. 14 **TE** Check Your Progress, pp. 25, 38 **TE** Performance Assessment: Chapter 1 Project Wrap-Up, p. 41	Science Explorer Internet Site
TR 1-1 Lesson Plan, p. 15 **TR** 1-1 Section Summary, p. 16 **TR** 1-1 Review and Reinforce, p. 17 **TR** 1-1 Enrich, p. 18 **TR** Chapter 1 Skills Lab, pp. 27–28	**SE** Section 1 Review, p. 25 **SE** Analyze and Conclude, p. 27 **TE** Ongoing Assessment, pp. 19, 21, 23 **TE** Performance Assessment, p. 25 **TR** 1-1 Review and Reinforce, p. 17	Exploring Physical Science Videodisc, Unit 3 Side 1, "Travel" Audiotapes: English-Spanish Summary 1-1 Transparency 1, "Exploring Motion Graphs" Interactive Student Tutorial CD-ROM, M-1
TR 1-2 Lesson Plan, p. 19 **TR** 1-2 Section Summary, p. 20 **TR** 1-2 Review and Reinforce, p. 21 **TR** 1-2 Enrich, p. 22 **TR** Chapter 1 Real-World Lab, pp. 29–31 **SES** Book F, *Inside Earth,* Chapter 1	**SE** Section 2 Review, p. 31 **SE** Analyze and Conclude, p. 33 **TE** Ongoing Assessment, p. 29 **TE** Performance Assessment, p. 31 **TR** 1-2 Review and Reinforce, p. 21	Exploring Earth Science Videodisc, Unit 3 Side 1, "Everything on Your Plate" Exploring Earth Science Videodisc, Unit 3 Side 1, "Journey to the Bottom of the Sea" Audiotapes: English-Spanish Summary 1-2 Interactive Student Tutorial CD-ROM, M-1
TR 1-3 Lesson Plan, p. 23 **TR** 1-3 Section Summary, p. 24 **TR** 1-3 Review and Reinforce, p. 25 **TR** 1-3 Enrich, p. 26	**SE** Section 3 Review, p. 38 **TE** Ongoing Assessment, pp. 35, 37 **TE** Performance Assessment, p. 38 **TR** 1-3 Review and Reinforce, p. 25	Exploring Physical Science Videodisc, Unit 3 Side 1, "Light as a Feather" Audiotapes: English-Spanish Summary 1-3 Interactive Student Tutorial CD-ROM, M-1
TR Chapter 1 Performance Assessment, pp. 186–188 **TR** Chapter 1 Test, pp. 189–192	**SE** Chapter Review, pp. 39–41 **TR** Chapter 1 Performance Assessment, pp. 186–188 **TR** Chapter 1 Test, pp. 189–192 **CTB** Test M–1	Computer Test Bank, Test M-1 Interactive Student Tutorial CD-ROM, M-1

Key: **SE** Student Edition
CTB Computer Test Bank
ISAB Inquiry Skills Activity Book
TE Teacher's Edition
SES Science Explorer Series Text
PTA Product Testing Activities by *Consumer Reports*
TR Teaching Resources
ISLM Integrated Science Laboratory Manual
IES Interdisciplinary Explorations Series

Meeting the National Science Education Standards and AAAS Benchmarks

National Science Education Standards	Benchmarks for Science Literacy	Unifying Themes
Science as Inquiry (Content Standard A) ◆ **Use appropriate tools and techniques to gather, analyze, and interpret data** Students make distance and time measurements, then analyze and interpret their data. *(Chapter Project; Skills Lab)* ◆ **Design and conduct an experiment** An experiment is designed and conducted to determine what distance is necessary beyond the out-of-bounds line on a basketball court. *(Real-World Lab)* ◆ **Use mathematics in all aspects of scientific inquiry** Students measure time and distance and calculate speed. *(Chapter Project; Section 1, 2; Skills Lab; Real-World Lab)* Students calculate acceleration. *(Section 3)* **Physical Science** (Content Standard B) ◆ **Motions and forces** Students learn how to describe the motion of an object. They also learn to represent motion on a graph. *(Section 1)* Students learn how to calculate acceleration. *(Section 3)* **Earth and Space Science** (Content Standard C) ◆ **Structure of the earth system** Students apply knowledge about the Earth's moving plates and calculate the speed and distance of their motion. *(Section 2)*	**3A Technology and Science** The history of speed and transportation is discussed with emphasis on the progress of technology. *(Section 1)* **4F Motion** Objects in motion have a direction and speed that can be changed. *(Sections 1, 3)* **9B Symbolic Relationships** Students quantify speed and acceleration using equations and graph the motion of various objects. *(Sections 1, 2; 3; Skills Lab)* **10A Displacing the Earth from the Center of the Universe** Students learn that motion is relative to a given reference point. *(Section 1)* **12B Computation and Estimation** Students determine units of measurement, estimate distances, and compare numbers in measurements of speed and acceleration. *(Sections 2, 3; Chapter Project, Real-World Lab)*	◆ **Evolution** The Earth's plates move at a measurable velocity so scientists can predict how they will change over time. *(Section 2)* ◆ **Patterns of Change** As an object accelerates, its motion changes as it slows down, speeds up, or changes direction. *(Sections 1, 2, 3; Real-World Lab)* ◆ **Scale and Structure** The idea of scale is emphasized with SI units and unit conversions. SI units can be used for very large and very small speeds. *(Sections 1 and 2)* ◆ **Systems and interactions** Earth's tectonic plates comprise a complex system with many different types of interactions as plates collide, pull apart, or slide past each other. *(Sections 1 and 2)* ◆ **Modeling** Students conduct an activity to measure speed. An experiment is designed and conducted to determine what distance is necessary between the out-of-bounds line and a wall so that a basketball player can stop before hitting the wall. *(Skills Lab, Real-World Lab)*

Media and Technology

Exploring Physical Science Videodisc

◆ **Section 1** "Travel" examines some of the factors that affect travel. Frame of reference, speed, and direction are discussed.

Exploring Earth Science Videodisc

◆ **Section 2** "Everything on Your Plate" illustrates how geologic activity occurs at divergent, convergent, and strike-slip plate boundaries.

◆ **Section 2** "Journey to the Bottom of the Sea" provides evidence of sea-floor spreading by examining trenches, mountain ranges, and continental rocks under the sea.

Interactive Student Tutorial CD-ROM

◆ **Chapter Review** Interactive questions help students to self-assess their mastery of key chapter concepts.

Student Edition Connection Strategies

◆ **Section 1** **Integrating Mathematics,** p. 18
Math Toolbox, p. 19
Social Studies Connection, p. 20
Science and History, pp. 22–23

◆ **Section 2** **Integrating Earth Science,** p. 28

◆ **Section 3** **Integrating Space Science,** p. 36

Visit the Science Explorer Internet site to find an up-to-date activity for Chapter 1 of *Motion, Forces, and Energy.*

ACTIVITY	Time (minutes)	Materials Quantities for one work group	Skills
Section 1			
Discover, p. 16	15	**Consumable** masking tape **Nonconsumable** meter stick, stopwatch	Inferring
Try This, p. 18	5 min, 6–8 times during 1 day	**Consumable** No special materials are required.	Observing, Interpreting data, Drawing conclusions
Skills Lab, pp. 26–27	40	**Consumable** masking tape **Nonconsumable** skateboard, meter stick, protractor, flat board about 1.5 m long, small piece of sturdy cardboard, supports to prop up the board (books, boxes), 2 stopwatches or wristwatches with a stopwatch function	Measuring
Section 2			
Discover, p. 28	20	**Consumable** honey, masking tape, damp cloths or paper towels **Nonconsumable** spoon, plate, books or blocks, metric ruler, stopwatch or clock	Observing, Inferring
Sharpen Your Skills, p. 29	15	**Consumable** No special materials are required.	Predicting
Real-World Lab, pp. 32–33	50	**Nonconsumable** wooden meter stick, tape measure, 2 stopwatches or watches with second hands	Measuring Calculating Inferring
Section 3			
Discover, p. 34	15	**Consumable** masking tape **Nonconsumable** meter stick, stopwatch	Inferring

A list of all materials required for the Student Edition activities can be found on pages T14–T15. You can order Materials Kits by calling 1-800-828-7777 or by accessing the Science Explorer Internet site at **www.science-explorer.phschool.com.**

Speeds à la Carte

While moving objects are very common in our daily lives, measuring the motion of an object is a very sophisticated notion. In this chapter, students will be introduced to three of the useful ways of measuring and describing motion: speed, velocity, and acceleration. The Chapter Project allows students to develop and practice techniques used to measure motion.

Purpose In this project, students will identify and measure the motion of several different objects.

Skills Focus Students will be able to
- ◆ measure distance and time accurately;
- ◆ record data in lists or tables;
- ◆ apply concepts learned in class to calculate speed;
- ◆ communicate their work on display cards.

Project Time Line Students can begin measuring speeds the first week. Some measurements can be completed in a very short period of time, although others, such as the rate at which grass grows, may take longer. Most students should be able to complete all of their measurements within one week. Allow another week for students to prepare display cards for presenting the speeds that they measured. Before beginning the project, see Chapter 1 Project Teacher Notes on pages 8–9 in Teaching Resources for more details on carrying out the project. Also, distribute the students' Chapter 1 Project Student Overview and Worksheets and Scoring Rubric on pages 10–14 in Teaching Resources.

Suggested Shortcuts Although the project is written to be completed by students individually at home, they could complete parts of the project in groups in the classroom. You may wish to adjust the requirements of each level of success to better match the cooperative capabilities of small groups of students. To ensure that all students have ample opportunities to measure speed, have each student measure at least one speed at home and in class.

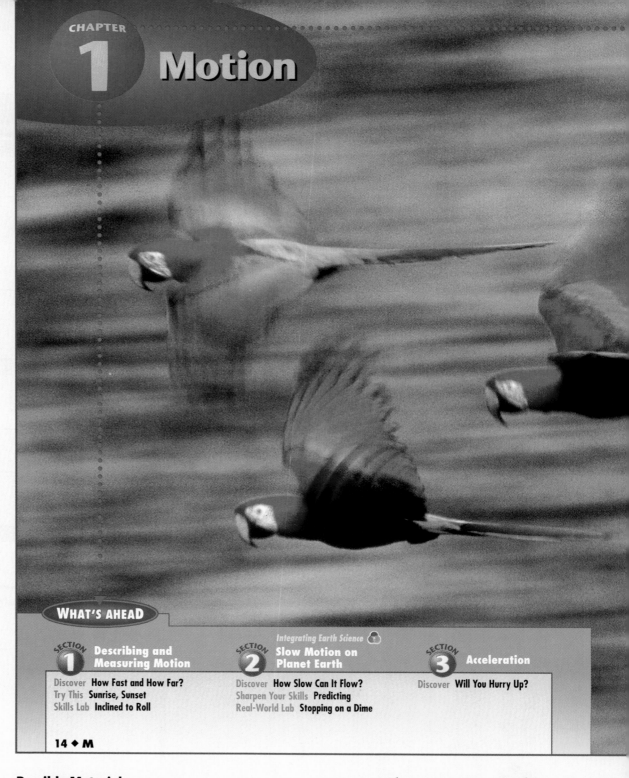

CHAPTER 1

Motion

WHAT'S AHEAD

14 ◆ M

Possible Materials
- ◆ metric ruler to measure centimeters and millimeters
- ◆ device to measure meters such as meter sticks, tape measures, or strings marked in meters
- ◆ timing device such as a stop watch or clock

Launching the Project To introduce the project and to stimulate student interest, show students several toys that move in various ways, such as wind up cars or other toys. Some of these should move in straight lines with constant speed, some can move in other ways. Or have one volunteer walk in a straight line, another walk in a circle, while a third walks randomly. Ask: **What are some other examples of motion?** *(Sample: a cloud moving in the sky, an acorn falling from an oak tree, a sprinter running down a track)* **How can we describe different types of motion?** *(Measure distance and time, create a map showing the various positions)*

Allow time for students to read the Chapter Project Overview on pages 10–11 in Teaching

PROJECT 1

Speeds à la Carte

Imagine that you have traveled thousands of miles to visit the tropics of South America. Suddenly, vivid reds and blues brighten the green of the rain forest as a group of macaws swoop down and perch above you in a nut tree. They squawk at each other as they crack nuts with their powerful jaws and eat the meat. In a few minutes they spread their wings to take off, and vanish from sight. The macaws cracking nuts, flapping their wings, and flying through the forest are all examples of motion. Your plane flight to South America is another.

In this chapter, you will learn how to describe and measure motion. You will find examples of motion and describe how fast different objects move. You will measure the speeds of various common moving things.

Your Goal To identify several examples of motion and measure how fast each one moves. You will arrange your results from slowest to fastest.

Your project must

- include careful distance and time measurements
- use your data to calculate the speed of each example
- provide display cards that show data, diagrams, and calculations
- follow the safety guidelines in Appendix A

Get Started Brainstorm with a group of your classmates several examples of motion. For example, you might consider a feather falling, the water level rising in a bathtub, or the minute hand moving on a clock. Which examples will be easy to measure? Which will be more challenging?

Check Your Progress You'll be working on this project as you study this chapter. To keep your project on track, look for Check Your Progress boxes at the following points.

Section 1 Review, page 25: Create a data table.
Section 3 Review, page 38: Repeat measurements and make calculations.

Wrap Up At the end of the chapter (page 41), you will compare the speeds recorded by the class.

These red-and-green macaws live in the Amazon River basin in Peru.

Resources. Then encourage discussions on measuring speed and answer any initial questions students may have. Pass out copies of the Chapter 1 Project Worksheets on pages 12–13 in Teaching Resources for students to review. Make sure students understand the the requirements. Have students review the rubric and set goals for their work.

Program Resources

- **Teaching Resources** Chapter 1 Project Teacher's Notes, pp. 8–9; Chapter 1 Project Overview and Worksheets, pp. 10-13; Chapter 1 Project Scoring Rubric, p. 14

Performance Assessment

The Chapter 1 Project Scoring Rubric on page 14 of Teaching Resources will help you evaluate how well students complete the Chapter 1 Project. You may wish to share the scoring rubric with your students so they are clear about what will be expected of them. Students will be assessed on

- how carefully they measured and how thoroughly they recorded data;
- their explanations of how they calculated the speeds;
- the clarity of their data and the associated units of measurement in each step of their written displays;
- the thoroughness and organization of their display cards.

Section 1 Describing and Measuring Motion

Objectives

After completing the lesson, students will be able to

- explain when an object is in motion and how motion is relative to a reference point;
- calculate an object's speed and velocity using SI units of distance;
- graph motion showing changes in distance as a function of time.

Key Terms motion, reference point, International System of Units (SI), meter, speed, velocity

1 Engage/Explore

Activating Prior Knowledge

Invite students to list various kinds of movement on the board. Ask: **How did you know the object moved?** *(Sample: Because I saw it change position.)* Then ask: **Did the object appear to move slowly or quickly? How could you tell?** *(Sample: The plane appeared to move slowly.)* Explain to students that everything around us is moving in some way.

Discover Activity

Skills Focus inferring
Materials *meter stick, stopwatch, masking tape*
Time 15 minutes
Tips Tape a long piece of masking tape to the ground as a starting line. Place another piece of tape 5 m from the first piece for Step 1. Tell students to use a third piece of tape to mark their location after 5 seconds for Step 2. Remind students to walk at a normal pace for the first two measurements. Ask: **How can you change the distance that you travel in 5 seconds?** *(Walk or run faster or slower, take larger or smaller steps.)*
Think It Over The faster you walk, the greater the distance you go in a certain time. If you walk for a longer time at a given speed, you travel a greater distance. If you walk a longer distance in a given amount of time, you are walking faster.

Section 1 Describing and Measuring Motion

Discover Activity

How Fast and How Far?

1. Find out how long it takes you to walk 5 meters at a normal pace. Record your time.
2. Now find out how far you can walk in 5 seconds if you walk at a normal pace. Record your distance.
3. Repeat Steps 1 and 2, walking slower than your normal pace. Then repeat Steps 1 and 2, walking faster than your normal pace.

Think It Over
Inferring What is the relationship between the distance you walk, the time it takes you to walk, and your walking speed?

Guide for Reading

- When is an object in motion?
- How can you find the speed and velocity of an object?

Reading Tip Before you read, rewrite the headings in the section as questions. As you read, look for answers.

It's three o'clock and school is over! You hurry out of class to enjoy the bright afternoon. A light breeze is blowing. A few clouds are lazily drifting across the sky, and colorful leaves float down from the trees. Two birds fly playfully over your head. A bunch of frisky squirrels chase one another up a tree. You spend a few minutes with some friends who are kicking a ball around. Then you head home.

Does anything strike you about this afternoon scene? It is filled with all kinds of motion: blowing, drifting, fluttering, flying, and chasing. There are simple motions and complicated motions, motions

▼ Gray squirrels

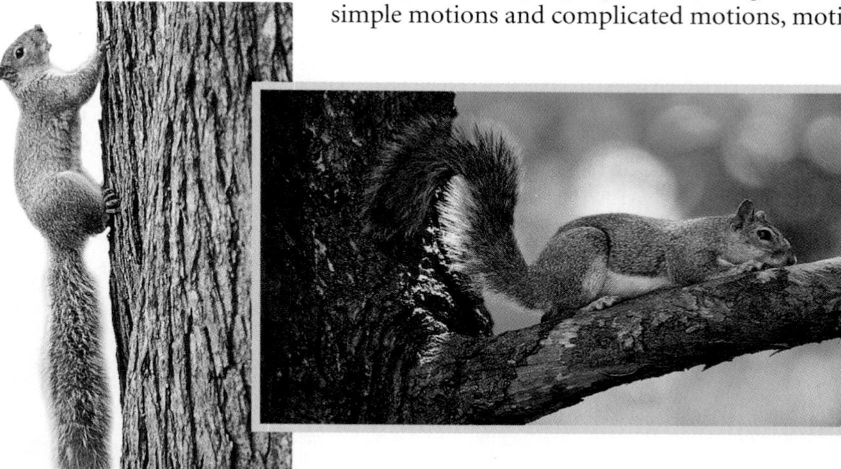

Reading Strategies

Reading Tip Discuss with students how they might rewrite each heading as a question. For example, they could write "How do I know when something is in motion?" for *Recognizing Motion.* Have students write down their questions. Suggest they leave space by each question so they can answer questions as they read.

Vocabulary Concepts and definitions in physics are often described by mathematical formulas. Tell students that if they do not understand the way a concept is explained in the text, they can look for a formula.

Study and Comprehension Suggest students write new definitions and formulas on note cards while they are working on the section. Make sure they include the formulas for calculating constant speed and average speed as well as the definition of velocity.

Figure 1 Whether or not an object is in motion depends on the reference point you choose. *Comparing and Contrasting* *Which people are moving if you compare them to the escalator? Which people are moving if you compare them to Earth?*

that are over in a moment, and motions that continue all afternoon. How else can you describe all of these examples of motion? There is actually a great deal to understand about how and why all these things move as they do. In this section, you will learn how scientists describe and measure motion.

Recognizing Motion

Deciding if an object is in motion isn't as easy as it sounds. For example, you are probably sitting as you read this paragraph. Are you moving? Other than your eyes blinking and your chest moving up and down, you would probably say that you (and this book) are not moving. An object is in **motion** when its distance from another object is changing. Since the distance between you and this book is not changing, you conclude that neither you nor the book is moving.

At the same time that you think you are sitting still, you are actually moving about 30 kilometers every second. At that speed, you could travel from New York City to Los Angeles in about 2 minutes! You are moving because you are on planet Earth, which is orbiting the sun. Earth moves about 30 kilometers every second, so you and everything else on Earth are moving at that speed as well.

Whether an object is moving or not depends on your point of view. If you compare the books on a desk to the floor beneath them, they are not moving.

2 Facilitate

Recognizing Motion

Language Arts Connection

Read aloud an action-filled poem such as "Paul Revere's Ride" by Longfellow. Ask: **What words and phrases does the poet use to describe motion?** *(Sample: raced, crept)* Explain that poets use descriptive language to help readers and listeners understand the poem. **learning modality: verbal**

Building Inquiry Skills: Applying Concepts

Materials *globes, measuring tape*
Time 15 minutes

Have students work in small groups. Ask them to locate their home state on the globe. Then ask them to locate Tokyo, Japan. Have them use the measuring tape to find the distance on the globe between their state and Tokyo. Have a volunteer rotate the globe one-half turn starting from the home state. **Why doesn't our state get closer to or farther away from Japan when the globe turns?** *(Japan is moving at the same rate as everything else on the globe.)* **cooperative learning**

Using the Visuals: Figure 1

Draw students' attention to the person at the top of the "up" escalator. Ask: **Which people are moving relative to this person?** *(The people on the "down" escalator)* Then ask: **Why isn't this person at the top moving from the point of view of the person a few steps behind him?** *(The distance between them stays the same.)* **learning modality: visual**

Program Resources

◆ **Teaching Resources** 1-1 Lesson Plan, p. 15; 1-1 Section Summary, p. 16

Media and Technology

Audiotapes English-Spanish Summary 1-1

Answers to Self-Assessment

Caption Question

Figure 1 The people standing still on each escalator are not moving with respect to each other if each escalator is used as a reference point. The people walking on the escalator are moving with respect to the escalator. All the people are moving with respect to Earth.

Ongoing Assessment

Writing Have students write a paragraph about their trip to school in the morning describing everything they saw that was moving.

Recognizing Motion, continued

Skills Focus observing
Time 5 minutes, 6 to 8 times during 1 day
Tips Students should pick a place for their observations that they can visit throughout the day, and mark the spot. Have students draw a sketch of their observation area from their reference point, complete with buildings and trees. Direct students to record the position of the sun on their sketches. Remind them to include the time of observation. Ask: **How did the position of the sun at lunch time compare with the position of the sun in the morning and late afternoon?** *(The sun appeared higher in the sky at lunch time than it appeared at other times.)*
Expected Outcome Students should observe that the sun moves across the sky throughout the day. However, they should conclude that they see the sun as moving because they use the things around them as reference points. If they view the same information, but use the sun as a reference point, they can show that Earth is moving.
Extend Using a flashlight and a globe or large ball, have students model the motion of the Earth and the sun. By marking a spot on the ball, students can demonstrate how the sun appears to move from the perspective of someone on Earth. **learning modality: visual**

Including all Students

Students who are still mastering English may have increased difficulty understanding the words in this section that indicate motion. Pair them with native English speakers and have partners find such words, list them, then form sentences using the words.
limited English proficiency

Figure 2 Both the Hubble Space Telescope and the astronaut are actually moving rapidly through space. But compared to the Hubble Space Telescope, the astronaut is not moving and can therefore complete necessary repairs.

Sunrise, Sunset

ACTIVITY

Earth moves around the sun. But it is the sun that appears to move. Doesn't it?

1. Choose a spot from which you can observe the sky throughout one day.
2. From the same spot, observe the sun at 6 to 8 different times during the day. **CAUTION:** *Be careful not to look directly at the sun.* Describe its position by comparing it with things around you, such as trees and buildings.
3. Draw a diagram of the sun throughout the day.

Observing What reference point(s) did you use to study the sun? Did the sun appear to move when compared with those reference points? Did it move?

But if you compare them to the sun, the books are moving quite rapidly. Earth and the sun are different reference points. A **reference point** is a place or object used for comparison to determine if something is in motion. **An object is in motion if it changes position relative to a reference point.** You assume that the reference point is stationary, or not moving.

If you have ever been on a slow-moving train, you know that you may not be able to tell the train is moving unless you look out the window. A nearby building is a good reference point, and a glance at it will tell you if you and the train are moving. But it is important to choose your reference point carefully. Have you ever been in a school bus stopped right next to another school bus? Suddenly, you think your bus is moving backward. When you look out the window on the other side, you find that your bus isn't moving at all. Actually, the other bus is moving forward! Your bus seemed to be moving backward because you used the other bus as a reference point. You assumed your reference point was stationary. But in fact, your reference point—the other bus—was really moving.

Describing Distance

INTEGRATING MATHEMATICS To describe motion further, you need to use units of measurement. Whether you realize it or not, you use units, or standard quantities, all the time. You might, for example, measure 2 cups of milk for a recipe, swim 100 yards after school, or buy 3 pounds of fruit at the store. Cups, yards, and pounds are all units.

Scientists all over the world use the same system of units so that they can communicate information clearly. This system of

Background

Integrating Science Throughout recorded time, civilizations have devised methods of measurement. Units of measurement are often based on parts of the human body. For example, the Egyptians called the distance from the fingertips to the elbow a *cubit.* Even our own U.S. system has some units based on body parts. One example is the *foot.* The standard system of units we use today is a relatively modern innovation. At one time, practically every nation on Earth used a different system of units. This made commerce and trade between nations very difficult. Today, even when different units of measurement are used (such as feet or gallons) they are defined in terms of the standard system of units.

measurement is called the **International System of Units,** or in French, Système International (SI). SI is a system based on the number ten. This makes calculations with the system relatively easy.

The basic SI unit of length is the **meter** (m). A meter is a little longer than a yard. The Eiffel Tower in Figure 3 is measured in meters. To measure the length of an object smaller than a meter, scientists use the metric unit called the centimeter (cm). The prefix *centi-* means "one hundredth." A centimeter is one hundredth of a meter, so there are 100 centimeters in a meter. The beautiful butterfly in Figure 3 is measured in centimeters. For even smaller lengths, the millimeter (mm) is used. The prefix *milli-* means "one thousandth." So there are 1,000 millimeters in a meter. In the International System large objects, or long distances, are measured in kilometers (km). The prefix *kilo-* means "one thousand." There are 1,000 meters in a kilometer.

SI units are also used to describe quantities other than length. You can find more information about SI units in the Skills Handbook on page 204 of this textbook.

☑ *Checkpoint* *What unit would you use to describe the width of your thumb?*

Converting Units

When you convert one metric unit to another, you must move the decimal point.

1. How many millimeters are in 14.5 meters? You are converting from a larger unit to a smaller one, so you multiply. There are 1,000 millimeters in a meter. To multiply by 1,000, move the decimal to the right three places.
   14.500 m = 14,500. mm
   There are 14,500 mm in 14.5 m.
2. Convert 1,200 centimeters to meters. You are converting from a smaller unit to a larger one, so you divide (move the decimal to the left).
   1,200. cm = 12.00 m
   1,200 cm equals 12 m.

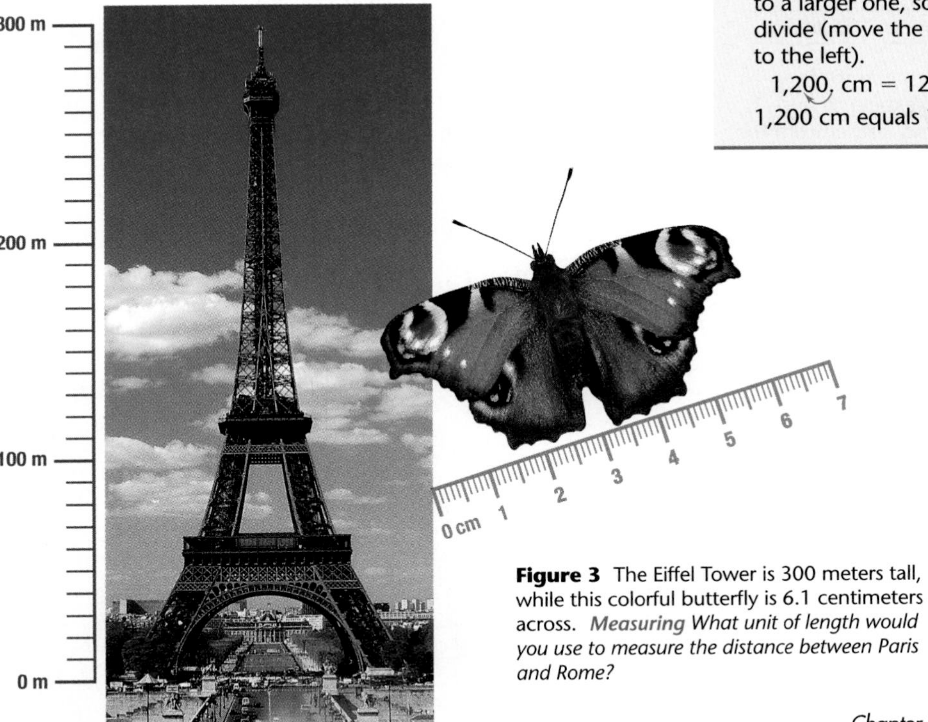

Figure 3 The Eiffel Tower is 300 meters tall, while this colorful butterfly is 6.1 centimeters across. *Measuring What unit of length would you use to measure the distance between Paris and Rome?*

Describing Distance

Integrating Mathematics

ACTIVITY

Materials *meter sticks, classroom items such as a chalkboard, desk, chair, eraser, stapler, sheet of paper*
Time 20 minutes

Challenge students to create a metric measurement inventory of the classroom. Students can measure a variety of 10 or more objects. Have them determine the appropriate unit of measurement for each object and record their findings. Ask: **What was the smallest object you measured? What unit did you use?** *(Sample: paper clip, staple, push pin; millimeter)* **Then ask: What was the largest object you measured? What unit did you use?** *(Sample: chalkboard, bookshelf; meter)* **learning modality: logical/mathematical**

Math TOOLBOX

ACTIVITY

Time 15 minutes
Tips For Problem 1, show students a meter stick that is divided into millimeters. Ask: **If there are 1,000 mm on 1 meter stick, then how many mm are on 2 meter sticks?** *(2,000)* **On 7.5 meter sticks?** *(7,500)* Then write out the problem 14.5 m × 1,000 mm = 14,500 mm. Ask: **Where is the decimal point in the number 14,500? How many places did it move?** *(To the right of the last zero; 3 places to the right)* For Problem 2, ask: **How many centimeters are in 1 meter?** *(100)* Then write out the problem 1,200 cm ÷ 100 = 12 m. Ask: **If the decimal point for 1,200 centimeters is to the right of the zero, which direction did it move when you converted from centimeters to meters?** *(To the left)* **learning modality: logical/mathematical**

Media and Technology

Exploring Physical Science Videodisc
Unit 3, Side 1, "Travel"

Chapter 1

Answers to Self-Assessment

Caption Question

Figure 3 The distance between Paris and Rome would be measured in kilometers.

☑ *Checkpoint*

You would measure the width of your thumb in millimeters or centimeters

Ongoing Assessment

Skills Check Have students measure the width and length of their index finger in millimeters and convert the answer to centimeters.

Calculating Speed

Social Studies CONNECTION

After students have read the feature, point out that cities are not symmetrical and the "spokes" may be several different widths. City growth is also limited by geographic constraints and legal requirements as well as transportations needs.

In Your Journal Ask students how many kilometers a person could go in one hour along each of the routes. That distance represents the greatest distance people are willing to drive. Students should realize that they would expect to find homes built farther from the center of the city on Highway 1 and Red Rail. Each transportation route should extend away from the city center in a different direction. Have students choose a scale (for example, 1 mm = 1 km) and measure the distance in mm along the transportation route equal to the number of kilometers a person could travel in one hour. Since these distances represent the maximum distance a person is willing to travel, they mark the city boundaries.

Students can save their maps in their portfolios.

Addressing Naive Conceptions

Some students may think objects that have "speed" must move fast. Direct their attention to a clock. Explain that even though the tip of the hour hand on the clock may move very slowly, it still travels at a measurable speed. Have students measure the circumference of a clock by wrapping a piece of string around the clock and measuring the string with a ruler. Ask: **How long does it take the tip of the hour hand to travel around the clock's face one time?** *(12 hours)* **What is its speed?** *(Answers should be the length of the circumference divided by 12 hours.)* Students can also calculate the speed of the minute and second hands. **learning modality: visual**

Social Studies CONNECTION

Speed affects the shape of cities. Because people want to travel quickly, they live close to major transportation routes—highways and railroads. Thus a city often looks like a hub with spokes coming out of it along the transportation routes.

In Your Journal

People prefer not to travel more than one hour from home to work. The table shows a city's travel routes.

Route	Average Speed
Highway 1	75 km/h
Highway 2	55 km/h
Blue Rail	60 km/h
Red Rail	75 km/h
Main Street	35 km/h

Along which two routes would you expect to find people living farther from the center of the city? Explain why. Draw a map of what you think this city might look like.

Calculating Speed

Scientists use SI units to describe the distance an object travels. A car, for example, might travel 90 kilometers. An ant might travel 2 centimeters. If you know the distance an object travels in a certain amount of time, you know the speed of the object. To be more exact, the **speed** of an object is the distance the object travels in one unit of time. Speed is a type of rate. A rate tells you the amount of something that occurs or changes in one unit of time.

To calculate the speed of an object, divide the distance the object travels by the amount of time it takes to travel that distance. This relationship can be written as follows.

$$Speed = \frac{Distance}{Time}$$

Speed measurements consist of a unit of distance divided by a unit of time. If you measure distance in meters and time in seconds, you express speed in meters per second (m/s). (The slash is read as "per.") If you measure distance in kilometers and time in hours, you express speed in kilometers per hour (km/h).

If a car travels 90 kilometers in one hour, the car is traveling at a speed of 90 km/h. An ant that moves 2 centimeters in one second is moving at a speed of 2 centimeters per second, or 2 cm/s. The ant is much slower than the car.

Constant Speed A ship traveling across the ocean may move at the same speed for several hours. Or a horse cantering across a field may keep a steady pace for several minutes. If so, the ship and the horse travel at constant speeds. If the speed of an object does not change, the object is traveling at a constant speed. When an object travels at a constant speed, you know that its speed is the same at all times during its motion.

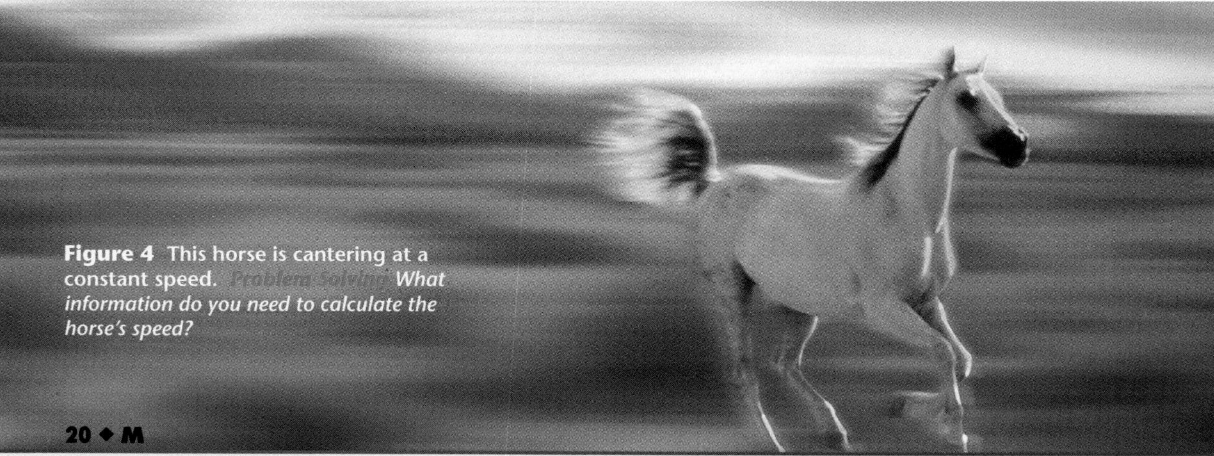

Figure 4 This horse is cantering at a constant speed. *Problem Solving What information do you need to calculate the horse's speed?*

Background

History of Science Sundials, invented about 3,500 years ago, measure time by the shadow cast by the sun as it crosses the sky. Water clocks, which measure time by the movement of dripping water, were used about 3,500 years ago. By the early eighteenth century, mechanical clocks with cogs and wheels gained or lost only about a second per day. Today, most clocks and watches are powered by a vibrating quartz crystal and are extremely accurate.

Figure 5 The cyclists do not travel at a constant speed throughout this cross-country race. *Comparing and Contrasting How does average speed differ from constant speed?*

If you know the distance an object travels in a given amount of time, you can use the formula for speed to calculate the object's constant speed. Suppose, for example, that the horse in Figure 4 is moving at a constant speed. Find the horse's speed if it canters 21 meters in 3 seconds. Divide the distance traveled, 21 meters, by the time, 3 seconds, to find the horse's speed.

$$\text{Speed} = \frac{21 \text{ m}}{3 \text{ s}} = 7 \text{ m/s}$$

The horse's speed is 7 meters per second, or 7 m/s.

Average Speed Most objects do not move at constant speeds for very long. The cyclists in Figure 5, for example, change their speeds many times during the race. They might glide along on level ground, move more slowly as they climb steep inclines, and dash down hills. Occasionally, they stop to fix a tire.

Unlike the horse described earlier, you cannot use any one speed to describe the motion of the cyclists at every point during the race. You can, however, find the average speed of a cyclist throughout the entire race. To find the average speed, divide the total distance traveled by the total time.

Suppose a cyclist travels 32 kilometers during the first two hours of riding, and 13 kilometers during the next hour. The average speed of the cyclist during the trip is the total distance divided by the total time.

$$\text{Total distance} = 32 \text{ km} + 13 \text{ km}$$

$$\text{Total time} = 2 \text{ h} + 1 \text{ h}$$

$$\text{Average speed} = \frac{45 \text{ km}}{3 \text{ h}} = 15 \text{ km/h}$$

The average speed of the cyclist is 15 kilometers per hour.

☑ *Checkpoint* *How do you calculate average speed?*

Building Inquiry Skills: Calculating

Ask students what information they need to know to determine the speed of an object. *(The distance it moved and the amount of time it took to move that distance)* Then have them calculate the speed of the following objects:

- a baseball that moves 11 m in 1 s *(11 m ÷ 1 sec = 11 m/s)*
- a car that travels 70 km in 1.75 h *(70 km ÷ 1.75 hr = 40 km/hr)*

learning modality: logical/mathematical

Inquiry Challenge

ACTIVITY

Materials *two or three wind-up toys per group, stopwatches, metric rulers, masking tape*
Time 40 minutes
Tips Have students bring toys from home. Challenge students to discover which wind-up toy reaches the highest speed. Students can work in small groups. Have students mark off a "test track" on the floor with masking tape, then measure how long it takes for each toy to travel the length of the track. Suggest students perform at least three trials for each toy and calculate an average speed from the results. To determine if the toy is changing speed during the run, students can compare the average speed of a certain toy measured over two or three different distances. Ask students to describe any changes in each toy's speed during each trial. *(The toys may slow down as they move down the track)* Ask: **For each trial, are you measuring constant speed or average speed?** *(average speed)* After students complete their trials, have a final race with each group choosing one toy that they think will go fastest over a distance chosen by you. **cooperative learning**

Answers to Self-Assessment

Caption Questions

Figure 4 The distance the horse traveled and the time it took to travel that distance
Figure 5 Average speed is the total distance traveled divided by the total time. Constant speed does not change.

☑ *Checkpoint*

Divide the total distance traveled by the total time.

Ongoing Assessment

Skills Check Have students find the speed of an asteroid that travels 4,500 km in 60 s. *(4,500 km ÷ 60 s = 75 km/s)*

Describing Velocity

Real-Life Learning

Obtain a set of hurricane-tracking charts from your local weather service. Have students follow weather reports to track the daily progress of any hurricanes. Have students calculate the average speed of a hurricane based on the data they gather. If hurricane charts are unavailable, charts showing the movement of high- or low-pressure systems can be substituted. Ask: **How is this type of information useful to weather forecasters?** *(It helps them predict how long it will take for a hurricane to reach a region so they can warn people who live there.)* **learning modality: visual**

Describing Velocity

Knowing the speed at which something travels does not tell you everything about its motion. For example, if a weather forecaster announces that a severe storm is traveling at 25 km/h, would you prepare for the storm? Storms usually travel from west to east. If you live to the west of the storm and the storm is traveling to the east, you need not worry. But if the storm is moving to the west, take cover.

It is important to know not only the speed of the storm, but also its direction. **When you know both the speed and direction of an object's motion, you know the velocity of the object.**

The Speed of Transportation

The speed with which people can travel from one place to another has increased over the years.

1885

Benz Tricycle Car Introduced

This odd-looking vehicle was the first internal combustion (gasoline-powered) automobile sold to the public. Although it is an ancestor of the modern automobile, its top speed was only about 15 km/h—not much faster than a horse-drawn carriage.

1800 1850

1818

National Road Constructed

The speed of transportation has been limited largely by the quality of roadways. The U.S. government paid for the construction of a highway named the Cumberland Road. It ran from Cumberland, Maryland, to Wheeling, in present-day West Virginia. Travel by horse and carriage on the roadway was at a speed of about 11 km/h.

1869

Transcontinental Railroad

After more than six and a half years of work, railroad tracks from each side of the country met in Utah, just north of Great Salt Lake. Passengers could now travel across the United States by steam-powered trains. A cross-country trip took about a week at an average speed of 30 km/h.

Speed in a given direction is called **velocity**. If you know the velocity at which an object is moving, you know two different things about the object's motion—its speed and its direction. A weather forecaster may give the speed of the storm as 25 km/h, but you don't know its velocity unless you know that the storm is moving 25 km/h westward.

Air traffic controllers must keep very close track of the velocities of all of the aircraft under their control. These velocities change more often than the velocities of storm systems. An error in determining a velocity, either in speed or in direction, could lead to a collision.

In Your Journal

The distance between Wheeling, West Virginia, and Cumberland, Maryland, is 258 kilometers. How many hours would it take to travel this distance for each of the vehicles in the time line if they each traveled at the speed shown? Record your results on a bar graph.

1908

Ford Model T Mass-Produced

Between 1908 and 1927, over 15 million of these automobiles were sold. The Model T had a top speed of 65 km/h.

1956

Inauguration of the Interstate Highway System

The passage of the Federal Aid Highway Act established the Highway Trust Fund. This act allowed the construction of the Interstate and Defense Highways. Nonstop transcontinental auto travel became possible. Speed limits in many parts of the system were more than 100 km/h.

1900 **1950** **2000**

1936

***Pioneer Zephyr* Introduced**

The first diesel passenger train in the United States was the *Pioneer Zephyr*. The *Zephyr* set a long-distance record, traveling from Chicago to Denver at an average speed of 125 km/h for more than 1,633 km.

1983

TGV in Motion

First introduced in 1983, this French high-speed train now has a top speed of 300 km/h. On its route from Paris to Lyon, it averages 152.6 km/h.

SCIENCE & *History*

Review each item along the timeline with students. Ask: **How do you think improvements in transportation affected the lives of people living at that time?** *(Sample: They could go farther to find a job, get supplies, or visit relatives.)* Then ask: **What do you think are some negative effects of widespread rapid transportation?** *(Sample: increased pollution, damage to the environment, accidents at high speeds may be deadlier)*

In Your Journal Allow students to use calculators to calculate how long the journeys would take. *(Horse and Carriage on Cumberland Road—23.5 hours; Transcontinental Railroad—8.6 hours; Benz tricycle car—17.2 hours; Ford Model T —4.0 hours; Pioneer Zephyr—2.0 hours; Interstate Highway—2.6 hours; TGV—1.7)* **learning modality: logical/ mathematical**

Cultural Diversity

The United States has built an elaborate system of highways for public and freight transportation, while the rail system is primarily used for transportation of heavy freight. Other countries, such as France and Japan, have constructed sophisticated high speed rail systems for public transportation. In small groups, allow students to discuss the relative advantages and disadvantages of primarily using automobiles for public transportation (as opposed to high-speed rail). Have students relate the contrasting systems of public transportation to the availability of natural resources, such as petroleum. Students may also relate preferences for different modes of public transportation to cultural differences.

Background

Facts and Figures The fastest animals are:
- on land, the cheetah (96 km/h)
- in the water, the sailfish (109 km/h)
- in the air, the peregrine falcon (198 km/h)

Program Resources

- **Teaching Resources** 1-1 Review and Reinforce, p. 17; 1-1 Enrich, p. 18

Media and Technology

Transparencies "Exploring Motion Graphs," Transparency 1

Interactive Student Tutorial CD-ROM M-1

Ongoing Assessment

Writing Invite students to write brief summaries of the major changes in transportation over the past 200 years.

Graphing Motion

EXPLORING Motion Graphs

Draw students' attention to the first graph. They should recognize that the jogger travels 170 m each minute. To show that speed is constant, choose another point on the graph and calculate the average speed. Have students copy the graph and extend the line to predict how long she would have to jog to travel 2,550 m. *(15 min)* As students examine the second graph, ask: **What happened during the sixth through eighth minutes?** *(The jogger stopped.)* Then ask students: **What effect did the stop have on the jogger's average speed?** *(Average speed was lowered: 1,200 m ÷ 10 min = 120 m/min.)* Ask: **What was the difference in the jogger's average speed between the first and second day?** *(50 m/min)* Compare the angle of the slope in the first and third graphs. *(The angle of the slope in the first graph is greater.)* Ask: **How fast would the jogger be traveling if the graph was flat?** *(0 m/min)*

Extend Take students to a running track. Pair students. Ask each pair to create their own motion graphs based on their own actual motion. For example, one student jogs, then walks, and rests, (1 min for each). The partner records what the other student is doing and the distance he or she travels. Then partners reverse roles. They then work together to graph their data. Pairs share their graphs with the class and ask the class to determine what the student was doing. **learning modality: logical/mathematical**

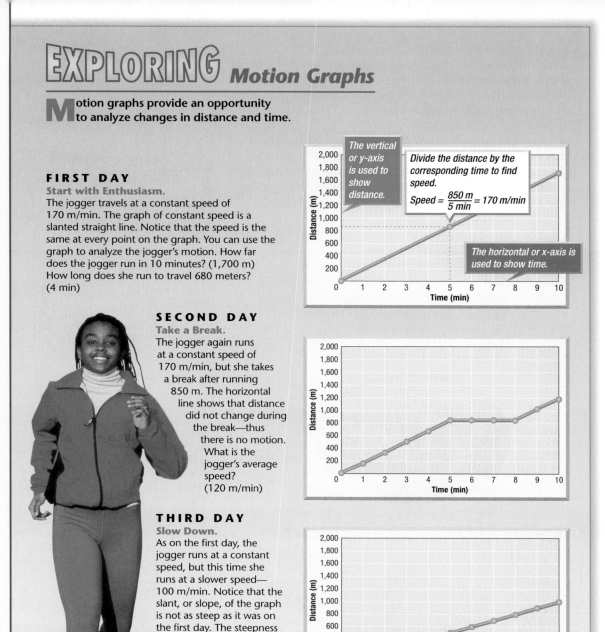

EXPLORING Motion Graphs

Motion graphs provide an opportunity to analyze changes in distance and time.

FIRST DAY

Start with Enthusiasm.

The jogger travels at a constant speed of 170 m/min. The graph of constant speed is a slanted straight line. Notice that the speed is the same at every point on the graph. You can use the graph to analyze the jogger's motion. How far does the jogger run in 10 minutes? (1,700 m) How long does she run to travel 680 meters? (4 min)

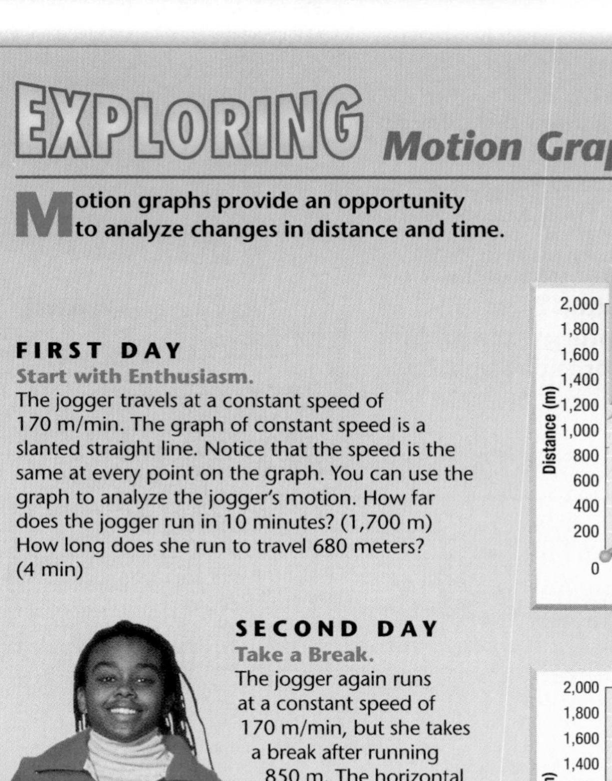

SECOND DAY

Take a Break.

The jogger again runs at a constant speed of 170 m/min, but she takes a break after running 850 m. The horizontal line shows that distance did not change during the break—thus there is no motion. What is the jogger's average speed? (120 m/min)

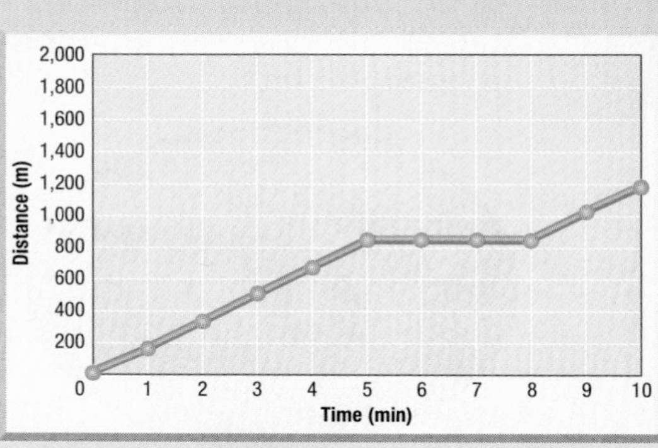

THIRD DAY

Slow Down.

As on the first day, the jogger runs at a constant speed, but this time she runs at a slower speed—100 m/min. Notice that the slant, or slope, of the graph is not as steep as it was on the first day. The steepness of the slope is related to the speed. The faster the speed, the steeper the slope. How far does the jogger run in 10 minutes on this day? (1,000 m)

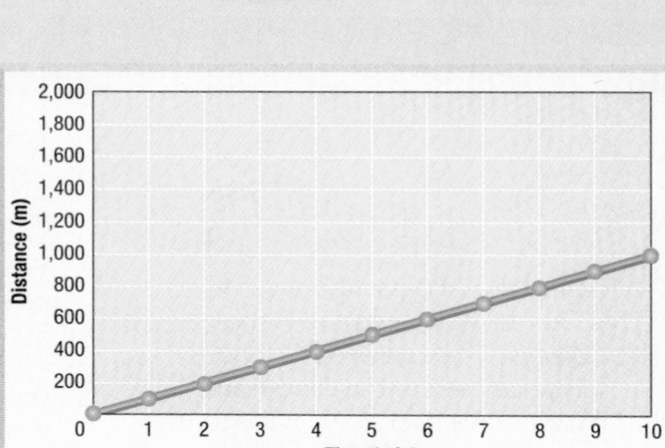

Stunt pilots make spectacular use of their control over the velocity of their aircraft. To avoid colliding with other aircraft, these skilled pilots must have precise control of both speed and direction. Stunt pilots use this control to stay in close formation while flying graceful maneuvers.

Figure 6 During a complicated maneuver an airplane's direction changes continuously, along with its speed.

Graphing Motion

You can show the motion of an object on a line graph in which you plot distance against time. A point on the graph represents the location of an object at a particular time. By tradition, time is shown on the *x*-axis and distance on the *y*-axis. A straight line (a line with a constant slant, or slope) represents motion at a constant speed. The steepness of the slope depends on how quickly or slowly the object is moving. The faster the motion, the steeper the slope, because the object moves a greater distance in a given amount of time. A horizontal line represents an object that is not moving at all. To see examples of how graphs represent motion, read about the jogger in *Exploring Motion Graphs* on page 24.

Section 1 Review

1. Why do you need a reference point to know if an object is moving?
2. What is the difference between an object's speed and an object's velocity?
3. A bamboo plant grows 15 centimeters in 4 hours. At what average speed does the plant grow?
4. **Thinking Critically Problem Solving** The distance traveled by two crawling babies is shown in the table. Graph the information and determine which baby moves at constant speed throughout the entire trip. What is that baby's speed? Describe the speed of the other baby.

Time (s)	**Baby Scott Distance** (m)	**Baby Sarah Distance** (m)
1	0.5	1
2	1	2
3	1.5	2.5
4	2	2.5
5	2.5	3.5

Check Your Progress

CHAPTER PROJECT 1

To measure each object's speed, you will need to know how far it moves in a certain amount of time. Create a data table to record your measurements and to show the speeds you calculate. Be sure to choose the best units for each speed measurement. To measure fast speeds, you may choose to measure distance in meters and time in seconds. For slower speeds you may choose to measure distance in centimeters or millimeters, and time in minutes or hours.

3 Assess

Section 1 Review Answers

1. Motion involves a change in position relative to some reference point.
2. Speed describes the rate at which an object moves. Velocity is speed in a given direction.
3. The plant grows at an average speed of 15 cm/4 h, or 3.75 cm/h.
4. Baby Scott moves at a constant speed, 0.5 m/s so the graph will have constant slope. Baby Sarah moves at 1.0 m/s for the first two seconds, slows down to 0.5 m/s, stops, then moves at a speed of 1.0 m/s for the last second.

Check Your Progress

CHAPTER PROJECT 1

Draw an example on the board of how to record information neatly in a project log. This example should show a sketch of the measurement, a list or table of data collected, and a step-by-step calculation of the object's speed. Assign the Chapter Project Worksheet 1, which will provide students with hints and ideas for making the measurements required for this project.

Performance Assessment

Skills Check Give each student a photocopy of the same map. Ask them to pick two places on the map, A and B. Have them use the scale on the map to measure the direct distance between A and B. Ask: **If it takes 2 hours to get from A to B, what speed are you going?** *(Sample: Washington, DC to San Francisco, CA; speed 2,400 km/h)* **What is your velocity?** *(Answers must include speed and direction. Sample: Washington, DC, to San Francisco, CA; velocity 2,400 km/h west.)*

Skills Lab

Measuring

Inclined to Roll

Preparing for Inquiry

Key Concept After an object rolls down a ramp, it will be going faster if the incline is steeper.

Skills Objective Students will be able to

- measure speed using time taken to travel a certain distance;
- measure the effect of the incline of the ramp on the average speed of an object rolling down the ramp;
- begin to think about acceleration.

Time 40 minutes

Advance Planning If you have not yet taught the skill of measuring, see pages 188–189 of the Skills Handbook. Buy 4 ft × 8 ft sheets of 1/4-in plywood or pegboard and have them cut crosswise into six ramps 16 in wide. Many hardware stores will cut the sheets for you. Since these ramps would be 4 feet long, the starting line on the ramp would be at 1 m. This lab requires plenty of space and may need to be done in a gym or outdoors.

Alternative Materials If no student in a group has a skateboard, ask other students to bring extras. Students can also use four-wheeled toys. If protractors are unavailable, have students measure the height of the ramp at the starting line. This height can be used instead of angle to measure ramp incline.

Skills Lab

Measuring

Inclined to Roll

In this lab, you will practice the skills of measuring time and distance to find the speed of a moving object.

Problem

How does the steepness of a ramp affect how fast an object moves across the floor?

Materials

skateboard
meter stick
protractor
masking tape
flat board, about 1.5 m long
small piece of sturdy cardboard
supports to prop up the board (books, boxes)
two stopwatches

Procedure

1. In your notebook, make a data table like the sample. Include space for five angles.
2. Lay the board flat on the floor. Using masking tape, mark a starting line in the middle of the board. Mark a finish line on the floor 1.5 m beyond one end of the board. Place a barrier after the finish line.
3. Prop up the other end of the board to make a slight incline. Use a protractor to measure the angle that the board makes with the ground. Record the angle in your data table.
4. Working in groups of three, have one person hold the skateboard so that its front wheels are even with the starting line. As the holder releases the skateboard, the other two students should start their stopwatches.
5. One timer should stop his or her stopwatch when the front wheels of the skateboard reach the end of the incline.
6. The second timer should stop his or her stopwatch when the front wheels reach the finish line.

DATA TABLE

Angle (degrees)	Trial Number	Time 1 (to bottom) (s)	Time 2 (to finish) (s)	Avg Time 1 (s)	Avg Time 2 (s)	Avg Time 2 – Avg Time 1 (s)	Avg Speed (m/s)
	1						
	2						
	3						
	1						
	2						
	3						
	1						
	2						

Guiding Inquiry

Invitation Have students predict what they think they will find. Ask: **Have you ever ridden a roller coaster or bicycled down a hill? How did the incline of the hill affect your average speed?** *(Faster on a steeper hill)* **How did you judge how fast you were traveling?** *(Samples: Trees went by faster; air rushed by faster)* Emphasize that speed is measured relative to an object.

Introducing the Procedure

- Refer students to the photo illustrating the experimental setup.
- Show students how to use the stopwatches. Have students roll the skateboard down the ramp a few times to practice using the stopwatches before they collect data.

Troubleshooting the Experiment

- Make sure students begin with a very small incline.
- Make sure the skateboard rolls smoothly at the transition from the ramp to the ground.

Expected Outcome

- As the ramp incline increases, the time taken to travel from starting line to bottom of ramp (Average Time 1) will decrease.
- As the ramp incline increases, the time taken to travel from bottom of ramp to finish line (Average Time 2 - Average Time 1) will decrease. Thus, average speed will increase as ramp incline increases.

Analyze and Conclude

1. Average speed is distance traveled on floor (distance from bottom of ramp to finish line or 1.5 m) divided by time on floor (Average Time 2 – Average Time 1).

7. Repeat Steps 4–6 two more times. If your results for the three times aren't within 0.2 seconds of one another, carry out more trials.
8. Record all times in your data table in the columns labeled Time 1 and Time 2.
9. Repeat Steps 3–8 four more times, making the ramp gradually steeper each time.
10. For each angle of the incline, complete the following calculations and record them in your data table.
    a. Find the average time the skateboard takes to get to the bottom of the ramp (Time 1).
    b. Find the average time the skateboard takes to get to the finish line (Time 2).
    c. Subtract the average Time 1 from the average Time 2.

Analyze and Conclude

1. How can you find the average speed of the skateboard across the floor for each angle of incline? Determine the average speed for each angle and record it in your data table.
2. Which is your manipulated variable and which is your responding variable in this experiment? Explain why. (For a discussion of manipulated and responding variables, see the Skills Handbook.)
3. On a graph, plot the speed of the skateboard (on the y-axis) against the angle of the ramp (on the x-axis). Connect the points on your graph.
4. What does the shape of your graph show about the relationship between the speed and the angle of the ramp?
5. **Think About It** Do you think your method of timing was accurate? Did the timers start and stop their stopwatches exactly at the appropriate points? Explain anything that might have prevented accurate timing.

Design an Experiment

A truck driver transporting new cars needs to roll the cars off the truck. You offer to design a ramp to help with the task. What measurements might you make that would be useful? Design an experiment to test your ideas.

2. The manipulated variable is ramp incline and the responding variable is average speed.

3.

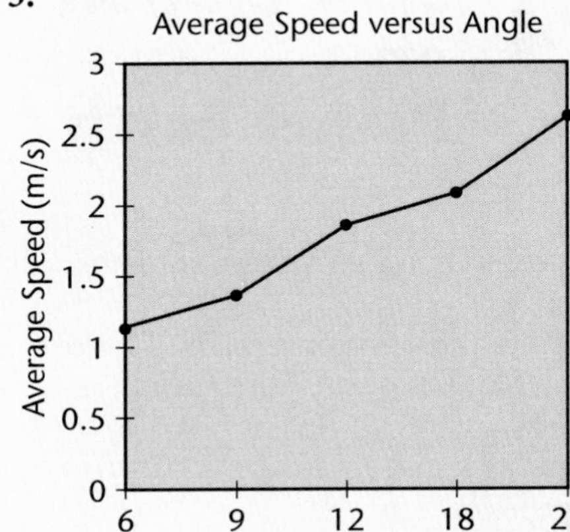

4. Speed will increase as the incline goes from small (0 degrees) to large (45 or more degrees).

5. Many students could time a particular run. The average of all students could then be used. Alternatively, an electric timing device as used during athletic events could be utilized.

Extending the Inquiry

Design An Experiment Students need to know the weight of the cars and the distance between the left and right wheels so that the ramp could be wide enough and strong enough. To measure the angle of the ramp, measure the height of the ramp rather than trying to use a small protractor. To make sure this will work, students can compare the height of their ramp at the start line with the angle measured using a protractor. They can plot height on the x-axis and angle on the y-axis.

Sample Data Table

Angle (degrees)	Time 1 (to bottom) (s)	Time 2 (to finish) (s)	Avg Time 2 – Avg Time 1 (s)	Avg Speed (m/s)
6	1.47	2.75	1.28	1.17
9	1.31	2.40	1.09	1.38
12	1.06	1.88	0.82	1.83
18	0.87	1.58	0.71	2.11
27	0.71	1.28	0.57	2.63

Safety

Tell students to be careful when carrying boards. Tell students not to stand on the skateboards, or roll them at other people. Review the safety guidelines in Appendix A.

Program Resources

- **Teaching Resources** Chapter 1 Skills Lab, pp. 27–28

Integrating Earth Science

Section 2 Slow Motion on Planet Earth

Objectives

After completing the lesson, students will be able to

- ◆ explain the slow movement of Earth's plates and calculate their speed.

Key Term plates

1 Engage/Explore

Activating Prior Knowledge

Show students a map of the Atlantic Ocean, showing the coastlines of North and South America, Europe, and Africa. Ask them which pieces might fit together like a jigsaw puzzle. *(The coastlines of Africa and South America do fit together.)* If you have a map that shows the continental shelf, the fit will be even better.

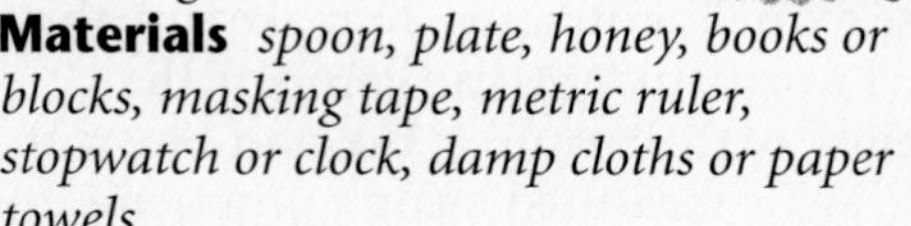

Discover Activity

Skills Focus observing, inferring
Materials *spoon, plate, honey, books or blocks, masking tape, metric ruler, stopwatch or clock, damp cloths or paper towels*
Time 20 minutes
Tips Refrigerate the honey if possible. Students should prop up the plates using books or blocks. Provide damp cloths or paper towels to clean up any spilled honey. Write the equation for calculating speed on the board: Speed = Distance ÷ Time. Ask: **What distance will you use to complete the calculation?** *(2 cm)* Divide the class into groups of two or three. Allow students to complete their calculations and compare results.
Think It Over You can tell an object is moving if it changes position over a period of time. If the object moves too slowly, you need to observe it over longer periods of time. The growth of hair and the movement of the hour hand on a clock are too slow to see.

Integrating Earth Science 

Section 2 Slow Motion on Planet Earth

Discover Activity

How Slow Can It Flow?

1. Put a spoonful of honey on a plate.
2. Lift one side of the plate just high enough that the honey is visibly flowing.
3. Reduce the angle of the plate a small amount so that the honey appears to be barely moving. Prop up the plate at this angle.
4. Using a ruler, place a piece of tape 2 cm from the bottom edge of the honey.
5. Time how long it takes the honey to flow to the tape. Use this information to calculate the speed of the honey.

Think It Over
Forming Operational Definitions How can you tell that an object is moving if it doesn't appear to be moving at first glance? Can you think of some other examples of motion that are too slow to see?

Guide for Reading

- ◆ How does the theory of plate tectonics describe the movement of Earth's continents?

Reading Tip Before you read, preview Figure 8, and describe what you think is happening.

Have you ever noticed that Earth's landmasses resemble pieces of a giant jigsaw puzzle? It's true—take a look at a map of the world. The east coast of South America, for example, would fit nicely with the west coast of Africa. The Arabian Peninsula, as shown in the satellite photo below, would fit perfectly with the northeastern coast of Africa. Since the 1600s, people have wondered why Earth's landmasses look as if they would fit together. After all, land can't move—or can it?

What Are Earth's Plates?

Earth's rocky outer shell consists of broken pieces that fit together like a jigsaw puzzle. The upper layer of Earth consists of more than a dozen major pieces called **plates.** The boundaries between the plates are cracks in Earth's crust. The various plates are shown in Figure 7.

Scientists use this concept of plates to explain how landmasses have changed over time. **According to their explanation, known as the theory of plate tectonics, Earth's plates move ever so slowly in various directions.** Sometimes they pull away

Satellite photo of Africa and the Arabian Peninsula ▼

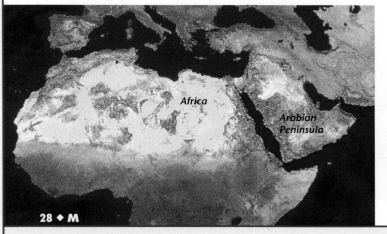

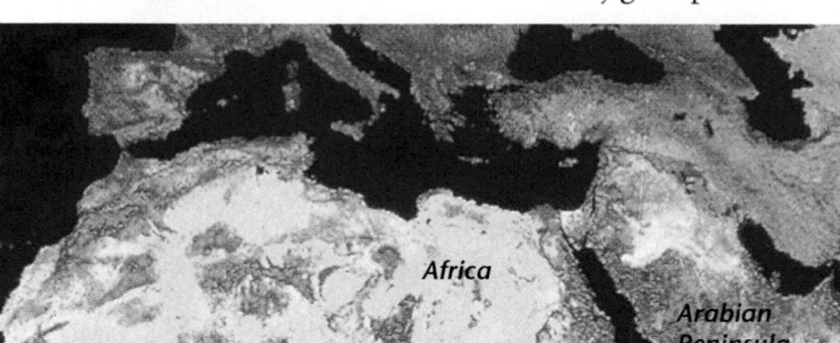

28 ◆ M

Reading Strategies

Reading Tip As students preview Figure 8, elicit their predictions about the speed of the continents. Point out that there is an enormous amount of time between the pictures. Ask students to think of other objects that might move as slowly.

Study and Comprehension Tell students there are three important things for them to learn from this section. Have them glance over the text and identify what they are. Guide them to see that they should learn

- ◆ what the theory of plate tectonics is;
- ◆ how to calculate distance from speed and time; and
- ◆ how to convert units using a conversion factor.

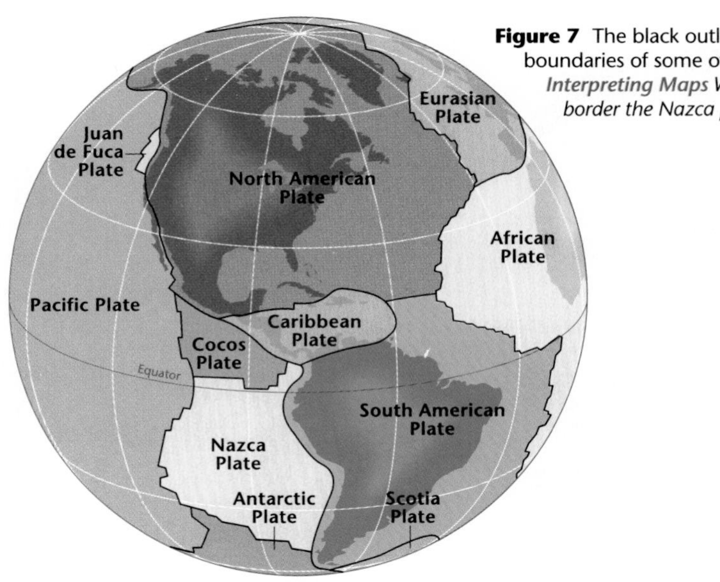

Figure 7 The black outlines show the boundaries of some of Earth's plates. *Interpreting Maps Which plates border the Nazca plate?*

from each other, sometimes they push toward each other, and sometimes they slide past each other.

☑ *Checkpoint* *What is the name scientists use for pieces of Earth's upper layer?*

How Fast Do Plates Move?

The speed with which Earth's plates move is very slow indeed. Some small plates can move as much as several centimeters per year, whereas others move only a few millimeters per year.

Knowing how far a plate moves in a certain amount of time enables scientists to calculate the average speed of the plate. This, in turn, enables scientists to explain how Earth's surface has changed over time. And it helps them to predict how it will change in the future. Figure 8 on pages 30–31 shows an estimate of how the continents have moved in the past and how they may move in the future.

Calculating Distance Suppose scientists study a particular plate over the course of a year. They find that the plate moves a distance of 5 centimeters. Thus the speed at which the plate moves is 5 centimeters divided by one year, or 5 cm/yr.

How can you use the speed of a plate to predict how far the plate will move in 1,000 years? To find distance, rearrange the speed formula: Distance = Speed × Time. This formula tells you

Predicting ACTIVITY

Los Angeles, on the Pacific Plate, is slowly moving northwest. San Francisco, on the North American plate, is slowly moving southeast. These two cities are moving toward each other at a rate of about 5 cm/yr. If the two cities are now 554,000 m apart, how long will it take for the two cities to be next to each other?

2 Facilitate

What Are Earth's Plates?

Using the Visuals: Figure 7

Have students examine the map. Find a plate boundary. Ask: **What would happen at a boundary where plates are pushing together?** *(Answers may vary. Sample: Mountains may form)* **learning modality: visual**

How Fast Do Plates Move?

Sharpen your Skills

Predicting ACTIVITY

Materials *none*
Time 10 minutes
Tips Write the formula for speed on the board: Speed = Distance ÷ Time. Ask: **How does speed depend on distance?** *(Speed increases as distance increases.)* **How does speed depend on time?** *(Speed decreases as time increases.)* Write the formula for time on the board (Time = Distance ÷ Speed) Remind students that all distances in the equation must first be changed to the same unit. Guide students' calculations using these steps:
554,000 m × 100 cm/m = 55,400,000 cm
Time = 55,400,000 cm ÷ 5 cm/yr
Time = 11,080,000 yr
Extend Give students a map of California and ask them to find San Francisco and Los Angeles. Have them try to figure out where the fault runs based on the information in the text.

Ongoing Assessment

Writing Calculate the distance that a plate will move if it moves at a speed of 4 cm/yr for 8,000,000 years *(32,000,000 cm)*

Program Resources

◆ **Teaching Resources** 1-2 Lesson Plan, p. 19; 1-2 Section Summary, p. 20
Science Explorer Series "Inside Earth," Chapter 1, has information on continental drift and plate tectonics.

Media and Technology

Audiotapes English-Spanish Summary 1-2

Answers to Self-Assessment

Caption Question

Figure 7 Antarctic, South American, Cocos, Caribbean, Pacific

☑ *Checkpoint*

Pieces of Earth's crust are called plates.

How Fast Do Plates Move?, continued

Using the Visuals: Figure 8

Help students identify the portions of the southern land mass that became South America, Africa, and India. Have students trace the movement of these land masses between 135 million years ago to 100 million years ago. Ask: **How did the movements of the plates affect South America, Africa and India between 100 million years ago and now?** *(All three moved north. India collided with Eurasia.)* **If South America, Africa and India continue moving in the same direction, predict what will happen?** *(South America will move north, the Mediterranean will disappear as Africa crashes into Europe, and the Himalayas will continue to pile up.)* **learning modality: visual**

Building Inquiry Skills: Problem Solving

Materials *number cubes, index cards, poster board, markers, tokens to use as game pieces*
Time 1 class period

ACTIVITY

Before class, prepare sufficient game cards so that each group will have at least 10 cards. Create conversion problems using units of time, distance, and speed and create other problems solving for speed, reading graphs, and so on. Print each problem on one side of an index card and write the answer on the other side. You may wish to have some of your more capable students help you create cards. Allow students to work in groups to design the game board. Some students in each group can create the board, including spaces such as "Lose a Turn," "Roll Again," and "Go Back 2 Spaces." The remaining students can write down the game rules. The basic rule should be that players must correctly answer a conversion problem before rolling the number cubes and advancing across the board. **learning modality: logical/mathematical**

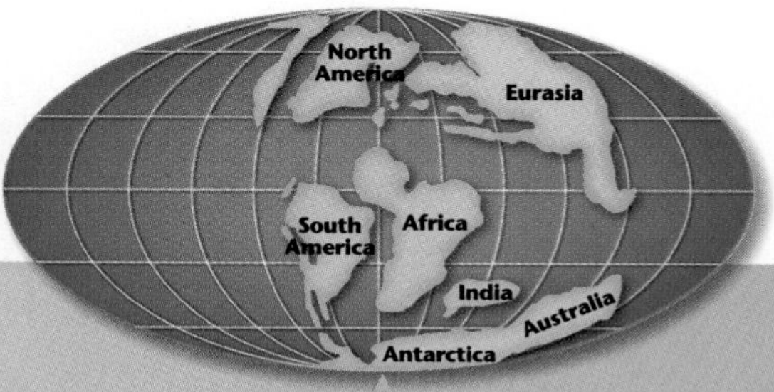

250 Million Years Ago **135 Million Years Ago** **100 Million Years Ago**

Figure 8 The shapes and positions of Earth's continents have changed greatly over time and will continue to change in the future. *Interpreting Maps Locate Australia on the map. How does its position change over time?*

to multiply the speed of the plate by the time during which the plate travels at that speed.

$$\text{Distance} = \frac{5\text{ cm}}{1\text{ yr}} \times 1{,}000\text{ yr} = 5{,}000\text{ cm}$$

The plate moves 5,000 centimeters in 1,000 years. Since 5,000 is a large number, try expressing this distance in meters. Recall that there are 100 centimeters in 1 meter, so you can divide by 100 by moving the decimal to the left two places.

$$5{,}000.\text{ cm} = 50.00\text{ m}$$

So in 1,000 years, which is well over ten average lifetimes, this plate moves only 50 meters. Walking at a brisk pace, you can probably travel the same distance in about 30 seconds!

Converting Units Suppose you want to know the speed of the plate in centimeters per day rather than centimeters per year. You can convert from one unit of measurement to another by using a conversion factor, a fraction in which the numerator and denominator are equal. In this example, 1 year is equal to 365 days. So you choose a conversion factor from these two possibilities.

$$\frac{1\text{ yr}}{365\text{ d}} = 1 \quad \text{or} \quad \frac{365\text{ d}}{1\text{ yr}} = 1$$

Background

History of Science In the 1960s, Harry Hess proposed the hypothesis of sea-floor spreading. His hypothesis stated that rising volcanic material along a mid-ocean ridge pushed the older hardened rock away from the ridge in two directions. This movement, in turn, acted like a conveyor belt for the floating continents. Hess's discovery led to an understanding of how the continents moved.

Earth's continents and other landmasses also move as the plates that carry them move toward or away from each other. When plates collide or split apart, new land features, such as mountains, form.

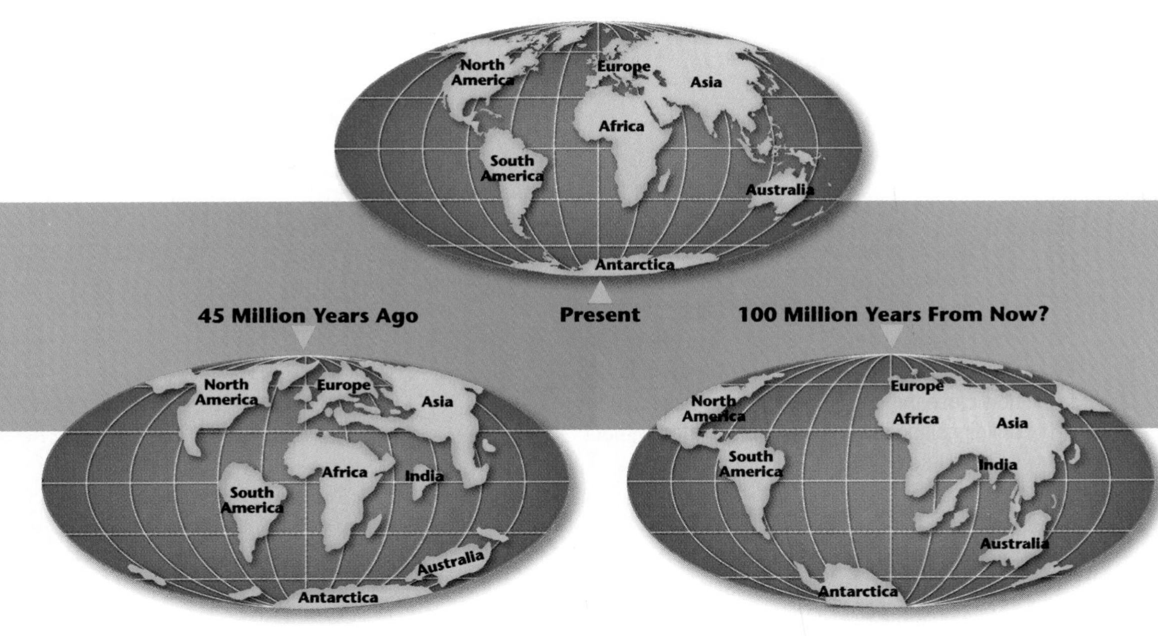

The conversion factor you need is the one that will allow you to cancel the years units. This factor is the one that has years in the numerator.

$$\frac{5\ cm}{1\ yr} \times \frac{1\ yr}{365\ d} = 0.0137\ cm/d$$

So you can describe the speed of this plate as 5 centimeters per year or as 0.0137 centimeters per day.

Section 2 Review

1. What is the theory that explains the slow movement of continents on Earth's surface?
2. Give two reasons why you don't notice the land moving beneath you. (*Hint*: Remember reference points.)
3. Suppose you are studying the motion of one of Earth's plates. What units would you probably use to describe its speed? Explain why.
4. **Thinking Critically Problem Solving** A certain plate moves 5 mm in 100 days. What is its speed in mm/d? What is its speed in mm/yr?

Science at Home

Have each member of your family measure the length of the white part at the end of one fingernail. Write down the results (and which finger you used) and mark your calendar for a date in exactly three weeks. On that day, measure the new length of the white part of the same fingernail. Then calculate the speed, in millimeters per day, at which your fingernail grew. Discuss with your family how your results compare with the typical speed with which continents move.

Media and Technology

Exploring Earth Science Videodisc
Unit 3, Side 1, "Everything on Your Plate"

Chapter 6

Exploring Earth Science Videodisc
Unit 3, Side 1, "Journey to the Bottom of the Sea"

Chapter 5

Program Resources

◆ **Teaching Resources** 1-2 Review and Reinforce, p. 21; 1-2 Enrich p. 22

Answers to Self-Assessment

Caption Question

Figure 8 Over time, Australia moved north.

3 Assess

Section 2 Review Answers

1. The theory of plate tectonics
2. Because the movement is slow and because you do not change position relative to the reference point, the plate
3. Use cm/yr or mm/yr because plates travel very slowly.
4. 0.05 mm/d; 18.25 mm/yr

Science at Home

Materials *metric ruler*
Tips Encourage students to involve at least one or two family members of different ages. Students should record the measurements in millimeters. Suggest that students and family members take measurements of more than one finger in case a particular fingernail breaks during the three-week period. Students should find that fingernail growth rate is similar to the movement of Earth's plates.

Performance Assessment

Skills Check Calculate the distance in meters that a continental plate will travel if it moves at a speed of 2 cm/yr for 5 million years. *(100,000 m)*

Real-World Lab

You and Your Community

Stopping on a Dime

The school has decided to put in a new basketball court in a small area between two buildings. Safety is an important consideration in the design of the court. You and your friends volunteer to find out experimentally how close the out-of-bounds lines can be to the buildings and still allow players to stop without running into a wall.

Problem

What distance is necessary between the out-of-bounds line and a wall so that a player can stop before hitting the wall?

Skills Focus

measuring, calculating, inferring

Materials

wooden meter stick
tape measure
2 stopwatches or watches with second hands

Procedure

Part I Reaction Time

1. Have your partner suspend a wooden meter stick between your thumb and index finger, as shown. Your thumb and index finger should be about three centimeters apart.
2. Your partner will drop the meter stick without giving you any warning. You will try to grab it with two fingers.
3. Note the level at which you grabbed the meter stick and use the chart shown to determine your reaction time. Record the time in the class data table.
4. Reverse roles with your partner and repeat Steps 1 through 3.

Reaction Time

Distance (cm)	Time (s)	Distance (cm)	Time (s)
15	0.175	25	0.226
16	0.181	26	0.230
17	0.186	27	0.235
18	0.192	28	0.239
19	0.197	29	0.243
20	0.202	30	0.247
21	0.207	31	0.252
22	0.212	32	0.256
23	0.217	33	0.260
24	0.221	34	0.263

Real-World Lab

You and Your Community

Stopping on a Dime

Preparing for Inquiry

Key Concept Students will use measurements of reaction times, running speeds, and stopping distances to help them decide where a basketball court should be located.

Skills Objective Students will be able to
- measure reaction time, maximum speed, and stopping distance;
- use reaction time, maximum speed, and stopping distance to calculate the total distance a student could travel after crossing an out-of-bounds line;
- infer how reaction time, speed, and stopping distance influence total distance

Time 40 minutes

Advance Planning Reserve time and space on the school field or in the gymnasium for Part II of the lab.

Guiding Inquiry

Invitation Have students think about the importance of using measurements and calculations to infer a suitable location of a basketball court. Ask: **When you run out of bounds on a basketball court, what determines how long it takes you to stop?** *(Sample: running speed)*

Introducing the Procedure

- Give students specific instructions concerning where running speed and stopping distance will be measured. Show them where the timer should stand, where the runner will begin, and in which direction the runner should run.
- Tell students that the distance a basketball player will run past an out-of-bounds line depends on three things. First, on how fast the player is running when he or she goes out of bounds (maximum running speed). Second, on how long it takes the player to realize that he or she is out of bounds (reaction time). Third, on how far a player travels after realizing that he or she needs to stop (stopping distance).

Expected Outcome

A typical reaction time is about 0.2 seconds. A typical running speed is about 5 m/s which produces a stopping distance of about 3 m. Reaction time plus stopping distance means that there should be a safety margin of around 4 m.

Troubleshooting the Experiment

Make sure students do not slow down before reaching the 25-meter mark. Be sure that the person dropping the meter stick does not inadvertently signal the person catching.

Analyze and Conclude

1. Find the student with the lowest time for running the course. Divide the distance (25 m) by this time to get the maximum running speed in meters per second.
2. The maximum running speed multiplied by the slowest reaction time tells how far the fastest running student would travel out of bounds in meters if he or she had the slowest

CLASS DATA TABLE			
Student Name	Reaction Time (s)	Running Time (s)	Stopping Distance (m)

Part II Stopping Distance

5. On the school field or in the gymnasium, mark off a distance of 25 m.
6. Have your partner time how long it takes you to run the course at full speed. **CAUTION:** *Be sure to remove any obstacles from the course.* After you pass the 25-m mark, come to a stop as quickly as possible and remain standing. You must not slow down before the mark.
7. Have your partner measure the distance from the 25-m mark to your final position. This is the distance you need to come to a complete stop. Enter your time and distance into the class data table.
8. Reverse roles with your partner. Enter your partner's time and distance into the class data table.

Analyze and Conclude

1. How can you calculate the average speed of the student who ran the 25-m course the fastest? Find this speed.
2. Multiply the speed of the fastest student (calculated in Question 1) by the slowest reaction time listed in the class data table. Why would you be interested in this product?
3. Add the distance calculated in Question 2 to the longest stopping distance in the class data table. What does this total distance represent?
4. Explain why it is important to use the fastest speed, the slowest reaction time, and the longest stopping distance in your calculations.
5. What other factors should you take into account to get results that apply to a real basketball court?
6. **Apply** Suppose the distance between the out-of-bounds line and the wall in a playground or gymnasium is, according to your calculations, too short for safety. Suggest some strategies that could be used (other than moving the wall) for making that playground safer.

Getting Involved

Visit a local playground and examine it from the viewpoint of safety. Use what you learned about stopping distance as one of your guidelines, but also try to identify other potentially unsafe conditions. Write a letter to the department of parks or to the officials of your town informing them of your findings.

Safety

All students should run in the same direction. Students should not be allowed to walk across the area where running speeds are being measured. Review the safety guidelines in Appendix A.

Program Resources

- **Teaching Resources** Chapter 1 Real-World Lab, pp. 29–31

reaction time before realizing that he or she needed to stop. The distance represents how far the fastest runner, with the slowest reaction time, would travel out of bounds before being able to react and stop.

3. Adding the longest stopping distance tells how much farther the student in Question 2 will travel before coming to a complete stop if that student also had the longest measured stopping distance.

4. It's the "worst case scenario." You are calculating the maximum distance it could take a student to stop. In reality, students will either be slower runners or will react faster or will have a shorter stopping distance. Thus all students should be able to stop in a distance that is shorter than you have calculated. To show that this is true, students can calculate how far they would travel given their own measured maximum speed, reaction time, and stopping distance.

5. A player may go out of bounds running sideways, jumping, or stumbling. A player might not immediately realize that he or she is out of bounds. These factors might increase the distance the player traveled.

6. You could add a wide yellow line to let players know when they are approaching the out of bounds. This would alert them to react sooner. You could also place cushions on the wall to reduce the risk of injury in a collision.

Extending the Inquiry

Getting Involved Students should check to make sure that there is enough distance between the out-of-bounds line and any obstructions (trees, walls, parking areas, roads). Students should realize that lines indicating where spectators should sit or stand would prevent a possible collision with a player. Students should note that basketball posts are very close to the court and perhaps should be wrapped in foam. Students should look for cracks in the playing surface.

Acceleration

Objectives

After completing the lesson, students will be able to
- ◆ describe what happens to the motion of an object as it accelerates;
- ◆ calculate the acceleration of an object and graph changing speed and distance of an accelerating object.

Key Term acceleration

1 Engage/Explore

Activating Prior Knowledge

Ask a volunteer to blow up a balloon and hold the opening firmly shut. Say: **Describe the motion of the balloon right now.** *(The balloon is not moving.)* Then ask: **What could you do to make the balloon move?** *(Release it.)* Now have the volunteer release the balloon. Make sure it is released toward a wall, well away from other students. Ask students to describe when the balloon changed speed or direction as it flew. *(More or less continuously, from the moment of release until it landed)* Tell students in this section they investigate changing speed and direction.

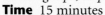

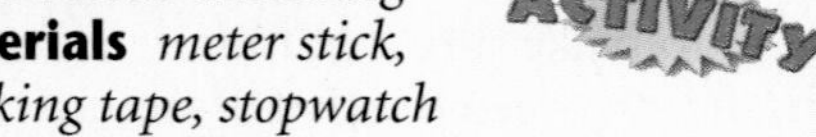

Skills Focus inferring
Materials *meter stick, masking tape, stopwatch*
Time 15 minutes
Tips Take students to a large open area or a long hallway where they will not disturb others. When students begin walking, suggest they walk very slowly, and gradually increase their speed until they are moving as fast as they can without running. Caution them not to run.
Think It Over The faster you speed up, the less time it takes to walk the course.

3 Acceleration

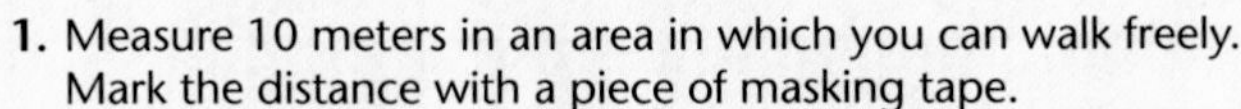

Will You Hurry Up?

1. Measure 10 meters in an area in which you can walk freely. Mark the distance with a piece of masking tape.
2. Walk the 10 meters in such way that you keep moving faster throughout the entire distance. Have a partner time you.
3. Repeat Step 2, but try to walk the 10 meters in less time than you did before. Try it again, but this time walk it in twice the amount of time as the first. Remember that you must keep speeding up throughout the entire 10 meters.

Think It Over
Inferring How is the change in your speed related to the time during which you walk the 10-meter course?

GUIDE FOR READING

- ◆ What happens to the motion of an object as it accelerates?
- ◆ How is acceleration calculated?

Reading Tip As you read, list the three different types of acceleration. Then give several examples of each.

The pitcher winds up. She throws. The ball speeds to the batter and, *crack*—off the bat it goes. It's going, it's going, it's gone—a home run!

Before falling beyond the fence, the softball went through several changes in its motion. It started moving from the pitcher's hand, sped up, stopped moving at the bat, changed direction, and eventually slowed down. Most examples of motion involve similar changes. In fact, it is rare for any motion to stay the same for very long. You can describe changes in motion in much the same way as you did when you learned how to describe motion in terms of speed and velocity.

Acceleration in Science

Consider a car stopped at a red light. When the light changes to green, the driver of the car gently steps on the accelerator. As a result, the car speeds up, or accelerates. In everyday language, *acceleration* means "speeding up."

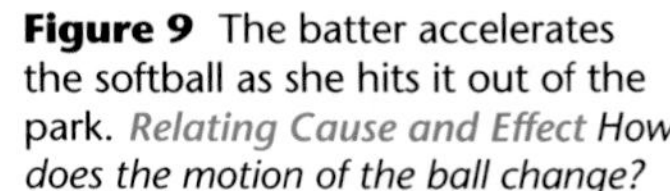

Figure 9 The batter accelerates the softball as she hits it out of the park. *Relating Cause and Effect How does the motion of the ball change?*

Acceleration has a more precise definition in science. **Acceleration** is the rate at which velocity changes. Recall that velocity has two components (speed and direction). Acceleration involves a change in either of these components. **In science, acceleration refers to increasing speed, decreasing speed, or changing direction.**

READING STRATEGIES

Reading Tip For each kind of acceleration, challenge students to identify at least three examples of objects in motion not in the text. *(Sample: Increasing speed—car starting from stopped position; decreasing speed—jet landing on a runway; changing direction—moon orbiting Earth)* Once students' lists are complete, invite them to share ideas with each other.

Concept Mapping As they complete the section, students can form a concept map using the following terms: *acceleration, time, speed, direction, distance.*

Increasing Speed Any time the speed of an object increases, the object experiences acceleration. Can you think of examples of acceleration? A softball accelerates when the pitcher throws it, and again when a bat hits it. A car that begins to move from a stopped position or speeds up to pass another car is accelerating.

People can experience acceleration as well. The runners in Figure 10 increase their speed to sprint down the track. A figure skater will accelerate as he speeds up before jumping into the air. Similarly, a gymnast might accelerate as she runs into a tumbling routine. You accelerate as you speed up to catch the bus for school.

Decreasing Speed Just as objects can speed up, they can also slow down. Motion in which speed decreases is also considered acceleration in science. This change in speed is sometimes called deceleration, or negative acceleration.

Can you think of examples of deceleration? A softball decelerates as it rolls to a stop. A car decelerates when it comes to a stop at a red light. A jet decelerates as it lands on an aircraft carrier. The diver in Figure 10 decelerates as he travels through the water.

Changing Direction A car on a highway may be traveling at constant speed. Thus you may be tempted to conclude that it is not accelerating. Recall, however, that velocity involves *both* speed and direction. Therefore, an object can be accelerating even if its speed is constant. The car, for example, will be accelerating if it follows a gentle curve in the road or changes lanes. The skaters in Figure 10 accelerate as they round the turns on the track.

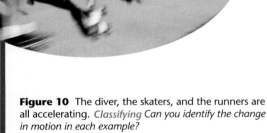

Figure 10 The diver, the skaters, and the runners are all accelerating. *Classifying Can you identify the change in motion in each example?*

2 Facilitate

Acceleration in Science

Addressing Naive Conceptions

Students may not realize that acceleration can involve speeding up or slowing down. Ask students which of these statements could be true:

- When you step on the gas, the car accelerates.
- When you step on the brake, the car accelerates.

Explain that both statements are correct, because acceleration is defined as any change in velocity. Slowing down, or deceleration, is negative acceleration. **learning modality: verbal**

Inquiry Challenge

ACTIVITY

Materials *marble, cardboard tubes, scissors, masking tape, books or blocks*
Time 40 minutes
Tips To demonstrate the ways an object can accelerate, invite students to construct tracks for marbles. Organize students in small groups. They can cut the cardboard tubes in half lengthwise and join the sections with masking tape. Tracks must be long enough for the marble to show all forms of acceleration. Tell students the tracks must make the marble speed up, slow down, and change direction. Ask: **How can you arrange the track so that the marble speeds up?** *(Make it so that the marble rolls downward.)* **Slows down?** *(Make it so that it has an upward-sloping section.)* **Changes direction?** *(Make it have a curve.)* **learning modality: kinesthetic**

Program Resources

- **Teaching Resources** 1-3 Lesson Plan, p. 23; 1-3 Section Summary, p. 24
- **Integrated Science Laboratory Manual** M-1, "Measuring Speed"

Media and Technology

Audiotapes English-Spanish Summary 1-3

Answers to Self-Assessment

Caption Questions

Figure 9 The ball accelerates toward the bat, stops as it strikes the bat, then accelerates in the opposite direction as the bat pushes it forward.
Figure 10 The runners are speeding up, the diver is changing direction and slowing down, and the skaters are changing direction.

Ongoing Assessment

Drawing Have students make sketches that show three ways an object can accelerate. *(Sketches should show acceleration by speeding up, slowing down, and changing direction.)*

Acceleration in Science, continued

Integrating Space Science

Materials *bicycle, tape, construction paper, scissors* ACTIVITY
Time 5 minutes

Make a construction-paper arrow. Tape it to the bicycle wheel so that it points in the direction the wheel will move when spinning. Slowly spin the wheel. Ask: **In what direction is the arrow pointing?** *(In different directions)* Ask: **Does the arrow have acceleration? Explain.** *(Yes, because it changes direction.)* Point out that just like the arrow, the moon, Earth, and satellites accelerate because they constantly change direction. **learning modality: visual**

Calculating Acceleration

Using the Visuals: Figure 12

Have students draw a line graph plotting the data for the airplane. Ask students to describe the graph. *(The graph is a straight line sloping up to the right.)* Ask students what this tells them about constant acceleration. *(The speed changes by the same amount each second.)* **learning modality: logical/ mathematical**

Building Inquiry Skills: Calculating

Students may have difficulty understanding units of acceleration. Ask them to imagine that they are riding in a car traveling at 40 km/hr. Exactly 1 minute later, the speedometer reads 80 km/hr. Ask: **What was the change in speed?** *(40 km/hr)* Then ask: **What was the change in time?** *(1 min)* Finally, ask: **If you watched the speedometer during that minute, what would you expect to see?** *(The needle moving slowly from 40 km/hr to 80 km/hr)* Since acceleration is the change in speed over a period of time, the acceleration is written as 40 km/hr per min, or 40 km/hr/min. **learning modality: logical/ mathematical**

Figure 11 Both the moon and the Ferris wheel are accelerating because they are changing direction. *Making Generalizations What path does the moon follow?*

Many objects continuously change direction without changing speed. The simplest example of this type of motion is circular motion, or motion along a circular path. The seats on the Ferris wheel accelerate because they move in a circle.

INTEGRATING SPACE SCIENCE In a similar way, the moon accelerates because it is continuously changing direction. Just as Earth revolves around the sun, the moon revolves around Earth. Another object that continuously accelerates is an artificial satellite orbiting Earth.

☑ *Checkpoint* ***How is it possible for a car to be accelerating if its speed is a steady 65 km/h?***

Calculating Acceleration

Acceleration describes the rate at which velocity changes. **To determine the acceleration of an object, you must calculate the change in velocity during each unit of time.** This is summarized by the following formula.

$$\text{Acceleration} = \frac{\text{Final velocity} - \text{Initial velocity}}{\text{Time}}$$

If velocity is measured in meters/second and time is measured in seconds, the unit of acceleration is meters per second per second. This unit is written as m/s^2. This unit may sound peculiar at first. But acceleration is the change in velocity per unit of time and velocity is the change in distance per unit of time. Therefore, acceleration has two units of time. Suppose velocity is measured in kilometers/hour and time is measured in hours. Then the unit of acceleration becomes kilometers per hour per hour, or km/h^2.

Background

Facts and Figures All objects in the solar system are accelerating in some way or another.

Comets travel in elliptical orbits. As they approach the sun, comets accelerate because their speed increases and their direction of motion changes. After the comet has moved past the sun and is headed back toward deep space, it is still accelerating because it is slowing down and changing direction.

Geostationary satellites appear to remain suspended above a spot on Earth's equator. However, they are not really stationary because, to stay over the same spot on the equator, they must move with constant speed completely around Earth once in 24 hours. Geostationary satellites are still accelerating because their direction of motion is constantly changing.

If the object's speed and direction change by the same amount during each unit of time, the acceleration at any time during its motion is the same. If, however, the acceleration varies, you can describe only the average acceleration.

For an object moving without changing direction, the acceleration of the object is the change in its speed during one unit of time. Consider, for example, a small airplane moving on a runway. The speed of the airplane at the end of each of the first 5 seconds of its motion is shown in Figure 12.

To calculate the acceleration of the airplane, you must first subtract the initial speed (0 m/s) from the final speed (40 m/s). This gives the change in speed, 40 m/s. Then divide the change in speed by the time, 5 seconds. The acceleration is 40 m/s divided by 5 seconds, which is 8 m/s^2.

The acceleration tells you how the speed of the airplane in Figure 12 changes during each second. Notice that after each interval of one second, the speed of the airplane is 8 m/s greater

Change in Speed Over Time

Time (s)	Speed (m/s)
0	0
1	8
2	16
3	24
4	32
5	40

Figure 12 The speed of the airplane increases by the same amount each second.

Sample Problem

A roller coaster car rapidly picks up speed as it rolls down a slope. As it starts down the slope, its speed is 4 m/s. But 3 seconds later, at the bottom of the slope, its speed is 22 m/s. What is its average acceleration?

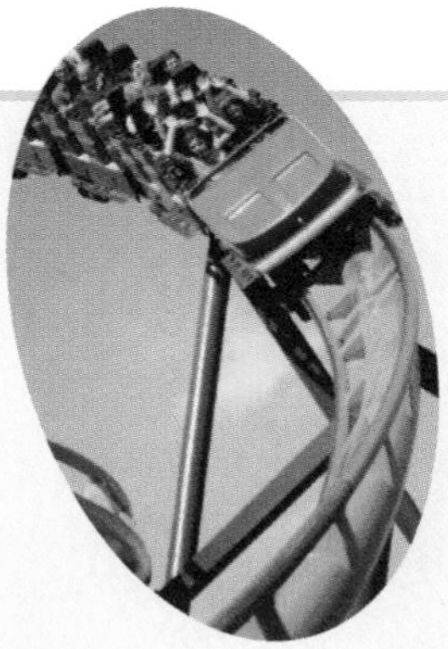

Analyze. You know the initial velocity and final velocity of the car, and the length of time during which its velocity changed. You are looking for its acceleration.

Write the formula.

$$\text{Acceleration} = \frac{\text{Final velocity} - \text{Initial velocity}}{\text{Time}}$$

Substitute and solve.

$$\text{Acceleration} = \frac{22 \text{ m/s} - 4 \text{ m/s}}{3 \text{ s}}$$

$$\text{Acceleration} = \frac{18 \text{ m/s}}{3 \text{ s}}$$

$$\text{Acceleration} = 6 \text{ m/s}^2$$

Think about it. The answer is reasonable. If the car's velocity increases by 6 m/s each second, its velocity will be 10 m/s after one second, 16 m/s after two seconds, and 22 m/s after three seconds.

Practice Problem

1. A car advertisement states that a certain car can accelerate from rest to 90 km/h in 9 seconds. Find the car's average acceleration.
2. An eagle accelerates from 15 m/s to 22 m/s in 4 seconds. What is the eagle's average acceleration?

Including All Students

Students who are still mastering English may not understand the difference between speed and acceleration. When students say a car is "fast," they usually mean the car accelerates rapidly. Have students use speed and acceleration words in sentences such as: *The runner ____ quickly at the start, but could not keep up her ____ to the finish line.* **limited English proficiency**

Sample Problem

Identify the main parts of the problem for students. Ask: **What is the initial velocity?** *(4 m/s)* **What is the final velocity?** *(22 m/s)* **How long did it take for the roller coaster to get from the top to the bottom of the slope?** *(3 s)* Ask students to complete the calculation. Follow up by asking: **What happens to the velocity each second?** *(It increases by 6 m/s.)* **learning modality: logical/ mathematical**

Practice Problems

1. 10 km/hr/s
2. 1.75 m/s^2

Real-Life Learning

Ask students to describe what happens when they ride a bike down a steep hill. *(You move faster and faster.)* Then ask: **Suppose you reach the bottom of a hill traveling 20 km/hr. What additional information do you need to find your acceleration rate?** *(Speed at the top of the hill; time it took to go from the top to the bottom of the hill)* **learning modality: logical/mathematical**

Media and Technology

Exploring Physical Science Videodisc

Unit 3, Side 1, "Light as a Feather"

Chapter 4

Answers to Self-Assessment

Caption Question

Figure 11 The moon takes a circular path around Earth (Some students may know that the moon's orbit is slightly elliptical.).

Checkpoint

If the car is turning, it would be changing direction and therefore accelerating.

Ongoing Assessment

Skills Check A badminton shuttlecock leaves the racquet traveling 30 m/s. It goes over the net 0.5 seconds later with a speed of 10 m/s. Calculate the average acceleration.

Graphing Acceleration

Using the Visuals: Figure 13

Draw student's attention to the line graphs in the figure. Ask: **How is the graph of change in distance over time different from the graph of change in speed over time?** *(The change-in-distance graph curves upward instead of being a straight line.)* Then ask: **What would happen to the curved graph if the acceleration rate slowed?** *(The curve would look more like the distance versus time graphs in Section 1.)* **learning modality: logical/mathematical**

3 Assess

Section 3 Review Answers

1. Increasing speed—a plane taking off; decreasing speed—a car braking; changing direction—a bicycle turning.
2. Acceleration = (Final velocity − Initial velocity)/ Time
3. The horse is accelerating because it is continually changing direction.
4. The car could have accelerated at $2 m/s^2$ for 12 s, $4 m/s^2$ for 6 s, or $6 m/s^2$ for 4 s. There are an infinite number of ways for the speed increase to have happened.

CHAPTER PROJECT 1

Check Your Progress

Talk with the whole class about ways to make measurements more accurately. Explain to students why taking several measurements and then calculating the average improves accuracy. Show students ways to organize their calculations to model good problem-solving techniques.

Performance Assessment

Oral Presentation Divide the class into small groups. Have each group write a short scenario involving an object being accelerated, then exchange scenarios with another group and sketch a graph of speed versus time for the scenario. Finally, have each class present their findings to the class.

Changes in Speed and Distance Over Time

Time (s)	Speed (m/s)	Distance (m)
0	0	0
1	10	5
2	20	20
3	30	45
4	40	80
5	50	125

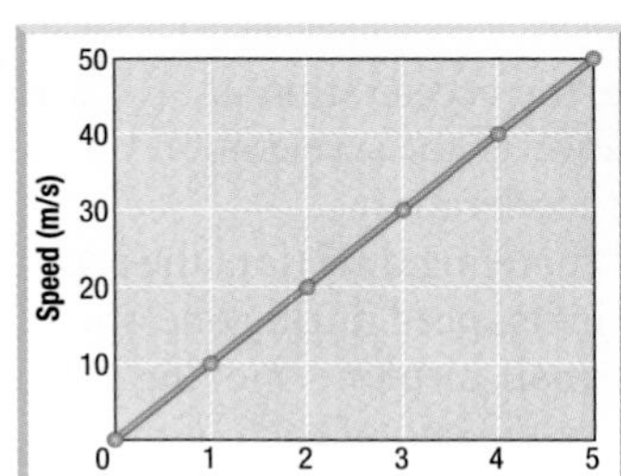

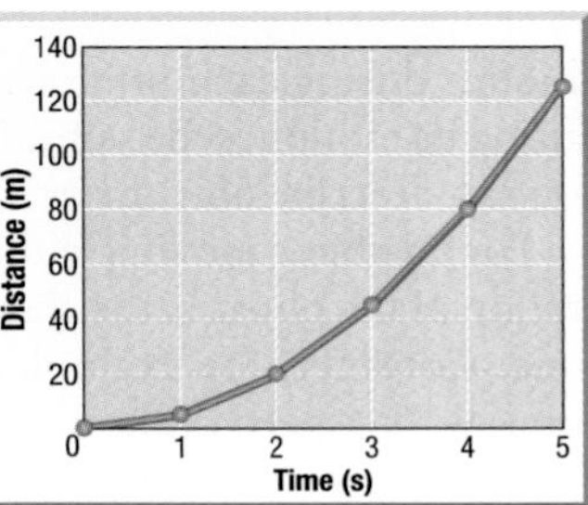

Figure 13 These graphs plot the motion of an accelerating object. *Predicting How would the slope of the speed and time graph change if the object were accelerating more rapidly? More slowly? What do you think the graph of a decelerating object would look like?*

than during the previous interval. So after one second, its speed is 8 m/s. After two seconds, its speed is 8 m/s + 8 m/s, or 16 m/s, and so on. Since the acceleration of the airplane does not change during the 5 seconds, you can use this formula for any time interval during the five seconds. Try it.

Graphing Acceleration

You can use a graph to analyze the motion of an object that is accelerating. Figure 13 shows the data for an object that is accelerating at $10 m/s^2$. The graph showing speed versus time is a slanted straight line. The straight line shows that acceleration is constant. For every increase of one second, the speed increases by 10 m/s. Thus the graphed line rises the same amount each second. If the object accelerated by a different amount each second, the graph would not be a straight line.

The graph of distance versus time is a curved line. This tells you that the distance traveled by the accelerating object varies each second. As the speed increases, the graph curves upward.

Section 3 Review

1. What three kinds of change in motion are called acceleration? Give an example of each.
2. What formula is used to calculate acceleration?
3. A horse trots around a large circular track, maintaining a constant speed of 5 m/s. Is the horse accelerating? Explain.
4. **Thinking Critically Problem Solving** A car is creeping down a deserted highway at 1 m/s. Sometime later, its speed is 25 m/s. This could have happened if the car accelerated at $3 m/s^2$ for 8 seconds. Is this the only way the increase in speed could have happened? Explain.

CHAPTER PROJECT 1

Check Your Progress

You can improve the accuracy of your speed estimations by repeating measurements and by using averaged data. Make all your calculations in an organized, step-by-step manner. Prepare display cards that show how you calculated each speed.

Program Resources

◆ **Teaching Resources** 1-3 Review and Reinforce, p. 25; 1-3 Enrich, p. 26

Answers to Self-Assessment

Caption Question

Figure 13 If the object were accelerating more rapidly, then the slope of the speed and time line would be steeper. If it were accelerating more slowly, then the slope of the line would less steep. A decelerating object would produce a speed and time graph with a line that falls instead of rises.

STUDY GUIDE

Section 1 Describing and Measuring Motion

Key Ideas

- The motion of an object is determined by its change of position relative to a reference point.
- Speed is the distance an object travels in one unit of time. If an object moves at constant speed, its speed can be determined by dividing the distance it travels by the time taken. If an object's speed varies, then dividing distance by time gives you the object's average speed.
- When you state both the speed of an object and the direction in which it is moving, you are describing the object's velocity.

Key Terms

motion
reference point
International System of Units (SI)
meter
speed
velocity

Section 2 Slow Motion on Planet Earth

INTEGRATING EARTH SCIENCE

Key Idea

- The plates that make up Earth's outer layer move very slowly, only centimeters per year, in various directions.

Key Term

plate

Section 3 Acceleration

Key Ideas

- Acceleration is the rate at which velocity changes. It involves increasing speed, decreasing speed, or changing direction.
- Acceleration can be calculated by dividing the change in velocity by the amount of time it took that change to occur.

Key Term

acceleration

www.science-explorer.phschool.com

Program Resources

- **Teaching Resources** Chapter 1 Project Scoring Rubric, p. 14; Chapter 1 Performance Assessment Teacher Notes, pp. 186–187; Chapter 1 Performance Assessment Student Worksheet, p. 188; Chapter 1 Test, pp. 189–192

Media and Technology

Interactive Student Tutorial CD-ROM M-1

Computer Test Bank M-1 Test

CHAPTER 1 REVIEW

Reviewing Content:

Multiple Choice

1. d **2.** b **3.** b **4.** d **5.** a

True or False

6. true **7.** straight line **8.** plates **9.** true **10.** speed

Checking Concepts

11. From the reference point of the train, you are moving toward the rear of the train at walking speed. From the reference point of the ground, you are moving in the same direction as the train at a speed slightly less than the speed of the train.
12. The warbler has a greater speed, 12 m/s, compared to the hawk's 10 m/s.
13. The insect is accelerating because the direction of its motion is always changing.
14. The greater the slope, the greater the speed.
15. You could make a mark where it is today (a reference point), then come back after a certain period of time and make a mark to show where it is now. If it is still at the same reference point, it is not moving.
16. This assignment should generate interesting and useful responses. Check that the actual speeds students use are reasonable values for what they are describing.

Thinking Visually

17. Sample title: *Describing and Measuring Motion* **a.** reference point **b.** speed **c.** velocity

Applying Skills

18. Starting line to B = 2.0 cm; B to finish line = 5.0 cm
19. 2 cm/s
20. 1.0 cm/s^2

Thinking Critically

21. Sample: You can use the first 30-m interval as an initial velocity and compare it to the final velocity at the second 30-m interval. If they are the same, the car was not accelerating. If they are different, the car was accelerating.

CHAPTER 1 REVIEW

Reviewing Content

For more review of key concepts, see the Interactive Student Tutorial CD-ROM.

Multiple Choice

Choose the letter of the best answer.

1. A change in position with respect to a reference point is
a. acceleration. **b.** velocity.
c. direction. **d.** motion.

2. To find the average speed of an object,
a. add together its different speeds and divide by the number of speeds.
b. divide the distance it travels by the time taken to travel that distance.
c. divide the time it takes to travel a distance by the distance traveled.
d. multiply the acceleration by the time.

3. If you know a car travels 30 km in 20 minutes, you can find its
a. acceleration. **b.** average speed.
c. direction. **d.** graph

4. A child on a merry-go-round is accelerating because the child
a. is moving relative to the ground.
b. does not change speed.
c. is moving relative to the sun.
d. is always changing direction.

5. If you divide the increase in an object's speed by the time taken for that increase, you are determining the object's
a. acceleration. **b.** constant speed.
c. average speed. **d.** velocity.

True or False

If the statement is true, write true. If it is false, change the underlined word or words to make the statement true.

6. In a moving elevator, you are not moving from the reference point of the elevator.
7. The graph of distance versus time for an object moving at constant speed is a curve.
8. The upper layer of Earth is made of pieces called reference points.
9. Acceleration is a change in speed or direction.
10. The distance an object travels in one unit of time is called acceleration.

Checking Concepts

11. Suppose you walk toward the rear of a moving train. Describe your motion as seen from a reference point on the train. Then describe it from a reference point on the ground.
12. Which has a greater speed, a hawk that travels 600 meters in 60 seconds or a tiny warbler that travels 60 meters in 5 seconds? Explain.
13. An insect is on a compact disc that is put into a compact disc player. The disc spins around and the insect hangs on for dear life. Is the insect accelerating? Explain why or why not.
14. You have a motion graph for an object that shows distance and time. How does the slope of the graph relate to the object's speed?
15. How can you tell if an object is moving, if its motion is too slow to see?
16. Writing to Learn Suppose that one day some of the things that usually move very slowly start to go faster, while some things that usually move quickly slow to a snail's pace. Write a description of some of the strange events that might occur during this weird day. Include a few actual speeds as part of your description.

Thinking Visually

17. Copy the concept map about motion onto a separate sheet of paper. Then complete it and add a title. (For more on concept maps, see the Skills Handbook.)

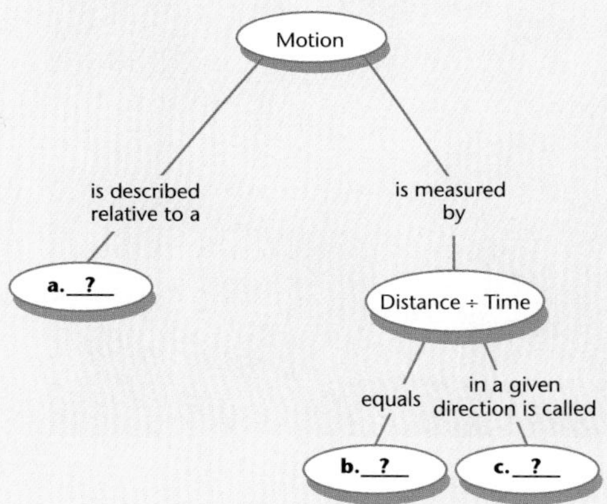

22. Since they left at the same time, the first driver had the greater average speed since that driver drove the same distance in less time, even though the second driver must have driven at higher speeds while in motion.
23. The family traveled a total distance of 160 km (80 km/hr × 1 hr + 40 km/hr × 2 hr) in 3 hours. So their average speed is 53.3 km/hr (160 km ÷ 3 hr = 53.3 km/hr). Simply adding the two speeds and dividing by 2 gives an incorrect answer because the family spent more time driving at the slower speed.

Applying Skills

Use the illustration of the motion of a ladybug to answer Questions 18–20.

18. Measuring Measure the distance from the starting line to line B, and from line B to the finish line. Measure to the nearest tenth of a centimeter.

19. Calculating Starting at rest, the ladybug accelerated to line B and then moved at constant speed until she reached the finish line. If she took 2.5 seconds to move from line B to the finish line, calculate her constant speed during that time.

20. Interpreting Data The speed you calculated in Question 19 is also the speed the ladybug had at line B (at the end of her acceleration). If she took 2 seconds to accelerate from the start line to line B, what is her acceleration during that time?

Thinking Critically

21. Making Generalizations You and a friend make two measurements. The first is the time that a car takes to travel one city block. The second is the time the car takes to travel the next city block. From these two measurements, explain how you can decide whether the car is moving at a steady speed or is accelerating.

22. Problem Solving Two drivers start at the same time to make a 100-km trip. The first driver takes 2 hours to complete the trip. The second driver takes 3 hours, but stops for an hour at the halfway point. Which driver had a greater average speed for the whole trip? Explain.

23. Applying Concepts A family takes a car trip. They travel for an hour at 80 km/h and then for 2 hours at 40 km/h. Find the average speed. (*Hint:* Remember to consider the total distance and the total amount of time.)

CHAPTER 1 REVIEW

Performance Assessment

CHAPTER PROJECT 1

Wrap Up

Presenting Your Project Organize your display cards so that they are easy to follow. Did you remember to put a title on each card stating the speed that was being measured? Place them in order from the lowest speed to the highest. Then display your cards to your class. Compare your results with those of other students.

Reflect and Record When you measured the same speed more than once, were the data always the same? Explain. What factors make measuring a speed difficult?

Getting Involved

In Your Community Contact the principal of a local elementary school and explain that you have been learning about motion. Volunteer to give a short lesson to a kindergarten class about motion that is too slow to see. Make a display with two or three of these motions and be prepared to demonstrate or explain a few others (such as molasses flowing down a plate, the minute hand of a clock, or a plant growing). Discuss how you know something is moving if you can't see it move.

Program Resources

◆ **Inquiry Skills Activity Book** Provides teaching and review of all inquiry skills

Performance Assessment

CHAPTER PROJECT 1

Wrap Up

Presenting Your Project

- ◆ Have students review each other's display cards in small groups for the easy and medium categories. Prepare a table on which students can record and compare their different values.
- ◆ Have individual students present their methods on the board for calculating the speeds from the difficult category. Share alternate methods for each measurement, and discuss discrepancies in students' answers.
- ◆ Have students convert all the speed measurements to m/s. The class can then put all the display cards in order from slowest to fastest, and the display can be put on the wall or made into a booklet showing a spectrum of speeds.

Reflect and Record The students probably got slightly different answers when they measured the same speed more than once. Multiple measurements improve accuracy. Measuring speed is difficult because it involves measuring two different things, distance and time, accurately.

Getting Involved

In Your Community If it is impractical in your community for individual students to physically visit elementary schools, you can modify the assessment by directing students to prepare a short lecture and demonstration they would give to a kindergarten class. Students can practice their lectures in small groups. Groups can evaluate each other's demonstrations, then give positive and constructive feedback. Check projects for correctness and feasibility.

Forces

Sections	Time	Student Edition Activities	Other Activities
CHAPTER PROJECT 2 **Newton Scooters** p. 43	Ongoing (3 weeks)	Check Your Progress, pp. 54, 61, 69 Wrap Up, p. 75	**TE** Chapter 2 Project Notes, pp. 42–43
1 The Nature of Force pp. 44–51 ◆ Explain how balanced and unbalanced forces are related to motion. ◆ State Newton's first law of motion and define inertia.	4 periods/ 2 blocks	**Discover** What Changes Motion?, p. 44 **Try This** Around and Around, p. 48 **Skills Lab: Interpreting Data** Forced to Accelerate, pp. 50–51	**TE** Including All Students, p. 45 **TE** Demonstration, p. 48 **TE** Science at Home, p. 49
2 Force, Mass, and Acceleration pp. 52–54 ◆ State Newton's second law of motion and explain how force and mass are related to acceleration.	1–2 periods/ 1 block	**Discover** How do the Rocks Roll?, p. 52	**TE** Demonstration, p. 53
3 Friction and Gravity pp. 55–63 ◆ Describe friction and identify the factors that determine the friction force between two surfaces. ◆ Explain how mass differs from weight. ◆ State the universal law of gravitation. ◆ Describe the effects of gravity and air resistance on an object in free fall.	4–5 periods/ $2\frac{1}{2}$ blocks	**Discover** Which Lands First?, p. 55 **Try This** Spinning Plates, p. 57 **Sharpen Your Skills** Calculating, p. 60 **Real-World Lab: You, the Consumer** Sticky Sneakers, pp. 62–63	**TE** Building Inquiry Skills: Designing Experiments, p. 56 **TE** Demonstration, p. 58 **TE** Inquiry Challenge, p. 59 **IES** "Mars the Next Frontier," pp. 20–21, 26–27 **ISLM** M-2, "Weight and the Force of Gravity"
4 Action and Reaction pp. 64–69 ◆ State Newton's third law of motion. ◆ Define and calculate momentum and state the law of conservation of momentum.	3 periods/ 1–2 blocks	**Discover** How Pushy Is a Straw?, p. 64 **Try This** Colliding Cars, p. 68	**TE** Including All Students, p. 65
5 *INTEGRATING SPACE SCIENCE* **Orbiting Satellites** pp. 70–72 ◆ Explain how a rocket lifts off the ground. ◆ Describe the forces that keep a satellite in orbit.	1–2 periods/ 1 block	**Discover** What Makes an Object Move in a Circle?, p. 70	**TE** Demonstration, p. 71 **TE** Science at Home, p. 72 **IES** "Mars the Next Frontier," pp. 22–23
Study Guide/Chapter Review pp. 73–75	1 period/ $\frac{1}{2}$ block		**ISAB** Provides teaching and review of all inquiry skills

For Standard or Block Schedule The Resource Pro® CD-ROM gives you maximum flexibility for planning your instruction for any type of schedule. Resource Pro® contains Planning Express®, an advanced scheduling program, as well as the entire contents of the Teaching Resources and the Computer Test Bank.

CHAPTER PLANNING GUIDE

Program Resources	Assessment Strategies	Media and Technology
TR Chapter 2 Project Teacher Notes, pp. 32–33 **TR** Chapter 2 Project Overview and Worksheets, pp. 34–37 **TR** Chapter 2 Project Scoring Rubric, p. 38	**SE** Performance Assessment: Chapter 2 Project Wrap Up, p. 75 **TR** Chapter 2 Project: Scoring Rubric, p. 38 **TE** Check Your Progress, pp. 54, 61, 69 **TE** Performance Assessment: Chapter 2 Project Wrap Up, p. 75	Science Explorer Internet Site
TR 2-1 Lesson Plan, p. 39 **TR** 2-1 Section Summary, p. 40 **TR** 2-1 Review and Reinforce, p. 41 **TR** 2-1 Enrich, p. 42 **TR** Chapter 2 Skills Lab, pp. 59–60	**SE** Section 1 Review, p. 49 **SE** Analyze and Conclude, p. 51 **TE** Ongoing Assessment, pp. 45, 47 **TE** Performance Assessment, p. 49 **TR** 2-1 Review and Reinforce, p. 41	Audiotapes: English-Spanish Summary 2-1 Exploring Physical Science Videodisc, Unit 3 Side 1, "Sir Isaac Newton" Transparency 2, "Exploring Combined Forces" Interactive Student Tutorial CD-ROM, M-2
TR 2-2 Lesson Plan, p. 43 **TR** 2-2 Section Summary, p. 44 **TR** 2-2 Review and Reinforce, p. 45 **TR** 2-2 Enrich, p. 46	**SE** Section 2 Review, p. 54 **TE** Ongoing Assessment, p. 53 **TE** Performance Assessment, p. 54 **TR** 2-2 Review and Reinforce, p. 45	Audiotapes: English-Spanish Summary 2-2 Exploring Physical Science Videodisc, Unit 3 Side 1, "Amusement Parks" Interactive Student Tutorial CD-ROM, M-2
TR 2-3 Lesson Plan, p. 47 **TR** 2-3 Section Summary, p. 48 **TR** 2-3 Review and Reinforce, p. 49 **TR** 2-3 Enrich, p. 50 **TR** Chapter 2 Real-World Lab, pp. 61–63 **SES** Book J, *Astronomy,* Chapters 1 and 2	**SE** Section 3 Review, p. 61 **SE** Analyze and Conclude, p. 63 **TE** Ongoing Assessment, pp. 57, 59 **TE** Performance Assessment, p. 61 **TR** 2-3 Review and Reinforce, p. 49	Audiotapes: English-Spanish Summary 2-3 Exploring Physical Science Videodisc, Unit 3 Side 1, "Light as a Feather" Transparencies 3, "Air Resistance"; 4, "Law of Universal Gravitation" Interactive Student Tutorial CD-ROM, M-2
TR 2-4 Lesson Plan, p. 51 **TR** 2-4 Section Summary, p. 52 **TR** 2-4 Review and Reinforce, p. 53 **TR** 2-4 Enrich, p. 54 **SES** Book B, *Animals,* Chapter 2	**SE** Section 4 Review, p. 69 **TE** Ongoing Assessment, p. 67 **TE** Performance Assessment, p. 69 **TR** 2-4 Review and Reinforce, p. 53	Audiotapes: English-Spanish Summary 2-4 Transparency 5, "Conservation of Momentum" Interactive Student Tutorial CD-ROM, M-2
TR 2-5 Lesson Plan, p. 55 **TR** 2-5 Section Summary, p. 56 **TR** 2-5 Review and Reinforce, p. 57 **TR** 2-5 Enrich, p. 58	**SE** Section 5 Review, p. 72 **TE** Ongoing Assessment, p. 71 **TE** Performance Assessment, p. 72 **TR** 2-5 Review and Reinforce, p. 57	Exploring Physical Science Videodisc, Unit 3 Side 1, "We Have Lift Off" Interactive Student Tutorial CD-ROM, M-2 Audiotapes: English-Spanish Summary 2-4
TR Chapter 2 Performance Assessment, pp. 193–195 **TR** Chapter 2 Test, pp. 196–199	**SE** Chapter Review, pp. 73–75 **TR** Chapter 2 Performance Assessment, pp. 193–195 **TR** Chapter 2 Test, pp. 196–199 **CTB** Test M-2	Interactive Student Tutorial CD-ROM, M-2 Computer Test Bank, M-2

Key: **SE** Student Edition; **CTB** Computer Test Bank; **ISAB** Inquiry Skills Activity Book; **TE** Teacher's Edition; **SES** Science Explorer Series Text; **PTA** Product Testing Activities by *Consumer Reports*; **TR** Teaching Resources; **ISLM** Integrated Science Laboratory Manual; **IES** Interdisciplinary Explorations Series

Meeting the National Science Education Standards and AAAS Benchmarks

National Science Education Standards	Benchmarks for Science Literacy	Unifying Themes
Physical Science (Content Standard B) ◆ **Motions and forces** Balanced forces, unbalanced forces, inertia, and Newton's first law of motion are presented for student analysis. *(Section 1)* Students learn how Newton's second law of motion explains the relationship between force, mass, and acceleration. *(Section 2)* Students examine the effect of friction and gravity on motion. *(Section 3)* Students learn Newton's third law of motion and the law of conservation of momentum. *(Section 4)* **Earth and Space Science** (Content Standard D) ◆ **Earth in the solar system** The idea that gravity attracts all objects in the universe is discussed. *(Section 3)* Students examine the forces affecting orbiting satellites. *(Section 5)* **Science and Technology** (Content Standard E) ◆ **Design a solution or a product** Students are challenged to design and build a vehicle powered only through Newton's third law of motion. *(Chapter Project)* ◆ **Evaluate completed technological designs or products** The amount of friction generated by different types of sneakers is measured. *(Real-World Lab)*	**3B Design and Systems** Students design a scooter based on Newton's principles of motion. *(Chapter Project)* **4F Motion** Balanced and unbalanced forces, inertia, friction, and momentum are discussed as students apply Newton's three laws of motion. *(Sections 1, 2, 3, 4)* **12C Manipulation and Observation** Students use force meters to calculate acceleration and weight. They assemble a scooter of their own design. *(Chapter Project, Skills Lab, Real-World Lab)* **12D Communication Skills** Students organize data in tables and graphs. *(Skills Lab, Real-World Lab)* **12E Critical-Response Skills** Students compare different types of sneakers and evaluate their usefulness for different activities. *(Real-World Lab)*	◆ **Systems and Interactions** Interactions between systems of objects are summarized in Newton's three laws of motion and the law of gravity. This includes interactions within the system of objects known as the Solar System. *(Chapter Project, Sections 1, 2, 3, 4, 5, Skills Lab)* ◆ **Stability** A system is stable and will remain stable as long as there are no unbalanced forces acting on it. *(Section 1)* ◆ **Patterns of Change** When change in a system occurs, the nature and magnitude of the change is determined by Newton's laws, especially Newton's second law relating force, mass, and acceleration. *(Sections 1, 2, 3, 4, Chapter Project, Skills Lab, Real-World Lab)* ◆ **Modeling** Students create models of vehicles. *(Chapter Project)*

Media and Technology

Exploring Physical Science Videodiscs

◆ **Section 1** "Sir Isaac Newton" takes viewers on an amusement park ride to introduce Newton's Laws of Motion and Gravitation.

◆ **Section 2** "Amusement Parks" a roller coaster ride models Newton's Laws of Motion.

◆ **Section 3** "Light as a Feather" introduces viewers to Newton's Law of Universal Gravitation and describes how gravity affects the acceleration of an object.

◆ **Section 5** "We Have Lift Off" shows how chemical energy produces the combustion needed to propel the space shuttle into orbit.

Interactive Student Tutorial CD-ROM

◆ **Chapter Review** Interactive questions help students to self-assess their mastery of key chapter concepts.

Student Edition Connection Strategies

◆ **Section 1** **Language Arts Connection,** p. 46 

◆ **Section 3** **Integrating Space Science,** p. 60 

◆ **Section 4** **Integrating Life Science,** p. 65

◆ **Section 5** **Integrating Space Science,** p. 70

www.science-explorer.phschool.com

Visit the Science Explorer Internet site to find an up-to-date activity for Chapter 2 of *Motion, Forces, and Energy.*

ACTIVITY	Time (minutes)	Materials Quantities for one work group	Skills
Section 1			
Discover, p. 44	10	**Nonconsumable** toy car, metal washers, heavy book	Observing
Try This, p. 48	15	**Consumable** thread, masking or cellophane tape **Nonconsumable** table tennis ball	Inferring
Skills Lab, p. 50–51	45	**Consumable** string, masking tape **Nonconsumable** skateboard; meter stick; spring scale, 5 N; stopwatch; several bricks or other large mass(es)	Interpreting Data
Section 2			
Discover, p. 52	10	**Nonconsumable** toy dump truck, several small rocks, spring scale	Observing
Section 3			
Discover, p. 55	15	**Nonconsumable** dime, nickel, quarter, ruler	Predicting
Try This, p. 57		**Nonconsumable** two identical pie plates, marbles	Drawing Conclusions
Sharpen Your Skills, p. 60	20	**Consumable** No special materials are required. **Nonconsumable** four objects, such as a shoe, a book, a spiral notebook, a pair of scissors; scale balance	Calculating
Real-World Lab, p. 62–63	45	**Consumable** tape **Nonconsumable** three or more different types of sneakers; spring scale, 20 N; mass set(s); spring scale, 5 N; large paper clip; balance	Forming Operational Definitions, Measuring, Controlling Variables
Section 4			
Discover, p. 64	15	**Consumable** plastic straw **Nonconsumable** rubber band, small- or medium-sized hard cover book, 4 marbles	Developing Hypotheses
Try This, p. 68	10	**Consumable** masking tape **Nonconsumable** two toy cars that are about the same mass and roll with relatively little friction	Predicting
Section 5			
Discover, p. 70	10	**Consumable** length of string no more than 1 m long **Nonconsumable** small object such as an empty thread spool, safety goggles	Forming Operational Definitions

A list of all materials required for the Student Edition activities can be found on pages T14–T15. You can order Materials Kits by calling 1-800-828-7777 or by accessing the Science Explorer Internet site at **www.science-explorer.phschool.com.**

CHAPTER PROJECT 2 Newton Scooters

In this chapter, students will be introduced to Newton's three laws of motion and learn how forces change all kinds of motion. The project has students design a vehicle that is propelled by an application of Newton's laws.

Purpose In this project, students will apply Newton's third law of motion by building a vehicle that moves forward by pushing back on something else.

Skills Focus Students will be able to
- identify and manipulate variables that affect the performance of the scooter;
- make a model of the scooter by drawing a diagram of the design;
- predict how the scooter will work based on the model;
- communicate the results of the activity to classmates through a demonstration.

Project Time Line Allow at least one week for students to brainstorm possible ideas for a vehicle. Drawing all the forces acting on the vehicle requires that they have read most of the chapter. Once given permission to begin building their vehicle, allow two or three weeks for students to build their vehicle and then troubleshoot problems that they encounter. Before beginning the project, see Chapter 2 Project Teacher Notes on pages 32–33 in Teaching Resources for more details on carrying out the project. Also distribute the Chapter 2 Project Overview and Worksheets and Scoring Rubric on pages 34–38 in Teaching Resources.

Possible Materials Provide a wide variety of materials from which students can choose. Some possibilities are listed below. Encourage students to suggest and use other materials as well. For example, an effective vehicle can be made from a milk carton with a balloon inside, floating in a basin of water.
- recycled materials from home
- toys or building block sets
- balloons
- straws
- fishing lines
- paper towel rolls
- a basin of water

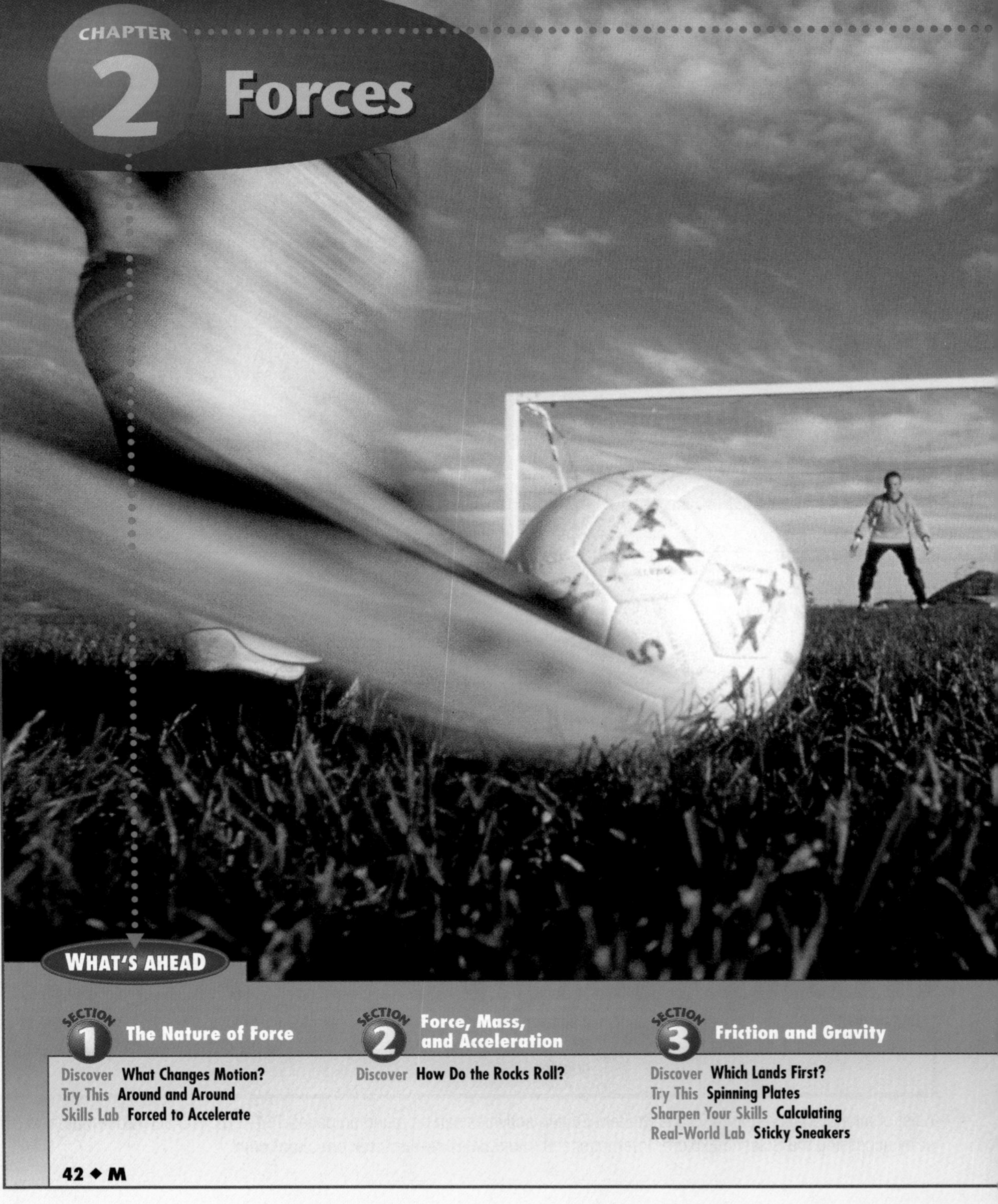

Launching the Project

Demonstrate the concept of Newton's third law of motion by releasing an inflated balloon into the air. Have the class discuss what makes the balloon move. Also discuss how a car moves forward when the wheels of the car push backward on the road. Allow time for students to read the description of the project in their text and the Chapter Project Overview on pages 34–35 in Teaching Resources. Pass out copies of the Chapter 2 Project Worksheets on pages 36–37 in Teaching Resources for students.

Allow the students to form groups. Have each group brainstorm vehicles other than four-wheeled cars and how they might power such vehicles without using any form of electricity or the force of gravity. Also have the students think about ways that they can keep vehicles going in a straight line. Tell students to apply what they learn about the forces in the chapter to their designs. Once they have acceptable designs, they may begin to build and test their vehicles.

PROJECT 2

Newton Scooters

A strong kick sends the soccer ball soaring toward the goal. The goalie does his best to stop the ball. Both the kicker and the goalie exert forces on the ball to change its motion. In this chapter you will learn how forces change all kinds of motion. You will find that there are forces acting on the ball even when it is soaring through the air.

In this chapter, you will learn how Newton's three basic laws of motion govern the relationship of forces and motion. You will use Newton's third law to build a scooter. Unlike the soccer ball, the scooter must move without being kicked!

Your Goal To design and build a vehicle that is powered only through Newton's third law of motion.

Your vehicle must

- move forward by pushing back on something
- not be powered by any form of electricity or use gravity in order to move
- travel a minimum distance of 1.5 meters
- be built following the safety guidelines in Appendix A

Get Started Brainstorm possible designs for your vehicle, but be careful not to lock yourself into a single idea. Remember that a car with wheels is only one type of vehicle. Try to think of ways to recycle household materials to build your vehicle.

Check Your Progress You'll be working on this project as you study this chapter. To keep your project on track, look for Check Your Progress boxes at the following points.

Section 2 Review, page 54: Determine factors that will affect the acceleration of your vehicle.

Section 3 Review, page 61: Draw a diagram of your proposed design.

Section 4 Review, page 69: Construct your vehicle and identify the force that propels it.

Wrap Up At the end of the chapter (page 75), demonstrate how your vehicle moves.

Both the kicker and the goalie use forces to control the motion of the soccer ball.

To conclude this project, students will make a class presentation of their vehicles demonstrating how their vehicles move and all the forces that act on them.

Program Resources

- **Teaching Resources** Chapter 2 Project Teacher's Notes, pp. 32–33; Chapter 2 Project Overview and Worksheets, pp. 34–37; Chapter 2 Project Scoring Rubric, p. 38

Performance Assessment

The Chapter 2 Project Scoring Rubric on page 38 of Teaching Resources will help you evaluate how well students complete the Chapter 2 Project. You may wish to share the scoring rubric with your students so they are clear about what will be expected of them. Students will be assessed on

- how well they planned their vehicle before building it, including consideration of all of the forces acting on it;
- the care with which the vehicle was built and the ability to modify the design after testing;
- the thoroughness and organization of their presentation, including explanations for all of the features of the vehicle.

The Nature of Force

Objectives

After completing the lesson, students will be able to

- explain how balanced and unbalanced forces are related to motion;
- state Newton's first law of motion and define inertia.

Key Terms force, net force, unbalanced force, balanced force, inertia, mass

1 Engage/Explore

Activating Prior Knowledge

Place a book in the middle of a table. Have students take turns moving the book, each using a different method. As obvious methods are used up, students will need to get more creative. They may use rubber bands, magnets, and springs. Ask the rest of the students to classify each method as a push or a pull. Ask: **What was required to make the book move?** *(A push or a pull)* **Did the book move when there was no push or pull?** *(no)*

Discover

Skills Focus observing
Materials *toy car, metal washers, heavy book*
Time 10 minutes
Tips Make sure students understand they should not fasten the washers to the top of the car. Have students record their predictions before they roll the car. Advise them not to push the car too hard or the washers will fall off the back.
Expected Outcome The car stops or bounces backward when it hits while the washers continue to move forward. The activity demonstrates inertia.
Think It Over The car stopped or bounced back while the washers kept moving forward. The force of the book stopped the forward motion of the car, but nothing stopped the forward motion of the washers.

Section 1 The Nature of Force

Discover — Activity

What Changes Motion?

1. Stack several metal washers on top of a toy car.
2. Place a heavy book on the floor near the car.
3. Predict what will happen to both the car and the washers if you roll the car into the book. Test your prediction.

Think It Over

Observing What happened to the car when it hit the book? What happened to the washers? What might be the reason for any difference between the motions of the car and the washers?

Guide for Reading

- **How are balanced and unbalanced forces related to motion?**
- **What is Newton's first law of motion?**

Reading Tip **As you read, use your own words to define each boldfaced word.**

An arrow soars through the air to its distant target. A long jumper comes to a sudden stop in a cloud of sand. You kick a soccer ball around your opponent. There is some type of motion involved in each of these activities. But why does each object move as it does? What causes an object to start moving, stop moving, or change direction? The answer is a force. In each of these activities, a force is exerted on, or applied to, an object.

What Is a Force?

In science the word *force* has a simple and specific meaning. A **force** is a push or a pull. When one object pushes or pulls another object, you say that the first object is exerting a force on the second object. You exert a force on a pen when you write, on a book when you lift it, on a zipper when you pull it, and on a

Reading Strategies

Reading Tip Have partners work together to define this section's boldfaced words. Partners can take turns defining the terms in his or her own words. Give students index cards so that they can write a term on one side and its definition on the other. Then partners can quiz each other on the term he or she did *not* define.

Study and Comprehension Reinforce concepts presented in this section by having students write descriptive captions for photographs shown. Instruct students to choose three photographs. Then direct them to write a new caption for each photograph. Suggest that students use up to three sentences for each caption. Invite volunteers to read aloud their completed captions while classmates study the photographs.

ball when you throw it. You exert a force on a pebble when you skim it across a pond, on a wagon when you pull it, and on a nail when you hammer it into a piece of wood.

Like velocity and acceleration, forces are described not only by how strong they are, but also by the *direction* in which they act. If you push on a door, you exert a force in a different direction than if you pull on the door.

Unbalanced Forces

Suppose you need to push a heavy box across a floor. When you push on the box, you exert a force on it. If a friend helps you, the total force exerted on the box is the sum of your force plus your friend's force. When two forces act in the same direction, they add together.

Figure 1 uses arrows to show the addition of forces. The head of each arrow points in the direction of a force. The width of each arrow tells you the strength of a force. A wider arrow shows a greater force. (When forces are shown in this book, the strength of a force will usually be shown by the width of an arrow.)

When forces act in opposite directions, they also add together. However, you must pay attention to the direction of each force. Adding a force acting in one direction to a force acting in the opposite direction is the same as adding a positive number and a negative number. So when two forces act in opposite directions, they combine by subtraction. If one force is greater than the other force, the overall force is in the direction of the greater force. You can see

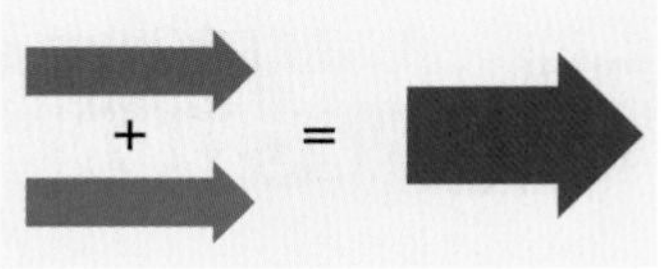

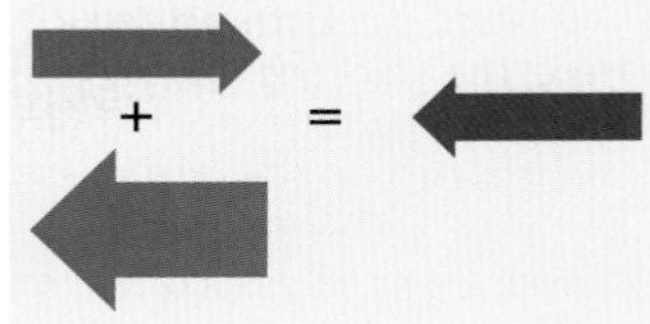

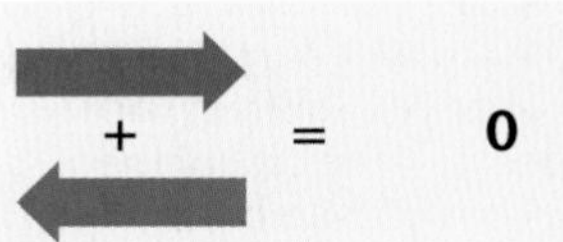

Figure 1 Two forces can combine so that they add together (top), or subtract from each other (center). They may also cancel each other (bottom).

Figure 2 The arrow, the jumper, and the soccer ball are all in motion. *Making Generalizations What makes an arrow fly through the air to its target, a long jumper thud to a stop, and a soccer ball change direction?*

2 Facilitate

What Is a Force?

Building Inquiry Skills: Applying Concepts

Have each student select a classroom object (such as a stapler, 3-hole punch, scissors, or desk drawer). Ask students to demonstrate how force is typically applied to each object and explain what happens when the force is applied. Help students recognize that all objects require a push or pull to put them into motion or to stop or change their motion. **learning modality: kinesthetic**

Unbalanced Forces

Including All Students

ACTIVITY

Assign students to two groups. Then have each group divide into two teams. Make sure teams consist of students that are matched in strength and height but unequal in number. For example, one team could have six students, the other four. The two teams will pull on opposite ends of a rope until one team moves. Inform students that, unlike many tug-of-wars they may have seen, this is not a competition, but a scientific experiment. Caution the team with more students not to pull so hard that the other team falls over. They should continue to pull only until one team moves. Ask: **Were both teams exerting forces?** *(yes).* **Which team exerted more force?** *(The larger team)* Since the forces are unbalanced, the net force moves both the rope and the team that exerts the smaller force. **cooperative learning**

Program Resources

◆ **Teaching Resources** 2-1 Lesson Plan, p. 39; 2-1 Section Summary, p. 40

Media and Technology

Audiotapes English-Spanish Summary 2-1

Answers to Self-Assessment

Caption Question

Figure 2 The force of the bow string on the arrow makes the arrow fly, the force of the ground on the jumper makes the long jumper stop, and the force of a toe on the ball makes the soccer ball change direction.

Ongoing Assessment

Writing Have students give two examples of force they have seen today. *(Answers will vary. Sample: I saw my dog push his food bowl and the teacher pick up a book.)*

Language Arts CONNECTION

The word *net* has several meanings. Some of the meanings are similar to net force (net profit, net effect) and some are different (fishing net). Pair native English speakers with students of limited English proficiency. Have partners take turns constructing sentences using the word *net* and giving the definition of the word as used in the sentence. To help students get started, write sample sentences on the board.

In Your Journal Encourage students to include other words that have multiple meanings as well as the terms in the book. Be sure students include the parts of speech. Students can use dictionaries as references. Sample: spring—a season (noun), a coil (noun); pound—a measurement of weight (noun), to smash something (verb); bat—a flying mammal (noun), to brush away (verb); bowl—a concave vessel for holding liquids (noun), to take part in the game of bowling (verb); row—a horizontal line (noun), to push oars through water and move a boat (verb) **limited English proficiency**

Balanced Forces

Using the Visuals: Figure 3

Direct students' attention to the stocking the dogs are pulling. Ask: **In what direction are forces being applied?** *(Toward each dog)* **If neither the dogs nor the stocking is moving, what can you infer about the amount of force each dog is placing on the stocking?** *(The pull of the dog on the left is balanced by the pull of the two dogs on the right.)* **What would happen to the stocking if the dog on the left suddenly let go? Why?** *(The stocking would move to the right because the forces would be unbalanced.)* **learning modality: visual**

Language Arts CONNECTION

You have learned that *net force* means "overall force." Have you heard the term *net profit?* Here, the adjective *net* describes the total amount of money left over after paying all expenses. For example, suppose you sell popcorn at a sports event to raise money for a class trip. Your *net profit* is the amount of money that is left after you subtract your expenses—the cost of the popcorn kernels, butter, salt, bags, and posters.

In Your Journal

Can you think of another meaning for the word *net?* Many words have more than one meaning. Here are just a few: *spring, pound, bat, bowl,* and *row.* Think of two meanings for each word. Use at least two of these words in sentences that show their different meanings. Add more words to the list.

what happens when the students in the center of the next page exert unequal forces in opposite directions.

In any situation, the overall force on an object after all the forces are added together is called the **net force.** When there is a net force acting on an object, the force is said to be unbalanced. An **unbalanced force** can cause an object to start moving, stop moving, or change direction. **An unbalanced force acting on an object will change the object's motion.** In other words, an unbalanced force will cause an object to accelerate. For example, if two unequal forces acting in opposite directions are applied to a box, the box will accelerate in the direction of the greater force.

Balanced Forces

Forces exerted on an object do not always change the object's motion. Consider the forces involved when the dogs in Figure 3 pull on a stocking in opposite directions. Even though there are forces acting on it, the motion of the stocking does not change. While one dog exerts a force on the stocking in one direction, the other dogs exert an equal force on the stocking in the opposite direction.

Equal forces acting on one object in opposite directions are called **balanced forces.** One force is exactly balanced by the other force. **Balanced forces acting on an object will not change the object's motion.** When you add equal forces exerted in opposite directions, the net force is zero. You can also see how balanced forces cancel in the example at the bottom of the next page. The box does not move at all.

☑ *Checkpoint Which cause change in motion—balanced forces or unbalanced forces?*

Figure 3 These dogs are exerting a great deal of force, but they aren't moving. *Applying Concepts What would happen if one of the dogs pulled harder? Explain why.*

46 ◆ M

Background

Integrating Science In the *Science Explorer* series, forces are represented by arrows whose width is proportional to the size of the force. Students who go on to take physics in high school will encounter forces represented by arrows whose length is proportional to the size of the force. There are advantages to both methods. For middle school students, width seems more intuitive as a means of representing sizes of forces. However, with geometric (graphical or trigonometric) methods of addition and subtraction of force vectors that are not in line, arrows with proportional length must be used to preserve the size and direction of resultant forces.

EXPLORING Combined Forces

What happens when two friends push on the same object? The forces they exert combine in different ways, depending on the directions in which they push.

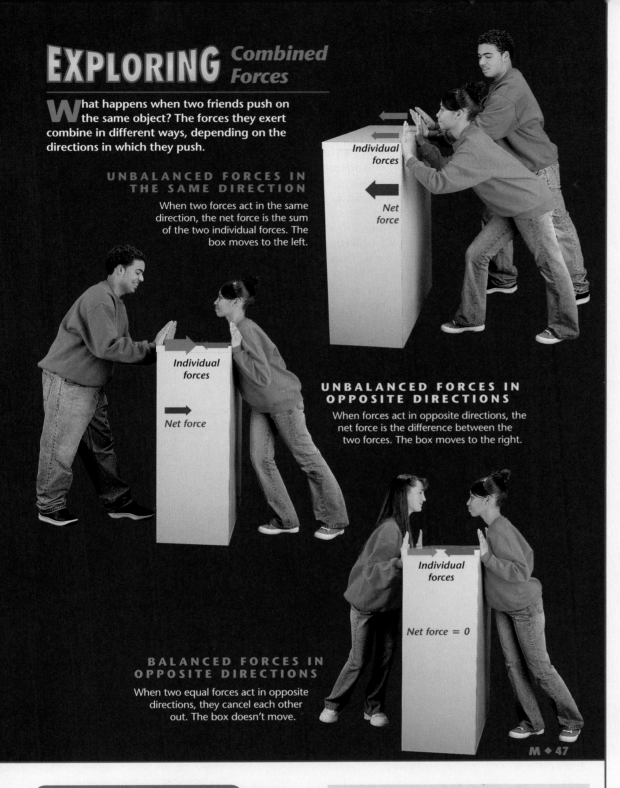

UNBALANCED FORCES IN THE SAME DIRECTION

When two forces act in the same direction, the net force is the sum of the two individual forces. The box moves to the left.

UNBALANCED FORCES IN OPPOSITE DIRECTIONS

When forces act in opposite directions, the net force is the difference between the two forces. The box moves to the right.

BALANCED FORCES IN OPPOSITE DIRECTIONS

When two equal forces act in opposite directions, they cancel each other out. The box doesn't move.

Media and Technology

Transparencies "Exploring Combined Forces," Transparency 2

Exploring Physical Science Videodisc Unit 3, Side 1, "Sir Isaac Newton"

Chapter 2

Answers to Self-Assessment

Caption Question

Figure 3 The forces will become unbalanced and the stocking, and perhaps one or two of the dogs, will move toward the dog that pulls harder. An object that is not moving will move when acted upon by an unbalanced force.

☑ Checkpoint

unbalanced forces

EXPLORING

Combined Forces

Guide students through the explanations in the visual by calling on volunteers to demonstrate the concepts. A student desk can be substituted for the heavy box shown. Some students may identify friction as a force acting on the box or desk. Tell them that in this activity, frictional force is ignored. To represent two forces in the same direction, have two students push the desk at the same time and in the same direction. Ask: **What is the net force acting on the desk?** *(The force of the first student's push added to the force of the second student's push)* Then have two other volunteers demonstrate two unequal forces in opposite directions. Suggest that one student push with one hand while the other pushes with two hands. Ask: **How would you calculate the net force?** *(Find the difference between the force of the first student's push and the force of the second student's push)* Then ask: **What happens to the desk when the forces acting on it are unequal?** *(The desk moves in the direction of the greater force.)* Finally, have two new volunteers demonstrate two equal forces acting in opposite directions. Ask: **What is the net force acting on the desk?** *(zero)* Then ask: **What happened to the desk when two equal forces push it from opposite directions?** *(The desk did not move.)*

Extend Have students identify other objects acted upon by equal and unequal forces and sketch the objects with arrows that represent the direction and strength of forces.

Students can save their sketches in their portfolios.

learning modality: visual

Ongoing Assessment

Drawing Have student sketch arm-wrestling matches in which balanced and unbalanced forces are demonstrated.

Newton's First Law of Motion

Skills Focus inferring

Materials *thread, masking or cellophane tape, table tennis ball*

Time 15 minutes

Tips Caution students to avoid releasing the table tennis ball so that it hits another person. Consider taking students outdoors or to an open area to reduce the chance that someone will get hit by a ball.

Inferring The ball will roll away if you let go of the thread when the ball is moving away from you. The ball will roll toward you if you let go of the thread when the ball is moving toward you. The inertia of the ball causes it to continue moving in the same direction that it was moving when it was released.

Extend Involve students in a game of tetherball and have them point out the effects of inertia on the movement of the ball. **learning modality: kinesthetic**

Demonstration

Materials *smooth cloth with no edge seam, several large, chrome-plated sockets (19–23 mm sizes work well)*

Time 10 minutes

Practice this demonstration before performing it in front of the class. Explain that this trick is not magic, just science. Place the cloth on a smooth table and arrange the sockets so that they are about 10 cm from the front edge of the cloth. The sockets should be placed so the the end with the square hole is down. Allow about 20 cm of the cloth to hang over the back edge of the table. Firmly grasp the edge of the cloth, lift your hands slightly, then snap the cloth straight down. Do not pull the cloth toward you, because you may lift it and you cannot pull it fast enough. The sockets should stay in place with little noticeable movement. Ask: **What kept the sockets in place?** *(inertia)*

Around and Around

An object moving in a circle has inertia.

1. Tape one end of a length of thread (about 1 m) to a table tennis ball.
2. Suspend the ball in front of you and swing it in a horizontal circle. Keep the ball about 2 or 3 cm above the floor.
3. Let go of the thread and observe the direction in which the ball rolls.
4. Repeat this several times, letting go of the thread at different points.

Inferring At what point do you need to let go of the thread if you want the ball to roll directly away from you? Toward you? Draw a diagram as part of your answer.

Newton's First Law of Motion

The ancient Greeks observed that objects have natural resting places. Objects move toward those places. A rock falls to the ground. A puff of smoke rises into the air. Once an object is in its natural resting place, it cannot move by itself. For an object to stay in motion, a force has to act on it.

Inertia In the early 1600s, the Italian astronomer Galileo Galilei questioned the idea that a force is needed to keep an object moving. He suggested that once an object is in motion, no push or pull is needed to keep it moving. Force is needed only to change the motion of an object. But whether it is moving or at rest, every object resists any change to its motion. This resistance is called inertia. **Inertia** (in UR shuh) is the tendency of an object to resist change in its motion.

You may have observed this yourself. A puck that rides on a cushion of air in an "air-hockey" game glides along quite freely once you push it. Similarly, a tennis ball flies through the air once you hit it with a racket. In both cases, the object continues to move even after you remove the force.

Galileo's ideas paved the way for the English mathematican Sir Isaac Newton. Newton discovered the three basic laws of motion in the late 1600s. The first of Newton's three laws of motion restates Galileo's idea. **Newton's first law of motion states that an object at rest will remain at rest. And an object that is moving at constant speed will continue moving at constant speed unless acted upon by an unbalanced force.** Newton's first law of motion is also called the law of inertia.

Figure 4 These crash-test dummies weren't wearing safety belts. ***Relating Cause and Effect*** *What caused them to move forward even after the car stopped?*

Background

History of Science Aristotle, Eratosthenes, Democritus, Thales, and many other ancient Greeks made important discoveries about science and nature. Beginning in the 1500s and through the late 1700s, philosophers and scientists reexamined their perceptions of the world around them and began to use the scientific method—experimentation and careful observation. It was during this time that Kepler and Galileo started to think and write about how things move. Kepler correctly described the motions of the planets, and Galileo first stated the most useful descriptions of how forces act on objects to cause acceleration. Sir Isaac Newton (1642–1727) restated and formalized these ideas about motion in his three laws of motion and the law of universal gravitation.

Inertia explains many common events. For example, if you are in a car that stops suddenly, inertia causes you to continue moving forward. The crash test dummies in Figure 4 don't stop when the car does. Passengers in a moving car have inertia. Therefore a force is required to change their motion. That force is exerted by the safety belt. If the safety belt is not worn, that force may be exerted by the windshield instead!

Mass Which is more difficult to move, a jar of pennies or a jar of plastic foam "peanuts"? Obviously, the jar of pennies is harder to move. What is the difference between the jar of pennies and the jar of plastic peanuts? After all, you can see in Figure 5 that both jars occupy the same amount of space, and so have the same volume. The difference is the amount of mass each one has. **Mass** is the amount of matter in an object. The jar of pennies has more mass than the jar of plastic peanuts.

Figure 5 The two jars have the same volume, but very different masses.

The SI unit of mass is the kilogram (kg). A small car might have a mass of 1,000 kilograms. A bicycle without a rider might have a mass of about 10 kilograms, and a student might have a mass of 45 kilograms. You describe the mass of smaller objects in terms of grams (1 kilogram = 1,000 grams). The mass of a nickel is about 5 grams.

The amount of inertia an object has depends on its mass. The greater the mass of an object, the greater its inertia. Mass, then, can also be defined as a measure of the inertia of an object.

Section 1 Review

1. What are the differences in how balanced and unbalanced forces affect motion?
2. What is inertia? How is it involved in Newton's first law of motion?
3. Two children who are fighting over a toy pull on it from opposite sides. The result is a stand-off. Explain this in terms of the net force.
4. **Thinking Critically** **Applying Concepts** Draw a diagram in which two forces acting on an object are unbalanced and a diagram in which two balanced forces act on an object. Use arrows to show the forces.

Science at Home

Fill a paper cup with water. Cover the cup with an index card and place a coin or paper clip in the center of the index card. Challenge your family members to move the coin from the card to the cup without touching the coin or holding on to the card. If they cannot think how to do it, show them how. Hold the cup and use your finger to flick the card with a sharp sideways force. The force doesn't have to be very strong, but it must be sharp. Explain what happens to the coin in terms of inertia.

3 Assess

Section 1 Review Answers

1. Balanced forces cancel out and do not change the motion of the object. Unbalanced forces cause an object to start moving, stop moving, or change speed or direction.
2. Inertia is a tendency of an object to resist any change in its motion. Newton's first law is called the law of inertia. The law states that an object at rest will remain at rest, and an object moving at constant speed will continue at a constant speed unless an unbalanced force acts on the object.
3. Because the toy does not move, each child must be pulling with the same amount of force. Because the forces are balanced, the net force equals zero.
4. Students' diagrams should resemble the force diagrams in *Exploring Combined Forces.*

Science at Home

Materials *paper cup, water, index card, coin or large paper clip*

Tips Suggest students practice the activity once or twice before challenging family members. Make sure students understand that the force applied to the card by flicking the edge of the card is not transferred to the coin or paper clip. The inertia of the coin resists the motion of the card so that the coin does not move to the side. When the card is no longer there to counteract the force of gravity, no force holds up the coin and it falls into the water.

Program Resources

◆ **Teaching Resources** 2-1 Review and Reinforce, p. 41; 2-1 Enrich, p. 42

Media and Technology

Interactive Student Tutorial CD-ROM M-2

Answers to Self-Assessment

Caption Question

Figure 4 The inertia of the dummies caused them to continue moving forward after the car stopped. The dummies stop only after a force from the airbag changes their motion.

Performance Assessment

Drawing Have students draw cartoon strips or diagrams which show ball games that illustrate Newton's first law of motion.

Students can save their cartoons in their portfolios.

Skills Lab

Interpreting Data

Forced to Accelerate

Preparing for Inquiry

Key Concept An unbalanced force causes an object to accelerate.

Skills Objective Students will be able to
- make observations of time and distance and calculate velocity and acceleration.
- graph data of acceleration vs. force;
- infer the relation between force and acceleration for constant mass.

Time 45 minutes

Advance Planning Ask volunteers to bring skateboards from home. Check calibration of the spring scales. Practice the experiment.

Alternative Materials You may be able to borrow carts or use old-fashioned roller skates in place of skateboards.

Guiding Inquiry

Invitation Put a skateboard on the floor and put a brick on it. Have a student accelerate it for about 1 meter using a spring scale. Ask students why the skateboard accelerated. Ask the students how they could investigate how acceleration depends on force.

Introducing the Procedure

- If needed, demonstrate how to zero and use a spring scale.
- Review the concepts of average speed and acceleration.
- Ask the students: **What are the manipulated and responding variables in this experiment?** *(Manipulated variable—force with which they pull the skateboard; responding variable—acceleration of the skateboard)*

Troubleshooting the Experiment

- If more mass is needed to keep the final velocity low, add bricks. Keep mass constant during the experiment.
- Be sure students zero the spring scale each time they use it. Point out that scale must be held horizontal and pulled straight.
- If the spring scale is calibrated in grams, multiply by 0.01 to obtain newtons.
- Remind students that for Steps 6–12, they should try to pull with constant force, not at a constant speed. Students should practice this before starting to record data.
- Be sure students round off their results to an appropriate number of digits.
- Remind students to measure force when the skateboard is moving, not the initial force to get it started moving (which will be higher).
- Students may want to pull using forces of 0.5 N, 1.0 N, and so on. Be sure to add the force reading from Step 5. For example, if it takes 0.2 N to keep the skateboard moving at constant speed, then the students should pull with 0.7 N, 1.2 N, and so on.
- In Question 3, students calculate the final speed from the average speed. They can do this because the acceleration is constant. Average speed = (Final speed − initial speed)/2. Since the initial speed is zero, Final speed = Average speed × 2.

Skills Lab

Interpreting Data

Forced to Accelerate

In this lab, you will practice the skill of interpreting data as you explore the relationship between force and acceleration.

Problem

How is the acceleration of a skateboard related to the force that is pulling it?

Materials

skateboard, meter stick, spring scale, 5 N, string, masking tape, stopwatch, several bricks or other large mass(es)

Procedure

1. Attach a loop of string to a skateboard. Place the bricks on the skateboard.
2. Using masking tape, mark off a one-meter distance on a level floor. Label one end "Start" and the other "Finish."
3. Attach a spring scale to the loop of string. Pull it so that you maintain a force of 2.0 N. Be sure to pull with the scale straight out in front. Practice applying a steady force to the skateboard as it moves.
4. Make a data table in your notebook like the one below.
5. Find the smallest force needed to pull the skateboard at a slow, constant speed. Do not accelerate the skateboard.
6. Add 0.5 N to the force in Step 5. This will be enough to accelerate the skateboard. Record this force on the first line of the table.
7. Have one of your partners hold the front edge of the skateboard at the starting line. Then pull on the spring scale with the force you found in Step 6.
8. When your partner says "Go" and releases the skateboard, maintain a constant force until the skateboard reaches the finish line.
9. A third partner should time how long it takes the skateboard to go from start to finish. Record the time in the column labeled Trial 1.
10. Repeat Steps 7, 8, and 9 twice more. Record your results in the columns labeled Trial 2 and Trial 3.
11. Repeat Steps 7, 8, 9, and 10, using a force that is 1.0 N greater than the force you found in Step 5.
12. Repeat steps 7, 8, 9 and 10 twice more. Use forces that are 1.5 N and 2.0 N greater than the force you found in Step 5. Record your results.

DATA TABLE

Force (N)	Trial 1 Time (s)	Trial 2 Time (s)	Trial 3 Time (s)	Avg Time (s)	Avg Speed (m/s)	Final Speed (m/s)	Acceleration (m/s^2)

Analyze and Conclude

1. For each force you used, find the average of the three times that you measured. Record the average in your data table.
2. Find the average speed of the skateboard for each force. Use this formula:

   Average speed = 1 m ÷ Average time

   Record this value for each force.
3. To obtain the final speed of the skateboard, multiply each average speed by 2. Record the result in your data table.
4. To obtain the acceleration, divide each final speed you found by the average time. Record the speed in your data table.
5. Make a line graph. Show the acceleration on the *y*-axis and the force on the *x*-axis. The *y*-axis scale should go from zero to about 1 m/s^2. The *x*-axis should go from zero to 3.0 newtons.
6. If your data points seem to form a straight line, draw a line through them.
7. Your first data point is the force required for an acceleration of zero. How do you know the force for an acceleration of zero?
8. According to your graph, how is the acceleration of the skateboard related to the pulling force?
9. **Think About It** Which variable is the manipulated variable? Which is the responding variable?

Design an Experiment

Design an experiment to test how the acceleration of the loaded skateboard depends on its mass. Think about how you would vary the mass of the skateboard. What quantity would you need to measure that you did not measure in this experiment? Do you have the equipment to make that measurement? If not, what other equipment would you need?

Expected Outcome

- The students should complete a data table similar to the sample provided.
- After calculating acceleration, the students should produce a graph showing that acceleration is proportional to force.
- Possible sources of error include improper use of the spring scale, calculating errors, and failing to pull with a constant force.

Analyze and Conclude

1. Answers may vary. If the mass is about 4 kg, and the force is 2.2 N, the time to accelerate for 1.0 m will be approximately 2 s.
2. Answers may vary. For the same combination, the average speed will be around 0.5 m/s.
3. Answers may vary. For the same combination, the final speed will be around 1 m/s.
4. Answers may vary. For the same combination, the acceleration will be around 0.5 m/s^2.
5. Answers may vary. Be sure to check for accuracy of graphing and comprehension of what the graph results mean.
6. Show students how to draw a "best-fit" line. Do not allow them to "connect the dots."
7. The force for an acceleration of zero was measured in Step 5 (at constant speed).
8. Acceleration is proportional to accelerating force.
9. The manipulated variable is the force; the responding variable is the acceleration.

Extending the Inquiry

Design an Experiment The new experiment should be essentially the same except that students should vary the mass (change the number of bricks) and keep the force constant.

Sample Data Table

Force for zero acceleration: 0.2 N

Force (N)	0.7	1.2	1.7	2.2
Trial 1 Time (s)				
Trial 2 Time (s)				
Trial 3 Time (s)				
Avg. Time (s)	4.4	3.2	2.5	2.0
Avg.Speed (m/s)	0.23	0.31	0.40	0.50
Final Speed (m/s)	0.46	0.62	0.80	1.00
Acceleration (m/s^2)	0.105	0.193	0.32	0.5

Safety

The skateboard can achieve a significant speed. It is safest to perform the experiment on the floor rather than on tables. Review the safety guidelines in Appendix A.

Program Resources

- **Teaching Resources** Chapter 2 Skills Lab, pp. 59–60

SECTION 2

Force, Mass, and Acceleration

Objectives

After completing the lesson, students will be able to

- state Newton's second law of motion and explain how force and mass are related to acceleration.

Key Term newton

1 Engage/Explore

Activating Prior Knowledge

Give pairs of students a flexible ruler and a small ball such as a golf ball. Have one student place one end of the ruler next to the ball. Ask the student to bend the ruler back, then release it to exert a small force against the ball on the floor. Once the ruler is released, have the pairs observe the motion of the ball. Students can repeat the activity, bending the ruler more and exerting a greater force against the ball. Have students compare the two forces and the motion of the ball. Ask: **How does changing the force of the ruler against the ball affect the motion of the ball?** *(The larger force causes more motion.)*

DISCOVER

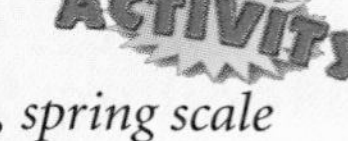

Skills Focus observing
Materials *toy dump truck, several small rocks, spring scale*
Time 10 minutes
Tips Encourage students to pull the truck with a steady force to get a reading on the spring scale that stays constant. Remind students to record the maximum reading on the spring scale each time they remove the rocks. Students should record their measurements in a data table.
Expected Outcome The students will probably notice that the same force causes the truck to accelerate more as rocks are removed (they may say it goes faster).
Think It Over Students should observe that as mass decreases, acceleration increases.

SECTION 2

Force, Mass, and Acceleration

DISCOVER ACTIVITY

How Do the Rocks Roll?

1. Place several small rocks in a toy dump truck. Hook a spring scale to the bumper of the truck.
2. Practice pulling the truck with the spring scale so that the reading on the scale stays constant.
3. Pull the truck with a constant force and observe its motion. Then remove a few rocks from the truck and pull it again with the same force.
4. Remove a few more rocks and pull the truck again. Finally, empty the truck and observe how it moves with the same constant force.

Think It Over

Observing How did changing the mass of the loaded truck affect its motion?

GUIDE FOR READING

- **How are force and mass related to acceleration?**

Reading Tip **As you read, use your own words to describe the relationship among force, mass, and acceleration.**

On a sunny afternoon you are baby-sitting for two boys who love wagon rides. You soon find that they enjoy the ride most if you accelerate quickly. They shout "Faster, faster!" and after a few minutes you sit down in the wagon to catch your breath. The smaller boy takes a turn pulling, but finds that he can't make the wagon accelerate nearly as fast as you can. How is the acceleration of the wagon related to the force pulling it? How is the acceleration related to the mass of the wagon?

Newton's Second Law of Motion

Newton's second law of motion explains how force, mass, and acceleration are related. **The net force on an object is equal to the product of its acceleration and its mass.** The relationship

READING STRATEGIES

Reading Tip Suggest students review the meanings of the terms *force, mass,* and *acceleration* before they begin to read. As they read, have them use their own words to describe the relationships among force, mass, and acceleration.

Vocabulary Explain to students that the word *mass* has several meanings other than its scientific meaning. Organize students in small groups. Provide each group with a dictionary and direct group members to read the various meanings of *mass.* Then challenge students in each group to write an original sentence for each of the different meanings.

among the quantities force, mass, and acceleration can be written in one equation.

$$Force = Mass \times Acceleration$$

People often refer to this equation itself as Newton's second law of motion.

As with any equation, you must pay attention to the units of measurement. When acceleration is measured in meters per second per second (m/s^2) and mass is measured in kilograms, force is measured in kilograms × meters per second per second ($kg \cdot m/s^2$). This long unit is called the newton (N), in honor of Isaac Newton. One **newton** equals the force required to accelerate one kilogram of mass at 1 meter per second per second.

$$1\ N = 1\ kg \times 1\ m/s^2$$

A student might have a mass of 40 kilograms. Suppose she is walking, and accelerates at 1 m/s^2. You can easily find the force she exerts by substituting mass and acceleration into the equation. You find that 40 kilograms × 1 m/s^2 is 40 newtons.

Sometimes you may want to write the relationship among acceleration, force, and mass in a different form.

$$Acceleration = \frac{Force}{Mass}$$

This form is found by rearranging the equation for Newton's second law.

Sample Problem

A 52-kg water-skier is being pulled by a speedboat. The force causes her to accelerate at 2 m/s^2. Calculate the force that causes this acceleration.

Analyze. You know the acceleration and the mass. You want to find the force.

Write the equation. $Force = Mass \times Acceleration$

Substitute and solve. $Force = 52\ kg \times 2\ m/s^2$

$Force = 104\ kg \times m/s^2 = 104\ kg \cdot m/s^2$

$Force = 104\ N$

Think about it. The answer tells you that a force of 104 N is required to accelerate the water-skier. This is not a large force, but you would not expect that a large force would be required to pull a skier over water.

Practice Problems

1. What is the force on a 1,000-kg elevator accelerating at 2 m/s^2?
2. How much force is needed to accelerate a 55-kg cart at 15 m/s^2?

Program Resources

◆ **Teaching Resources** 2-2 Lesson Plan, p. 43; 2-2 Section Summary, p. 44

Media and Technology

Audiotapes English-Spanish Summary 2-2

Interactive Student Tutorial CD-ROM M-2

Exploring Physical Science Videodisc Unit 3, Side 1, "Amusement Parks"

Chapter 3

2 Facilitate

Newton's Second Law of Motion

Demonstration

Materials *spring scale, 1-kg mass*
Time 15 minutes
Tips Point out to students that the increments on a spring scale are marked in newtons. Remind students that a newton is a unit of force, and that 1 N equals the force needed to accelerate a 1-kg mass at a rate of 1 m/s^2. Demonstrate 1 N of force by attaching the spring scale to the 1-kg mass and dragging the mass along a table. Ask: **How can you tell the amount of force it took to pull the mass?** *(Look at the measurement on the spring scale)* Have volunteers demonstrate forces less than and greater than 1 N. Ask: **What happens to the acceleration when the force on the mass increases?** *(It increases.)* Then write the equation Acceleration = Force/Mass on the board. Ask: **How does Newton's equation represent what you observed?** *(In the equation, as the value of the force gets larger, the value for acceleration also gets larger.)* **learning modality: visual**

Sample Problem

Make sure that students practice good problem solving skills. Have them write out the formula, substitute the known quantities, cancel the units and do the multiplication. Remind students that whatever mathematical operations are performed on the values are also performed on the units. Remind them that the $kg \cdot m/s^2$ has a special name, the newton (N).

Practice Problems

1. 1,000 kg × 2 m/s^2 = 2,000 N
2. 55 kg × 15 m/s^2 = 825 N

Ongoing Assessment

Skills Check Have students calculate the force needed to accelerate a 25-kg crate of bananas at a rate of 1.5 m/s^2. *(Force = 25 kg × 1.5 m/s^2 = 37.5 N)*

Changes in Force and Mass

Using the Visuals: Figure 6

Draw attention to this photograph to help students visualize how mass and acceleration are related. Ask:

- **How could you decrease the mass so that acceleration could increase?** *(Ask a child to step out of the wagon.)*
- **How could you increase acceleration without changing mass?** *(Increase force by pulling harder.)*
- **How could you apply what you learned about mass, force, and acceleration to make the wagon accelerate as much as possible?** *(Increase force and decrease mass at the same time.)*

learning modality: visual

3 Assess

Section 2 Review Answers

1. Force, mass, and acceleration; Force = Mass × Acceleration.
2. The acceleration increases.
3. You need to know the mass of the shopping cart.
4. If you double the force acting on an object, you have to double the mass of the object to keep the acceleration unchanged.

CHAPTER PROJECT 2

Check Your Progress

At this point, students should begin to sketch possible vehicle designs. Allow them to discuss their designs in small groups so that they can improve their vehicles. Have them brainstorm ways of increasing force or decreasing mass. For example: three wheels have less mass than four.

Performance Assessment

Oral Presentation Have students explain why the same force accelerates an empty wagon more than a wagon full of bricks. *(According to Newton's second law, if the mass is smaller, acceleration is larger for the same force.)*

Changes in Force and Mass

How can you increase the acceleration of the wagon? Look again at the equation for acceleration: Acceleration = Force ÷ Mass. One way to increase acceleration is by changing the force. According to the equation, acceleration and force change in the same way. An increase in force causes an increase in acceleration. So to increase the acceleration of the wagon, you can increase the force you use to pull it. You can pull harder.

Another way to increase acceleration is to change the mass. According to the equation, acceleration and mass change in opposite ways. This means that an increase in mass causes a decrease in acceleration. It also means that a decrease in mass causes an increase in acceleration. So to increase the acceleration of the wagon, you can decrease its mass. Instead of you, the boys should ride in the wagon.

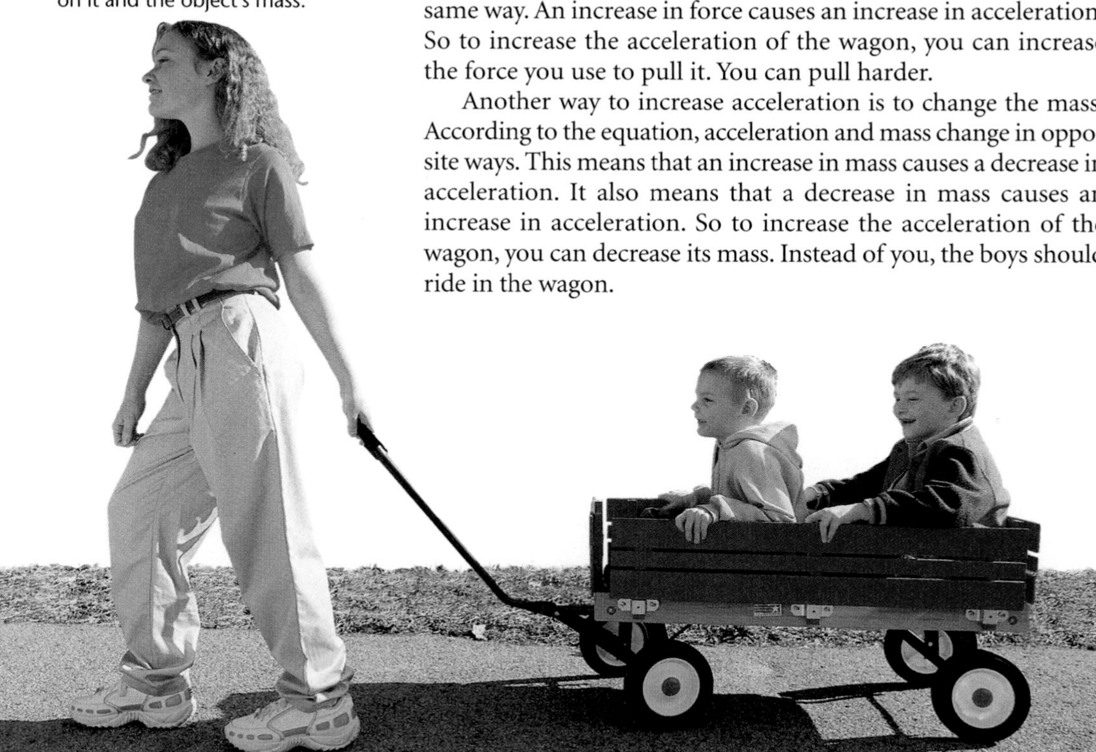

Figure 6 The acceleration of an object depends on the force acting on it and the object's mass.

Section 2 Review

1. What three quantities are related in Newton's second law of motion? What is the relationship among them?
2. When the force on an object increases, how does the object's acceleration change?
3. Suppose you know the acceleration of a shopping cart as it rolls down a supermarket aisle. You want to find the force with which it was pushed. What other information do you need in order to find the force?
4. **Thinking Critically Problem Solving** Suppose you doubled the force acting on an object. In what way could you change its mass to keep its acceleration unchanged?

CHAPTER PROJECT 2

Check Your Progress

The vehicle for your project will need to accelerate from a resting position. From Newton's second law of motion, you know that Acceleration = Force ÷ Mass. This means you have two ways of increasing acceleration: increasing force or decreasing mass. How can you either increase the force acting on your vehicle or decrease its mass?

Background

Facts and Figures In the U.S. Customary system of measurement, the pound is a unit of force, not mass. In this system, the unit for mass is the *slug*. 1 slug = 32.17 pounds. This unit of mass measurement is used widely by engineers but is rarely used by anybody else. When people say they want to take off a few "pounds," they probably mean they want to lose mass.

Program Resources

- **Teaching Resources** 2-2 Review and Reinforce, p. 45; 2-2 Enrich, p. 46

Section 3 Friction and Gravity

Discover

Which Lands First?

Do you think a quarter will fall more quickly than a dime? More quickly than a nickel? Record your predictions and find out!

1. Place a dime, a nickel, and a quarter along the edge of a desk.
2. Put a ruler behind the coins. Line it up with the edge of the desk.
3. Keeping the ruler parallel to the edge of the desk, push all three coins over the edge at the same time. Observe any time difference when the coins land.

Think It Over

Predicting Did you see a pattern in the time the coins took to fall? Use your observations about the coins to predict whether a soccer ball will fall more quickly than a marble. Will a pencil fall more quickly than a book? How can you test your predictions?

What happens if you push a book slowly across your desk and then let it go? Will it keep moving? Without actually pushing a book, you can predict that it will come to a stop. Now think about lifting a book above your desk and letting it go. Again, without actually dropping the book, you can predict that it will fall. In both of these situations, you first exert a force to change the motion of a book, and then you remove the force.

According to Newton's first law of motion, the book's motion changes only if an unbalanced force acts on it. A force should not be necessary to keep the book moving at a constant speed. So why does the book stop sliding after you push it? And why does the book fall back to the ground once you stop exerting a force to hold it up?

From Newton's first law of motion, we know that in each case another force must be acting on the book. Two other forces do indeed act on the book. When the book slides, the force of friction causes it to slow to a stop. When the book falls, the force of the gravity causes it to accelerate downward. In this section you will learn that these two forces affect nearly all motion.

Guide for Reading

- What factors determine the friction force between two surfaces?
- How does mass differ from weight?
- What is the law of universal gravitation?

Reading Tip As you read, compare and contrast friction and gravity.

Reading Strategies

Reading Tip Remind students that comparing is finding similarities and contrasting is finding differences. Suggest that students write *Friction* and *Gravity* as column headings on a sheet of paper. They can list information about each force as they read the section. Then instruct students to use a Venn diagram to organize their notes to show the similarities and differences.

Program Resources

- **Teaching Resources** 2-3 Lesson Plan, p. 47; 2-3 Section Summary, p. 48
- **Integrated Science Laboratory Manual** M-2, "Weight and the Force of Gravity"

Media and Technology

Audiotapes English-Spanish Summary 2-3

Section 3 Friction and Gravity

Objectives

After completing the lesson, students will be able to

- describe friction and identify the factors that determine the friction force between two surfaces;
- explain how mass differs from weight;
- state the universal law of gravitation;
- describe the effects of gravity and air resistance on an object in free fall.

Key Terms friction, sliding friction, rolling friction, fluid friction, gravity, free fall, projectile, air resistance, terminal velocity, weight

1 Engage/Explore

Activating Prior Knowledge

Stack two books on a table and tie a string around the bottom book. Attach a long elastic band to the string. Move the stack of books a short distance by pulling the elastic band. Have students observe how much the elastic band stretches. Now place several round pencils under the books. Move the books with the elastic band. Have students observe how much the elastic band stretches. Encourage the students to discuss what is happening in both cases.

Discover

Skills Focus predicting
Materials *dime, nickel, quarter, ruler*
Time 15 minutes
Tips Caution students to keep rulers parallel to the edge rather than lining up edge of coin with edge of desk.
Think It Over Students should observe that all the coins took the same time to fall. They should predict that the soccer ball and the marble, and the pencil and the book will all take the same time to fall. They can test their predictions by holding two of the objects at the same height, releasing them at the same time, and observing whether they land at the same time.

2 Facilitate

Friction

Using the Visuals: Figure 8

Have students measure the widths of the two friction arrows and the force exerted on the skiers and decide if the forces are balanced. (Have them refer to Figure 1 for a refresher on balanced and unbalanced forces.) If the forces are balanced, what is happening to the skiers? *(They have constant speed)* If the forces are not balanced, what is happening to the skiers? *(They are accelerating)* **learning modality: logical/mathematical**

Building Inquiry Skills: Designing Experiments

ACTIVITY

Materials *spring scale, wooden block, wooden board, various materials such as sandpaper, carpeting, and aluminum foil.*
Time 20 minutes

Allow students to compare the friction generated by a rough and smooth surface. Have them run their fingers over the sandpaper or carpet and compare with the table top. Ask: **How would you describe the texture of a surface that produces a lot of friction?** *(Rough or gritty)* Suggest students design an experiment to investigate the friction created by different surfaces. If the small wooden blocks don't have hooks, wrap rubber bands around the blocks and attach paper clips to the rubber bands to serve as connectors. The students will attach the spring scale to the block and drag it across a smooth surface and then across a rough surface. If students drag the block at a constant speed, then the forces are balanced and the spring scale reading is equal to the friction force. Encourage students to collect various materials to test different surfaces. Students should conclude that the rougher the surfaces of the two objects, the greater the friction between them. **learning modality: kinesthetic**

Figure 7 If you look at a polished metal surface under a special microscope, you'll find that it is actually quite rough. *Predicting What would a rough surface look like?*

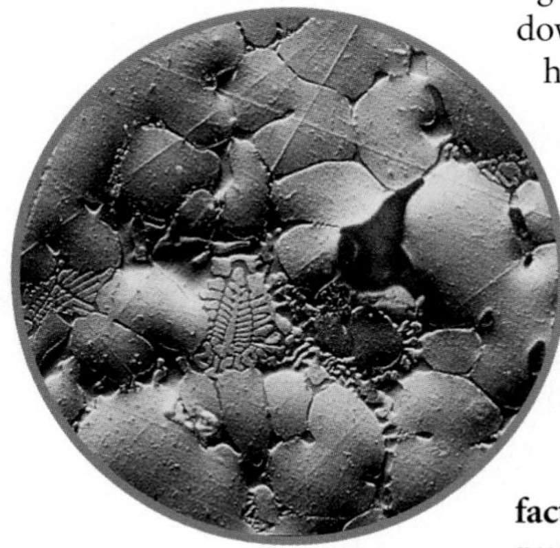

Friction

When you push a book across a table, the surface of the book rubs against the surface of the table. In the same way, the skin of a firefighter's hands rubs against the polished metal pole as she slides down. Although surfaces may seem quite smooth, they actually have many irregularities. When two surfaces rub, the irregularities of one surface get caught on those of the other surface. The force that one surface exerts on another when the two rub against each other is called **friction.**

The Nature of Friction Friction acts in a direction opposite to the object's direction of motion. Without friction, the object would continue to move at constant speed forever. Friction, however, opposes motion. Eventually friction will cause an object to come to a stop.

The strength of the force of friction depends on two factors: the types of surfaces involved and how hard the surfaces push together. Rough surfaces produce greater friction than smooth surfaces. The skiers in Figure 8 get a fast ride because there is very little friction between their skis and the snow. The reindeer would not be able to pull them over a rough surface such as sand. The force of friction also increases if the surfaces push harder against each other. If you rub your hands together forcefully, there is more friction than if you rub your hands together lightly.

Figure 8 These reindeer can't fly. But they can give an exciting ride to the two Finlanders on skis.

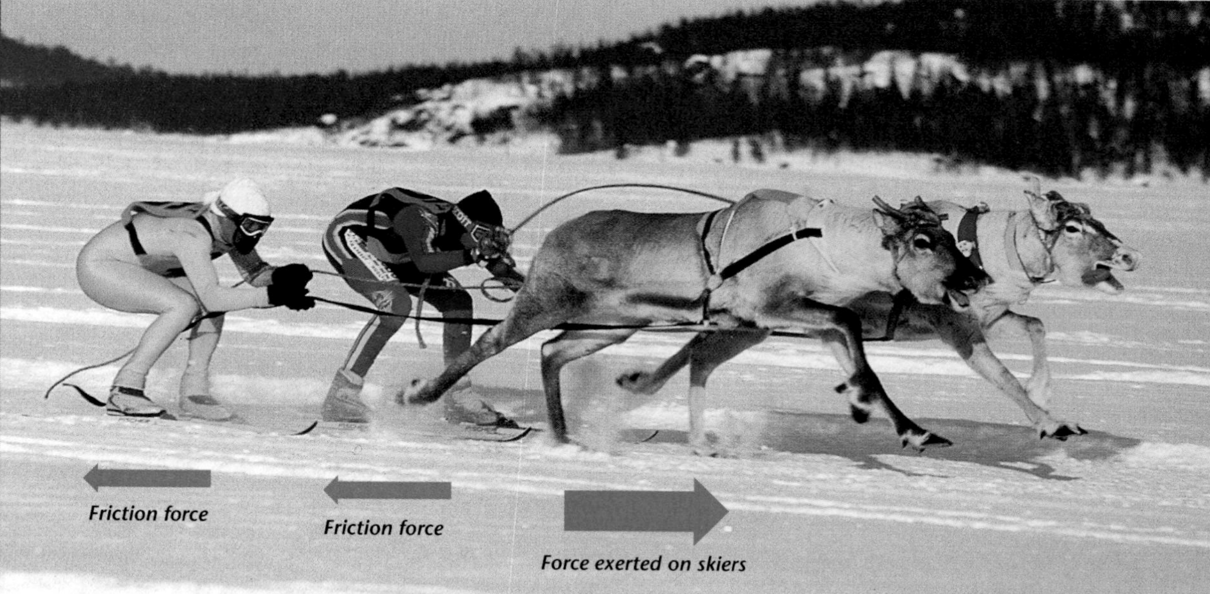

Background

Integrating Science Earth's surface is made up of separate plates that move relative to one another. At some boundaries, the plates are slowly sliding past each other at the rate of 10 centimeters or so a year. However, friction sometimes temporarily prevents the plate boundaries from sliding. Thus stress can build up over a long time until the force gets large enough to overcome the friction. When the plates finally do slip, the shaking of Earth's crust can cause earthquake waves that spread over a large area. Some scientists have suggested drilling wells and pumping water into the plate boundaries. This would lubricate the boundaries and reduce friction, thus allowing the plates to slide past each other more easily.

Figure 9 Friction enables these students to draw on the pavement. Friction also enables the metalworker to smooth a metal surface. *Inferring* *How can you tell that the grinder is producing heat?*

Is Friction Useful or Not? Is friction necessarily a bad thing? No—whether or not friction is useful depends on the situation. You are able to walk, for example, because friction acts between the soles of your shoes and the floor. Without friction your shoes would only slide across the floor, and you would never move forward. An automobile moves because of friction between its tires and the road. Thanks to friction you can light a match and you can walk on a sidewalk.

Friction is so useful that at times people want to increase it. If you are walking down a snow-covered hill, you might wear rubber boots or spread sand to increase the friction and slow you down. Ballet dancers spread a sticky powder on the soles of their shoes so that they do not slip on the dance floor.

Controlling Friction There are different kinds of friction. When solid surfaces slide over each other, the kind of friction that occurs is called **sliding friction.** When an object rolls over a surface, the kind of friction that occurs is **rolling friction.** The force needed to overcome rolling friction is much less than the force needed to overcome sliding friction.

Ball bearings are one way of reducing friction between two surfaces. Ball bearings are small, smooth steel balls. The balls roll between rotating metal parts. The wheels of in-line skates, skateboards, and bicycles all have ball bearings. Many automobile parts have ball bearings as well.

The friction that occurs when an object moves through a fluid is called **fluid friction.** The force needed to overcome fluid friction is usually less than that needed to overcome sliding friction. The fluid keeps surfaces from making direct contact and thus reduces friction. The moving parts of machines are bathed in oil so that they can slide past each other with less friction.

☑ *Checkpoint* *What are two ways to reduce friction?*

Spinning Plates

ACTIVITY

Find out if the force of rolling friction is really less than the force of sliding friction.

1. Stack two identical pie plates together. Try to spin the top plate.
2. Now separate the plates and fill the bottom of one pie plate loosely with marbles.
3. Place the second plate in the plate with marbles.
4. Try to spin the top plate again. Observe the results.

Drawing Conclusions What applications are there for the rolling friction modeled in this activity?

Skills Focus drawing conclusions

ACTIVITY

Materials *two identical pie plates, marbles*

Time 10 minutes

Tips Shallow bowls may be substituted for the pie plates. Allow students to work in groups to complete the activity. After students complete Step 1, ask: **What kind of friction occurred?** *(Sliding friction)* In Step 2, 10 to 20 marbles are sufficient. Students should not fill the pie plate. After Step 4, ask: **What kind of friction occurred?** *(Rolling friction)*

Drawing Conclusions Students should conclude that rolling friction is less than sliding friction because the plate moves more easily once the marbles are added.

Extend Students can put enough water in the bottom pie plate to make the top plate float, then repeat the experiment. The result of this activity will be similar to that of the activity with marbles, because the water acts as a lubricant to reduce friction. **learning modality: visual**

Real Life Learning

Ask students to name several lubricants that they have encountered. *(Sample: motor oil in a car, grease for a bicycle chain)* Ask: **Why do lubricants reduce friction?** (*Lubricants replace sliding friction with fluid friction.)*

Media and Technology

Exploring Physical Science Videodisc Unit 3, Side 1, "Light as a Feather"

Answers to Self-Assessment

Caption Questions

Figure 7 A rough surface would look even rougher under a microscope, with more hills and valleys than a smooth surface.

Figure 9 The metal surface is glowing and sparks are flying.

☑ *Checkpoint*

Ball bearings and oil or other lubricants

Ongoing Assessment

Writing Have students write a sentence or two describing a situation where friction is both a help and a hindrance. *(Sample: Friction slows a car and increases gasoline use but also allows the wheels to push the car forward and helps to keep the car on the road.)*

Students can save their sentences in their portfolios.

Gravity

Building Inquiry Skills: Applying Concepts

Ask students the following questions about the nature of gravitational force. Ask: **What happens to a ball if you hold it out in front of you and then release it?** *(It falls down to the ground.)* **What force acts on the ball?** *(gravity)* **Is the ball falling faster when it leaves your hand or when it is just about to hit the ground?** *(When it is about to hit the ground)* **Why?** *(Because gravity causes the ball to continue accelerating.)* **learning modality: logical/mathematical**

Using the Visuals: Figure 11

Explain to students that the five frames of the two balls in A were photographed within fractions of a second. Ask: **What is happening to the velocity of the two balls as they fall? How can you tell?** *(The velocity is increasing because the distance between the images increases.)* Ask students to state which ball in B is a projectile and to explain their reasoning *(The ball on the right, because it also moves horizontally)* **learning modality: visual**

Demonstration

Materials *plastic ruler with groove, two marbles, books, tongue depressor*
Time 10 minutes

Make a small dent in the top of a tongue depressor, near the end, about 0.5 cm from the edge. Tape the tongue depressor perpendicular to the edge of the desk, so that the dent is just beyond the edge of the desk. Place a ruler on top of and centered over the tongue depressor. The end of the ruler should be close to the edge of the desk. Raise the opposite end of the ruler with a book or two. Balance a marble in the dent and allow another marble to roll down the groove. The rolling marble should very lightly brush the other marble so that both drop off the tongue depressor at the same time. Before you release the marble to roll down the groove, ask students to predict if the marbles will hit the floor at the same time. *(yes)* **learning modality: logical/mathematical**

Figure 10 As soon as they jump from their airplane, skydivers begin accelerating. *Predicting Will a skydiver with greater mass accelerate more quickly than a skydiver with less mass?*

Gravity

Friction explains why a book comes to a stop when it is pushed. But why does the same book fall to the ground if you lift it and let it go? Newton realized that a force acts to pull objects straight down toward the center of Earth. He called this force gravity. **Gravity** is the force that pulls objects toward Earth.

Free Fall When the only force acting on a falling object is gravity, the object is said to be in **free fall.** An object in free fall accelerates as it falls. Do you know why? In free fall the force of gravity is an unbalanced force, and unbalanced forces cause an object to accelerate.

How much do objects accelerate as they fall? Near the surface of Earth, the acceleration due to the force of gravity is 9.8 m/s^2. This means that for every second an object is falling, its velocity increases by 9.8 m/s. Suppose that an object is dropped from the top of a building. Its starting velocity is 0 m/s. At the end of the first second of falling, its velocity is 9.8 m/s. After two seconds, its velocity is 19.6 m/s (9.8 m/s + 9.8 m/s). After 3 seconds the velocity is 29.4 m/s. The velocity increases as long as the object falls.

While it may seem hard to believe at first, all objects in free fall accelerate at the same rate regardless of mass. If you do not believe that the rates are the same, look at the two balls in Figure 11A.

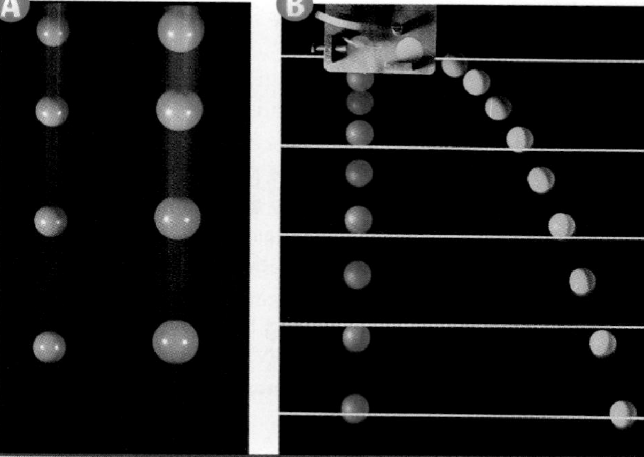

Figure 11 A. Two balls with different masses are dropped to the ground. In a vacuum they would fall at exactly the same rate, regardless of their masses. **B.** A special device is used to drop one ball vertically and throw another ball horizontally at the same time.

Projectile Motion Rather than dropping a ball straight down, what happens if you throw it horizontally? An object that is thrown is called a **projectile** (pruh JEK tul). Will a projectile land on the ground at the same time as an object dropped straight down?

An object that is simply dropped and one that is thrown horizontally are both in free fall. The horizontal motion of the thrown object does

Background

Integrating Science Gravity influences growing plants in two ways. The shoots of most plants grow away from the soil or away from Earth toward the sun. The roots of most plants grow downward into the soil or toward the center of Earth. When a seedling is planted on its side—or even upside down—its roots will change direction and grow downward. The shoot will change direction and grow upward. This tendency is called gravitropism.

Other factors also control plant growth. Hydrotropism means roots will grow toward a source of water. Phototropism is the tendency of shoots to grow toward a source of light. These tendencies make it possible to grow plants even in the absence of gravity, as in a space station.

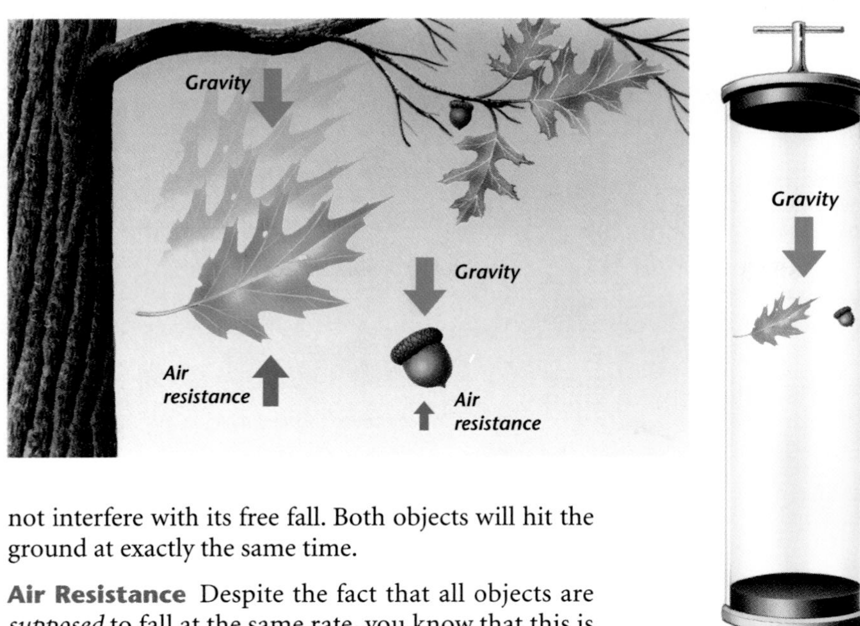

not interfere with its free fall. Both objects will hit the ground at exactly the same time.

Air Resistance Despite the fact that all objects are *supposed* to fall at the same rate, you know that this is not always the case. For example, an oak leaf flutters slowly to the ground, while an acorn drops straight down. Objects falling through air experience a type of fluid friction called **air resistance.** Remember that friction is in the direction opposite to motion, so air resistance is an upward force. Air resistance is not the same for all objects. The greater the surface area of an object, the greater the air resistance. That is why a leaf falls more slowly than an acorn. In a vacuum, where there is no air, all objects fall with exactly the same rate of acceleration.

Air resistance increases with velocity. So as a falling object speeds up, the air resistance against it increases. Eventually, the air resistance equals the force of gravity. Remember that when forces are balanced, there is no acceleration. So although the object continues to fall, its velocity no longer increases. This velocity, the greatest velocity the object reaches, is called **terminal velocity**.

☑ *Checkpoint* *At what rate does an object in free fall accelerate?*

Weight The force of gravity on a person or object at the surface of a planet is known as **weight.** When you step on a bathroom scale, you are determining the force with which Earth is pulling you. Do not confuse weight with mass! **Weight is a measure of the force of gravity on an object, and mass is a measure of the amount of matter in that object.**

Figure 12 When air is present, air resistance exerts an upward force on objects. *Inferring The oak leaf and the acorn fall at the same rate in the tube on the right. Is there any air resistance?*

Inquiry Challenge

ACTIVITY

Students may be assigned to groups to complete this activity. Instruct them to unfold a sheet of notebook paper or a paper napkin. Have them release the paper and time how long it takes for it to float to the ground. Then have them roll up the same tissue paper into a small ball. Release the ball and time how long it takes the ball to reach the ground Ask: **Which paper took the longest to reach the ground?** *(the flat piece)* **Why?** *(It had more air resistance.)* **learning modality: kinesthetic**

Addressing Naive Conceptions

Most people use the term *weight* when they mean *mass.* Help students to recognize the difference by telling them that you know of a revolutionary way to lose weight. Explain that all you have to do is take a trip to the moon and you will weigh about one-sixth of what you weigh on Earth. Ask: **Why wouldn't this weight-loss system have the effect most people want?** *(Because the amount of matter in the person's body would not change.)* Remind students that weight refers to the force of gravity on an object and that decreasing gravity decreases weight but not mass. **learning modality: verbal**

Ongoing Assessment

Writing Have students describe how a feather and a brick fall from the roof of a 50-m building. Then have them describe how the objects fall if they are dropped inside of a 50-m tall tube from which the air has been removed. Be sure students describe the forces acting upon the objects in both cases. *(The objects will not hit the ground at the same time when dropped from the building. Air resistance acts upon the flat surface of the feather so that it takes longer to fall than the brick. In the tube with no air, there is no air resistance so the objects will fall at the same rate.)*

Media and Technology

Transparencies "Air Resistance," Transparency 3

Answers to Self-Assessment

Caption Question

Figure 10 No. All the sky divers accelerate at the same rate. The rate of acceleration does not depend on mass.

Figure 12 No, if there were air resistance, it would exert more upward force on the leaf and the leaf would fall more slowly.

☑ *Checkpoint*

9.8 m/s^2

Sharpen your Skills

Calculating

ACTIVITY

Materials *four distinct objects, such as a shoe, a book, a spiral notebook, a pair of scissors; scale balance*
Time 20 minutes
Tips This activity can help reinforce the difference between weight and mass. Have students create a data table for their estimates, measurements, and calculations. You may wish to provide a sample calculation for converting mass to weight.
Extend Suggest students find the mass of one of their shoes, then find its weight in newtons.

Universal Gravitation

Using the Visuals: Figure 13

Ask students: **Why do the arrows in the figure point toward each other?** *(The force attracts the objects toward each other so each force arrow points to the other object.)* Point out to students the parts of the diagram with the thickest arrows. Ask: **How could you increase the gravitational force between the objects?** *(Add mass to the objects or decrease the distance between the objects.)* Have students draw their own diagrams to indicate what decreasing the mass of the objects might look like. **learning modality: logical/mathematical**

Integrating Space Science

Discuss the problems created by humans living for an extended period in a low or zero gravity environment during space flight.

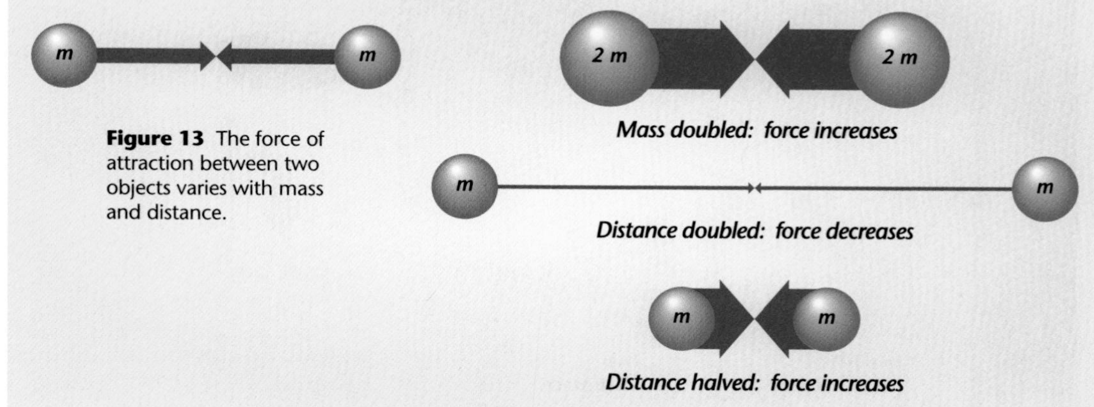

Figure 13 The force of attraction between two objects varies with mass and distance.

Since weight is a force, you can rewrite Newton's second law of motion, Force = Mass × Acceleration, to find weight.

Weight = Mass × Acceleration due to gravity

Weight is usually measured in newtons, mass in kilograms, and acceleration due to gravity in m/s^2. So a 50-kilogram person weighs 50 kg × 9.8 m/s^2 = 490 newtons on Earth's surface.

Universal Gravitation

Newton realized that Earth is not the only object that exerts a gravitational force. Instead, gravity acts everywhere in the universe. Gravity is the force that makes an apple fall to the ground. It is the force that keeps the moon orbiting around Earth. It is also the force that keeps all the planets orbiting around the sun.

What Newton discovered is now called the law of universal gravitation. **The law of universal gravitation states that the force of gravity acts between all objects in the universe.** Any two objects in the universe, without exception, attract each other. This means that you are not only attracted to Earth, but you are also attracted to all the other objects around you! Earth and the objects around you are attracted to you as well.

Why don't you notice that the objects around you are pulling on you? After all, this book exerts a gravitational force on you. The reason is that the strength of the force depends on the masses of the objects involved. The force of gravity is much greater between you and Earth than between you and your book.

INTEGRATING SPACE SCIENCE Although your mass would remain the same on another planet or moon, your weight would be different. For example, the force of gravity on Earth's moon is about one sixth that on Earth. Your weight on

Sharpen your Skills

Calculating

ACTIVITY

You can determine the weight of an object if you measure its mass.

1. Estimate the weight of four objects. (*Hint:* An apple weighs about 1 N.)
2. Find the mass of each object. If the measurements are not in kilograms, convert them to kilograms.
3. Multiply each mass by 9.8 m/s^2 to find the weight in newtons.

How close to actual values were your estimates?

Background

Facts and Figures Gravity is much weaker than electrical, magnetic, or any other forces in nature. Magnetic and electric forces can both attract and repel, but as far as we know, gravity only attracts. Gravity is not blocked by anything. Even though gravity is the weakest of the forces, it is the force that holds the universe together.

Program Resources

Science Explorer Series *Astronomy*, Chapter 1 gives additional information about the moon and space flight, and Chapter 2 discusses the other planets in the solar system.

- **Interdisciplinary Exploration Series** "Mars the Next Frontier," pp. 20–21, 26–27
- **Teaching Resources** 2-3 Review and Reinforce, p. 49; 2-3 Enrich, p. 50

Figure 14 This astronaut jumps easily on the moon. *Comparing and Contrasting How do his mass and weight on the moon compare to his mass and weight on Earth?*

the moon, then, would be about a sixth of what it is on Earth. That is why the astronaut in Figure 14 can leap so easily.

If the gravitational force depends on mass, you might then expect to notice a force of attraction from a massive object, such as the moon or the sun. But you do not. The reason is that the gravitational force also depends on the distance between the objects. The farther apart the objects are, the weaker the force.

Astronauts travel great distances from Earth. As they travel from Earth toward the moon, Earth's gravitational pull becomes weaker. At the same time, the moon's gravitational pull becomes stronger. At the surface of the moon an astronaut feels the pull of the moon's gravity, but no longer notices the pull of Earth's gravity.

Section 3 Review

1. What factors determine the strength of the friction force when two surfaces slide against each other?
2. What is the difference between weight and mass?
3. State the law of universal gravitation in your own words.
4. **Thinking Critically Problem Solving** A squirrel drops a nut over a cliff. What is the velocity of the nut after 3 seconds? After 5 seconds? After 10 seconds? (Ignore air resistance. Remember that the acceleration due to gravity is 9.8 m/s^2.)

CHAPTER PROJECT 2

Check Your Progress

Draw a diagram of your vehicle. Use labeled arrows to show each place that a force is acting on it. Be sure to include friction forces in your diagram. Brainstorm ways to reduce forces that slow down your vehicle.

3 Assess

Section 3 Review Answers

1. The types of surfaces, and how hard the surfaces push together.
2. Weight is a measure of the force of gravity acting on an object. Mass is a measure of the amount of matter in that object.
3. Every object exerts a force of gravity on every other object in the universe. This force is proportional to both objects' mass, and inversely proportional to the distance between them.
4. After 3 seconds: 29.4 m/s; after 5 seconds: 49 m/s; after 10 seconds: 98 m/s

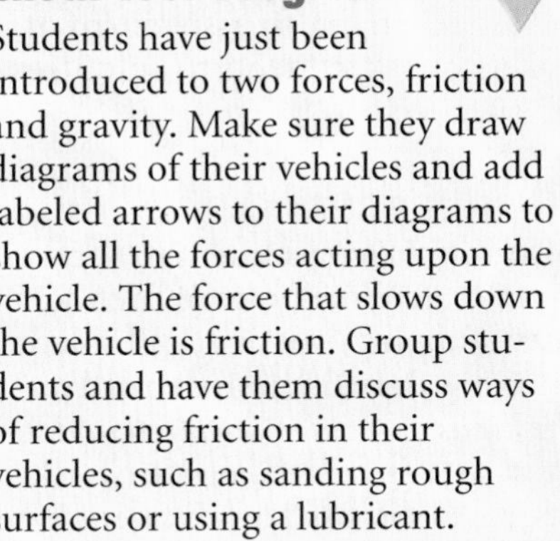

CHAPTER PROJECT 2

Check Your Progress

Students have just been introduced to two forces, friction and gravity. Make sure they draw diagrams of their vehicles and add labeled arrows to their diagrams to show all the forces acting upon the vehicle. The force that slows down the vehicle is friction. Group students and have them discuss ways of reducing friction in their vehicles, such as sanding rough surfaces or using a lubricant.

Media and Technology

Transparencies "Law of Universal Gravitation," Transparency 4

Interactive Student Tutorial CD-ROM M-2

Answers to Self-Assessment

Caption Question

Figure 14 Although his mass is the same, his weight is lower on the moon.

Performance Assessment

Writing Ask students to imagine they are playing basketball on a planet with either less friction than Earth or lower gravity. Have students write paragraphs that describe how the motion of the players and the ball would be different from a game on Earth.

Students can save their paragraphs in their portfolios.

Real-World Lab

You, the Consumer

Sticky Sneakers

The appropriate sneaker for an activity should have a specific type of tread to grip the floor or the ground. In this lab you will test different sneakers by measuring the amount of friction between the sneakers and a table.

Problem

How does the amount of friction between a sneaker and a surface compare for different types of sneakers?

Skills Focus

forming operational definitions, measuring, controlling variables

Materials

three or more different types of sneakers

spring scale, 20 N   mass set(s)   tape

spring scale, 5 N   large paper clip   balance

Procedure

1. Sneakers are designed to deal with various friction forces, including these:
   - starting friction, which is involved when you start from a stopped position
   - forward-stopping friction, which is involved when you come to a forward stop
   - sideways-stopping friction, which is involved when you come to a sideways stop
2. Prepare a data table in which you can record each type of friction for each sneaker.
3. Find the mass of each sneaker. Then put masses in each sneaker so that the total mass of the sneaker plus the masses is 1,000 g. Spread the masses out evenly inside the sneaker.
4. You will need to tape the paper clip to each sneaker and then attach a spring clip to the paper clip. To measure
   - starting friction, attach the paper clip to the back of the sneaker
   - forward-stopping friction, attach the paper clip to the front of the sneaker
   - sideways-stopping friction, attach the paper clip to the side of the sneaker

DATA TABLE

Sneaker	Starting friction (N)	Sideways-stopping friction (N)	Forward-stopping friction (N)
A			
B			

Real-World Lab

You, the Consumer

Sticky Sneakers

Preparing for Inquiry

Key Concept Sneaker soles illustrate three kinds of friction.

Skills Objective Students will be able to
- form operational definitions of starting friction, forward-stopping friction, and sideways-stopping friction;
- measure the force required to overcome friction;
- control variables such as total mass.

Time 45 minutes

Advance Planning Assemble the spring scales, paper clips, tape, balance and mass sets. Bring in an assortment of sneakers or ask students to volunteer their sneakers.

Guiding Inquiry

Invitation Have a student in sneakers demonstrate three types of friction forces: stopping, starting, and sideways. Ask: **What does friction depend on?** *(The kinds of surfaces involved and how hard the surfaces push together.)* Ask students to discuss how different kinds of sneakers might have different kinds of friction.

Introducing the Procedure
- If necessary, demonstrate how to zero and use a spring scale.
- Show students how to measure the force of sliding friction with a spring scale by pulling an object with a slow, constant speed.
- Ask students which way they should pull a sneaker to measure stopping friction. *(Forward, so that the friction force on the shoe is toward the back of the shoe).* Ask similar questions about starting friction and sideways-stopping friction.

Troubleshooting the Experiment
- Be sure students check the zero of the spring scale each time they use it. If the spring scale is calibrated in grams, students can multiply by 0.01 to obtain a reading in newtons.
- Point out that the scale must not be angled to the side or up or down while it is used, as this changes the reading.

Expected Outcome

Students should have a table with a column for each kind of friction, showing the force of friction for each kind of sneaker.

Analyze and Conclude

1. The manipulated variable is the sneaker sole. The responding variable is the amount of friction.

2. For stopping friction: the sneaker is moving at a constant speed, therefore, the friction force and the pulling force must be balanced (equal). The pulling force is indicated by the spring scale. For starting friction, the pulling force must overcome the friction force in order to make the sneaker move. At the point where the sneaker starts to move, the two forces are almost equal.

3. It is a fair test of the friction as long as the amount of friction in each sneaker depends on mass in the same way.

5. To measure starting friction, pull the sneaker backward until it starts to move. Use the 20-N spring scale first. If the reading is less than 5 N, use a 5-N scale. The force necessary to make the sneaker start moving is equal to the friction force. Record the starting friction force in your data table.
6. To measure either type of stopping friction, use the spring scale to pull each sneaker at a slow, constant speed. Record the stopping friction force in your data table.
7. Repeat Steps 3 and 4 for the remaining sneakers.

Analyze and Conclude

1. What are the manipulated and responding variables in this experiment? Explain. (See the Skills Handbook for a discussion of experimental variables.)
2. Why is the reading on the spring scale equal to the friction force in each case?
3. Do you think that using a sneaker with a small amount of mass in it is a fair test of the friction of the sneakers? (Consider the fact that sneakers are used with people's feet inside them.) Explain your answer.
4. Draw a diagram that shows the forces acting on the sneaker for each type of motion.
5. Why did you pull the sneaker at a slow speed to test for stopping friction? For starting friction, why did you pull a sneaker that wasn't moving?
6. Which sneaker had the most starting friction? Which had the most forward stopping friction? Which had the most sideways stopping friction?
7. Can you identify a relationship between the type of sneaker and the type of friction you observed? What do you observe about the sneakers that would cause one to have better traction than another?
8. **Apply** Wear a pair of your own sneakers. Start running and notice how you press against the floor with your sneaker. How do you think this affects the friction between the sneaker and the floor? How can you test for this variable?

Getting Involved

Go to a store that sells sneakers. If possible take a spring scale and, with the clerk's permission, do a quick friction test on sneakers designed for different activities. Also, note the materials they are made of, the support they provide for your feet, and other features. Then decide whether it is necessary to buy specific sneakers for different activities.

shoes exert more sideways-stopping friction.

7. One type of sneaker may provide better traction than another because the soles are made of a different material, they have different treads, or have worn treads or rubber soles hardened with age.

8. When you press against the floor when starting to run, you increase the force with which the sneaker and floor press against each other, increasing the friction force. To test for this variable, students could repeat the lab after adding weights to each sneaker. A suitable weight could be made by filling several resealable plastic bags with sand. These could be stuffed into the sneaker before measuring each type of friction.

Extending the Inquiry

Getting Involved Remind students they must go to the store with an adult supervisor and ask permission from the store clerk before carrying out the friction test. Remind students to compare sneakers of about the same mass. Students will probably find there are not big differences in friction between different types of sneakers. The same type of sneakers should exhibit about the same amount of each type of friction.

4. See students' diagrams. Diagrams should be clearly labeled with force arrows reflecting the size of the force and the direction.

5. You pull the sneaker at a slow speed to test stopping friction because when you stop, the sneaker is sliding slowly along the ground. You pull a sneaker that is not moving for starting friction because when you start running the sneaker is not moving yet.

6. Answers will vary. Running sneakers exhibit more starting friction. Basketball sneakers exert more stopping friction. Tennis

Sample Data Table

Brand of Sneaker	Starting friction (N)	Sideways stopping (N)	Forward stopping (N)
A	6.3	4.5	4.8
B	4.6	3.7	3.6
C	4.4	3.3	3.4

Program Resources

◆ **Teaching Resources** Chapter 2 Real-World Lab, pp. 61–63

Action and Reaction

Objectives

After completing the lesson, students will be able to
- ◆ state Newton's third law of motion;
- ◆ define and calculate momentum and state the law of conservation of momentum.

Key Terms momentum, law of conservation of momentum

1 Engage/Explore

Activating Prior Knowledge

Invite a volunteer to sit facing forward on a wide skateboard with his or her feet up. Once the student is steady on the board, give him or her a basketball to toss to you. Ask students: **What happened to the student on the skateboard when he or she tossed the ball?** *(The student moved backward as he or she tossed the ball.)* Ask: **What made the ball move?** *(a force)* **Where did the force come from?** *(The person on the skateboard)* **What made the person on the skateboard move?** *(a force)* **Where did this force come from?** *(It must have come from the ball.)*

DISCOVER

Skills Focus developing hypotheses
Materials *rubber band, hard cover book, marbles, plastic straw*
Time 15 minutes
Tips Have students work in pairs. Make sure that they do not produce a twisting motion and that they release the straw and the book at the same time. Allow several attempts to master the technique.
Think It Over Students should observe that the book and straw moved in opposite directions, and the straw moved faster than the book. One hypothesis might be that the straw exerted a force on the book and the book exerted a force on the straw.

Section 4 Action and Reaction

DISCOVER — ACTIVITY

How Pushy Is a Straw?

1. Stretch a rubber band around the middle of the front cover of a small or medium-sized hardcover book.
2. Place four marbles in a small square on a table. Carefully place the book on the marbles so that the cover with the rubber band is on top.
3. Hold the book steady by placing one index finger on the center of the binding. Then, as shown in the illustration, push a straw against the rubber band with your other index finger.

4. Push the straw so that the rubber band stretches about ten centimeters. Then let go of both the book and the straw at the same time.

Think It Over

Developing Hypotheses What did you observe about the motion of the book and the straw? Write a hypothesis to explain what happened in terms of the forces on the book and the straw.

GUIDE FOR READING

- ◆ What is Newton's third law of motion?
- ◆ What is the law of conservation of momentum?

Reading Tip Before you read, preview the illustrations and predict what *action* and *reaction* mean.

Imagine that you are an astronaut making a space walk outside your space station. In your excitement about your walk, you lose track of time and use up all the fuel in your jet pack. How do you get back to the station? Your jet pack is empty, but it can still get you back to the station if you throw it away. To understand how, you need to know Newton's third law of motion.

Newton's Third Law of Motion

Newton realized that forces are not "one-sided." Whenever one object exerts a force on a second object, the second object exerts a force back on the first object. The force exerted by the second object is equal in strength and opposite in direction to the first force. Newton called one force the "action" and the other force the "reaction." **Newton's third law of motion states that if one object exerts a force on another object, then the second object exerts a force of equal strength in the opposite direction on the first object.**

Figure 15 A hammer exerts a force on a nail, pushing it into a piece of wood. At the same time, the nail exerts a force back on the hammer, causing its motion to come to a sudden stop.

READING STRATEGIES

Reading Tip Indicate to students that illustrations and their captions can give them an idea of the content. Encourage students to preview the illustrations in this section and then predict what this section covers. Have students record any questions that come to mind as they view the illustrations.

Study and Comprehension Write the four major headings in the section on separate note cards. Place the cards face down and invite volunteers to choose a card and summarize the information presented under that heading.

Vocabulary Emphasize to students that *conservation* has a special meaning in physical science. Have partners take turns explaining the terms *conservation of momentum* and *conservation of natural resources* and give examples of each.

Equal but Opposite You may already be familiar with examples of Newton's third law of motion. Perhaps you have watched figure skaters and have seen one skater push on the other. As a result, both skaters move—not only the skater who was pushed. The skater who pushed is pushed back with an equal force, but in the opposite direction.

The speeds with which the two skaters move depend on their masses. If they have the same mass, they will move at the same speed. But if one skater has a greater mass than the other, she will move backward more slowly. Although the action and reaction forces will be equal and opposite, the same force acting on a greater mass results in a smaller acceleration. Recall that this is Newton's second law of motion.

Now can you figure out how to return from your space walk? In order to get a push back to the space station, you need to push on some object. You can remove your empty jet pack and push it away from you. In return, the jet pack will exert an equal force on you, sending you back to the safety of the space station.

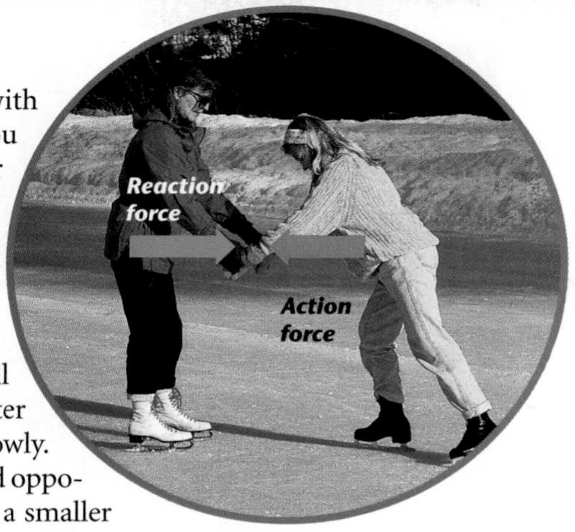

Figure 16 One skater pushes gently on the other. The result is that the other skater pushes back with an equal force—even if she isn't trying. *Applying Concepts Which of Newton's laws describes this phenomenon?*

Action-Reaction in Action Newton's third law is in action all around you. When you walk, you push the ground with your feet. The ground pushes back on your feet with an equal and opposite force. You go forward when you walk because the ground is pushing you! A bird flies forward by exerting a force on the air with its wings. The air pushes back on those wings with an equal force that propels the bird forward.

A squid applies Newton's third law of motion to move itself through the water. The squid exerts a force on the water that it expels from its body cavity. At the same time, the water exerts an equal and opposite force on the squid, causing it to move.

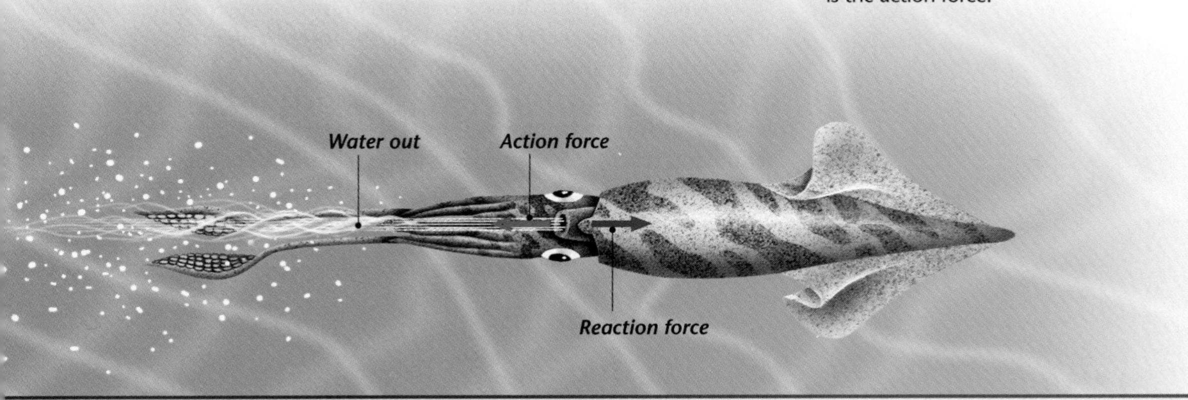

Figure 17 When a squid pushes water out, the expelled water pushes back and forces the squid to move ahead (to the right). The force the squid exerts on the water is the action force.

2 Facilitate

Newton's Third Law of Motion

Building Inquiry Skills: Interpreting Illustrations

Have students collect examples of action and reaction forces from daily life. They can draw a picture of the example or use photographs from magazines. Have students use a marker to draw arrows on pictures to indicate the direction of action and reaction forces. Ask: **What two characteristics describe action and reaction forces?** *(They are equal and opposite.)* **learning modality: logical/mathematical**

Integrating Life Science

Inform students that several sea animals other than squid employ action and reaction forces as they move. These animals use a similar form of jet propulsion to move around. Scallops escape danger by snapping their shells together and forcing out water. This action pushes the scallops backward in a burst of speed. **learning modality: verbal**

Including All Students

ACTIVITY

Some students may wonder how we know the action-reaction forces are equal. Obtain a plastic ruler with a groove down the middle. Have students work in pairs to experiment with two marbles by rolling them along this groove. When a rolling marble collides with a stationary marble, the rolling marble stops and the stationary marble starts rolling. Students should recognize that the force required to stop the rolling marble is the same size as the force required to start the stationary marble. **learning modality: kinesthetic**

Ongoing Assessment

Skills Check Have students apply Newton's third law of motion to a pogo stick. Ask: **What are the action and reaction forces in a pogo stick jump?**

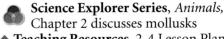

Program Resources

- **Science Explorer Series**, *Animals*, Chapter 2 discusses mollusks
- **Teaching Resources** 2-4 Lesson Plan, p. 51; 2-4 Section Summary, p. 52

Media and Technology

Audiotapes English-Spanish Summary 2-4

Answers to Self-Assessment

Caption Question

Figure 16 Newton's third law of motion

Newton's Third Law of Motion, continued

Using the Visuals: Figure 18B

Have students indicate the direction in which each player in Figure 18B applies a force. Then have them indicate the direction of the reaction force. *(There are two pairs of action and reaction forces.)* Challenge students to describe the size of all four forces illustrated. What happens to all the forces if the player on the left exerts a larger force on the ball than the player on the right. *(The action reaction pairs are still equal, but the forces exerted by the hands on the ball would be unbalanced. The ball would move to the right.)* **learning modality: visual**

Addressing Naive Conceptions

Some students may confuse balanced forces with action and reaction forces. Place a book on the table. Ask students to list all of the forces acting on the book. Ask: **Why doesn't the book move?** *(The forces are balanced.)* **What is pulling down on the book?** *(gravity)*. **What is pushing up on the book?** *(the table)* **If the table is pushing up on the book, what is the book doing to the table?** *(pushing down)* The force of gravity on the book and the force of the table on the book are balanced forces. They both act on the book. The force of the book on the table and the force of the table on the book are an action-reaction pair. One acts on the book, the other acts on the table.

Including All Students

Students whose first language is not English may not recognize the difference between the words *action* and *reaction* or *balanced* and *unbalanced.* Ask all students to supply other instances of words using the prefixes *un-* and *re-* with which they are familiar. *(Sample: tie—untie, do—redo, play—replay)* **limited English proficiency**

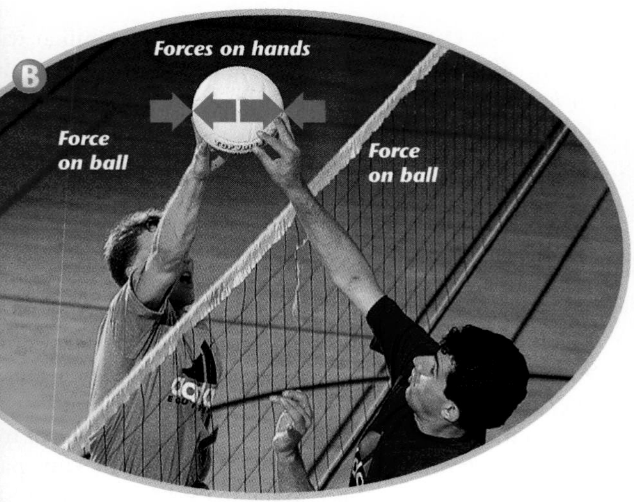

Figure 18 In these photographs, red arrows show action forces and blue arrows show reaction forces. **A.** The player's wrists exert the action force. **B.** As two players jump for the ball, the ball exerts reaction forces on both of them.

Do Action-Reaction Forces Cancel? In Section 1 you learned that balanced forces, which are equal and opposite, add up to zero. In other words, balanced forces cancel out. They produce no change in motion. Why then don't the action and reaction forces in Newton's third law of motion cancel out as well? After all, they are equal and opposite.

To answer this question, you have to consider the object on which the forces are acting. Look, for example, at the two volleyball players in Figure 18B. When they hit the ball from opposite directions, each of their hands exerts a force on the ball. If the forces are equal in strength, but opposite in direction, the forces cancel out. The ball does not move either to the left or to the right.

Newton's third law, however, refers to forces on two different objects. If only one player hits the ball, as shown in Figure 18A, the player exerts an upward action force on the ball. In return, the ball exerts an equal but opposite downward reaction force back on her wrists. One force is on the ball, and the other is on the player. The action and reaction forces cannot be added together because they are acting on different objects. Forces can be added together only if they are acting on the same object.

☑ *Checkpoint* ***Why don't action and reaction forces cancel each other?***

Background

Integrating Science Personal watercraft (jet skis) are also propelled with action-and-reaction force pairs. The watercraft pushes a strong jet of water backward, and this jet of water pushes the watercraft forward. An exposed propeller would be dangerous in the event of an accident, so the propeller is concealed in a pump for safety reasons. Water is drawn in through an intake and expelled at the back. Jet airplanes use a similar principle by drawing air in through the engine intake, mixing the air with hot combustion gases, and expelling the mixture through the rear of the engine. In both cases, the craft is propelled forward by a reaction to the force required to expel a fluid backwards.

Momentum

When Newton presented his three laws of motion, he used two different words to describe moving objects. He used the word velocity, but he also wrote about something that he called the "quantity of motion." What is this quantity of motion? Today we call it momentum. The **momentum** (moh MEN tum) of an object is the product of its mass and its velocity.

Momentum = Mass × Velocity

What is the unit of measurement for momentum? Since mass is measured in kilograms and velocity is measured in meters per second, the unit for momentum is kilogram-meters per second (kg·m/s). Like velocity and acceleration, momentum is described by its direction as well as its quantity. The momentum of an object is in the same direction as its velocity.

The more momentum an object has, the harder it is to stop. You can catch a baseball moving at 20 m/s, for example, but you cannot stop a car moving at the same speed. Why does the car have more momentum than the ball? The car has more momentum because it has a greater mass.

A high velocity also can produce a large momentum, even when mass is small. A bullet shot from a rifle, for example, has a large momentum. Even though it has a small mass, it travels at a high speed.

Sample Problem

Which has more momentum: a 3-kg sledgehammer swung at 1.5 m/s or an 4-kg sledgehammer swung at 0.9 m/s?

Analyze. You know the mass and velocity of two different objects. You need to determine the momentum of each.

Write the formula. *Momentum = Mass × Velocity*

Substitute and solve. *(a) 3 kg × 1.5 m/s = 4.5 kg·m/s*

(b) 4 kg × 0.9 m/s = 3.6 kg·m/s

Think about it. The lighter hammer has more momentum than the heavier one, because it is swung at a greater velocity—almost twice as fast.

Practice Problems

1. A golf ball travels at 16 m/s, while a baseball moves at 7 m/s. The mass of the golf ball is 0.045 kg and the mass of the baseball is 0.14 kg. Which has greater momentum?
2. What is the momentum of a bird with a mass of 0.018 kg flying at 15 m/s?

Answers to Self-Assessment

☑ Checkpoint

The forces are acting on different objects.

Momentum

Building Inquiry Skills: Inferring

To help students understand that momentum depends upon the mass and velocity of a moving object, ask: **If a fire engine and a tricycle are rolling at a speed of 5 km/h, which would be easier to stop? Why?** *(The tricycle; it has less mass and less momentum.)* **Can a bullet and an automobile have the same momentum? Explain.** *(Yes, a bullet with a small mass that is moving very fast can have the same momentum as a car with a greater mass that is moving very slowly.)* **When a truck driver begins to brake, what happens to the momentum of the truck? Explain.** *(The truck's momentum decreases because its velocity decreases.)* **learning modality: logical/mathematical**

Sample Problem

When working through mathematical problems, always model good techniques. Write the formula, substitute known quantities, then perform the mathematical operations. Remind students to manipulate the units as well. There is no special name for the unit of momentum, it is always written as kg•m/s.

Practice Problems

1. 0.045 kg × 16 m/s = 0.72 kg•m/s
   0.14 kg × 7 m/s = 0.98 kg•m/s
   The baseball has greater momentum.
2. 0.018 kg × 15 m/s = 0.27 kg•m/s

Ongoing Assessment

Drawing Direct students to draw a diagram showing the direction and relative size of the action and reaction forces exerted when a person jumps. Students' diagrams should include force arrows showing a downward force from the person to the ground and an upward force from the ground to the person.

Conservation of Momentum

TRY THIS — ACTIVITY

Skills Focus predicting
Materials *two toy cars with the same mass and low-friction wheels, masking tape*
Time 10 minutes
Tips If the cars collide with too much force, friction, which is an external force, will affect the conservation of momentum. Ask: **What happens to the velocity of the moving car when it sticks to the stationary car?** *(It decreases.)* **What happens to the velocity of the stationary car when it sticks to the moving car?** *(It increases.)* Immediately after the collision, the first car's velocity was reduced by one-half, so both cars now have half the original velocity, but together they have twice the mass. Therefore, in the absence of friction, momentum would be conserved.
Predicting Since students know that momentum is conserved, some will predict that it will be conserved in this case. Other students may realize the cars will stop and predict that momentum is not conserved. The momentum of the cars is zero after the collision, but it was also zero before the collision because they were moving in opposite directions. Thus, momentum is conserved.
learning modality: kinesthetic

Using the Visuals: Figure 19

Visual learners should be able to understand the material in this section based on a careful examination of Figure 19. Make sure students understand the tilt in the cars is a visual means of communicating motion. Have students use small objects, such as toy cars or blocks, to model each event as they describe it verbally. For example, students might say that in event A, both cars are moving before the collision, and X has greater speed. After the collision, both cars are moving and Y has greater speed. **learning modality: visual**

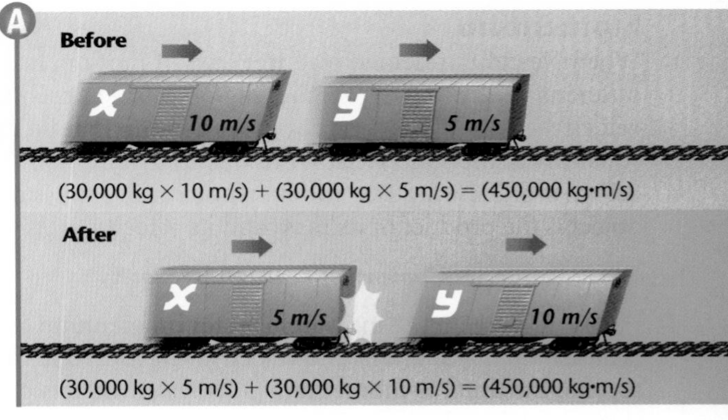

Figure 19 In the absence of friction, momentum is conserved when two train cars collide. This is true regardless of whether the train cars bounce off each other or couple together during the collision. *Interpreting Diagrams In which diagram is all of the momentum transferred from car X to car Y?*

Colliding Cars — ACTIVITY

Momentum is always conserved—even by toys!

1. Find two nearly identical toy cars that roll easily.
2. Make two loops out of masking tape (sticky side out). Put one loop on the front of one of the cars and the other loop on the back of the other car.
3. Place the car that has tape on the back on the floor. Then gently roll the other car into the back of the stationary car. Was momentum conserved? How do you know?

Predicting What will happen if you put masking tape on the fronts of both cars and roll them at each other with equal speeds? Will momentum be conserved in this case? Test your prediction.

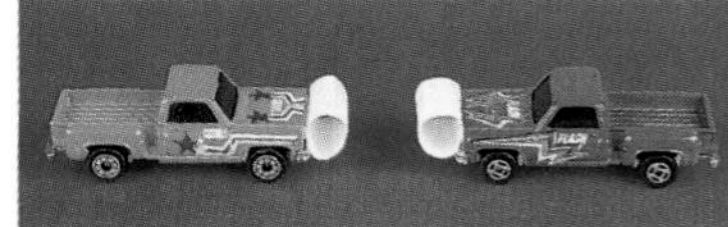

Conservation of Momentum

You know that if someone bumps into you from behind, you gain momentum in the forward direction. Momentum is useful for understanding what happens when an object collides with another object. When two objects collide in the absence of friction, momentum is not lost. This fact is called the law of conservation of momentum. The **law of conservation of momentum** states that the total momentum of the objects that interact does not change. The quantity of momentum is the same before and after they interact. **The total momentum of any group of objects remains the same unless outside forces act on the objects.** Friction is an example of an outside force.

Before you hear the details of this law, you should know that the word *conservation* means something different in physical science than in everyday usage. In everyday usage, conservation means saving resources. You might conserve water or fossil fuels, for example. In physical science, the word conservation refers to conditions before and after some event. A quantity that is conserved is the same after an event as it was before the event.

Two Moving Objects Look at the two train cars traveling in the same direction on a track shown in Figure 19A. Car X is traveling at 10 m/s and car Y is traveling at 5 m/s. Eventually, car X will catch up with car Y and bump into it. During this collision, the speed of each car changes. Car X slows down to 5 m/s, and car Y speeds up to 10 m/s. Momentum is conserved—the momentum of one train car decreases while the momentum of the other increases.

One Moving Object Suppose that car X moves down the track at 10 m/s and hits car Y, which is not moving. Figure 19B shows that after the collision, car X is no longer moving, but car Y is

Background

History of Science Conservation of momentum is the oldest of the great conservation laws of physics. Conservation of momentum is a direct result of Newton's third law. When one object exerts a force on another it changes the momentum of that object. However, the second object also exerts a force on the first object and changes that object's momentum. As a result, the total momentum stays the same.

The law of conservation of momentum was soon followed by laws of conservation of mass, conservation of energy, and conservation of electric charge. These laws unify physics and connect physics to all other sciences. The laws allow scientists to analyze complex interactions between objects without knowing precise details.

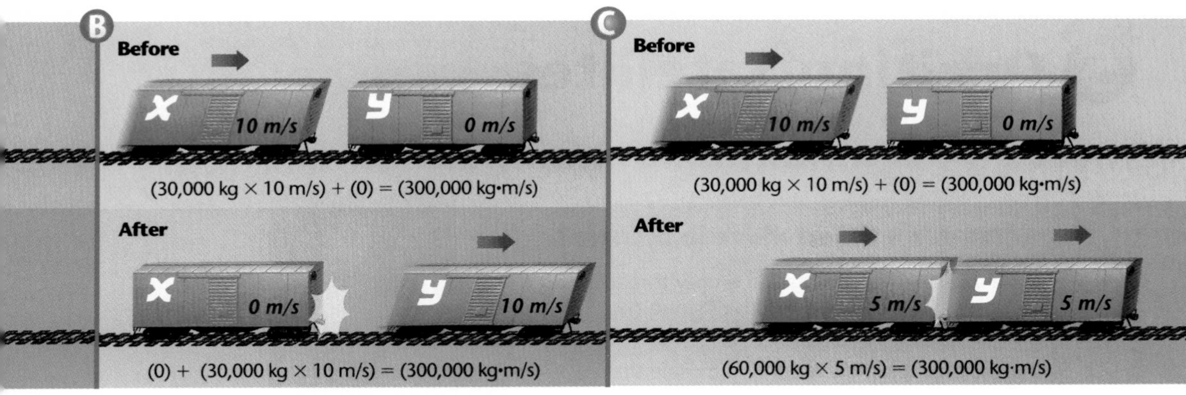

moving. Even though the situation has changed, momentum is still conserved. The total momentum is the same before and after the collision. This time, all of the momentum has been transferred from car X to car Y.

Two Connected Objects Now suppose that, instead of bouncing off each other, the two train cars couple together when they hit. Is momentum still conserved? The answer is yes. You can see in Figure 19C that the total momentum before the collision is again 300,000 kg·m/s. But after the collision, the coupled train cars make one object with a total mass of 60,000 kilograms (30,000 kilograms + 30,000 kilograms). The velocity of the coupled trains is 5 m/s—half the velocity of car X before the collision. Since the mass is doubled, the velocity must be divided in half in order for momentum to be conserved.

Section 4 Review

1. According to Newton's third law of motion, how are action and reaction forces related?
2. How is momentum conserved?
3. Suppose you and a friend, who has exactly twice your mass, are on skates. You push away from your friend. How does the force with which you push your friend compare to the force with which your friend pushes you? How do your accelerations compare?
4. **Thinking Critically Comparing and Contrasting** Which has more momentum, a 250-kg dolphin swimming at 6 m/s, or a 450-kg manatee swimming at 2 m/s?

Check Your Progress (CHAPTER PROJECT 2)

Construct your vehicle. Is your vehicle powered according to Newton's third law of motion? Add to your diagram so that it shows the force exerted by your vehicle and the force exerted on your vehicle to make it move. What exerts the force that moves your vehicle? Be ready to explain the diagram to other students.

3 Assess

Section 4 Review Answers

1. Action and reaction forces are equal but act in opposite directions.
2. The total momentum is exactly the same before and after a collision.
3. The force with which you push your friend is equal and opposite to the force with which your friend pushes you (even if your friend is not deliberately "pushing"). You accelerate faster than your friend and roll back further because your mass is less.
4. The dolphin has a greater momentum (1,500 kg•m/s) than the manatee (900 kg•m/s).

Check Your Progress (CHAPTER PROJECT 2)

Allow students to work in pairs as they add force arrows to their diagrams and verify that they are using Newton's third law. They should be able to explain to their partner how each force acts and how this is in accord with the third law. Working in pairs and explaining to their partner gives students practice for the class presentation.

Program Resources

◆ **Teaching Resources** 2-4 Review and Reinforce, p. 53; 2-4 Enrich, p. 54

Media and Technology

Interactive Student Tutorial CD-ROM M-2

Transparencies "Conservation of Momentum," Transparency 5

Answers to Self-Assessment

Caption Question

Figure 19 Diagram B

Performance Assessment

Skills Check Have students write and solve a problem in which they must calculate the momentum of two objects before and after a collision. Have students compare their problems and solutions in small groups.

Students can save their problems and solutions in their portfolios.

Section 5 Orbiting Satellites

Objectives

After completing the lesson, students will be able to
- ◆ explain how a rocket lifts off the ground;
- ◆ describe the forces that keep a satellite in orbit.

Key Terms satellite, centripetal force

1 Engage/Explore

Activating Prior Knowledge

Ask students if they have seen a launching of the space shuttle on television. Encourage a volunteer to describe the launch. Invite students who enjoy model rocketry to tell about their hobby to the class. Compare the launching of a rocket to the way a squid propels itself. Call students' attention to the photograph of a shuttle launch and have them describe the action-reaction force pair that produces lift.

Discover Activity

Skills Focus forming operational definitions
Materials *small object such as an empty thread spool, length of string no more than 1 m long, safety goggles*
Time 10 minutes
Tips Caution students not to swing the object near another person. Have them wear safety goggles during the activity. In Step 3, students may predict that the spool will move more slowly or that it won't make it over the top. In Step 4, several variables are related to the length of the string. Students may find that it takes less force to keep the object moving at the same speed when the length of the string is increased.
Think It Over The object is moving in a circle and is constantly accelerating. The force that keeps the object accelerating in a circle is the pulling force of the string.

Section 5 Orbiting Satellites

Discover Activity

What Makes an Object Move in a Circle?

1. Tie a small mass, such as an empty thread spool, to the end of a length of string (no more than one meter long).
2. Swing the object rapidly around in a circle that is perpendicular to the floor. Make sure no one is near the swinging object, and don't let it go!
3. Predict what will happen if you decrease the speed of the object. Test your prediction.
4. Predict how the length of the string affects the motion of the object. Test your prediction.

Think It Over
Forming Operational Defintions Describe the motion of the object. How do you know that the string exerts a force?

GUIDE FOR READING

- ◆ **How does a rocket lift off the ground?**
- ◆ **What keeps a satellite in orbit?**

Reading Tip **As you read, make a list of main ideas and supporting details about rockets and satellites.**

What would it be like to be at Cape Canaveral in Florida for a space shuttle launch? The countdown is broadcast over a loudspeaker—ten—nine—eight—seven—six—five—four. White steam comes out of the base of the rocket—three—two—one. The rocket rises into space and begins to turn slightly and roll. The noise hits you, and the ground shakes. With an astonishingly loud rumble, the rocket rises in the distance. Everyone cheers. You watch the rocket until it is too far away to see.

How Do Rockets Lift Off?

The awesome achievement of lifting a rocket into space against the force of gravity can be explained using Newton's third law of motion. As a rocket burns fuel, it expels exhaust gases. When the gases are forced out of the rocket, they exert an equal and opposite force back on

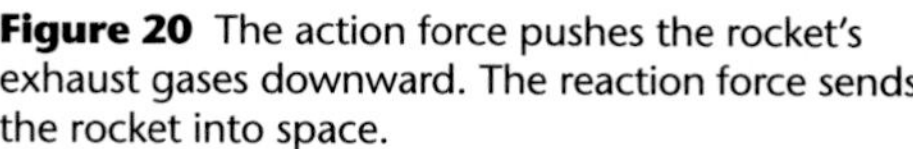

Figure 20 The action force pushes the rocket's exhaust gases downward. The reaction force sends the rocket into space.

Reading Strategies

Reading Tip Remind students that a main idea is an important point an author makes about a topic. Supporting details are the facts that support a main idea. Suggest that students use this format to list main ideas and supporting details.
Main idea 1: ____________
Supporting detail: ____________
Supporting detail: ____________

Vocabulary Explain that the word *satellite* comes from a Latin word that means "attendant" or "guard." Have students work with partners to check dictionary meanings of *satellite.* Then instruct pairs to use this information to write about similarities between an artificial *satellite* and a *satellite* office.

the rocket. **A rocket can rise into the air because the gases it expels with a downward force exert an equal but opposite force on the rocket.** As long as this upward pushing force, called thrust, is greater than the downward pull of gravity, there is a net force in the upward direction. As a result, the rocket accelerates upward.

☑ *Checkpoint When a rocket is launched, what is the direction of the reaction force?*

What Is a Satellite?

Rockets are often used to carry satellites into space. A **satellite** is any object that travels around another object in space. An artificial satellite is a device that is launched into orbit around Earth. Artificial satellites are designed for many purposes. They are used in space research, communications, military intelligence, weather analysis, and geographical surveys.

Circular Motion Artificial satellites travel around Earth in an almost circular path. Recall that an object traveling in a circle is accelerating because it is constantly changing direction. If an object is accelerating, there must be a force acting on it to change its motion. Any force that causes an object to move in a circle is called a **centripetal force** (sen TRIP ih tul). The word *centripetal* means "center-seeking." For a satellite, the centripetal force is the gravitational force that pulls the satellite toward the center of Earth.

Satellite Motion If gravity pulls satellites toward Earth, why doesn't a satellite fall, as a ball thrown into the air would? The answer is that satellites do not travel straight up into the air. Instead, they move around Earth. If you throw a ball horizontally, for example, it will move out in front of you at the same time that it is pulled to the ground. If you throw the ball faster, it will land even farther in front of you. The faster you throw a projectile, the farther it travels before it lands.

Figure 21 As this rocket moves higher, its path tilts more and more. Eventually its path is parallel to Earth's surface. *Predicting How will the direction of the accelerating force change?*

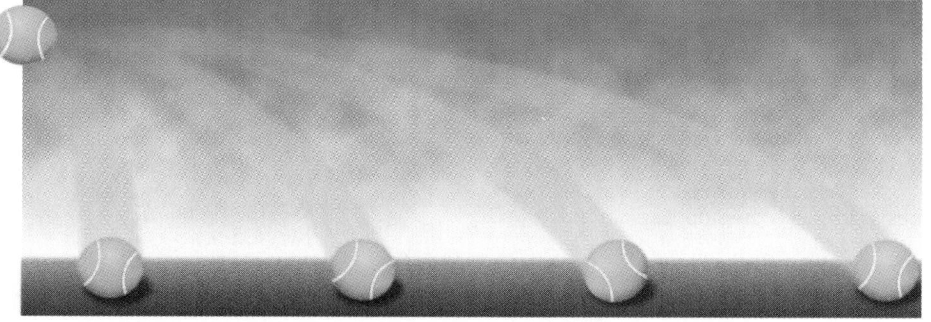

Figure 22 The faster a projectile like this ball is thrown, the farther it travels before it hits the ground.

2 Facilitate

How Do Rockets Lift Off?

Demonstration

Materials *plastic water rocket, hand air pump, safety goggles*
Time 15 minutes plus time for rocket assembly

This demonstration uses a plastic water rocket and must be done outdoors. Water rockets can be purchased from science supply companies. The rocket uses compressed air to expel a mixture of water and air from the rocket nozzle. CAUTION: *These water rockets are safe, but the manufacturer's recommendations must be followed exactly. Students should wear goggles and observe from a safe distance.* After the launch, challenge students to identify the action and reaction forces that acted as the rocket lifted off the ground. *(The compressed air exerted a downward force on the water, expelling it from the rocket. The water exerted an upward force on the rocket.)* Then ask students which unbalanced forces are responsible for the rocket's upward movement. *(The upward force of the water on the rocket is greater than the downward pull of gravity.)* **learning modality: visual**

What Is a Satellite?

Building Inquiry Skills: Inferring

Ensure that students grasp how forces act on a satellite by asking: **Earth travels around the sun, so there must be a force acting on it to change the direction of its motion. What is that force?** *(The sun's gravity)* **learning modality: logical/mathematical**

Ongoing Assessment

Drawing Have students draw a diagram of the Earth-moon system and draw and label the centripetal force acting on the moon.

Program Resources

- **Teaching Resources** 2-5 Lesson Plan, p. 55; 2-5 Section Summary, p. 56
- **Interdisciplinary Exploration Series** "Mars the Next Frontier," pp. 22–23

Media and Technology

Audiotapes English-Spanish Summary 2-5

Answers to Self-Assessment

Caption Question

Figure 21 The direction of the force gradually changes from vertical to horizontal.

☑ *Checkpoint*

The direction of a rocket's reaction force is upward.

3 Assess

Section 5 Review Answers

1. According to Newton's third law, since the rocket exerts a force when it pushes the gas out backward, the gas exerts an equal and opposite force on the rocket, pushing it upward.
2. As the satellite falls, the surface of Earth curves away.
3. No. For satellites in low orbit, the force of gravity is almost as large as it would be on the surface. Satellites stay in orbit because they fall and move along the orbit at the same time.
4. All three factors increase acceleration. The decrease in air resistance allows the rocket to accelerate faster because there is less air resistance pushing the rocket in the opposite direction. The decrease in gravity allows the rocket to accelerate faster because there is less gravity pulling the rocket back toward Earth. The decrease in the rocket's mass increases acceleration because the same force acting on a smaller mass causes a greater acceleration.

Science at Home

ACTIVITY

Materials *child's plastic bucket, water*

Tips If students have difficulty spinning the bucket, suggest they tie a rope to the handle. Warn students that if they spin the bucket too slowly, the water will spill out when the bucket gets to the top of the circle. If they spin the bucket fast enough, the bucket will "catch" the water before the water spills out due to gravity.

Performance Assessment

Writing Tell students they have received a letter from a person wondering about what will happen when the geostationary communications satellites orbiting Earth run out of fuel. Have students write paragraphs explaining why the communications satellites are not really stationary and why they don't need fuel to stay in orbit.

Students can save their paragraphs in their portfolios.

Figure 23 A projectile with enough velocity will move in a circular orbit around Earth. *Interpreting Diagrams The force of gravity is always toward the center of Earth. How does the direction of gravity compare to the direction of the projectile's motion at any point?*

Isaac Newton wondered what would happen if you were on a high mountain and were able to throw a stone as fast as you wanted. The faster you threw it, the farther away it would land. At a certain speed, the path of the object would match the curve of Earth. Although the stone would keep falling due to gravity, Earth's surface would curve away from the stone at the same rate. Thus the object would circle Earth, as in Figure 23.

Satellites in orbit around Earth continually fall toward Earth, but because Earth is curved they travel around it. In other words, a satellite is a projectile that falls around Earth rather than into it. A satellite does not need fuel because it continues to move ahead due to its inertia. At the same time, gravity continuously changes the satellite's direction. The speed with which an object must be thrown in order to orbit Earth turns out to be 7,900 m/s! This speed is almost 200 times as fast as a pitcher can throw a baseball.

Satellite Location Some satellites, such as the space shuttle, are put into low orbits. The time to complete a trip around Earth in a low orbit is about 90 minutes. Other satellites are sent into higher orbits. At these distances, the satellite travels more slowly and takes longer to circle Earth. For example, communications satellites travel about 40,000 kilometers above the surface. At this height they circle Earth once every 24 hours. Since Earth rotates once every 24 hours, a satellite above the equator always stays above the same point on Earth as it orbits.

Section 5 Review

1. Use action-reaction forces to explain why a rocket can lift off the ground.
2. Why doesn't an orbiting satellite fall back to Earth?
3. Is it correct to say that satellites stay in orbit rather than falling to Earth because they are beyond the pull of Earth's gravity? Explain.
4. **Thinking Critically Applying Concepts** When a rocket travels higher, air resistance decreases as the air becomes less dense. The force of gravity also decreases because the rocket is farther from Earth, and the rocket's mass decreases as its fuel is used up. Explain how acceleration is affected.

Science at Home

Fill a small plastic bucket halfway with water and take it outdoors. Challenge a family member to swing the bucket in a vertical circle. Explain that the water won't fall out at the top if the bucket is moving fast enough. Tell your family member that if the bucket falls as fast as the water, the water will stay in the bucket. Relate this activity to a satellite that also falls due to gravity, yet remains in orbit.

72 ◆ M

Media and Technology

Exploring Physical Science Videodisc Unit 3, Side 1, "We Have Lift Off"

Chapter 10

Program Resources

- **Teaching Resources** 2-5 Review and Reinforce, p. 57; 2-5 Enrich, p. 58

Answers to Self-Assessment

Caption Question

Figure 23 For a projectile in orbit, the direction of the force of gravity is perpendicular to the projectile's motion.

Section 1 The Nature of Force

Key Ideas

- The sum of all the forces acting on an object is the net force.
- Unbalanced forces change the motion of an object, whereas balanced forces do not.
- According to Newton's first law of motion, an object at rest will remain at rest and an object in motion will continue in motion at constant speed unless the object is acted upon by an unbalanced force.

Key Terms

force, net force, unbalanced force, balanced forces, inertia, mass

Section 2 Force, Mass, and Acceleration

Key Idea

- Newton's second law of motion states that the net force on an object is the product of its acceleration and its mass.

Key Term

newton

Section 3 Friction and Gravity

Key Ideas

- Friction is a force that one surface exerts on another when they rub against each other.
- Weight is a measure of the force of gravity on an object, and mass is a measure of the amount of matter that an object contains.
- The force of gravity acts between all objects in the universe.

Key Terms

friction, sliding friction, rolling friction, fluid friction, gravity, free fall, projectile, air resistance, terminal velocity, weight

Section 4 Action and Reaction

Key Ideas

- Newton's third law of motion states that every time there is an action force on an object, the object will exert an equal and opposite reaction force.
- The momentum of an object is the product of its mass and its velocity.
- The law of conservation of momentum states that the total momentum is the same before and after an event, as long as there are no outside forces.

Key Terms

momentum
law of conservation of momentum

Section 5 Orbiting Satellites

Integrating Space Science

Key Ideas

- A rocket burns fuel and produces gases. The rocket pushes these gases downward. At the same time, the gases apply an equal force to the rocket, pushing it upward.
- Even though a satellite is pulled downward by gravity, it stays in orbit because it is moving so quickly. Earth's surface curves away from the satellite at the same rate that the satellite falls.

Key Terms

satellite, centripetal force

ACTIVITY

USING THE INTERNET

www.science-explorer.phschool.com

Program Resources

- **Teaching Resources** Chapter 2 Project Scoring Rubric, p. 38; Chapter 2 Project Performance Assessment Teacher Notes, pp. 193–194; Chapter 2 Performance Assessment Student Worksheet, p. 195; Chapter 2 Test, pp. 196–199

Media and Technology

Interactive Student Tutorial CD-ROM M-2

Computer Test Bank M-2 Test

CHAPTER 2 REVIEW

Reviewing Content: Multiple Choice

1. b **2.** a **3.** a **4.** d **5.** c

True or False

6. equal and opposite to **7.** matter or inertia **8.** true **9.** true **10.** true

Checking Concepts

11. Air resistance on the flat sheet is greater than the air resistance on the crumpled paper.
12. The force on an object equals acceleration times mass.
13. The fluids keep surfaces from making direct contact and thus reduce friction.
14. Both erasers hit the ground at the same time. While one is thrown horizontally, they both accelerate downward at the same rate.
15. Your mass would stay the same, but your weight on the asteroid would be less because the asteroid pulls you less strongly than the Earth.
16. The cleats dig into the ground and prevent sliding.
17. Yes. The pavement exerts a force on the ball.
18. Answers will vary. Drawing should resemble the art on Figure 24. The satellite is accelerating since it is changing direction.
19. Students write original material. The answer should include a description of each kind of force involved in the event, how those forces changed the motion of objects involved in the event, and how the objects interacted.

Thinking Visually

20. a. opposite to the direction of the motion **b.** types of surfaces involved and how hard the surfaces push together **c.** between any two objects **d.** masses and distance

Applying Skills

21. Left ball before: 0.4 kg × 2 m/s = 0.8 kg•m/s; right ball before: 0.4 kg × 0 m/s = 0 kg•m/s; left ball after: 0.4 kg × 0.5 m/s = 0.2 kg•m/s; right ball after: 0.4 kg × 1.5 m/s = 0.6 kg•m/s

CHAPTER 2 REVIEW

Reviewing Content

For more review of key concepts, see the Interactive Student Tutorial CD-ROM.

Multiple Choice

Choose the letter of the best answer.

1. When two equal forces act in opposite directions on an object, they are called
   a. friction forces.
   b. balanced forces.
   c. centripetal forces.
   d. gravitational forces.
2. When an unbalanced force acts on an object, the force
   a. changes the motion of the object.
   b. is canceled by another force.
   c. does not change the motion of the object.
   d. is equal to the weight of the object.
3. The resistance of an object to any change in its motion is called
   a. inertia. b. friction.
   c. gravity. d. weight.
4. According to Newton's second law of motion, force is equal to mass times
   a. inertia. b. weight.
   c. direction. d. acceleration.
5. The product of an object's mass and its velocity is called the object's
   a. net force. b. weight.
   c. momentum. d. gravitation.

True or False

If the statement is true, write true. If it is false, change the underlined word or words to make the statement true.

6. According to Newton's third law of motion, whenever you exert a force on an object, the object exerts a force back on you that is greater than your force.
7. Mass is a measure of the amount of force that an object has.
8. Weight is the measure of the force of gravity exerted on an object.
9. Conservation in science refers to the amount of some quantity staying the same before and after an event.
10. The force that causes a satellite to orbit Earth is gravity.

Checking Concepts

11. Explain why a flat sheet of paper dropped from a height of 2 meters will not accelerate at the same rate as a sheet of paper crumpled into a ball.
12. Explain how force, mass, and acceleration are related.
13. Why do slippery fluids such as oil reduce sliding friction?
14. One student tosses a chalkboard eraser horizontally so that the eraser hits the ground 5 meters away. At exactly the same time, another student drops an eraser. Which eraser hits the ground first? Explain.
15. Compare your mass and weight on Earth with your mass and weight on an asteroid, which is much smaller than Earth.
16. Why do athletes' shoes often have cleats on them?
17. When you drop a golf ball to the pavement, it bounces up. Is a force needed to make it bounce up? If so, what exerts the force?
18. Draw a diagram showing the motion of a satellite around Earth. Is the satellite accelerating?
19. **Writing to Learn** You are a reporter for a local television station, and you like to give your stories a physical-science twist. Write a story for the evening news in which you describe an event in terms of the forces involved. Use a catchy title.

Thinking Visually

20. **Compare/Contrast Table** Copy the compare/contrast table below on a separate sheet of paper. Complete the table to compare and contrast friction and gravity. (For more information on compare/contrast tables see the Skills Handbook.)

Force	Direction of Force	Force Depends Upon
Friction	a. ?	b. ?
Gravity	c. ?	d. ?

22. Total momentum before: 0.8 kg•m/s + 0 g•m/s = 0.8 kg•m/s; total momentum after: 0.2 kg•m/s + 0.6 kg•m/s = 0.8 kg•m/s; yes, the law of conservation is satisfied. Total momentum before the collision is equal to total momentum after the collision.
23. Students' designs will vary, but should include a high-friction surface to demonstrate how friction will decrease the momentum.

Thinking Critically

24. When walking on land, you push the ground and the ground pushes back with an equal force on you. On the boat, you push the boat and the boat pushes back with an equal force on you. You move forward but the boat is also free to move backward.
25. 30 N
26. The skateboard stops, but you will keep moving forward because of inertia.
27. The crumpled paper, because it has less air resistance.

Applying Skills

Use the illustration showing a collision between two balls to answer Questions 21–23.

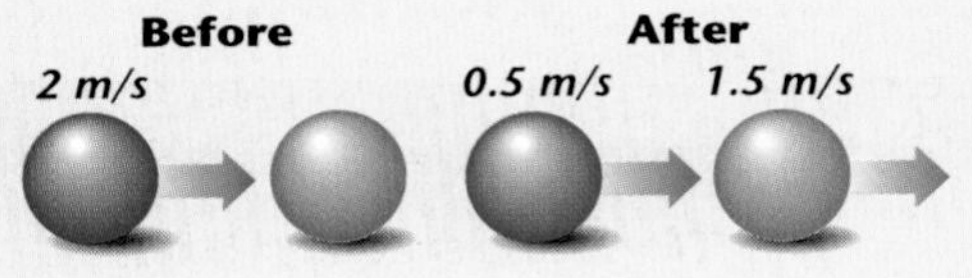

21. **Calculating** Use the formula for momentum to find the momentum of each ball before and after the collision. Assume the mass of each ball is 0.4 kg.
22. **Inferring** Find the total momentum before and after collision. Is the law of conservation of momentum satisfied in this collision? Explain.
23. **Designing Experiments** Design an experiment in which you could show that momentum is not conserved between the balls when friction is strong.

Thinking Critically

24. **Comparing and Contrasting** If you stand up in a rowboat and take a step toward the dock, you may fall in the water. Explain what happens in this situation. How is it similar to what happens when you take a step on land? How is it different?
25. **Problem Solving** If a toy train has a mass of 1.5 kg and accelerates at a rate of 20 m/s^2, what is the amount of force acting on it?
26. **Applying Concepts** You are riding fast on a skateboard when your wheel suddenly gets stuck in a crack on the sidewalk. Using the term *inertia*, explain what happens.
27. **Predicting** Suppose you drop a sheet of paper to the ground. Then you crumple the paper and drop it again from the same height. Which takes less time to reach the ground? Explain why.

Performance Assessment

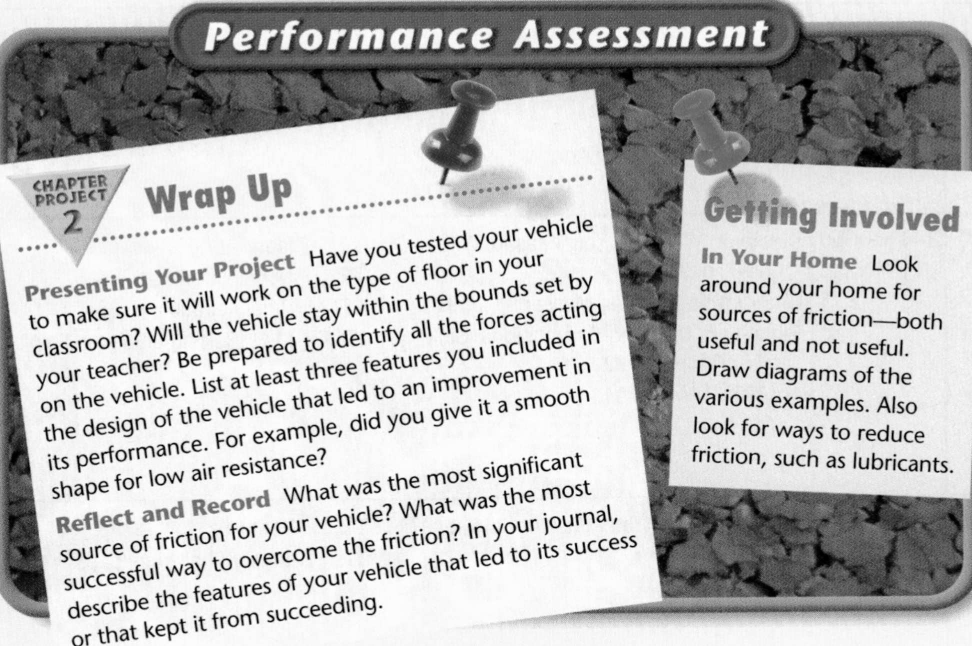

Wrap Up

CHAPTER PROJECT 2

Presenting Your Project Have you tested your vehicle to make sure it will work on the type of floor in your classroom? Will the vehicle stay within the bounds set by your teacher? Be prepared to identify all the forces acting on the vehicle. List at least three features you included in the design of the vehicle that led to an improvement in its performance. For example, did you give it a smooth shape for low air resistance?

Reflect and Record What was the most significant source of friction for your vehicle? What was the most successful way to overcome the friction? In your journal, describe the features of your vehicle that led to its success or that kept it from succeeding.

Getting Involved

In Your Home Look around your home for sources of friction—both useful and not useful. Draw diagrams of the various examples. Also look for ways to reduce friction, such as lubricants.

Program Resources

◆ **Inquiry Skills Activity Book** Provides teaching and review of all inquiry skills

Performance Assessment

Wrap Up

CHAPTER PROJECT 2

Presenting Your Project Allow time for students to test their vehicles. Remind students to include a diagram identifying the forces. Encourage students to incorporate Newton's first two laws of motion when they explain the features of their design that improved performance.

Reflect and Record After all presentations have been completed, have students discuss the sources of friction for the different vehicles. Encourage them to compare design features with their classmates as they evaluate their own vehicles.

Getting Involved

In Your Home To help students get started, have them narrow their search for friction to one room in the home such as the kitchen. Give examples of useful friction, such as nonslip flooring. Have students suggest ways to reduce friction that is not useful.

CHAPTER 3

Forces in Fluids

Sections	Time	Student Edition Activities	Other Activities
CHAPTER PROJECT 3 **Staying Afloat** p. 77	Ongoing (2 weeks)	Check Your Progress, pp. 89, 96 Wrap Up, p. 103	**TE** Chapter 3 Project Notes, pp. 76–77
1 **Pressure** pp. 78–83 ◆ Define and calculate pressure. ◆ Recognize that pressure decreases at higher altitudes and increases at greater depths. ◆ Identify and explain examples of balanced pressures.	4 periods/ 2 blocks	**Discover** Can You Blow Up a Balloon in a Bottle?, p. 78 **Sharpen Your Skills** Hypothesizing, p. 80 **Real-World Lab: How It Works** Spinning Sprinklers, pp. 84–85	**TE** Building Inquiry Skills: Controlling Variables, p. 79 **TE** Math Toolbox, p. 79 **TE** Addressing Naive Conceptions, p. 80 **TE** Demonstration, p. 81 **TE** Real-Life Learning, p. 82 **TE** Using the Visuals, p. 82 **IES** "Riddles of the Pharaohs," p. 33
2 **Transmitting Pressure in a Fluid** pp. 86–89 ◆ State Pascal's principle and recognize applications of the principle. ◆ Explain how a hydraulic system works.	2 periods/ 1 block	**Discover** How Does Pressure Change?, p. 86	**TE** Building Inquiry Skills: Making Models, p. 88 **TE** Integrating Life Sciences, p. 88
3 **Floating and Sinking** pp. 90–96 ◆ Define the buoyant force and its effect. ◆ State Archimedes' principle. ◆ Explain how the density of an object determines whether it floats or sinks.	3–4 periods/ $1\frac{1}{2}$ blocks	**Discover** What Can You Measure With a Straw?, p. 90 **Sharpen Your Skills** Measuring, p. 91 **Skills Lab: Drawing Conclusions** Sink and Spill, pp. 92–93 **Try This** Dive!, p. 94	**TE** Inquiry Challenge, p. 91 **TE** Demonstration, p. 94 **TE** Demonstration, p. 95 **ISLM** M-3 "Raising a Sunken Ship"
4 *INTEGRATING TECHNOLOGY* **Applying Bernoulli's Principle** pp. 97–100 ◆ State Bernoulli's principle. ◆ Explain the application of Bernoulli's principle to flight.	2 periods/ 1 block	**Discover** Does Water Push or Pull?, p. 97	**TE** Demonstration, p. 98 **TE** Inquiry Challenge, p. 98
Study Guide/Chapter Review pp. 101–103	1 period/ $\frac{1}{2}$ block		**ISAB** Provides teaching and review of all inquiry skills

For Standard or Block Schedule The Resource Pro® CD-ROM gives you maximum flexibility for planning your instruction for any type of schedule. Resource Pro® contains Planning Express®, an advanced scheduling program, as well as the entire contents of the Teaching Resources and the Computer Test Bank.

CHAPTER PLANNING GUIDE

Program Resources	Assessment Strategies	Media and Technology
TR Chapter 3 Project Teacher Notes, pp. 64–65 **TR** Chapter 3 Project Overview and Worksheets, pp. 66–69 **TR** Chapter 3 Project Scoring Rubric, p. 70	**SE** Performance Assessment: Chapter 3 Project Wrap Up, p. 103 **TE** Performance Assessment: Chapter 3 Project Wrap Up, p. 103 **TE** Check Your Progress, pp. 89, 96 **TR** Chapter 3 Project Scoring Rubric, p. 70	Science Explorer Internet Site
TR 3-1 Lesson Plan, p. 71 **TR** 3-1 Section Summary, p. 72 **TR** 3-1 Review and Reinforce, p. 73 **TR** 3-1 Enrich, p. 74 **TR** Chapter 3 Real-World Lab, pp. 87–89 **SES** Book D, *Human Biology and Health,* Chapter 5	**SE** Section 1 Review, p. 83 **SE** Analyze and Conclude, p. 85 **TE** Ongoing Assessment, pp. 79, 81 **TE** Performance Assessment, p. 83 **TR** 3-1 Review and Reinforce, p. 73	Audiotapes: English-Spanish Summary 3-1 Interactive Student Tutorial CD-ROM, M-3
TR 3-2 Lesson Plan, p. 75 **TR** 3-2 Section Summary, p. 76 **TR** 3-2 Review and Reinforce, p. 77 **TR** 3-2 Enrich, p. 78 **SES** Book B, *Animals*, Chapter 2	**SE** Section 2 Review, p. 89 **TE** Ongoing Assessment, pp. 87 **TE** Performance Assessment, p. 89 **TR** 3-2 Review and Reinforce, p. 77	Audiotapes: English-Spanish Summary 3-2 Interactive Student Tutorial CD-ROM, M-3
TR 3-3 Lesson Plan, p. 79 **TR** 3-3 Section Summary, p. 80 **TR** 3-3 Review and Reinforce, p. 81 **TR** 3-3 Enrich, p. 82 **TR** Chapter 3 Skills Lab, pp. 90–91	**SE** Section 3 Review, p. 96 **SE** Analyze and Conclude, p. 93 **TE** Ongoing Assessment, pp. 91, 95 **TE** Performance Assessment, p. 96 **TR** 3-3 Review and Reinforce, p. 81	Exploring Earth Science Videodisc, Unit 3 Side 1, "Isto What?"; Exploring Physical Science Videodisc, Unit 3 Side 1, "Density Column" Audiotapes: English-Spanish Summary 3-3 Transparencies 6, "Floating and Sinking"; 7, "Density" Interactive Student Tutorial CD-ROM, M-3
TR 3-4 Lesson Plan, p. 83 **TR** 3-4 Section Summary, p. 84 **TR** 3-4 Review and Reinforce, p. 85 **TR** 3-4 Enrich, p. 86	**SE** Section 4 Review, p. 100 **TE** Ongoing Assessment, p. 99 **TE** Performance Assessment, p. 100 **TR** 3-4 Review and Reinforce, p. 85	Audiotapes: English-Spanish Summary 3-4 Transparency 8, "Exploring Wings" Exploring Physical Science Videodisc, Unit 3 Side 1, "How an Airplane Flies" Interactive Student Tutorial CD-ROM, M-3
TR Chapter 3 Performance Assessment, pp. 200–202 **TR** Chapter 3 Test, pp. 203–206	**SE** Chapter Review, p. 101–103 **TR** Chapter 3 Performance Assessment, pp. 200–202 **TR** Chapter 3 Test, pp. 203–206 **CTB** Test M-3	Computer Test Bank, Test M-3 Interactive Student Tutorial CD-ROM, M-3

Key: **SE** Student Edition
CTB Computer Test Bank
ISAB Inquiry Skills Activity Book
TE Teacher's Edition
SES Science Explorer Series Text
PTA Product Testing Activities by *Consumer Reports*
TR Teaching Resources
ISLM Integrated Science Laboratory Manual
IES Interdisciplinary Explorations Series

Meeting the National Science Education Standards and AAAS Benchmarks

National Science Education Standards	Benchmarks for Science Literacy	Unifying Themes
Science as Inquiry (Content Standard A) ◆ **Develop descriptions, explanations, predictions, and models using evidence** Students model a rotating lawn sprinkler to determine the factors that affect the speed of its rotation. *(Real-World Lab)* ◆ **Communicate scientific procedures and explanations** Students follow a scientific procedure and communicate their findings as they examine the relationship between the buoyant force on an object and the weight of the water the object displaces. *(Skills Lab)* ◆ **Using mathematics in all aspects of scientific inquiry** Students calculate pressure. *(Section 1)* Measurements of force and volume are taken and buoyant force is calculated. *(Skills Lab)* **Physical Science** (Content Standard B) ◆ **Properties and changes of properties in matter** Students explore the densities of specific objects and determine why objects float or sink. *(Section 3)* **Science and Technology** (Content Standard E) ◆ **Implement a proposed design** Students construct a small-scale boat that can carry cargo and float. *(Chapter Project)*	**1C The Scientific Enterprise** Students learn how the contributions of scientists Blaise Pascal and Daniel Bernoulli improved our understanding of fluid pressure and the motion of fluids. *(Sections 2, 4)* **3B Design and Systems** As students design small-scale boats they take constraints into account and propose solutions to improve their designs. *(Chapter Project)* **4D The Structure of Matter** Matter is composed of moving particles. A liquid or fluid is a form of matter with distinct properties. Different forms of matter have different physical properties, such as pressure and density. *(Sections 1, 2, 3, 4; Skills Lab)* **11B Models** Modeling the rotation of a lawn sprinkler allows students to think about the application of pressure and force to making sprinklers spin. *(Real-World Lab)*	◆ **Systems and Interactions** The movement of a fluid affects its pressure on an object. When the forces of fluid pressure are confined they are equally transmitted to objects. *(Sections 1, 2, 4)* ◆ **Scale and Structure** Different forms of matter have different densities. The buoyant force on an object is equal to the weight of the fluid displaced by the object. *(Section 3; Chapter Project; Skills Lab)* ◆ **Modeling** Students model the effects of pressure on the motion of fluids. *(Section 4; Real-World Lab)*

Media and Technology

Exploring Earth Science Videodisc

◆ **Section 3** "Isto What?" explains the concept of isostasy using an ice cube and a cargo ship as examples.

Exploring Physical Science Videodisc

◆ **Section 3** "Density Column" helps viewers explore the concept of density as they learn how it is calculated.

◆ **Section 4** "How an Airplane Flies" introduces viewers to the forces that act on an airplane during flight.

Interactive Student Tutorial CD-ROM

◆ **Chapter Review** Interactive questions help students to self-assess their mastery of key chapter concepts.

Student Edition Connection Strategies

◆ **Section 1** **Math Toolbox,** p. 79
Integrating Life Science, p. 81

◆ **Section 2** **Social Studies Connection,** p. 87 
Integrating Life Science, p. 89

◆ **Section 4** **Integrating Technology,** p. 97

www.science-explorer.phschool.com

Visit the Science Explorer Internet site to find an up-to-date activity for Chapter 3 of *Motion, Forces, and Energy*.

ACTIVITY	Time (minutes)	Materials Quantities for one work group	Skills
Section 1			
Discover, p. 78	10	**Consumable** small balloon **Nonconsumable** 2 L plastic bottle, straw	Developing Hypotheses
Real-World Lab, pp. 84–85	45	**Consumable** fishing line, 50 cm **Nonconsumable** 6 empty soda cans with tabs, waterproof marker, beaker or wide-mouth jar, stopwatch or clock with second hand, 4d common nail, 10d common nail, 20d common nail, large basin to catch water	Making Models, Designing Experiments, Controlling Variables
Section 2			
Discover, p. 86	10	**Consumable** water **Nonconsumable** 2-L plastic bottle with cap	Observing
Section 3			
Discover, p. 90	20	**Consumable** plastic straw, water, sugar **Nonconsumable** metric ruler, scissors, waterproof clay, waterproof marker, glass, spoon	Predicting
Sharpen your Skills, p. 91	5	**Nonconsumable** wooden block, metric ruler	Measuring
Skills Lab, pp. 92–93	45	**Consumable** salt, paper towel **Nonconsumable** beaker, 400-mL; beaker, 250-mL; balance; jar with water tight lid, about 30 mL	Drawing Conclusions
Try This, p. 94	20	**Consumable** plastic straw **Nonconsumable** scissors, paper clips, beaker, 2 L plastic bottle	Drawing Conclusions
Section 4			
Discover, p. 97	10	**Nonconsumable** plastic spoon, plastic fork, faucet	Inferring

A list of all materials required for the Student Edition activities can be found beginning on page T14. You can order Materials Kits by calling 1-800-828-7777 or by accessing the Science Explorer Internet site at **www.science-explorer.phschool.com.**

Staying Afloat

In this chapter, students will be introduced to the principles of buoyancy that allow some objects to float while others sink. They will apply these principles to design a boat that will float even though it is made of metal and loaded with heavy cargo.

Purpose Students will have the opportunity to design, build, test, and modify a boat. Then students test their boats' abilities to carry cargo without capsizing.

Skills Focus After completing the Chapter 3 Project, students will be able to

- ◆ build a boat out of metal;
- ◆ design and test the boat so that it can hold 50 pennies for 10 seconds;
- ◆ describe the scientific reasoning behind design modifications to the rest of the class.

Project Time Line The entire project will require at least two weeks. Set aside one or two class periods at the end of the project for students to present their boats in class.

For more detailed information on planning and supervising the chapter project, see Chapter 3 Project Teacher Notes, pages 64–65 in Teaching Resources.

Possible Materials cans, metal plates or bowls, aluminum foil, sheet metal, wire, tin snips, pennies, dishpan or bath tub, meter stick, string

Suggested Shortcuts You may wish to divide the class into small groups to carry out the project. You can make this project less involved by specifying the materials that should be used by all students. For example, limit the choices of materials to aluminum foil and metal plates or bowls.

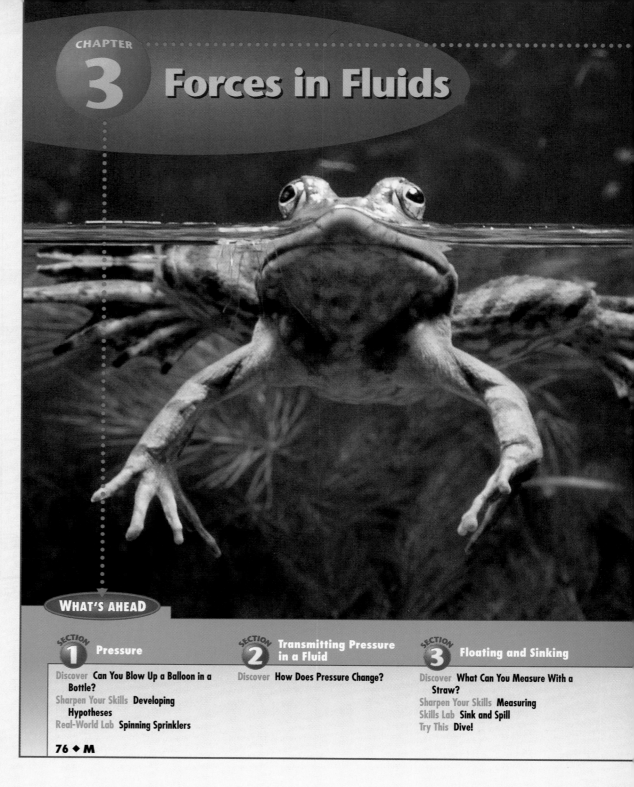

CHAPTER 3

Forces in Fluids

WHAT'S AHEAD

SECTION 1 Pressure

Discover **Can You Blow Up a Balloon in a Bottle?**
Sharpen Your Skills **Developing Hypotheses**
Real-World Lab **Spinning Sprinklers**

SECTION 2 Transmitting Pressure in a Fluid

Discover **How Does Pressure Change?**

SECTION 3 Floating and Sinking

Discover **What Can You Measure With a Straw?**
Sharpen Your Skills **Measuring**
Skills Lab **Sink and Spill**
Try This **Dive!**

76 ◆ M

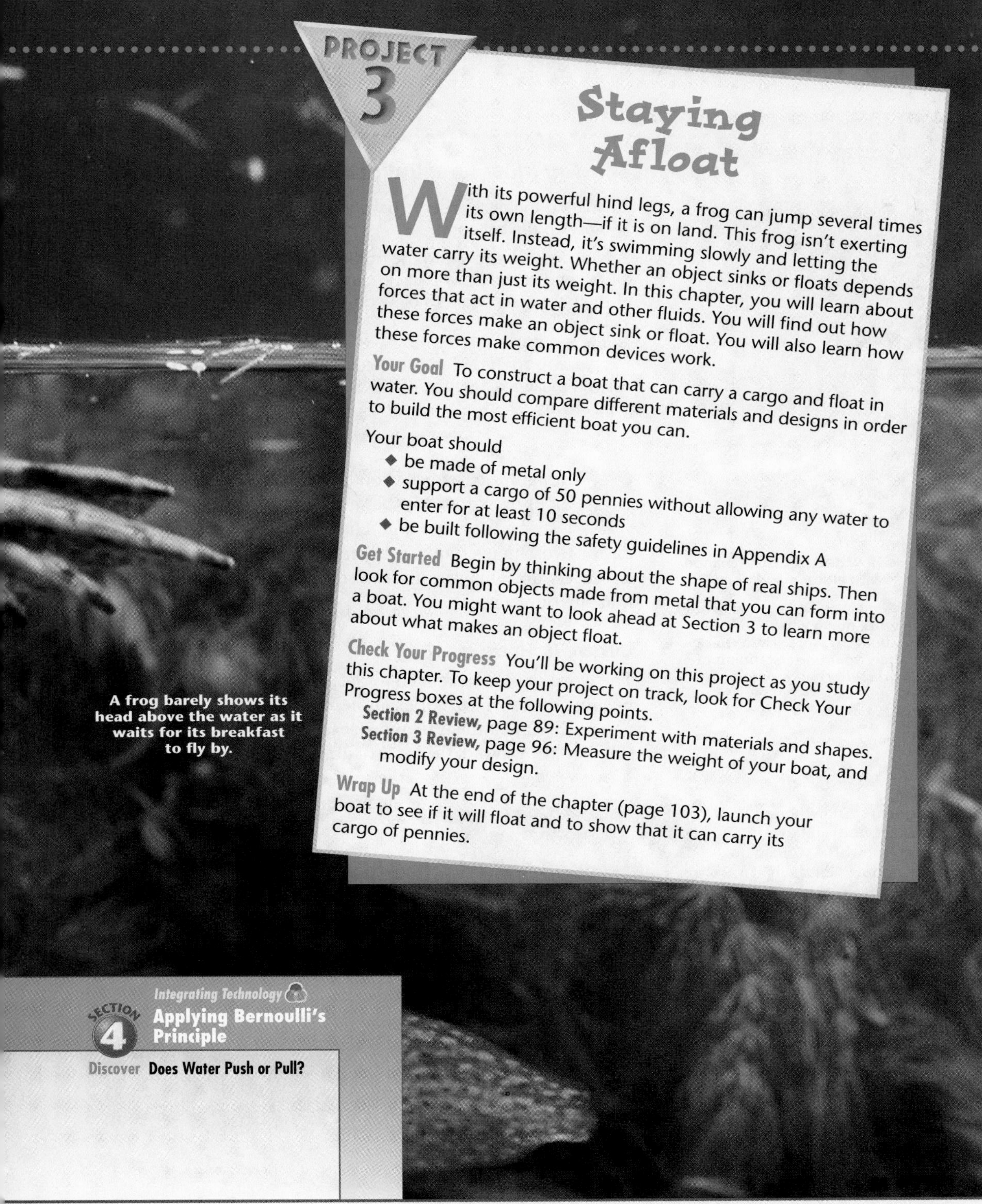

PROJECT 3
Staying Afloat

With its powerful hind legs, a frog can jump several times its own length—if it is on land. This frog isn't exerting itself. Instead, it's swimming slowly and letting the water carry its weight. Whether an object sinks or floats depends on more than just its weight. In this chapter, you will learn about forces that act in water and other fluids. You will find out how these forces make an object sink or float. You will also learn how these forces make common devices work.

Your Goal To construct a boat that can carry a cargo and float in water. You should compare different materials and designs in order to build the most efficient boat you can.

Your boat should
- be made of metal only
- support a cargo of 50 pennies without allowing any water to enter for at least 10 seconds
- be built following the safety guidelines in Appendix A

Get Started Begin by thinking about the shape of real ships. Then look for common objects made from metal that you can form into a boat. You might want to look ahead at Section 3 to learn more about what makes an object float.

Check Your Progress You'll be working on this project as you study this chapter. To keep your project on track, look for Check Your Progress boxes at the following points.
Section 2 Review, page 89: Experiment with materials and shapes.
Section 3 Review, page 96: Measure the weight of your boat, and modify your design.

Wrap Up At the end of the chapter (page 103), launch your boat to see if it will float and to show that it can carry its cargo of pennies.

Integrating Technology
SECTION 4 Applying Bernoulli's Principle
Discover Does Water Push or Pull?

A frog barely shows its head above the water as it waits for its breakfast to fly by.

Program Resources

- **Teaching Resources** Chapter 3 Project Teacher Notes, pp. 64–65; Chapter 3 Project Overview and Worksheets, pp. 66–69; Chapter 3 Project Scoring Rubric, p. 70

Launching the Project Fill a 500-mL beaker halfway with water. Place the beaker where all students can see it. Choose a laboratory cork and a small stone that have the same mass. Ask: **What will happen when these are dropped in the water?** *(Many students will predict that the stone will sink and the cork will float.)* Demonstrate by placing the cork and the stone in the water. Ask students to explain why the stone sank. *(At the beginning of this chapter, most students will say that the stone is heavier rather than denser.)* Place the stone and the cork on a balance to demonstrate that they are the same weight. Explain to students that very heavy things can still float if they are shaped to hold a lot of air. Explain to students that in the Chapter 3 Project, they will design and test boats out of metal that can carry a cargo of 50 pennies without sinking. To help students get started, hand out Chapter 3 Project Overview and Worksheets, pages 66–69 in Teaching Resources. You may also wish to pass out the Chapter 3 Project Scoring Rubric, page 70, at this time.

Performance Assessment

Use the Chapter 3 Project Scoring Rubric to assess students' work. Students will be assessed on
- how well the boat meets the size and material specifications;
- how well they document the testing procedure and observations;
- how well they revise the design of the boat based on the results of testing;
- how well the boat performs;
- the clarity and organization of the presentation to the class.

Pressure

Objectives

After completing the lesson, students will be able to
- ◆ define and calculate pressure;
- ◆ recognize that pressure decreases at higher altitudes and increases at greater depths;
- ◆ identify and explain examples of balanced pressures.

Key Terms pressure, pascal, fluid

1 Engage/Explore

Activating Prior Knowledge

Have students take turns placing one hand inside a plastic bag and plunging the covered hand into clean water at room temperature. The water should be in a container deep enough for students to submerge their arms up to the elbow and the plastic bag should be long enough to cover the student's arm to above the elbow. A new garbage can and a tall kitchen bag would work well. Ask: **What did it feel like?** *(Most students will say that the water exerted pressure on their arms.)* **How did the plastic bag affect what you felt?** *(The bag allowed students to feel pressure without feeling the water on their skin.)*

Discover Activity

Skills Focus developing hypotheses
Materials *small balloon, 2 L plastic bottle, straw*
Time 10 minutes
Tips Make sure the mouth of the balloon is outside the bottle. Caution students not to hold the straw near their eyes in Step 2.
Expected Outcome In Step 1 the balloon will inflate until it seals the neck of the bottle. With the straw, the balloon will continue to inflate easily.
Think It Over Blowing up the balloon compressed the air trapped inside the bottle, making it difficult to blow the balloon up any farther. Inserting the straw allowed air inside the bottle to escape.

Section 1 Pressure

Discover Activity

Can You Blow Up a Balloon in a Bottle?

1. Holding the neck, insert a balloon into an empty bottle. Try to blow up the balloon.
2. Now insert a straw into the bottle, next to the balloon. Keep one end of the straw sticking out of the container as shown in the photo. Try again to blow up the balloon.

Think It Over
Developing Hypotheses Did holding the straw next to the balloon make a difference? If it did, develop a hypothesis to explain why.

Guide for Reading
- ◆ What causes pressure in fluids?
- ◆ How does pressure change with altitude and depth?

Reading Tip **Before you read, write down what you know about pressure. Then check how your understanding of pressure changes as you read.**

Think of the last time you heard a friend say "I'm under a lot of pressure!" Maybe she was talking about having two tests on the same day. That sort of pressure is over in a day or two. But everyone is under another kind of pressure that never lets up. This pressure, as you will learn, is due to the air that surrounds you!

What Is Pressure?

The word *pressure* is related to the word *press.* It refers to a force pushing on a surface. For example, when you lean against a wall, you push against the wall and so exert pressure on it. When you stand on the ground, the force of gravity pulls you downward. So the soles of your shoes push down on the ground and exert pressure on it.

Figure 1 Snowshoes make it easier to travel in deep snow. The woman on the right wishes she had a pair.

Reading Strategies

Reading Tip Before students read the section, have them create charts with three columns, with the headings *What I Know, What I Want to Know,* and *What I Learned.* Have students fill in the first two columns with information and questions about pressure. As students read the section, have them fill in the third column. Invite volunteers to share the information on their charts.

Study and Comprehension Pair students. Give one student in each pair a notecard that says, *Describe what causes pressure in fluids.* Give the other student a card that says, *Tell how pressure changes with altitude and depth.* Have students review the section. Encourage them to make notes on information that relates to the instructions on their notecards. Then direct partners to take turns giving oral summaries of the information called for on their notecards.

Force and Pressure Suppose you try to walk on top of deep snow. Most likely you will sink into the snow, much as the woman on the right in Figure 1. But if you walk with snowshoes, you will be able to walk without sinking. The downward force you exert on the snow—your weight—doesn't change. Your weight is the same whether you wear boots or snowshoes. So what's the difference?

The difference is the size of the area over which your weight is distributed. When your weight is distributed over the smaller area of the soles of your boots, you sink. When your weight is distributed over the much larger area of the snowshoes, you don't sink. The larger area results in less downward pressure on the snow. So force and pressure are closely related, but they are not the same thing.

Calculating Pressure The relationship of force, area, and pressure is summarized by this formula.

$$Pressure = \frac{Force}{Area}$$

Pressure is equal to the force exerted on a surface divided by the total area over which the force is exerted. Force is measured in newtons (N). When area is measured in square meters (m^2), the SI unit of pressure is the newton per square meter (N/m^2). This unit of pressure is also called the **pascal** (Pa): $1\ N/m^2 = 1\ Pa$.

A smaller unit of measure for area is often more practical to use, such as a square centimeter instead of a square meter. When square centimeters are used, the unit of pressure is N/cm^2.

Area

Area is the measure of a surface. The area of a rectangle is found by multiplying the length by the width. The area of the rectangle below is $2\ cm \times 3\ cm$, or $6\ cm^2$.

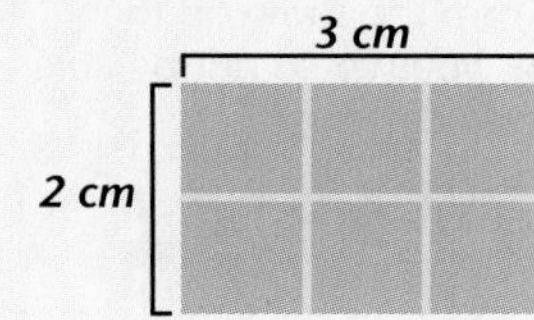

Notice that area is written as cm^2. This is read as "square centimeter."

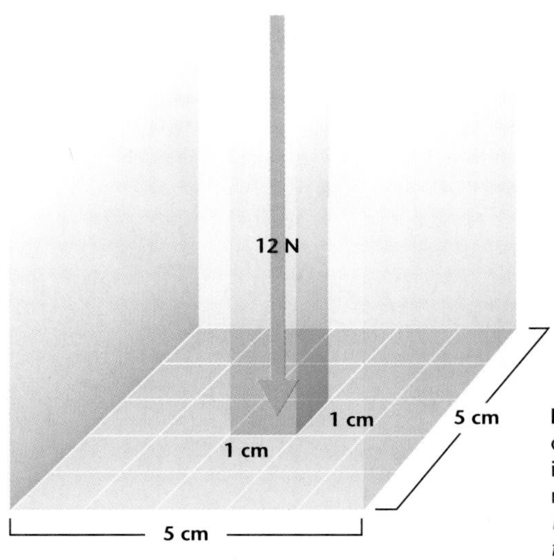

Figure 2 The force a fluid exerts on each square centimeter in the illustration is 12 N. So the resulting pressure is $12\ N/cm^2$. *Problem Solving What is the total force on the entire bottom surface?*

2 Facilitate

What Is Pressure?

Building Inquiry Skills: Controlling Variables

Materials *modeling clay; assortment of rigid container lids; waxed paper; 100-g and 500-g masses or other small, heavy objects*
Time 15 minutes

Organize students into small groups and have them spread a 1.0 cm layer of modeling clay onto sheets of waxed paper. Show students lids from bottled drinks, baby food jars, or similar containers, and ask them to predict which lids will leave deeper dents. Students should place a lid on the clay, set the 100-g mass on top, and observe how the clay looks after 5 seconds. Ask: **Did smaller lids exert more or less pressure?** *(Smaller lids left a deeper mark; they exerted more pressure under the same force.)* Repeat the activity with a heavier mass and compare the results. **learning modality: kinesthetic**

Math TOOLBOX

ACTIVITY

Time 15 minutes
Tips Draw a 2 cm × 3 cm rectangle on an overhead projector and divide it into 1-cm squares. Have students count the squares to verify that the rectangle is $6\ cm^2$. Then have students find the areas of several rectangular objects.

Ongoing Assessment

Skills Check Have students perform the following calculations:

- A solid block of wood has a square base 1 m × 1 m and weighs 5,000 N. How much pressure does it exert on the floor underneath. *(Pressure = 5,000 N/1 m² = 5,000 Pa)*
- A baseball strikes a catcher's mitt with a force of 200 N. If the area the ball strikes is 0.003 m², what is the pressure exerted on the mitt? *(Pressure = 200 N/0.003 m² = 66,667 Pa)*

Program Resources

- **Teaching Resources** 3-1 Lesson Plan, p. 71; 3-1 Section Summary, p. 72

Answers to Self-Assessment

Caption Question

Figure 2 300 N ($12\ N/cm^2 \times 5\ cm \times 5\ cm$) = $12\ N/cm^2 \times 25\ cm^2$ = 300 N

Media and Technology

Audiotapes English-Spanish Summary 3-1

Fluid Pressure

Addressing Naive Conceptions

Some students may think that only liquids are fluids. Have students partially blow up one balloon and fill a second balloon partway with water. Both balloons should be tied. Have students squeeze the balloons and observe what happens. Ask: **What happens to the fluid inside the air-filled balloon when it is squeezed?** *(The air moves or flows from one side to the other.)* **What happens to the fluid inside the water-filled balloon?** *(The water moves or flows from one side to the other.)* Guide students to infer that both the gas and the liquid are fluids because they flow. **learning modality: kinesthetic**

Building Inquiry Skills: Relating Cause and Effect

Ask students: **If you decreased the number of molecules in a gas and kept the gas in the same container, what would happen to the pressure?** *(It would decrease. The force of fewer molecules would be added to make up the pressure exerted by the gas.)* **learning modality: logical/mathematical**

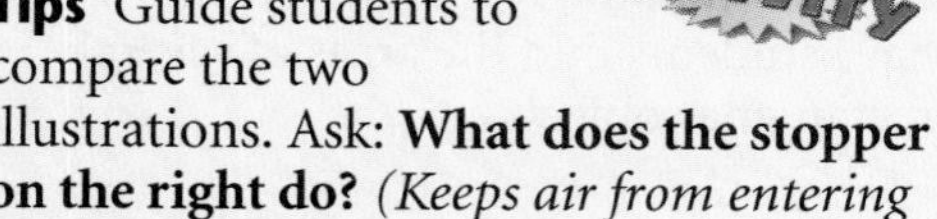

Developing Hypotheses

Time 10 minutes
Tips Guide students to compare the two illustrations. Ask: **What does the stopper on the right do?** *(Keeps air from entering the bottle)*
Expected Outcome A typical hypothesis states that if the bottle is stopped, then the stopper prevents air pressure from pushing down on the fluid so that the fluid can rise up into the straw.
Extend Challenge students to explain why it is necessary to pierce the lid of a large juice can in two places to make the juice pour out easily. **learning modality: visual**

Developing Hypotheses

If you took a sip from the straw on the left, you would be able to drink the lemonade. But if you took a sip from the straw on the right, you would not be able to quench your thirst.

What is the difference between the two illustrations? What can you conclude about how you drink through a straw? Write a hypothesis that explains why you can drink through one straw and not the other.

You can produce a lower pressure by increasing the area a force acts on. Or you can work the other way around. You can produce a much higher pressure by decreasing the area a force acts on. For instance, the blades of ice skates have a very small surface area. They exert a much higher pressure on the ice than ordinary shoes would.

Fluid Pressure

In this chapter, you will learn about the pressure exerted by fluids. A **fluid** is a substance whose shape can easily change. As a result, a fluid is able to flow. Both liquids and gases have this property. Air, helium, water, and oil are all fluids.

Fluids exert pressure against the surfaces they touch. To understand how fluids exert forces on surfaces, you must think about the particles that make up the fluid. Fluids, like all matter, are made up of molecules. These molecules are tiny particles that are much too small to be seen using your eyes or even a good microscope. One liter of water contains about 33 trillion trillion molecules (that's 33 followed by 24 zeros)!

In fluids, molecules are constantly moving in all directions. In air, for example, molecules are moving around at high speeds. They are constantly colliding with each other and with any surface that they meet.

As each molecule collides with a surface, it exerts a force on the surface. **All of the forces exerted by the individual molecules in a fluid add together to make up the pressure exerted by the fluid.** The number of particles is so large that you can consider the fluid as if it were not made up of individual particles. Thus fluid pressure is the total force exerted by the fluid divided by the area over which the force is exerted.

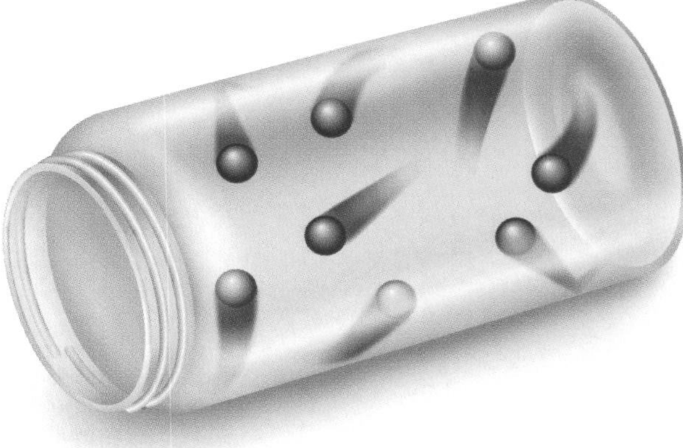

Figure 3 In a gas, molecules move at different speeds in all directions. As they hit surfaces, the molecules exert forces on those surfaces. The total force divided by the area of the surface gives the pressure of the gas. *Inferring Do you think that the pressure inside the jar is the same as the pressure outside the jar? How can you tell?*

Background

Facts and Figures The fluids in the human body exert pressure that balances the pressure of Earth's atmosphere. In order to travel beyond Earth, astronauts have to wear special pressurized suits to balance the pressure of their bodies. Without these pressurized suits, their body fluids would begin to boil and evaporate.

Because the atmosphere in the Space Shuttle can be kept at a constant pressure, shuttle passengers do not have to wear suits. In fact, they usually wear comfortable clothes or flight suits. During launch and re-entry, however, cabin pressure may drop, so astronauts on shuttles wear partially-pressurized suits. These suits contain air bladders that automatically fill with air to maintain pressure on the astronauts' bodies.

On a spacewalk, astronauts are no longer protected by the controlled pressure of the shuttle. Because there is no atmosphere in space, spacewalking astronauts must wear suits that maintain a pressure high enough to balance the pressure of the astronauts' bodies.

Fluid Pressure All Around

Hold your hand out in front of you, palm up. You are holding up a weight equivalent to that of a washing machine. How can this be? You are surrounded by a fluid that presses down on you all the time. This fluid is the mixture of gases that makes up Earth's atmosphere. The pressure exerted by the air is usually referred to as air pressure, or atmospheric pressure.

Air exerts pressure because it has mass. You may forget that air has mass, but each cubic meter of air around you has a mass of about 1 kilogram. The force of gravity on this mass produces air pressure. The pressure from the weight of air in the atmosphere is great because the atmosphere is over 100 kilometers high.

Air pressure at sea level is about 10.13 N/cm^2. Think about a square measuring one centimeter by one centimeter on the palm of your hand. Air is pushing against that small square with a force of 10.13 newtons. The total surface area of your hand is probably about 100 square centimeters. So the total force due to the air pressure on your hand is about 1,000 newtons.

☑ *Checkpoint* *Why does the atmosphere exert pressure on you?*

Balanced Pressures

How could your hand possibly support the weight of the atmosphere when you don't feel a thing? In a fluid that is not moving, pressure at a given point is exerted equally in all directions. Air is pushing down on the palm of your hand with 10.13 N/cm^2 of pressure. It is also pushing up on the back of your hand with the same 10.13 N/cm^2 of pressure. These two pressures balance each other exactly.

INTEGRATING LIFE SCIENCE So why aren't you crushed even though the air pressure outside your body is so great? The reason again has to do with a balance of pressures. Pressure inside your body balances the air pressure outside your body. But where does the pressure inside your body come from? It comes from fluids within your body. Some parts of your body, such as your lungs, sinus cavities, and your inner ear, contain air. Other parts of your body, such as your cells and your blood, contain liquids.

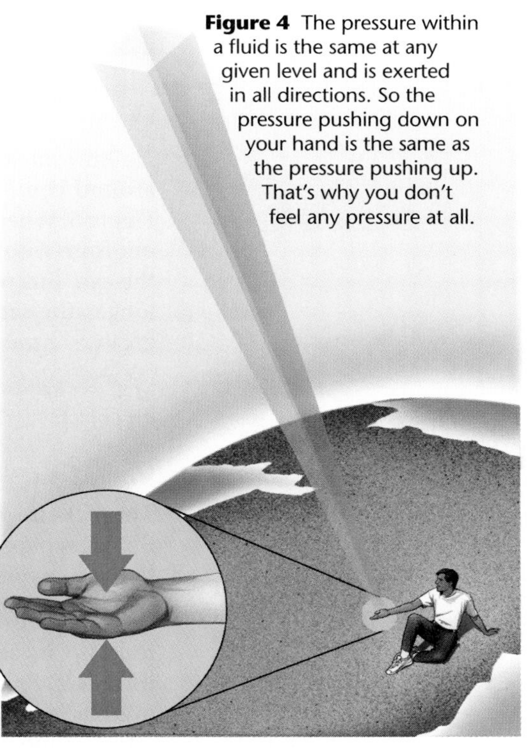

Figure 4 The pressure within a fluid is the same at any given level and is exerted in all directions. So the pressure pushing down on your hand is the same as the pressure pushing up. That's why you don't feel any pressure at all.

Fluid Pressure All Around

Demonstration

Materials *unopened jar with cap that says "Safety button will pop up if seal is broken."*

Time 10 minutes

Explain that the pressure inside the jar is less than the pressure outside. Before the seal is broken, the greater pressure outside the jar pushes the cap down. Have students press the button on the jar, noting that it does not move. Direct them to listen closely as you open the jar. Ask them to infer what happens when the seal is broken. *(The inside pressure becomes the same as the outside pressure.)* Ask: **How could you tell the seal was broken?** *(The button moved; you could hear air rush into the jar.)* **learning modality: visual**

Balanced Pressures

Integrating Life Science

Point out that astronauts and deep-sea divers explore areas where the pressure is much greater or smaller than normal atmospheric pressure. Encourage interested students to contact a local diving shop or certified diving instructor to find out how the special equipment worn by deep-sea divers controls the pressure. **learning modality: verbal**

Program Resources

- **Interdisciplinary Exploration Series** "Riddles of the Pharaohs," p. 33
- **Science Explorer Series** *Human Biology and Health,* Chapter 5, has more information about respiration.

Answers to Self-Assessment

Caption Question

Figure 3 Yes. The jar is open so that the molecules are free to move in and out of the jar, making the pressure equal.

☑ *Checkpoint*

The atmosphere is a large mass of air, and the force of gravity on the air above an object produces air pressure on the object.

Ongoing Assessment

Drawing Have students draw diagrams showing beakers of water and label the fluid pressures acting on the beakers. *(Student diagrams should include the fluid pressure of water on the bottom and sides of the beaker, and air pressure on the surface of the water and on the outside of the beaker.)*

Balanced Pressures, continued

Real-Life Learning

Materials *daily newspapers from the previous week or so*
Time 10 minutes

Have students save weather maps from a local newspaper for one week. Point out the high and low pressure areas marked on the maps. Explain that the air pressure is measured in inches of mercury, which refers to how high the air can push a column of mercury. Have students analyze their maps and compare the pressure readings to the weather conditions. Have pairs of students prepare a weather forecast and present it to the class. Encourage interested students to participate in weather school programs offered by local weather service offices or television stations. **learning modality: logical/ mathematical**

Variations in Fluid Pressure

Using the Visuals: Figure 6

Materials $\frac{1}{2}$ *gallon milk containers or similar containers*
Time 20 minutes

Have students examine the water streams in the photograph. Ask: **How can you tell which stream has more pressure?** *(The one with more pressure will have more force. It will be able to move farther.)* Make a vertical line of equally spaced holes in the side of a plastic milk jug. The easiest way to make the holes is to use tongs to hold a nail in a bunsen burner flame for a few moments, then poke the heated nail through the plastic side of the jug. Use caution when heating the nail. Fill the jug with water (while holding it over the sink) and have students draw the escaping streams of water and label them from least to greatest pressure. *(Students' drawings should show the greatest pressure at the bottom.)* **learning modality: visual**

Figure 5 A vacuum pump removes the air from a metal can. The pump produces dramatic results in a few moments. *Inferring Can you think of a way to crush the can without pumping out the air inside it? Explain why your idea works.*

Are you still having trouble believing that the air pressure around you is so high? Take a look at the metal container in Figure 5. When the can is filled with air, the air pressure pushing out from within the can balances the air pressure pushing in on the can. But when the air is removed from the can, there is no longer the same pressure pushing from within the can. The greater air pressure outside the can crushes it.

☑ *Checkpoint* ***What is the effect of balanced pressures acting on an object?***

Variations in Fluid Pressure

The pressure of a fluid is the same at any given level in the fluid. But what happens to pressure as you move up to a higher elevation or down to a deeper depth within a fluid?

Pressure and Elevation Have your ears ever "popped" as you rode up in an elevator? **Air pressure decreases as elevation increases.** Remember that air pressure at a given point results from the weight of air above that point. At higher elevations, there is less air above and therefore less weight of air to support.

Background

Integrating Science Scuba divers have to be careful not to rise to the surface too quickly. When atmospheric pressure decreases rapidly, humans can experience decompression sickness, a dangerous condition also known as *the bends.* This occurs when gases in their tissues come out of solution. Although oxygen is absorbed quickly, nitrogen bubbles form in the blood and cause severe muscle pain.

A different condition, known as *altitude sickness,* can occur when a person travels to high altitudes. This reaction can be severe and, unless the person returns to low altitude, possibly fatal. A person with altitude sickness may experience breathlessness, racing heartbeat, giddiness, headache, swelling of the legs and feet, gastrointestinal upsets, and weakness.

The fact that air pressure decreases as you move up in elevation explains why your ears pop. When the air pressure outside your body changes, the air pressure inside will adjust too, but more slowly. For a moment, the air pressure behind your eardrums is greater than it is outside. Your body releases this pressure with a "pop" so that the pressures are once again balanced.

Pressure and Depth Fluid pressure depends on depth. The pressure at one meter below the surface of a swimming pool is the same as the pressure one meter below the surface of a lake. But if you dive deeper into the water in either case, pressure becomes greater as you descend. The deeper you swim, the greater the pressure you feel. **Water pressure increases as depth increases.**

As with air, you can think of water pressure being due to the weight of the water above a particular point. At greater depths, there is more water above and therefore more weight to support. In addition, air in the atmosphere pushes down on the water. Therefore, the total pressure at a given point beneath the water results from the weight of the water plus the weight of the air above it. In the deepest parts of the ocean, the pressure is more than 1,000 times the air pressure you experience every day.

Figure 6 The strength of the stream of water coming out of the holes in the jug depends on the water pressure at each level. *Interpreting Photos At which hole is the pressure greatest?*

Section 1 Review

1. Explain how fluids exert pressure.
2. How does air pressure change as you move farther away from the surface of Earth? Explain why it changes.
3. Why aren't deep-sea fish crushed by the tremendous pressure of the water above them?
4. **Thinking Critically Applying Concepts** Why do you think an astronaut must wear a pressurized suit in space?
5. **Thinking Critically Comparing and Contrasting** Suppose a woman wearing high-heeled shoes has a mass of 50 kg and an elephant has a mass of 5,000 kg. Explain how the woman can exert pressure on a floor about three times the pressure exerted by the elephant.

Science at Home

Fill a small plastic container—a bottle or a cup—to the brim with water. Place a piece of cardboard over the entire opening of the container. Ask your family to predict what would happen if the container were turned upside down. Test the predictions by slowly turning the container upside down while holding the cardboard in place. Let go of the cardboard and see what happens. Without touching the cardboard, turn the container on its side. Use air pressure to explain why the cardboard stays in place and why the water stays in the container.

3 Assess

Section 1 Review Answers

1. The molecules of a fluid exert force when they collide with each other and with surfaces. The fluid pressure is the total force exerted divided by the area.
2. It decreases. As you move farther away from the Earth, there is less fluid above you. Less fluid has less weight, so pressure decreases.
3. Deep-sea fish are not crushed because their internal fluids and organs are at a pressure similar to those of their surroundings.
4. Space contains no air, so it exerts no air pressure on the astronaut's body, Astronauts wear pressurized suits to balance the pressure inside their bodies.
5. A woman wearing high-heeled shoes exerts force over a small area while an elephant exerts force over a large area. Because pressure depends on area, the woman can exert more pressure with less force.

Science at Home

Suggest that students first practice this activity outdoors or over a sink. Make sure there are no air bubbles in the cup with the cardboard. Encourage interested students to present this activity to their families as an illusion. The cardboard will remain on the cup and the water will remain inside. Students should explain that the air pushing up on the cardboard exerts a greater pressure than the water pushing down.

Program Resources

◆ **Teaching Resources** 3-1 Review and Reinforce, p. 73; 3-1 Enrich, p. 74

Media and Technology

Interactive Student Tutorial CD-ROM M-3

Answers to Self-Assessment

Caption Questions

Figure 5 The can will be crushed if enough additional pressure is applied from the outside, for example by putting it deep underwater.

Figure 6 The bottom hole has the greatest pressure.

Checkpoint

Balanced pressures cancel each other out.

Performance Assessment

Writing Have students write and illustrate a story describing the changes in fluid pressure experienced by a diver as he or she rises from the ocean floor to the surface. *(Students' stories should describe a decrease in water pressure as the diver rises.)*

Real-World Lab

How It Works

Spinning Sprinkler

Preparing for Inquiry

Key Concept The operation of a rotating lawn sprinkler can be explained by examining the factors that affect the pressure of water escaping from a can.

Skills Objectives Students will be able to
- make a model of a sprinkler;
- design an experiment to test factors affecting water pressure;
- control variables such as the size and number of the holes in the can.

Time 45 minutes

Advance Planning Obtain fishing line and nails. Rinse the soda cans to remove any residue that will attract insects. Obtain a sample sprinkler, or make a diagram of one.

Alternative Materials The lab can be done using clean one-quart or half-gallon milk containers. Follow the same procedure as with the cans, but have students count the number of spins in 30 seconds because the larger containers will not spin as fast as the cans.

Guiding Inquiry

Invitation Bring in a lawn sprinkler that operates by forcing water in one direction while spinning in the opposite direction. Ask: **What factors will affect how fast the sprinkler spins?** *(Pressure of escaping water, size and number of holes)* If a sprinkler of this type is not available, draw a diagram of one on the board and have the same discussion.

Introducing the Procedure Ask students to predict what factors will affect the can's rate of spinning based on the discussion about the sprinkler. *(Amount of water in the can, size and number of nail holes)*

Real-World Lab

How It Works

Spinning Sprinklers

There's nothing like running through a lawn sprinkler on a hot summer day. One type of sprinkler uses the pressure of the escaping water to cause it to spin. Its operation is similar to an ancient device known as Hero's engine. Hero's engine used the pressure of escaping steam to cause a sphere to spin.

Problem

What factors affect the speed of rotation of a lawn sprinkler?

Skills Focus

making models, designing experiments, controlling variables

Materials

6 empty soda cans with tabs attached
fishing line, 30 cm
waterproof marker
wide-mouth jar or beaker
stopwatch or clock with second hand
small nail
medium nail
large nail
large basin to catch water

Procedure  

1. Fill the jar with enough water to completely cover a can. Place it in the basin.
2. Bend up the tab of a can and tie the end of a length of fishing line to it. **CAUTION:** *Be careful not to cut yourself on the edge of the can opening.*
3. Place a mark on the can to help you keep track of how many times the can spins.
4. Using the small nail, make a hole in the side of the can about 1 cm up from the bottom. Poke the nail straight in. Then twist the nail until it makes a right angle with the radius of the can. See the diagram below. **CAUTION:** *Nails are sharp and should be used only to puncture the cans.*

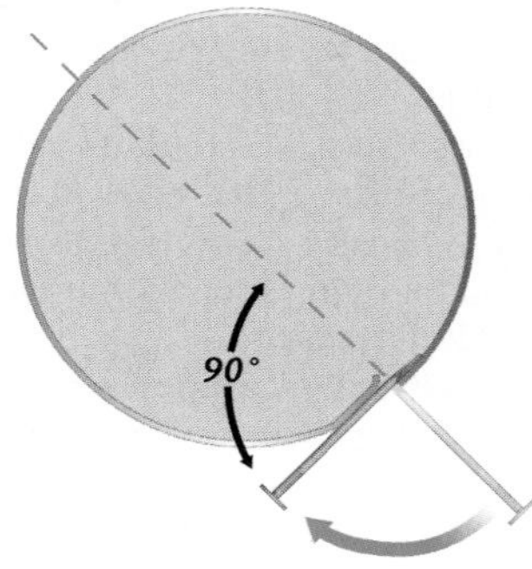

Sample Data Table

Nail Size	# of Holes	# of spins in 15 seconds
small	1	3
small	2	13
medium	1	18
medium	2	21
large	1	16 in 10 sec
large	2	11 in 6 sec

Nail Size	# of Holes	# of spins in 15 seconds
small	1	
small	2	
medium	1	
medium	2	
large	1	
large	2	

5. Submerge the can in the jar and fill the can to the top with water.
6. Quickly lift the can with the fishing line so that it is 1–2 cm above the water level in the jar. Count how many spins the can completes in 15 seconds. Record the result.
7. Design a way to investigate how the size of the hole affects the number of spins made by the can. Propose a hypothesis and then test the relationship. Record your results.
8. Design a way to investigate how the number of holes affects the number of spins made by the can. Propose a hypothesis and then test the relationship. Record your results.

Analyze and Conclude

1. How does the size of the hole affect the rate of spin of the can?
2. How does the number of holes affect the rate of spin of the can?
3. Explain the motion of the can in terms of water pressure.
4. Explain the motion of the can in terms of Newton's third law of motion (Chapter 2).
5. How could you make the can spin in the opposite direction?
6. What will cause the can to stop spinning?
7. You made a hole in the can at about 1 cm above the bottom of the can. Predict what would happen if you made the hole at a higher point on the can. How could you test your prediction?
8. **Apply** Use your observations to explain why a spinning lawn sprinkler spins.

Getting Involved

Many sprinkler systems use water pressure to spin the sprinklers. Examine one of these sprinklers to see the size, direction, and number of holes. What would happen if you put a second sprinkler in line with the first? If possible, try it.

Safety

Make sure students are careful to avoid sharp edges on the cans. Nails are sharp, make sure students use caution when handling the nails. For a more secure grip on the fishing line, tie a loop at the top. Students should be sure to hold the cans over the basin as the water escapes to prevent the floor from becoming slippery. Review the safety guidelines in Appendix A.

Program Resources

- **Teaching Resources** Chapter 3 Real-World Lab, pp. 87–89

Troubleshooting the Experiment

- Students must be sure to hold the cans over the large basin as the water escapes.
- The angle of the holes must be the same for all trials, as shown in the diagram.
- If the can drains in less than 15 seconds for any trial, it may be necessary to modify the procedure (fewer or smaller holes in the can, or more water in the can) and repeat that trial.
- Be sure to use new cans when investigating what might happen if the hole angles are reversed.

Expected Outcome

Results should illustrate that the more holes there are in the can, and the larger the holes are, the faster the can spins.

Analyze and Conclude

1. The larger the hole, the faster the rate of spin.
2. The greater the number of holes, the faster the rate of spin.
3. The water exerts a pressure due to its weight. The force of the water escaping from the hole in the can causes the can to spin in the opposite direction.
4. A force equal and opposite to the force of the water is exerted on the can, so the can spins in the direction opposite to the direction of the water.
5. Bending the hole in the opposite direction will cause the can to spin in the opposite direction.
6. The can will stop spinning when the water level falls below the holes.
7. Holes made at a higher point on the can will reduce the water pressure, thus reducing the speed of spinning.
8. Students should use Newton's Third Law of Motion to explain why a spinning lawn sprinkler spins. They should explain that the water pressure and the size and number of holes will affect the speed of rotation.

Extending the Inquiry

Getting Involved A second sprinkler on the same line will reduce the pressure in each. The water from the second sprinkler may interfere with the water from the first, so some factors that need to be considered include the distance between sprinklers and the directions of their rotations.

Section 2 Transmitting Pressure in a Fluid

Objectives

After completing the lesson, students will be able to
- ◆ state Pascal's principle and recognize applications of the principle;
- ◆ explain how a hydraulic system works.

Key Terms Pascal's principle, hydraulic devices

1 Engage/Explore

Activating Prior Knowledge

Show students a sealed bag of water. Ask: **What will happen if you squeeze one side of the bag?** *(The water will move to the other side of the bag.)* Encourage students to describe what happens to the fluid in the bag when you push on one part of it. *(It all moves.)*

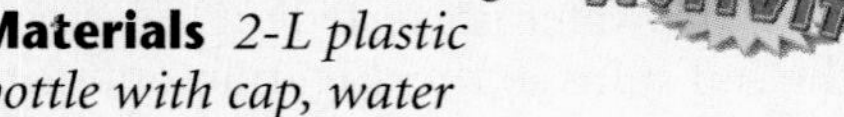

Skills Focus observing
Materials *2-L plastic bottle with cap, water*
Time 10 minutes
Tips Remove the label from the plastic bottle. Remind students to maintain a constant, firm pressure with their left thumbs. Encourage students to push in several different places on the bottle.
Think It Over The water pressure increases when you push in the bottle with your right thumb. You can tell because you can feel the pressure being exerted on your left thumb.

Section 2 Transmitting Pressure in a Fluid

Discover Activity

How Does Pressure Change?

1. Fill an empty two-liter plastic bottle to the top with water. Then screw on the cap tightly. There should be no bubbles in the bottle (or only very small bubbles).
2. Lay the bottle on its side. Pick a spot on the bottle, and push in with your left thumb.
3. With your right thumb, push in fairly hard on a spot at the other end of the bottle, as shown in the diagram. What does your left thumb feel?
4. Pick another spot on the bottle for your left thumb and repeat Step 3.

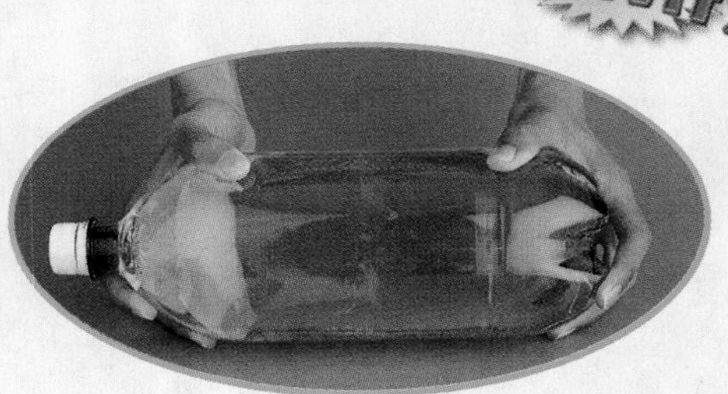

Think It Over

Observing When you push in with your right thumb, does the water pressure in the bottle increase, decrease, or remain the same? How do you know?

Guide for Reading

- ◆ What does Pascal's principle say about an increase in fluid pressure?
- ◆ How does a hydraulic device work?

Reading Tip **As you read, make a list of devices that apply Pascal's principle. Write one sentence describing each device.**

Piercing sirens shatter the morning quiet. Dark smoke rolls into the air. Bright flames shoot from a burning building. Firefighters arrive on the scene. Quickly, with the push of a button, a huge ladder is raised to the top floor. The firefighters climb up the ladder and soon have the blaze under control.

Thanks to equipment on the firetruck, this story has a happy ending. You might be surprised to discover that the truck is capable of using fluids to lift the ladder and its equipment to great heights. As you read on, you'll find out how.

Figure 7 A fire truck uses fluids under high pressure both to lift its ladder and to put out a fire.

Reading Strategies

Reading Tip To provide a structured format for the descriptions, have students write the name of the hydraulic device at the top of a sheet of paper and list the following topics in a column with space to record information as they read: *how input force is applied, how output force is applied, fluid used*

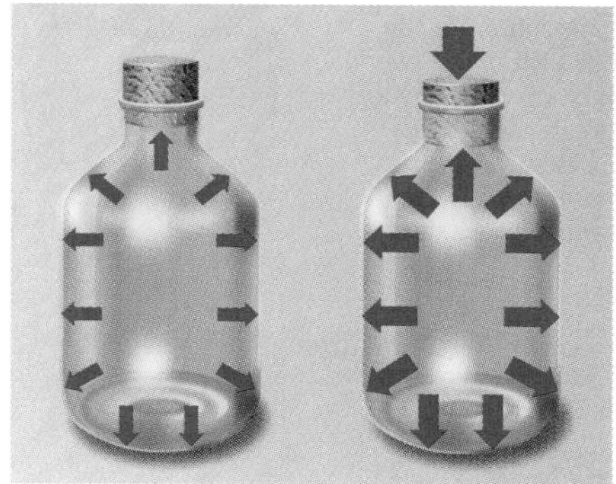

Figure 8 A liquid completely filling a bottle exerts pressure in all directions. When the stopper is pushed farther into the bottle, the pressure increases. *Predicting Suppose you poked a hole in the side of the bottle. What would happen when you pushed down on the stopper? Explain why.*

Pascal's Principle

As you learned in the last section, a fluid exerts pressure on any surface in contact with it. For example, the water in each bottle in Figure 8 exerts pressure on the entire inside surface of the bottle—up, down, and sideways.

What happens if you push the stopper down even farther? The water has nowhere to go, so it presses harder on the inside surface of the bottle. The pressure in the water increases everywhere in the bottle. This is shown by the increased width of the arrows on the right in Figure 8.

Pressure increases by the same amount throughout an enclosed, or confined, fluid. This fact was discovered in the 1600s by a French mathematician named Blaise Pascal. (Pascal's name is used for the unit of pressure.) **When force is applied to a confined fluid, an increase in pressure is transmitted equally to all parts of the fluid.** This relationship is known as **Pascal's principle.**

Force Pumps

What would happen if you increased the pressure at one end of a fluid in a container with a hole at the other end? If you have ever used a squeeze bottle or a tube of toothpaste, you already know what happens. Because it is not confined by the container, the fluid is pushed out of the opening. This simple example shows you how a force pump works. A force pump causes a fluid to move from one place to another by increasing the pressure in the fluid.

Your heart consists of two force pumps. One of them pumps blood to the lungs, where it can pick up oxygen from the air you breathe. This blood, now carrying oxygen, returns to your heart. It is then pumped to the rest of the body by the second pump.

☑ *Checkpoint* *What is the effect on fluid pressure if you press down on the stopper of a bottle full of water?*

Social Studies CONNECTION

The French mathematician and philosopher Blaise Pascal lived from 1623 until 1662. He first became famous for a mechanical calculator he designed before he was 21. He later explored the behavior of fluids, and was a pioneer in the mathematics of probability. Near the end of his life, he wrote about philosophical and religious subjects.

In Your Journal

Create a time line showing when the following people lived and worked: Galileo, Archimedes, Newton, Pascal, and Bernoulli. On your time line, write a brief description of each one's work.

2 Facilitate

Pascal's Principle

Using the Visuals: Figure 8

After students examine the diagram, ask: **As force is applied to the stopper, what happens?** *(Pressure increases inside the bottle and stays the same outside the bottle.)* **What will happen if the force on the stopper continues to increase?** *(The pressure inside will increase and the bottle could break.)* **learning modality: logical/mathematical**

Force Pumps

Real-Life Learning

Invite a nurse or certified CPR instructor to demonstrate the Heimlich maneuver. Explain that the diaphragm is a muscle under the lungs. Exerting force on the diaphragm increases lung pressure. Ask: **How does the Heimlich maneuver help a choking person?** *(It increases the lung pressure and forces the object out of the person's windpipe.)* **learning modality: visual**

Social Studies CONNECTION

Pascal began to write philosophical treatments of religious faith in 1655 and eventually joined a religious group at the monastery of Port Royal. While he continued to write scientific and religious works, they were published in the name of the monastery.

In Your Journal Encourage students to include interesting anecdotes on their time lines. Possible resources include biographies, the Internet, and encyclopedias. **learning modality: verbal**

Ongoing Assessment

Oral Presentation Ask students to identify two force pumps they have used. *(Sample answers include toothpaste tubes or ketchup squeeze bottles.)*

Program Resources

◆ **Teaching Resources** 3-2 Lesson Plan, p. 75; 3-2 Section Summary, p. 76

Media and Technology

Audiotapes English-Spanish Summary 3-2

Answers to Self-Assessment

Caption Question

Figure 8 When you push on the stopper, the water will spurt out of the hole with more force because there is more pressure acting on the water in the bottle.

☑ *Checkpoint*

The pressure increases throughout the water in the bottle.

Using Pascal's Principle

Including All Students

Have students brainstorm a list of English words that use the root *hydr-* (or *hydro*) which means "water." *(Sample: hydrant, hydroelectric, dehydrate, hydrothermal)* Write the words students suggest on the board. Then have volunteers give the dictionary definitions of the words. **limited English proficiency**

Building Inquiry Skills: Making Models

Materials *two different sizes of plastic "air piston" or similar devices, short piece of clear plastic tubing*
Time 20 minutes

ACTIVITY

Turkey basters or other similar devices could also be used in place of the air pistons. Fill the smaller air piston with water. Fill the larger air piston about half way. Attach the plastic tubing to the end of the larger air piston. Squeeze a small amount of water into the tubing. Attach the other end of the plastic tubing to the smaller air piston. The combination is now a working hydraulic system. Either piston can be depressed, forcing water through the tube into the other cylinder. If the larger piston is depressed, the displacement of the smaller piston will be larger. If the smaller piston is depressed, the larger piston will move a smaller distance, but be capable of exerting a larger force. **learning modality: kinesthetic**

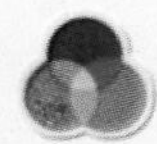

Integrating Life Science

ACTIVITY

You can demonstrate how the tube foot works with a small plastic dropper. Fill the dropper with water, squeeze out most of the water, and let the last drop fall on your skin. Still squeezing the bulb, hold the dropper tip against your wet skin and release it. Air pressure will hold the dropper in place. If you gently pull on the dropper, it will pull up the skin under the tip. **learning modality: visual**

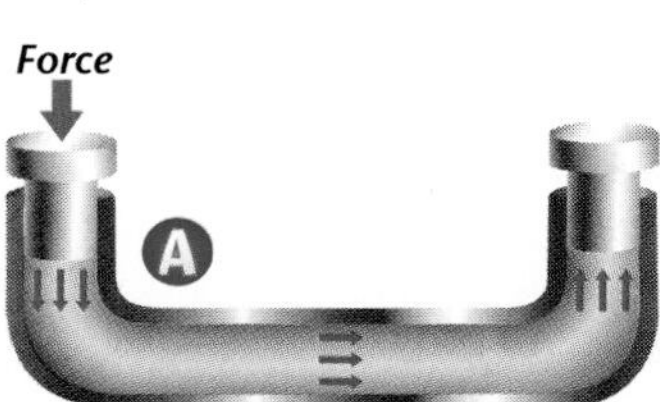

Figure 9 **A.** In a hydraulic device, a force applied to one piston increases the pressure in the fluid.

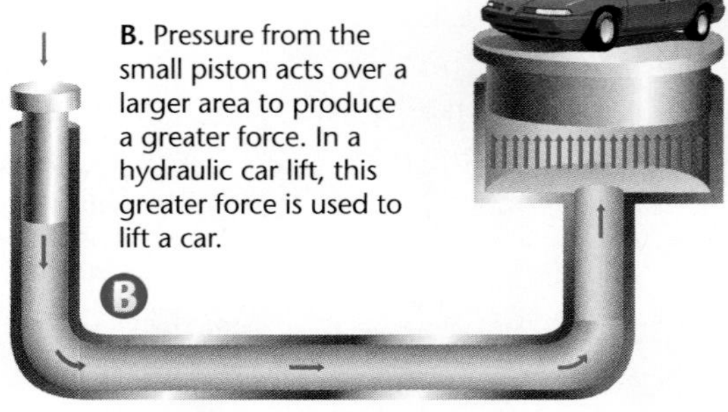

B. Pressure from the small piston acts over a larger area to produce a greater force. In a hydraulic car lift, this greater force is used to lift a car.

Using Pascal's Principle

Suppose you fill the small U-shaped tube shown in Figure 9A with water and push down on the piston on the left side. (A piston is similar to a stopper that can slide up and down inside the tube.) The increase in pressure will be transmitted to the piston on the right.

What can you determine about the force exerted on the right piston? According to Pascal's principle, both pistons will experience the same fluid pressure. If both pistons have the same area, then they will also experience the same force.

Now suppose that the right piston has a greater area than the left piston. For example, the small piston in the U-shaped tube in Figure 9B has an area of 1 square meter. The large piston has an area of 20 square meters. If you push down on the left piston with a force of 500 newtons, the increase in pressure on the fluid is 500 N/m^2. A pressure increase of 500 N/m^2 means that the force on every square meter of the piston's surface increases by 500 newtons. Since the surface area of the right piston is 20 square meters, the total increase in force on the right piston is 10,000 newtons. The push exerted on the left piston is multiplied twenty times on the right piston! Depending on the size of the pistons, you can multiply force by any amount.

Figure 10 The hydraulic brake system of a car multiplies the force exerted on the brake pedal.

Hydraulic Systems **Hydraulic systems** are designed to take advantage of Pascal's principle. **A hydraulic system multiplies a force by applying the force to a small surface area. The increase in pressure is then transmitted to another part of a confined fluid, which pushes on a larger surface area.** In this way, the force is multiplied. A common hydraulic system is used to lift the heavy ladder on a fire truck.

You also rely on Pascal's principle every time you ride in a car. The brake system of a car is a hydraulic system. A brake system with disc brakes is shown in simplified form in Figure 10. When a driver pushes down on

Background

Facts and Figures None of the hydraulic devices in modern aircraft and automobiles would have been possible without the work of Pascal. In fact, engineers began to develop many applications based on Pascal's work with fluids in the late 1800s.

One of the first hydraulic systems was built in 1882 in London, England. This system delivered pressurized water throughout the city in a system of pipes, provided the power to run factory machinery. In 1906, sailors on the *U.S.S. Virginia* used an oil hydraulic system to raise and lower the guns. The biggest advance came in the 1920s, when individual hydraulic units were developed. These units had a pump, controls, and a motor. They allowed people to develop hydraulic systems for transportation, farm machinery, and spacecraft.

Figure 11 A sea star exerts pressure on fluids in its cavities in order to move around. *Classifying Why are the tube feet considered part of a hydraulic device?*

the brake pedal, he or she pushes a piston. The piston exerts pressure on the brake fluid. The increased pressure is transmitted through the brake lines to pistons within the wheels of the car. Each of these pistons pushes on a brake pad. The brake pad then rubs against the brake disc, and the wheel's motion is slowed down by the force of friction. Because the brake system multiplies force, a person can stop a very large car with only a light tap on the brake pedal.

Pascal's Principle in Nature The sea stars shown in Figure 11 INTEGRATING LIFE SCIENCE use a natural hydraulic system called the water vascular system in order to move. Sea stars have rows of small suckers at the ends of their hollow tube feet. Each tube foot is filled with fluid. A valve is located at each foot. When the valve closes, the foot becomes a hydraulic container. As the sea star contracts different muscles, it changes the pressure in the fluid. The change in pressure causes the tube foot to either push down or pull up on the sucker. By the coordinated action of all of its tube feet, a sea star is able to move—even to climb straight up rock surfaces!

Section 2 Review

1. Explain Pascal's principle in your own words.
2. How does a hydraulic device multiply force?
3. What fluid is pumped by your heart?
4. **Thinking Critically** **Applying Concepts** How can you increase the force a hydraulic device produces without increasing the size of the force you apply to the small piston?
5. **Thinking Critically** **Comparing and Contrasting** How is the braking system of a car similar to the water vascular system of a sea star?

Check Your Progress

CHAPTER PROJECT 3

Experiment with various metal items in your home to see how they work as boats. Keep in mind that your designs don't have to look like real boats. Experiment with various shapes. Determine how the material and the shape relate to whether or not the boat floats or sinks. What works better: a wide but shallow boat or a narrow but deep boat? Keep a log that describes the material, the shape, and your results.

3 Assess

Section 2 Review Answers

1. If a force is exerted on a confined fluid, the pressure is transferred equally to all parts of the fluid.
2. The pressure on the smaller piston is transferred to the larger one. Because the pressure is the same and the area is larger, the force on the large piston is greater.
3. blood
4. Either decrease the size of the smaller piston, or increase the size of the larger piston.
5. In the brake system, pressure on a small area is transferred to pistons in the car's wheels. The sea star uses muscles to change the pressure in its tube feet so that they can either push up or down on its suckers.

Check Your Progress

CHAPTER PROJECT 3

Encourage students to record sketches of their designs and observations from their tests in their design log. Discuss how to experiment scientifically by altering and testing the effects of one variable at a time. For instance, students making aluminum foil boats might build and test three boats that are different heights but that are identical in every other way. Look for evidence of scientific experimentation in students' design logs.

Program Resources

- **Teaching Resources** 3-2 Review and Reinforce, p. 77; 3-2 Enrich, p. 78
- **Science Explorer Series,** *Animals,* Chapter 2, has more information about sea stars.

Media and Technology

Interactive Student Tutorial CD-ROM M-3

Answers to Self-Assessment

Caption Question

Figure 11 When the tube feet are closed, they enclose a fluid. The sea star moves by exerting pressure on this fluid so that the tube feet act like hydraulic devices.

Performance Assessment

Drawing Challenge students to invent a new hydraulic device. Instruct students to draw their new device on a sheet of notebook paper. Have them use labels and arrows to indicate a force applied to one area of the device and the effect of the force. *(Sample: A device to raise an elevator)*

Students can save their designs in their portfolios.

Floating and Sinking

Objectives

After completing the lesson, students will be able to

- define the buoyant force and its effect;
- state Archimedes' principle;
- explain how the density of an object determines whether it floats or sinks.

Key Terms buoyant force, Archimedes' principle, density

1 Engage/Explore

Activating Prior Knowledge

Fill a large basin with water and show students a variety of common objects, such as soap, blocks of wood, rubber duckies or other toys, cans of diet and regular soda (diet soda will float, regular soda will sink). Ask students to predict whether each object will float or sink. Record their predictions, then have volunteers test their predictions by putting each object into the water. Tell students that in this section, they learn why objects sink and float.

DISCOVER ACTIVITY

Skills Focus predicting
Materials *plastic straw, metric ruler, scissors, waterproof clay, waterproof marker, glass, water, sugar, spoon*
Time 20 minutes
Tips Make sure students place the straw firmly in the clay so that water cannot leak into the straw. Help students realize they should count the marks above the water to take measurements.
Expected Outcome In plain water, the hydrometer will float lower in the water. In sugar water, the hydrometer will float higher out of the water.
Think It Over Students should predict that the hydrometer will float higher out of the water when more sugar is added to the water.

Section 3 Floating and Sinking

DISCOVER ACTIVITY

What Can You Measure With a Straw?

1. Cut a plastic straw to a 10-centimeter length.
2. Use a waterproof marker to make marks on the straw that are 1 centimeter apart.
3. Roll a ball of modeling clay about 1.5 centimeters in diameter. Stick one end of the straw in the clay. You have constructed a hydrometer.
4. Place the hydrometer in a glass of water. If it sinks, remove some clay. About half of the straw should remain above water. Make sure no water gets into the straw.

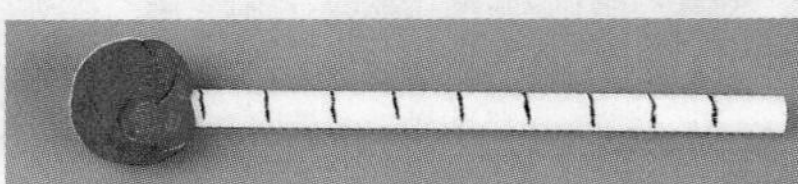

5. Dissolve 10 teaspoons of sugar in a glass of water. Try out your hydrometer in this liquid.

Think It Over

Predicting Compare your observations in Steps 4 and 5. Then predict what will happen if you use 20 teaspoons of sugar in a glass of water. Test your prediction.

GUIDE FOR READING

- What is the efffect of the buoyant force?
- What is Archimedes' principle?
- How does the density of an object determine whether it floats or sinks?

Reading Tip As you read, write a paragraph explaining how buoyancy and Archimedes' principle are related.

In April of 1912, the *Titanic* departed from England on its first and only voyage. It was as long as three football fields and as tall as a twelve-story building. It was the largest ship that had been built until that time, and its furnishings were the finest and most luxurious. The *Titanic* was also the most technologically advanced ship afloat. Its hull was divided into watertight compartments, and it was considered to be unsinkable.

Yet a few days into the voyage, the *Titanic* struck an iceberg. Two hours and forty minutes later, the bow of the great ship slipped underwater. As the stern rose high into the air, the ship broke in two. Both pieces sank to the bottom of the Atlantic Ocean. More than a thousand people died.

Figure 12 This painting shows the bow section of the *Titanic* resting on the sea floor.

READING STRATEGIES

Reading Tip Suggest students make notes or draw diagrams before they write paragraphs on the relationship between buoyancy and Archimedes' principle. Remind students that a paragraph is a group of related sentences that develop one main idea. A paragraph should have a topic sentence that states the main idea, supporting sentences, and a concluding sentence.

Program Resources

- **Teaching Resources** 3-3 Lesson Plan, p. 79; 3-3 Section Summary, p. 80
- **Integrated Science Laboratory Manual** M-3, "Raising a Sunken Ship"

How is it possible that a huge ship can float easily in water under certain conditions? Yet in a few hours the same ship can become a sunken wreck. And why does most of an iceberg lie hidden beneath the surface of the water? To answer these questions, you need to find out what makes an object float and what makes an object sink.

Buoyancy

If you have ever picked up an object under water, you know that it seems lighter in water than in air. Water exerts a force called the **buoyant force** that acts on a submerged object. **The buoyant force acts in the upward direction, against the force of gravity, so it makes an object feel lighter.**

As you can see in Figure 13, a fluid exerts pressure on all surfaces of a submerged object. Since the pressure in a fluid increases with depth, the upward pressure on the bottom of the object is greater than the downward pressure on the top. The result is a net force acting upward on the submerged object. This is the buoyant force.

A submerged object displaces, or takes the place of, a volume of fluid equal to its own volume. You can see this by looking at Figure 14. An object that floats on the surface of a fluid, however, displaces a smaller volume. It displaces a volume of fluid equal to the portion of the object that is submerged.

Archimedes' principle relates the amount of fluid a submerged object displaces to the buoyant force on the object. This relationship is named for its discoverer, the ancient Greek mathematician Archimedes. **Archimedes' principle states that the buoyant force on an object is equal to the weight of the fluid displaced by the object.**

☑ *Checkpoint* *Compare the direction of the buoyant force to the direction of the force of gravity.*

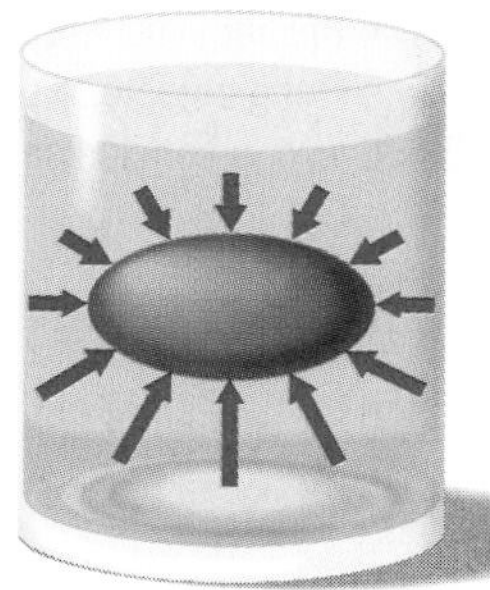

Figure 13 The pressure at the bottom of a submerged object is greater than the pressure at the top. The result is a net force in the upward direction. *Applying Concepts What is this upward force called?*

Figure 14 The volume of water displaced by an object is equal to the volume of the object. If the object floats, the volume of displaced water is equal to the volume of the portion of the object that is under water.

Sharpen your Skills

Measuring ACTIVITY

How can you measure an object's volume?

Measure in centimeters (cm) the length, width, and height of a wooden block. Then multiply length times width times height. The product is the volume. Volume has units of cubic centimeters (cm^3).

Media and Technology

Audiotapes English-Spanish Summary 3-3

Exploring Earth Science Videodisc Unit 3, Side 1, "Isto What?"

Chapter 1

Answers to Self-Assessment

Caption Question

Figure 13 The upward force is called buoyant force.

☑ *Checkpoint*

The buoyant force acts upward, and the force of gravity acts downward.

2 Facilitate

Buoyancy

Including All Students

Students who are still mastering English may need extra help to understand the term *buoyancy.* Ask students to describe a buoy. *(Sample: a buoy is a large floating object used to mark channels or water hazards.)* Have students draw pictures of buoys that include arrows showing the buoyant force. **limited English proficiency**

Sharpen your Skills

Measuring

Materials *wooden block, metric ruler* ACTIVITY
Time 5 minutes
Tips Suggest students create a data table to record their measurements and volumes.
Expected Outcome Students should find the volume of the block in cm^3.
Extend Challenge students to calculate the volume of the room using a meter stick. **learning modality: logical/mathematical**

Inquiry Challenge

Materials *assorted small classroom objects, graduated cylinder or beaker, water, metric ruler* ACTIVITY
Time 15 minutes
Tips Challenge groups of students to find the volumes of regularly shaped objects by measuring them with a ruler and comparing the resultant calculation of volume with the measured volume of water they displace.
Extend Challenge students to find the volume of irregularly shaped objects. **learning modality: kinesthetic**

Ongoing Assessment

Skills Check Ask students to describe the relationship between the volume and weight of the water an object displaces and its buoyant force.

Skills Lab

Drawing Conclusions

Sink and Spill

Preparing for Inquiry

Key Concept The buoyant force on an object is equal to the weight of the fluid displaced by the object (Archimedes' principle).

Skills Objective Students will be able to:
- perform calculations;
- interpret data;
- draw conclusions on how the buoyant force on a floating object is related to the weight of the displaced water.

Time 45 minutes

Advance Planning Assemble the beakers, balance, salt, paper towels, and small jars with lids. Baby food jars may serve as small watertight jars. Prepare any solutions you will need if you plan to use a liquid other than water.

Alternative Materials Instead of water, part of the class can use sugar water, salt water, or vegetable oil. A denser material than salt, such as iron filings, could be used to fill the jar.

Guiding Inquiry

Invitation You may want to perform this lab before you cover Archimedes' principle in class. Tell students that in this lab they will compare the buoyant force of the water to the weight of the water displaced, a comparison first made by Archimedes.

Introducing the Procedure
Discuss ways students might determine the weight of water displaced when an object sinks or floats. Explain the method used in this lab—subtracting the weight of the dry paper towel and 250-mL beaker from their weight *after* the spill.

Skills Lab

Drawing Conclusions

Sink and Spill

In this lab, you will use data on floating and sinking objects to practice the skill of drawing conclusions.

Problem

How is the buoyant force on a floating object related to the weight of the water it displaces?

Materials

paper towels
beaker, 250 mL
triple-beam balance
beaker, 600 mL
table salt
jar with watertight lid, about 30 mL

Procedure  

1. Preview the procedure and copy the data table into your notebook.
2. Find the mass, in grams, of a dry paper towel and the 250-mL beaker together. Multiply the mass by 0.01. This gives you the weight in newtons. Record it in your data table.
3. Carefully fill the 600-mL beaker to the very top with water. Put the 250-mL beaker, with the dry paper towel under it, next to the spout of the 600-mL beaker.
4. Place a small amount of salt in the jar. (The jar and salt must be able to float in water.) Then find the mass of the dry jar (with its cover on) in grams. Multiply the mass by 0.01. Record this weight in your data table.
5. Gently lower the jar into the 600-mL beaker. (If the jar sinks, take it out and remove some salt. Repeat Steps 3 and 4.) Estimate the fraction of the jar that is underwater, and record it.
6. Once all of the displaced water has been spilled, find the total mass of the paper towel and 250-mL beaker containing the water. Multiply the mass by 0.01 and record the result in your data table.
7. Empty the 250-mL beaker. Dry off the beaker and the jar.
8. Repeat Steps 3 through 7 several more times. Each time fill the jar with a different amount of salt, but make sure the jar still floats.

DATA TABLE

Jar	Weight of Empty 250-mL Beaker and Dry Paper Towel (N)	Weight of Jar, Salt, and Cover (N)	Weight of 250-mL Beaker with Displaced Water and Paper Towel (N)	Fraction of Jar Submerged in Water	Buoyant Force (N)	Weight of Displaced Water (N)
1						
2						
3						

Safety

Caution students not to spill liquid on the floor, as it could become slippery. Caution students to use care handling glass objects. Review the safety guidelines in Appendix A.

Program Resources

- **Teaching Resources** Chapter 3 Skills Lab, pp. 90–91

9. Calculate the buoyant force for each trial and record it in your data table. (*Hint:* When an object floats, the buoyant force is equal to the weight of the object.)
10. Calculate the weight of the displaced water in each case. Record it in your data table.

Analyze and Conclude

1. In each trial, the jar had a different weight. How did this affect the way that the jar floated?
2. The jar had the same volume in every trial. Why did the volume of displaced water vary?
3. What can you conclude about the relationship between the buoyant force and the weight of the displaced water?
4. Can you suggest places where errors may have been introduced?
5. **Think About It** If you put too much salt in the jar, it will sink. What can you conclude about the buoyant force in this case? How can you determine the buoyant force for an object that sinks?

Design an Experiment

How do you think your results would change if you used a different liquid that is more dense or less dense than water? Design an experiment to test your hypothesis. What liquid or liquids will you use? Will you need equipment other than what you have used for this experiment? If so, what will you need? If you carry out your new experiment, be sure to have your teacher check your design before you begin.

Sample Data Table

Jar	Weight of Empty 250-mL Beaker and Dry Paper Towel (N)	Weight of Jar, Salt, and Cover (N)	Weight of 250-mL Beaker with Displaced Water and Paper Towel (N)	Amount of Jar Submerged in Water	Buoyant Force (N)	Weight of Displaced Water (N)
1	1.08	0.26	1.33	1/4	0.25	0.25
2						
3						

Troubleshooting the Experiment

- Make sure students perform the lab on a level surface.
- Remind students to multiply their mass readings by .01 to convert them to newtons. They can round the forces to the nearest hundredth of a newton.
- Make sure students capture all the displaced water. If they do not, errors will be introduced.

Expected Outcome

The weight of the displaced water will be equal to the buoyant force, which in turn is equal to the weight of the jar, salt, and cover.

Analyze and Conclude

1. Because the volume remains constant, the lighter the jar, the higher it floated.
2. The amount of displaced water depends only on the volume of jar that is submerged. Since this varied each time, so did the amount of displaced water.
3. The buoyant force is the same (or close to) the weight of the displaced water.
4. Errors may be introduced in capturing all of the spilled water. If any of the water is lost, the measured weight of the displaced water will be less than the actual amount.
5. If a jar sinks, the buoyant force is less than the weight of the jar. However, the buoyant force will still be equal to the weight of the displaced water, which can be found using the method from this lab.

Extending the Inquiry

Design an Experiment A typical hypothesis states that if a liquid that is denser than water is used, the same jar would float higher and a smaller volume of liquid will be displaced. Students should plan to repeat this lab using a denser liquid than water, such as corn syrup or glycerin, to test this hypothesis.

Floating and Sinking

Using the Visuals: Figure 15

Draw students' attention to the relative sizes of the force arrows in the images. Ask: **What information do the arrows give you about the forces involved?** *(In the diagrams on the left and right, the weight of the displaced water is equal to the object's weight. In the middle, the object's weight is greater.)* **learning modality: visual**

Density

Demonstration

Materials *modeling clay, clear plastic container, water, paper towels*
Time 15 minutes

Have students who have difficulty understanding the text examine Figure 17 on page 96. Then fill a clear plastic container three-quarters full of water. Make a small clay ball. Have students predict whether the ball will float, then drop it into the water. Remove the ball, dry it, and shape it into a small boat. Have students predict whether the boat will float, then try it. Elicit the fact that the ball sinks because it is more dense than water. The boat floats because its overall density is less than water. Since it displaces more water, it floats. **limited English proficiency**

TRY THIS

Skills Focus drawing conclusions
Materials *plastic straw, scissors, paper clips, jar, 1–2 L plastic bottle*
Time 20 minutes
Tips Have students test the diver in the jar. If the diver is less than 0.5 cm above the water, it may sink in the bottle.
Expected Outcome When the bottle is squeezed, the pressure on the water increases, causing it to enter the straw. Students may conclude that the diver sinks because it has greater density.
Extend Challenge students to find a way to remove the diver from the bottle without emptying the bottle. *(Fill the bottle to the top and the diver will rise to the surface.)* **learning modality: kinesthetic**

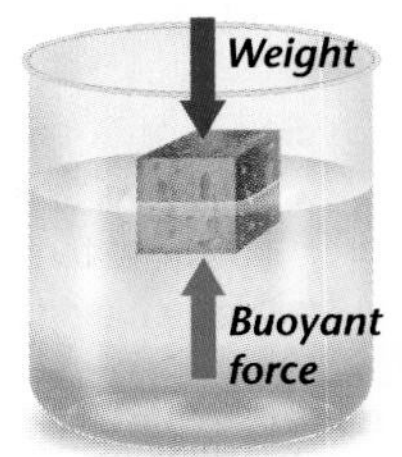

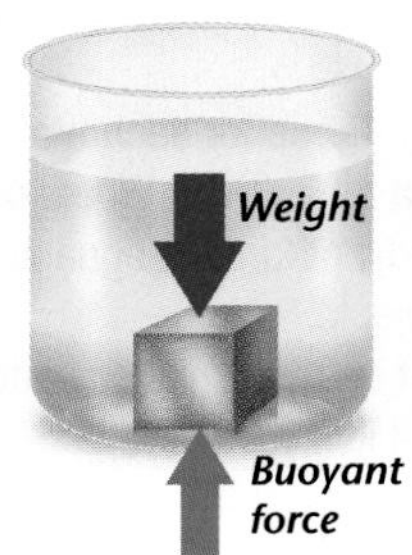

Figure 15 The illustration shows the forces on three different cubes. All three cubes have the same volume. *Comparing and Contrasting* *Why don't all three cubes float?*

TRY THIS

Dive! ACTIVITY

In this activity you will construct a device called a Cartesian diver.

1. Bend a plastic straw into a U shape and cut the ends so that each side is about 4 cm long. Attach the ends with a paper clip.
2. Attach additional paper clips to the first paper clip. The straw should float with its top about half a centimeter above the surface. This is the diver.
3. Fill a plastic jar or bottle almost completely with water. Drop the diver in, paper clips first. Then put the lid on the jar.
4. Slowly squeeze and release the jar several times.

Drawing Conclusions Explain the behavior of the diver.

Floating and Sinking

Remember that there is always a downward force on a submerged object. That force is the weight of the object. If the weight of the object is greater than the buoyant force, the net force on a submerged object will be downward. The object will sink. If the weight of the object is less than the buoyant force, the object will begin to sink. It will only sink deep enough to displace a volume of fluid with a weight equal to its own. At that level, it will stop sinking deeper, and will float. If the weight of the object is exactly equal to the buoyant force, the two forces are balanced.

Density

Exactly why do some objects float and others sink? By comparing the density of an object to the density of a fluid, you can decide if it will float. But what is density?

The **density** of a substance is its mass per unit volume.

$$\text{Density} = \frac{\text{Mass}}{\text{Volume}}$$

For example, one cubic centimeter (cm^3) of lead has a mass of 11.3 grams, so its density is 11.3 g/cm^3.

$$\text{Density of lead} = \frac{11.3\ g}{1\ cm^3} = 11.3\ g/cm^3$$

In contrast, one cubic centimeter of cork has a mass of only about 0.25 gram. So its density is about 0.25 g/cm^3. You would say that lead is more dense than cork. The density of water is 1.0 g/cm^3, so it is less dense than lead but more dense than cork.

By comparing densities, you can explain the behavior of the objects shown in Figure 15. **An object that is more dense than the fluid in which it is immersed sinks. An object that is less dense than the fluid in which it is immersed floats to the surface.** And if the density of an object is equal to the density of the

Background

Integrating Science Many fishes control buoyancy by regulating the flow of gas into a swim bladder. The volume of gas, which is high in oxygen concentration, changes as the fish swims to different depths. When the fish swims upward, the bladder swells with gas and increases the buoyant force on the fish. When the fish swims downward, gases are removed from the bladder and the buoyant force decreases.

Not all fishes have oxygen-filled swim bladders. Sharks are a good example of fishes that do not have swim bladders. Most sharks must swim constantly in order to breathe. If they did not swim constantly, they would sink. Sharks' buoyancy is somewhat regulated by the oil in their large livers. However, because oil is much more dense than air, the livers of sharks are not as effective in controlling buoyancy as swim bladders are.

fluid in which it is immersed, the object neither rises nor sinks in the fluid. Instead it floats at a constant level.

Now you know why lead sinks: It is several times denser than water. Cork, which is less dense than water, floats. An ice cube floats in water because the density of ice is less than the density of water. But it's just a little less! So most of a floating ice cube is below the surface. Since an iceberg is really a very large ice cube, the part that you see above water is only a small fraction of the entire iceberg. This is one reason why icebergs are so dangerous to ships.

☑ *Checkpoint* ***To calculate the density of a substance, what two properties of the substance do you need to know?***

Densities of Substances Figure 16 shows several substances and their densities. Notice that liquids can float on top of other liquids. (You may have seen that salad oil floats on top of vinegar.) Notice also that the substances with the greatest densities are near the bottom of the cylinder.

Don't forget that air is also a fluid. Objects float in air if their densities are less than the density of air. A helium balloon rises because helium is less dense than air. An ordinary balloon filled with your exhaled breath, however, is more dense than air. So the balloon falls to the ground once you let go of it.

Changing the density of an object can make it float or sink in a given fluid. The density of a submarine, for example, is decreased when water is pumped out of its flotation tanks. The overall mass of the submarine decreases. Since its volume remains the same, its density decreases when its mass decreases. So the submarine will float to the surface. To dive, the submarine takes in water. In this way, it increases its mass (and thus its density), and sinks.

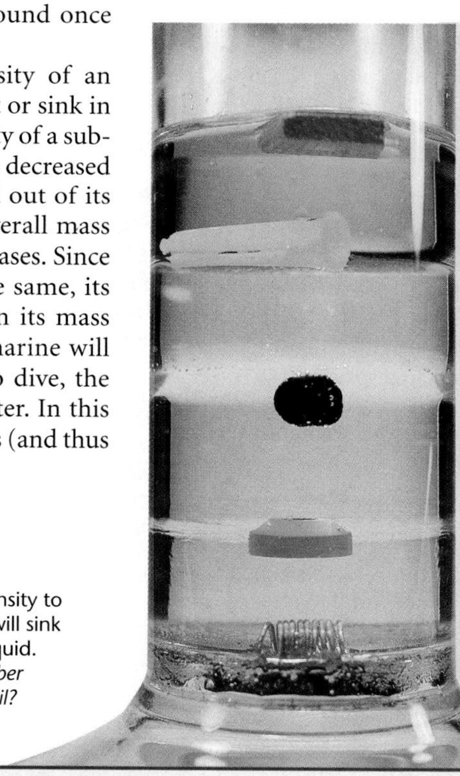

Substance	Density (g/cm^3)
Wood	0.7
Corn oil	0.925
Plastic	0.93
Water	1.00
Tar ball	1.02
Glycerin	1.26
Rubber washer	1.34
Corn syrup	1.38
Copper wire	8.8
Mercury	13.6

Figure 16 You can use density to predict whether an object will sink or float when placed in a liquid. *Interpreting Data Will a rubber washer sink or float in corn oil?*

Demonstration

ACTIVITY

Materials *tall, clear container; water, food coloring, rubbing alcohol, vegetable oil, water, tall glass, corn syrup, glycerin*
Time 15 minutes
Tips As a class, explore the densities of different solutions by floating liquids in a container similar to the one in Figure 16. Pour a layer of corn syrup, then pour in the glycerin. When the glycerin has settled, add liquids in this order—colored water, vegetable oil, and colored rubbing alcohol. Pour gently to avoid mixing. Ask: **How do the different liquids float on each other ?** *(The lightest or less dense liquids float on top of the heaviest or more dense liquids.)* **Which liquids have a density greater than water?** *(Corn syrup and glycerin)* **learning modality: visual**

Addressing Naive Conceptions

Many students may believe that whether an object sinks or floats depends on its weight, not its density. Ask students to look at Figure 16. Ask: **Why are the liquids in layers rather than mixed?** *(They have different densities.)* **What would happen if a tar ball twice as large as the one in the illustration were placed in the liquids?** *(It would rest in the same position.)* Ask students to explain how they can determine whether an object will sink or float. *(If the object is less dense than the fluid, it will float. If it is more dense, it will sink.)* **learning modality: visual**

Media and Technology

Transparencies "Floating and Sinking," Transparency 6

Exploring Physical Science Videodisc Unit 3, Side 1, "Density Column"

Chapter 5

Answers to Self-Assessment

Caption Questions

Figure 15 For a cube to float, the buoyant force must be greater than the weight of the cube.
Figure 16 A rubber washer will sink in corn oil.

☑ *Checkpoint*

To calculate density, you must know the mass and the volume.

Ongoing Assessment

Skills Check Have students design an experiment that uses water to tell whether a substance is corn oil or corn syrup. *(Pour the unknown substance into a glass of water. If it floats on the water, it is corn oil, it if sinks, it is corn syrup.)*

3 Assess

Section 3 Review Answers

1. The buoyant force acts upward on a submerged object. This makes the object seem lighter.
2. The buoyant force on an object equals the weight of the fluid displaced by the object.
3. If the density of the object is greater than that of water, the object will sink; if the object's density is less than the density of water, it will float.
4. The buoyant force equals the weight of the object, so the buoyant force is 340 N. The weight of the displaced water is equal to the weight of the object, so it is also 340 N.
5. The air pockets increase the volume of the canoe, but not its mass. This makes the canoe less dense than water even if the material the canoe is made of is more dense than water.

CHAPTER PROJECT 3

Check Your Progress

Make balances available for students to check the weights of their different designs. Students should add weight data to their design logs. Encourage students to brainstorm ideas for improving their designs. Help them to determine whether a boat sank because it was too dense, or if it capsized because it was unstable. Encourage students to find creative ways to solve the problems. Remind them to record everything they try in their design logs.

Performance Assessment

Writing Ask students to imagine that they are newspaper reporters the day after the *Titanic* sank. Have them write a column explaining why the unsinkable ship sank after striking an iceberg. *(Students' columns should describe how the water entering the ship increased the ship's density and caused it to sink.)*

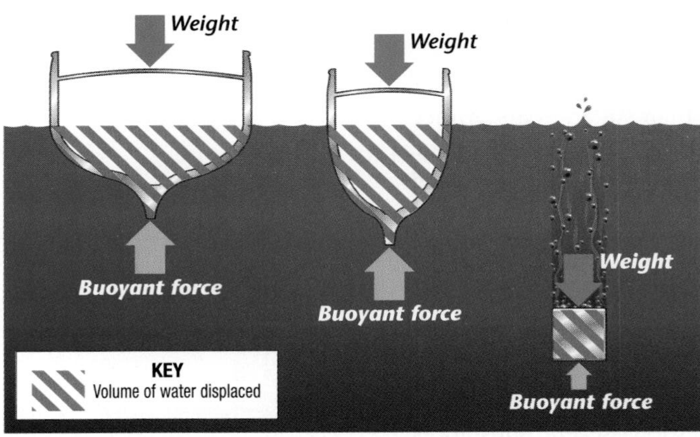

Figure 17 A solid cube of steel sinks when placed in water. A steel ship with the same weight floats.

Buoyancy and Density Another way of changing density is to change volume. In Figure 17, the amount of steel present in the three objects is the same. Yet two of the figures float, and one sinks. Solid steel sinks rapidly in water, and so will the hull of a ship that is full of water. Usually, however, the hull of a ship contains a large volume of air. This air reduces the ship's overall density, and so allows it to float.

You can explain why a ship floats not just in terms of density, but also by means of the force of buoyancy. Since the buoyant force is equal to the weight of the displaced fluid, the buoyant force will increase if more fluid is displaced. The amount of fluid displaced depends on the volume of a submerged object. A large object displaces more fluid than a small object. Therefore, the object with greater volume has a greater buoyant force acting on it—even if the objects have the same weight.

The shape of a ship causes it to displace a greater volume of water than a solid piece of steel of the same mass. The greater the volume of water displaced, the greater the buoyant force. A ship stays afloat as long as the buoyant force is greater than its weight.

Section 3 Review

1. How does the buoyant force affect a submerged object?
2. How does Archimedes' principle relate the buoyant force acting on an object to the fluid displaced by the object?
3. How can you use the density of an object to predict whether it will float or sink in water?
4. An object that weighs 340 N is floating on a lake. What is the buoyant force on it? What is the weight of the displaced water?
5. **Thinking Critically Applying Concepts** Some canoes have compartments on either end that are hollow and watertight. These canoes won't sink, even when they capsize. Explain why.

CHAPTER PROJECT 3

Check Your Progress

Don't be content with the first design that floats. Try several more, considering the characteristics that make your boat useful. How much space does your boat have for cargo? How does the weight of your boat affect the amount of cargo it can carry? (*Hint:* To measure the weight of each boat, see how many pennies will balance it on a double-pan balance.) Select your best boat and determine the number of pennies it can carry as it floats.

Media and Technology

Transparencies "Density," Transparency 7

Program Resources

◆ **Teaching Resources** 3-3 Review and Reinforce, p. 81; 3-3 Enrich, p. 82

SECTION 4 Applying Bernoulli's Principle

DISCOVER ACTIVITY

Does Water Push or Pull?

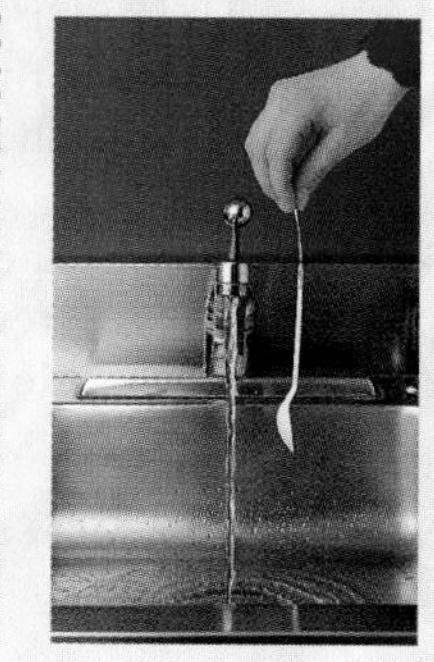

1. Hold a plastic spoon loosely by the edges of its handle so it is swinging freely between your fingers.
2. Turn on a faucet to produce a steady stream of water. Predict what will happen if you bring the curved back of the spoon into contact with the stream of water.
3. Test your prediction. Repeat the test several times.
4. Predict how your observations might change if you were to use a plastic fork instead of a spoon.
5. Test your prediction.

Think It Over

Inferring On what side of the spoon is the pressure lower? How do you know? Does the fork behave any differently from the spoon? If so, develop a hypothesis to explain why.

GUIDE FOR READING

- How is fluid pressure related to the motion of a fluid?

Reading Tip **Before you read, preview *Exploring Wings* and predict how you can explain flight in terms of fluid pressure.**

In December of 1903, Wilbur and Orville Wright brought an odd-looking vehicle to a deserted beach in Kitty Hawk, North Carolina. People had flown in balloons for more than a hundred years, but the Wright brothers' goal was something no one had ever done before. They flew a plane that was heavier (denser) than air! They had spent years experimenting with different wing shapes and surfaces, and they had carefully studied the flight of birds. Their first flight at Kitty Hawk lasted just 12 seconds. The plane flew 36 meters and made history.

What did the Wright brothers know about flying that allowed them to construct the first airplane? And how can the principles they used explain how a jumbo jet can fly across the country? The answer has to do with fluid pressure and what happens when a fluid moves.

Figure 18 On December 17, 1903, Wilbur Wright watched his brother Orville take off in *Flyer I*, the first successful airplane.

Bernoulli's Principle

So far in this chapter you have learned about fluids that are not moving. But what happens when a fluid, such as air or water, moves? Consider what happens if you hold a plastic spoon in a stream of running water. You might predict that the spoon would be pushed away by the water. But it is not. Surprisingly, the spoon is pushed toward the stream of water.

READING STRATEGIES

Reading Tip Guide students in previewing *Exploring Wings*. Have students read the sentence under the main heading. Then ask what the paragraph headings and the pictures suggest. Ask: **What do you think *Exploring Wings* is mostly about?** *(The relationship between the shape of a wing, the speed of the fluid through which the wing moves, and the pressure exerted by the fluid)*

Program Resources

- **Teaching Resources** 3-4 Lesson Plan, p. 83; 3-4 Section Summary, p. 84

Media and Technology

Audiotapes English-Spanish Summary 3-4

INTEGRATING TECHNOLOGY

SECTION 4 Applying Bernoulli's Principle

Objectives

After completing the lesson, students will be able to

- state Bernoulli's principle;
- explain the application of Bernoulli's principle to flight.

Key Terms Bernoulli's principle

1 Engage/Explore

Activating Prior Knowledge

Have students tear a strip of newspaper about 30 cm long and 3 cm wide, then hold one end of the strip near their bottom lip so that the strip hangs loosely down. Then blow gently across the top of the strip. Ask students to describe what happens. *(The strip rises)* **What force is pushing on the strip to make it rise?** *(The force must be from air pressure since nothing else is touching the strip.)* Explain to students that in this lesson, they will learn about the principles relating fluid motion to pressure.

DISCOVER

Skills Focus inferring
Materials *plastic spoon, plastic fork, faucet*
Time 10 minutes
Tips Elicit students' predictions before the activity. Remind students to hold the back of the spoon facing the stream of water. After Step 3, ask: **What happened to the spoon?** *(It moved toward the water.)* Then ask about the fork. *(It did not move.)*
Expected Outcome The spoon will move toward the stream of water. The fork will not.
Think It Over Students may conclud that the pressure is lower on the back of the spoon, but the fork does not move toward the water because the tines of the fork allow the air pressure to equalize.

2 Facilitate

Bernoulli's Principle

Demonstration

ACTIVITY

Inflate two small balloons and knot each one. Hang the balloons on strings so they hang with about 1 or 2 centimeters space between them. Have a volunteer gently blow air between the balloons. Ask students to observe what happens. *(The balloons move closer together.)* Ask: **Where do you think the pressure is the greatest?** *(On the outside, because the moving air between the balloons reduces the pressure.)* **learning modality: visual**

Objects in Flight

Inquiry Challenge

ACTIVITY

Materials *craft sticks, thin dowels, tissue paper, string, masking tape*
Time 40 minutes to design and build
Tips Have small groups design airplanes or gliders that use Bernoulli's principle to fly. Assign each student a task such as designer, assembler, and flight analyst. Allow students to test their designs outdoors. Challenge students to explain how the design of the plane or glider causes air to move more quickly over the top. **cooperative learning**

The behavior of the spoon demonstrates **Bernoulli's principle.** The Swiss scientist Daniel Bernoulli (bur NOO lee) found that the faster a fluid moves, the less pressure the fluid exerts. **Bernoulli's principle states that the pressure exerted by a moving stream of fluid is less than the pressure of the surrounding fluid.** The water running along the spoon is moving but the air on the other side of the spoon is not. The moving water exerts less pressure than still air. The result is that the greater pressure of the still air on one side of the spoon pushes the spoon into the stream of water.

Similarly, if you blow above a sheet of tissue paper, the paper will rise. Moving air blown over the tissue paper exerts less pressure than the still air below the paper. The greater pressure below the paper pushes it upward.

☑ *Checkpoint* ***How is the pressure exerted by a fluid related to how fast the fluid moves?***

Objects in Flight

Bernoulli's principle explains flight—from a small kite to a huge airplane. Objects can be designed so that their shapes cause air to move at different speeds above and below them. If the air moves faster above the object, pressure pushes the object upward. But if the air moves faster below the object, pressure pushes it downward. The shape of the sail of a ship is like an airplane wing. The difference in the pressure on the two sides of the sail moves the ship forward. Look through *Exploring Wings* to see how Bernoulli's principle can be applied to airplanes, birds, and race cars.

Bernoulli's Principle at Home

Bernoulli's principle can help you understand many common occurences. For example, you can sit next to a fireplace enjoying a cozy fire thanks to Bernoulli's principle. Smoke rises up the chimney partly because hot air rises, and partly because it is pushed. Wind blowing across the top of a chimney lowers the air pressure there. The higher pressure at the bottom then pushes air and smoke up the chimney.

Figure 19 Thanks to Bernoulli's principle, you can enjoy an evening by a warm fireplace without having the room fill up with smoke. *Making Generalizations Why does the smoke rise up the chimney?*

Background

History of Science Daniel Bernoulli (1700–1782) came from a family of esteemed scientists and mathematicians in Switzerland. His father, Johann Bernoulli, made many important contributions to mathematics, especially to the development of calculus. Johann and his brother Jakob were very competitive, and a new field of mathematical study called the calculus of variations developed from their arguments.

At the age of 25, Daniel Bernoulli and his brother Nicolaus joined the prestigious faculty of the St. Petersburg Academy of Sciences to teach mathematics. Later in life Daniel was elected to the Royal Society of London. Although most famous for his work on fluids, during his lifetime Daniel held academic posts in botany, anatomy, physiology, and physics. His work included studies in medicine, mechanics, mathematics, and oceanography.

EXPLORING Wings

Bernoulli's principle explains how air moving around a wing produces a force.

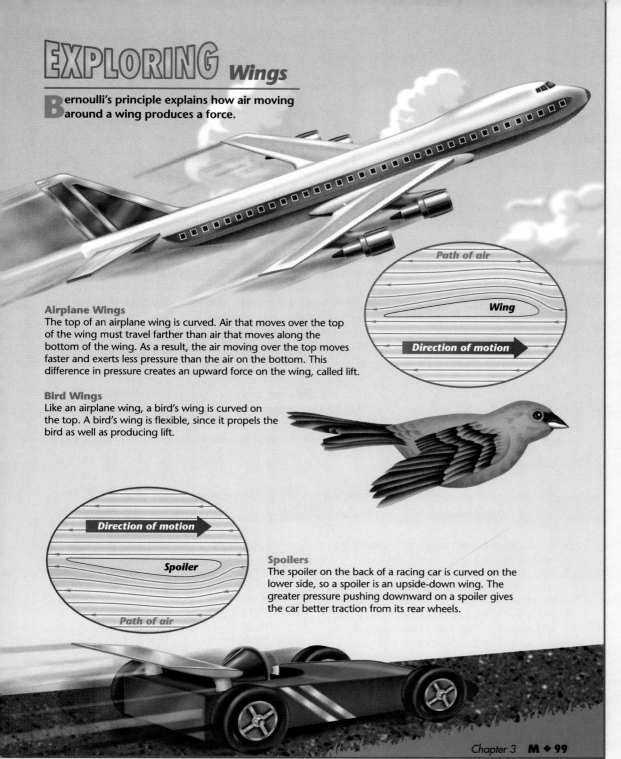

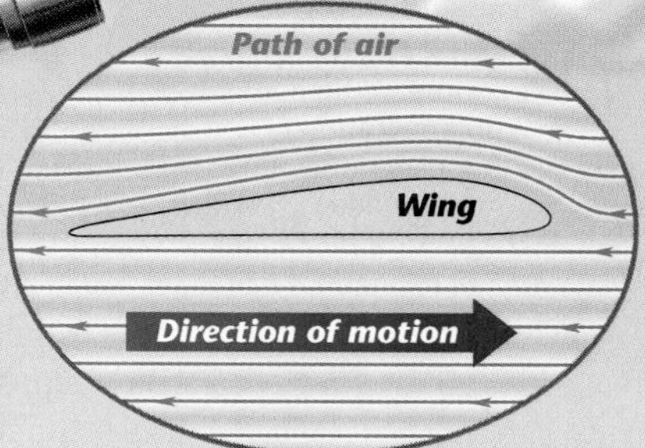

Airplane Wings
The top of an airplane wing is curved. Air that moves over the top of the wing must travel farther than air that moves along the bottom of the wing. As a result, the air moving over the top moves faster and exerts less pressure than the air on the bottom. This difference in pressure creates an upward force on the wing, called lift.

Bird Wings
Like an airplane wing, a bird's wing is curved on the top. A bird's wing is flexible, since it propels the bird as well as producing lift.

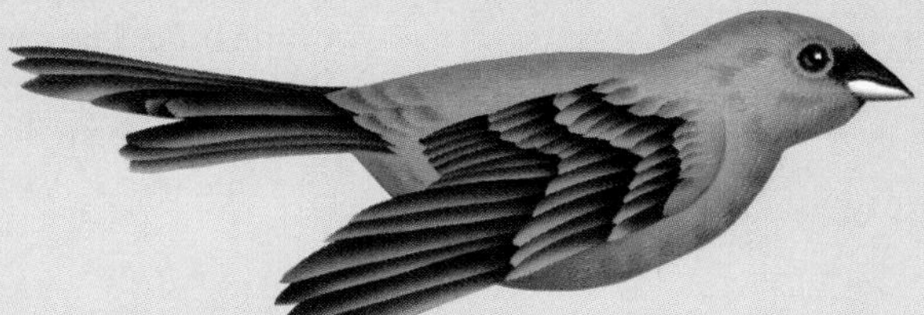

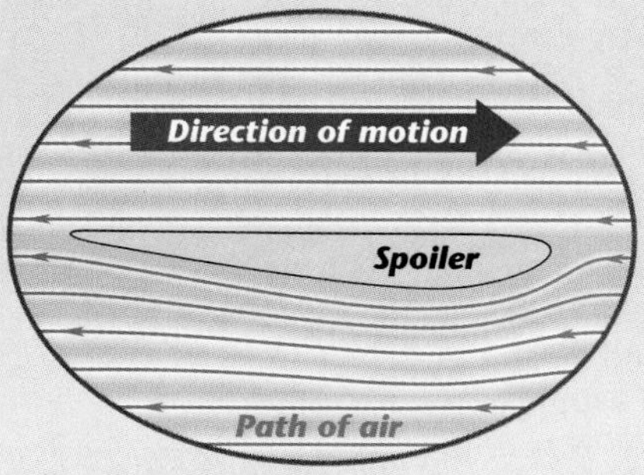

Spoilers
The spoiler on the back of a racing car is curved on the lower side, so a spoiler is an upside-down wing. The greater pressure pushing downward on a spoiler gives the car better traction from its rear wheels.

Media and Technology

Transparencies "Exploring Wings," Transparency 8

Exploring Physical Science Videodisc Unit 3, Side 1, "How an Airplane Flies"

Chapter 6

Answers to Self-Assessment

Caption Question

Figure 19 Hot air rises on its own. In addition, the wind across the top of the chimney lowers air pressure at the top of the chimney. This allows air to be pushed up from the bottom of the chimney.

✓ Checkpoint

The faster a fluid moves, the less pressure it exerts.

EXPLORING Wings

After students have had time to examine the visual, ask: **What fluid is moving?** *(air)* Ask: **Why is the top of an airplane wing curved?** *(So the air travels farther)* **What happens to the speed of the air that travels farther?** *(It increases.)* Ask: **How is this related to Bernoulli's principle?** *(The faster-moving air exerts less pressure.)* Have students explain why a spoiler on the back of a race car acts like an "upside down" wing. Direct students attention to the cross section of a bird's wing and ask them how a bird's wing is like an airplane wing and how it is different.

Extend Ask: **What would happen if an airplane flew into turbulent air?** *(Since the air would not flow smoothly above and below the wing, the wing might lose lift.)*
learning modality: visual

Bernoulli's Principle at Home

Real-Life Learning

Use Figure 19 and the description of fireplaces in the text to start a discussion of fire. Invite a member of the fire department to talk to the class about applications of Bernoulli's principle in fire fighting, such as backdrafts, updrafts, and fire safety. Encourage students to develop a list of questions before the talk. Prompt students to think about issues such as chimney flues, sparks and burning paper rising from a fire, and blowing on a fire to help it burn. Have students ask the speaker to explain how air pressure differences affect fire.
learning modality: verbal

Ongoing Assessment

Writing Have students give three examples of Bernoulli's principle.

3 Assess

Section 4 Review Answers

1. The pressure exerted by a moving fluid is lower than the pressure of the same fluid when it is not moving.
2. The air traveling above the wing is moving faster than the air traveling below the wing. The result is that air pressure above the wing is lower than air pressure below the wing. This causes an upward force, or lift, that allows the plane to fly.
3. Wind blowing over the roof exerts less pressure than the still air inside the house. The greater pressure inside the house pushes the roof upward.
4. The truck pulls air along with it. Because the air is moving at a greater speed than the air on the other side of your car, the greater pressure on the side of your car pushes your car toward the truck.

Science at Home

Materials *plastic straw, scissors, drinking glass or jar, water*
Tips Caution students to follow the directions carefully. Student must blow forcefully to make the atomizer work. Students should explain that the device works because the air blown over the straw lowers the pressure at the top of the straw. The greater pressure outside the straw pushes the water up the straw.

Performance Assessment

Writing Native Americans of many different tribes have built temporary and permanent dwellings that use a simple hole in the roof to allow smoke from a fire to escape. Have students write a paragraph using Bernoulli's principle to explain how this works. They should include a prediction of whether the smoke outlet works better with no wind or with wind.

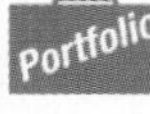

Students can save their paragraphs in their portfolios.

Figure 20 The spray of perfume from an atomizer is an application of Bernoulli's principle. *Applying Concepts Why is the perfume pushed up and out of the flask?*

Have you ever been hit in the legs by the shower curtain while taking a shower? The attack of the shower curtain can be explained by Bernoulli's principle. The stream of moving water inside the curtain drags air with it. The motion creates an area of low-pressure air. Air pressure outside the curtain, which is then greater, pushes the curtain inward.

Bernoulli's principle can help you understand the operation of other familiar devices. In the atomizer shown in Figure 20, you squeeze a rubber bulb. Squeezing the bulb causes air to move quickly past the top of the tube. The bottom of the tube is in the liquid in the flask. The moving air lowers the pressure at the top of the tube. The greater pressure in the flask pushes the liquid up into the tube. When the liquid reaches the air stream, the action of the air stream breaks it into small drops. The liquid comes out as a fine mist.

Section 4 Review

1. What does Bernoulli's principle say about the pressure exerted by a moving fluid?
2. Why does the air pressure above an airplane wing differ from the pressure below it? How is this pressure difference involved in flight?
3. **Thinking Critically Relating Cause and Effect** A roof is lifted off a building during a severe windstorm. Explain this in terms of Bernoulli's principle.
4. **Thinking Critically Applying Concepts** You are riding in a car on a highway when a large truck speeds by you. Explain why your car is forced toward the truck.

Science at Home

You can make your own atomizer using a straw. Cut a plastic straw part-way through. Hold one end of the straw in a glass of water and bend the other half of the straw at a right angle at the cut, as shown. Blow hard through the straw, making sure that no one is in the way! Show your device to your family. See if they know what it is and why it works. Explain the device to them in terms of Bernoulli's principle.

Program Resources

◆ **Teaching Resources** 3-4 Review and Reinforce, p. 85; 3-4 Enrich, p. 86

Answers to Self-Assessment

Caption Question

Figure 20 Air moves over the top of the tube when the bulb is squeezed. This lowers the pressure at the top of the tube. The higher pressure at the bottom of the tube pushes the perfume up the tube.

Section 1 Pressure

Key Ideas

- Pressure is the force per unit area on a surface.
- Fluid pressure results from the motion of the atoms or molecules that make up the fluid.
- Pressure at a given level in a fluid is the same in all directions. Pressure decreases with altitude and increases with depth.

Key Terms

pressure
pascal
fluid

Section 2 Transmitting Pressure in a Fluid

Key Ideas

- According to Pascal's principle, an increase in pressure on a confined fluid is transmitted equally to all parts of the fluid.
- A hydraulic device works by transmitting an increase in pressure from one part of a confined fluid to the other. A small force exerted over a small area at one place results in a large force exerted by a larger area at another place.

Key Terms

Pascal's principle
hydraulic system

Section 3 Floating and Sinking

Key Ideas

- The upward force on an object submerged in a fluid is called the buoyant force.
- The buoyant force on an object is equal to the weight of the fluid displaced by the object. This is Archimedes' principle.
- An object will sink, rise to the surface, or stay where it is in a fluid depending on whether its density is less than, greater than, or equal to the density of the fluid.

Key Terms

buoyant force
Archimedes' principle
density

Section 4 Applying Bernoulli's Principle

Integrating Technology

Key Idea

- The pressure in a fluid decreases as the speed of the fluid increases. This is Bernoulli's principle.

Key Term

Bernoulli's principle

Activity USING THE INTERNET
www.science-explorer.phschool.com

Program Resources

- **Teaching Resources** Chapter 3 Project Scoring Rubric, p. 70; Chapter 3 Performance Assessment Teacher Notes, pp. 200–201; Chapter 3 Performance Assessment Student Worksheet, p. 202; Chapter 3 Test, pp. 203–206

Media and Technology

Interactive Student Tutorial CD-ROM M-3

Computer Test Bank Test M-3

CHAPTER 3 REVIEW

Reviewing Content:

Multiple Choice

1. b **2.** a **3.** c **4.** d **5.** b

True or False

6. area **7.** decreases **8.** true **9.** displaced fluid **10.** true

Checking Concepts

11. You exert less pressure lying down. When you lie down, you spread the force of your weight out over a larger area, thus exerting less pressure.
12. Pressure = Force/Area = 14 N/7 cm^2 = 2 N/cm^2
13. The braking system of a car and the hydraulic lift in an auto shop are examples of hydraulic systems.
14. Air moves faster above a bird's curved wings, so the greater pressure below the wings pushes the bird upward.
15. In water, a greater upward force (the buoyant force) acts in the opposite direction of your weight. The net force, then, is less than in air.
16. Students should explain that pressure increases with depth.

Thinking Visually

17. a. pressure on fluid increases; **b.** pressure is transmitted throughout fluid; **c.** pressure pushes on larger piston; **d.** same pressure over greater area results in greater force ($P = F/A$)

Applying Skills

18. The object weighs less in water because the buoyant force on it in water is opposite to the force of gravity.
19. The buoyant force is 2.0 N (9.8 N − 7.8 N).
20. The volume of water is equal to the volume of the object. The weight of the volume of water is equal to the buoyant force on the object, 2.0 N.
21. The object will sink because the buoyant force is less than its weight.

Thinking Critically

22. The sphere must be hollow.
23. This method will increase the volume of displaced water, increasing the buoyant force. It will also decrease the ship's overall density.

CHAPTER 3 REVIEW

Reviewing Content

For more review of key concepts, see the Interactive Student Tutorial CD-ROM.

Multiple Choice

Choose the letter of the answer that best completes each statement.

1. Pressure can be measured in units of
   a. N. **b.** N/cm^2.
   c. N/cm. **d.** N/cm^3.
2. The operation of a hydraulic device can be explained in terms of
   a. Pascal's principle.
   b. Bernoulli's principle.
   c. Archimedes' principle.
   d. Newton's third law.
3. If the buoyant force on an object in water is greater than the object's weight, the object will
   a. sink.
   b. hover beneath the surface of the water.
   c. rise to the surface and float.
   d. be crushed by the water pressure.
4. A stone will sink in water because
   a. it is very heavy.
   b. its density is less than that of water.
   c. it has a small buoyant force on it.
   d. its density is greater than that of water.
5. Much of the lift that enables an airplane to fly can be explained using
   a. Pascal's principle.
   b. Bernoulli's principle.
   c. Archimedes' principle.
   d. Newton's first law.

True or False

If the statement is true, write true. If it is false, change the underlined word or words to make the statement true.

6. Pressure is force per unit of mass.
7. As you rise higher into the atmosphere, the air pressure increases.
8. The braking system of a car is an example of a hydraulic device.
9. You can determine the buoyant force on an object if you know the weight of the object.
10. The pressure exerted by a moving stream of fluid is less than the pressure exerted by the same fluid when it is not moving.

Checking Concepts

11. How does the amount of pressure you exert on the floor when you are lying down compare with the amount of pressure you exert when you are standing up?
12. You have a closed bottle of soda. The force on the bottle cap due to the carbonation of the soda is 14 N. If the area of the bottle cap is 7 cm^2, what is the pressure on the cap?
13. Name two hydraulic devices that an auto mechanic is familiar with.
14. Explain how Bernoulli's principle can keep a bird in the air.
15. Why do you seem to weigh more in air than you do in water?
16. **Writing to Learn** You have a job greeting vacationers who are learning to scuba dive. Prepare a brochure or handout explaining the pressure changes they should expect to experience as they dive. Be sure to describe the reasons for the changes.

Thinking Visually

17. **Flowchart** Create a flowchart that shows how a hydraulic device multiplies force. (For more on flowcharts, see the Skills Handbook.)

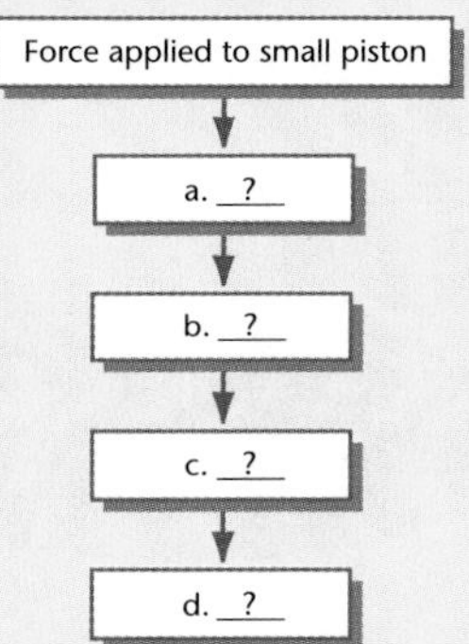

24. Take an object that floats in either of the liquids. If it sinks in the other liquid, the one it floats in is the denser liquid. If it floats in both, the one it floats higher in is the denser liquid.
25. The pressure above the kite is less than the pressure below it.

Applying Skills

Use the illustration to answer Questions 18–21. It shows an object being supported by a spring scale in and out of water.

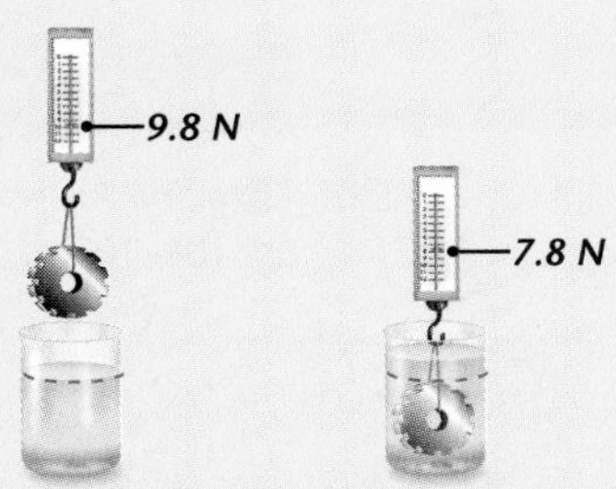

18. **Applying Concepts** Why is there a difference between the weight of the object in air and its weight in water?
19. **Calculating** What is the buoyant force on the object?
20. **Drawing Conclusions** What can you conclude about the volume of water above the dotted line?
21. **Predicting** If the spring scale were removed, would the object float or sink? How do you know?

Thinking Critically

22. **Developing Hypotheses** A sphere made of steel is put in water and, surprisingly, it floats. Develop a hypothesis to explain this observation.
23. **Applying Concepts** One method of raising a sunken ship to the surface is to inflate large bags or balloons inside its hull. Explain why this procedure could work.
24. **Designing Experiments** You have two fluids of unknown density. Suggest an experiment to determine which is denser without mixing the two fluids.
25. **Relating Cause and Effect** Your kite rises into the air as you run quickly on a windy day. Is the air pressure greater above the kite or below it? Explain your answer.

CHAPTER 3 REVIEW

Performance Assessment

CHAPTER PROJECT 3

Wrap Up

Presenting Your Project Test your boat to make sure it does not leak. Then display it for the class and demonstrate how it floats. Be sure to include the diagrams you drew of the different designs you tried. Display the observations and data you recorded for each design. Point out to your classmates the features you incorporated into your final design.

Reflect and Record Suppose you had no limitations on what materials you could use for your boat. Also suppose you could form your material into any shape you choose. In your journal, sketch and describe the boat you would design.

Getting Involved

In Your Community As you learned, the brakes in a car rely on a hydraulic system. All the parts of the brake system need to be in good working order. Speak to a local garage mechanic to learn what kinds of things can wear out or break in a car's brake system. Then prepare a display for your local library. Your display should explain how a car's brake system works and what can go wrong if the brakes are not properly serviced.

Program Resources

- **Inquiry Skills Activity Book** Provides teaching and review of all inquiry skills

Performance Assessment

CHAPTER PROJECT 3

Wrap Up

Presenting Your Project Encourage students to describe the design features of their boats and explain why they were included.

Prepare a basin of water in which students can test their boats. Use a basin large enough to test two boats at one time. To test the boats, have students float them and add pennies gently so that the momentum of the falling pennies doesn't push the lip of the boat underwater. The number of pennies supported by the boat is one less than the number required to sink it. After testing the boats, collect the students' design logs.

Reflect and Record Ask students to sketch and describe in their journal the boat they would design if material limitations were removed.

Getting Involved

In Your Community Students' displays should describe things that can go wrong with brakes, including how the pads can wear, and how the moving parts in the master cylinder and wheel cylinders can break. Students should include an explanation of how these problems affect the hydraulic system or how a particular hydraulic device such as an ABS system works.

Work and Machines

Sections	Time	Student Edition Activities	Other Activities
CHAPTER PROJECT 4 **The Nifty Lifting Machine** p. 105	Ongoing (2 weeks)	Check Your Progress, pp. 109, 128 Wrap Up, p. 137	**TE** Chapter 4 Project Notes, pp. 104–105
1 What Is Work? pp. 106–109 ◆ Identify when work is done on an object. ◆ Calculate the work done on an object.	2 periods/ 1 block	**Discover** What Happens When You Pull at an Angle?, p. 106 **Sharpen Your Skills** Inferring, p. 108	**TE** Integrating Mathematics, p. 108
2 Mechanical Advantage and Efficiency pp. 110–117 ◆ Explain what machines do and how they make work easier. ◆ Identify the difference between actual and ideal mechanical advantage. ◆ Calculate the efficiency of a machine.	6–7 periods/ $3\frac{1}{2}$ blocks	**Discover** Is it a Machine?, p. 110 **Try This** Going Up, p. 113 **Skills Lab: Designing Experiments** Seesaw Science, pp. 116–117	**TE** Building Inquiry Skills: Interpreting, p. 111 **TE** Including All Students, p. 112 **TE** Inquiry Challenge, p. 112 **IES** "Mill Life in the 1840's," pp. 10–11, 29
3 Simple Machines pp. 118–131 ◆ Describe the six types of simple machines. ◆ Calculate the ideal mechanical advantage of four types of simple machines. ◆ Define compound machines.	7 periods/ 3–4 blocks	**Discover** How Can You Increase Your Force?, p. 118 **Try This** Modeling a Screw, p. 121 **Sharpen Your Skills** Measuring, p. 127 **Real-World Lab: You and Your Community** Angling for Access, pp. 130–131	**TE** Real-Life Learning, p. 119 **TE** Demonstration, p. 120 **TE** Building Inquiry Skills: Predicting, p. 120; Measuring, p. 124; Interpreting Diagrams, p. 126 **TE** Visual Arts Connection, p. 122 **TE** Exploring the Three Classes of Levers, p. 123 **TE** Cultural Diversity, p. 122 **TE** Inquiry Challenge, p. 127 **IES** "Wagons West," p. 21 **ISLM** M-4, "Pulleys as Simple Machines"
4 *Integrating Life Science* **Machines in the Human Body** pp. 132–134 ◆ Explain how the body uses levers and wedges.	$1\frac{1}{2}$ periods/ 1 block	**Discover** Are You an Eating Machine?, p. 132	**TE** Building Inquiry Skills: Observing, p. 133
Study Guide/Chapter Review pp. 135–137	1 period/ 1/2 block		**ISAB** Provides teaching and review of all inquiry skills

For Standard or Block Schedule The Resource Pro® CD-ROM gives you maximum flexibility for planning your instruction for any type of schedule. Resource Pro® contains Planning Express®, an advanced scheduling program, as well as the entire contents of the Teaching Resources and the Computer Test Bank.

CHAPTER PLANNING GUIDE

Program Resources	Assessment Strategies	Media and Technology
TR Chapter 4 Project Teacher Notes, pp. 92–93 **TR** Chapter 4 Project Overview and Worksheets, pp. 94–97 **TR** Chapter 4 Project Scoring Rubric, p. 98	**SE** Performance Assessment: Chapter 4 Project Wrap Up, p. 137 **TR** Chapter 4 Project: Scoring Rubric, p. 98 **TE** Performance Assessment: Chapter 4 Project Wrap Up, p. 137 **TE** Check Your Progress, pp. 109, 128	Science Explorer Internet Site
TR 4-1 Lesson Plan, p. 99 **TR** 4-1 Section Summary, p. 100 **TR** 4-1 Review and Reinforce, p. 101 **TR** 4-1 Enrich, p. 102	**SE** Section 1 Review, p. 109 **TE** Ongoing Assessment, p. 107 **TE** Performance Assessment, p. 109 **TR** 4-1 Review and Reinforce, p. 101	English-Spanish Summary 4-1 Transparency 9, "Work and Force" Interactive Student Tutorial CD-ROM, M-4
TR 4-2 Lesson Plan, p. 103 **TR** 4-2 Section Summary, p. 104 **TR** 4-2 Review and Reinforce, p. 105 **TR** 4-2 Enrich, p. 106 **TR** Chapter 4 Skills Lab, pp. 115–117	**SE** Section 2 Review, p. 115 **SE** Analyze and Conclude, p. 117 **TE** Ongoing Assessment, pp. 111, 113 **TE** Performance Assessment, p. 115 **TR** 4-2 Review and Reinforce, p. 105	Audiotapes: English-Spanish Summary 4-2 Transparency 10, "Machines" Interactive Student Tutorial CD-ROM, M-4 Exploring Physical Science Videodisc, Unit 3 Side 1, "Work, Work, Work"
TR 4-3 Lesson Plan, p. 107 **TR** 4-3 Section Summary, p. 108 **TR** 4-3 Review and Reinforce, p. 109 **TR** 4-3 Enrich, p. 110 **TR** Chapter 4 Real-World Lab, pp. 118–119	**SE** Section 3 Review, p. 128 **SE** Analyze and Conclude, p. 131 **TE** Ongoing Assessment, pp. 119, 121, 123, 125, 127 **TE** Performance Assessment, p. 128 **TR** 4-3 Review and Reinforce, p. 109	Audiotapes: English-Spanish Summary 4-3 Exploring Physical Science Videodisc, Unit 3 Side 1, "Simple Machines" Transparency 11, "Exploring the Three Classes of Levers" Transparency 12, "Pulleys" Interactive Student Tutorial CD-ROM, M-4
TR 4-4 Lesson Plan, p. 111 **TR** 4-4 Section Summary, p. 112 **TR** 4-4 Review and Reinforce, p. 113 **TR** 4-4 Enrich, p. 114 **SES** Book D, *Human Biology and Health,* Chapter 2	**SE** Section 4 Review, p. 134 **TE** Ongoing Assessment, pp. 133 **TE** Performance Assessment, p. 134 **TR** 4-4 Review and Reinforce, p. 113	Audiotapes: English-Spanish Summary 4-4 Exploring Life Science Videodisc, Unit 4 Side 1, "Muscles and Bones" Transparency 13, "Exploring Levers in the Body" Interactive Student Tutorial CD-ROM, M-4
TR Chapter 4 Performance Assessment, pp. 207–209 **TR** Chapter 4 Test, pp. 210–213	**SE** Chapter Review, pp. 135–137 **TR** Chapter 4 Performance Assessment, pp. 207–209 **TR** Chapter 4 Test, pp. 210–213 **CTB** Test M-4	Interactive Student Tutorial CD-ROM, M-4 Computer Test Bank, M-4 Test

Key: **SE** Student Edition
CTB Computer Test Bank
ISAB Inquiry Skills Activity Book
TE Teacher's Edition
SES Science Explorer Series Text
PTA Product Testing Activities by *Consumer Reports*
TR Teaching Resources
ISLM Integrated Science Laboratory Manual
IES Interdisciplinary Explorations Series

Meeting the National Science Education Standards and AAAS Benchmarks

National Science Education Standards	Benchmarks for Science Literacy	Unifying Themes
Physical Science (Content Standard B) ◆ **Transfer of energy** Energy is transferred by the work of simple machines. *(Sections 1, 2, 3; Skills Lab; Chapter Project)* **Life Science** (Content Standard C) ◆ **Structure and function in living systems** Simple machines in the human body are a part of the muscular system, jaws, and teeth. *(Section 4)* **Science and Technology** (Content Standard E) ◆ **Design a solution or a product** Students use a combination of simple machines to build a machine that can lift a soup can. *(Chapter Project)* Students evaluate how the angle of a wheel-chair access ramp affects its usefulness. *(Real-World Lab)* ◆ **Evaluate completed technological designs or products** Students calculate the mechanical advantage and efficiency of different machines. *(Sections 2, 3)* **Science in Personal and Social Perspectives** (Content Standard F) ◆ **Science and technology in society** Students learn about ancient engineering marvels and how they were built using simple machines. *(Section 3)* Some of the ethical problems posed by automation in the work place are discussed. *(Science and Society)* Students design a ramp system that will provide wheel-chair access to a public library. *(Real-World Lab)*	**2B Mathematics, Science, and Technology** The use of mathematics to analyze work and machines has led to more efficient machines and improved mechanical technology. *(Sections 1, 2, 3; Real-World Lab)* **3C Issues in Technology** Students study how simple machines were used to make some of the most beautiful and useful structures in the world as well as how technology can improve life. The benefits and drawbacks of automation are discussed. *(Section 3; Real-World Lab; Science and Society)* **4E Energy Transformations** How simple machines transfer input force into output force is described. Students examine the relationship between force , distance , and direction in simple machines. *(Sections 1, 2, 3; Skills Lab)* **8C Energy Sources and Use** Students examine how some energy is lost in all simple machines. *(Sections 2,3)* **9B Symbolic Relationships** Students use equations to calculate work, mechanical advantage, and efficiency and determine how a change in one quantity affects other quantities in these equations. *(Sections 1, 2, 3; Skills Lab; Real-World Lab)* **11A Systems** Students examine the interconnectedness of simple machines in compound machines and systems such as the human body. *(Chapter Project; Sections 3, 4)*	◆ **Energy** Simple machines convert input force or energy to output force or energy. Simple machines may increase force, increase distance, or change direction. *(Sections 1, 2, 3, 4; Skills Lab; Real-World Lab)* ◆ **Scale and Structure** Simple machines can be found in the human body. Compound machines are made up of more than one simple machine. *(Sections 3, 4; Chapter Project)* ◆ **Unity and Diversity** Although simple machines differ in appearance or use, they all make work easier. *(Sections 1, 3, 4)* ◆ **Systems and Interactions** Compound machines are systems of simple machines that interact to increase mechanical advantage. *(Chapter Project)* ◆ **Modeling** Students model a compound machine by constructing a "lifting machine" consisting of two simple machines that work together. *(Chapter Project)*

Media and Technology

Exploring Life Science Videodiscs

◆ **Section 4** "Muscles and Bones" details the interdependence of the skeletal and muscular systems for an athlete in training.

Exploring Physical Science Videodiscs

◆ **Section 2** "Work, Work, Work" introduces viewers to a variety of simple machines and exemplifies how they can be used to make work easier.

◆ **Section 3** "Simple Machines" shows some everyday uses of simple machines including inclined planes, wedges, levers, pulleys, and wheels and axles.

Interactive Student Tutorial CD-ROM

◆ **Chapter Review** Interactive questions help students to self-assess their mastery of key chapter concepts.

Student Edition Connection Strategies

◆ **Section 1** **Integrating Mathematics,** p. 109

◆ **Section 2** **Integrating Mathematics,** p. 115
Math Toolbox, p. 115

◆ **Section 3** **Visual Arts Connection,** p. 122
Science & History, pp. 124–125
Science and Society, p. 129

◆ **Section 4** **Integrating Life Science,** p. 132

www.science-explorer.phschool.com

Visit the Science Explorer Internet site to find an up-to-date activity for Chapter 4 of *Motion, Forces, and Energy*.

Student Edition Activities Planner

ACTIVITY	Time *(minutes)*	Materials *Quantities for one work group*	Skills
Section 1			
Discover, p. 106	10	**Consumable** thin rubber band **Nonconsumable** mug	Developing Hypotheses
Sharpen Your Skills, p. 108	10	**Consumable** No special materials are required.	Forming Operational Definitions
Section 2			
Discover, p. 110	20	**Nonconsumable** objects that are machines such as pliers, corkscrew, blunt knife, can opener, screwdriver, hammer, jar lid, scissors, pencil sharpener, broom, hole punch, staple remover; objects that are not machines–eraser, pencil, chalk, paper, ruler, ball, book, dishcloth, coin, straw, salt shaker	Forming Operational Definitions
Try This, p. 113	15	**Consumable** 50-cm string or twine **Nonconsumable** small cooking pot, 20-N spring scale, pencil	Developing Hypotheses
Skills Lab, pp. 116–117	30	**Consumable** masking tape **Nonconsumable** meter stick; 28 pennies, post-1982; small object, mass about 50 g; dowel or other cylindrical object for pivot point, about 10 cm long and 3 cm in diameter	Designing Experiments
Section 3			
Discover, p. 118	15	**Nonconsumable** 2 broomsticks or dowels, long rope	Predicting
Try This, p. 121	10	**Consumable** sheet of paper, tape, string **Nonconsumable** long pencils, scissors, markers, ruler	Making a Model
Sharpen Your Skills, p. 127	10	**Consumable** No special materials are required.	Classifying
Real-World Lab, p. 130–131	55	**Consumable** No special materials are required. **Nonconsumable** board, at least 10 cm wide and 50 cm long; wooden block with eye-hook; spring scale, 0–5N; metric ruler; 4 books, about 2 cm thick; marker	Making Models, Measuring, Calculating
Section 4			
Discover, p. 132	10	**Consumable** crackers	Observing

A list of all materials required for the Student Edition activities can be found on pages T14–T15. You can order Materials Kits by calling 1-800-828-7777 or by accessing the Science Explorer Internet site at **www.science-explorer.phschool.com.**

The Nifty Lifting Machine

Modern society depends on complex machines, but even the most complex of machines can be thought of as a series of interconnected simple machines.

Purpose Students will demonstrate their understanding of simple machines by designing and building a device to reduce the input force required to lift a 600-g soup can 5 centimeters.

Skills Focus Students will be able to
- ◆ design a device that is a compound machine able to lift a 600-g load using less than a 600-g mass as an input force;
- ◆ build the device that they designed;
- ◆ calculate actual and ideal mechanical advantage
- ◆ explain to others how their device incorporates simple machines in its construction.

Project Time Line The project requires about four weeks. Before beginning the project, see Chapter 4 Project Teacher Notes on pages 92–93 in Teaching Resources for more details on carrying out the project. During week one, students should design their devices. In weeks two and three, students build and modify their prototypes. In week four, students should write short descriptions of their devices and demonstrate them to the class. Also distribute the Chapter 4 Project Student Overview and Worksheets and Scoring Rubric on pages 94–98 in Teaching Resources.

Suggested Shortcuts Have students work in small groups as a cooperative learning task. To ensure that every student will have ample opportunity to participate in the design of a compound machine, have them work alone during the first phase of the project. Students can then get together as a group to build one or more of the devices that group members have designed. Each group should consist of no more than four students.

Possible Materials Provide a wide variety of materials students can use to build their devices. Suitable materials include: wood scraps of all sizes, cardboard and plastic tubes, nails and screws, coat hangers, straws, spools, cups, cans, wire, toy wheels, toy cars, string, paper clips, and cardboard. Encourage students to suggest and use other materials as well. Have sanding paper and a light lubricating oil available for students to use when they build their devices. Sand will be needed to fill soup cans to 600 g for the load and to fill soup cans for input force.

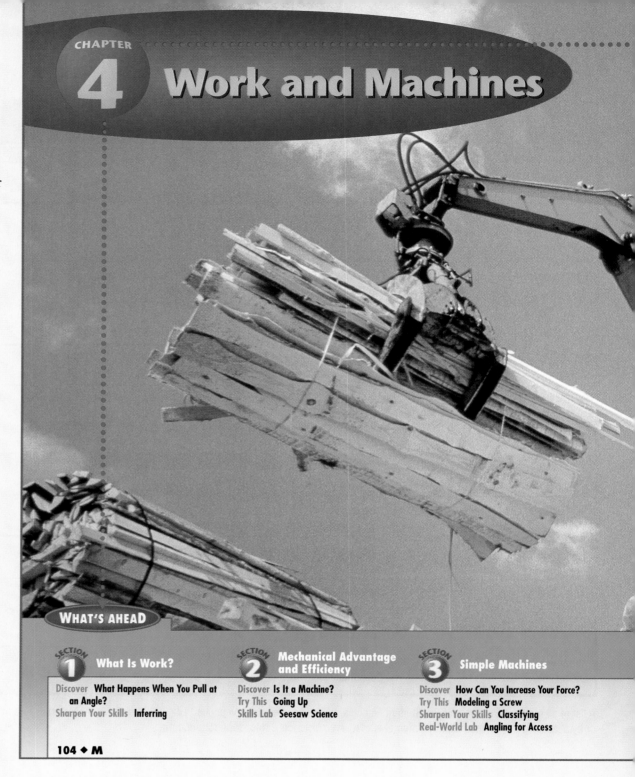

CHAPTER 4

Work and Machines

WHAT'S AHEAD

Section 1 What Is Work?
Discover **What Happens When You Pull at an Angle?**
Sharpen Your Skills **Inferring**

Section 2 Mechanical Advantage and Efficiency
Discover **Is It a Machine?**
Try This **Going Up**
Skills Lab **Seesaw Science**

Section 3 Simple Machines
Discover **How Can You Increase Your Force?**
Try This **Modeling a Screw**
Sharpen Your Skills **Classifying**
Real-World Lab **Angling for Access**

104 ◆ M

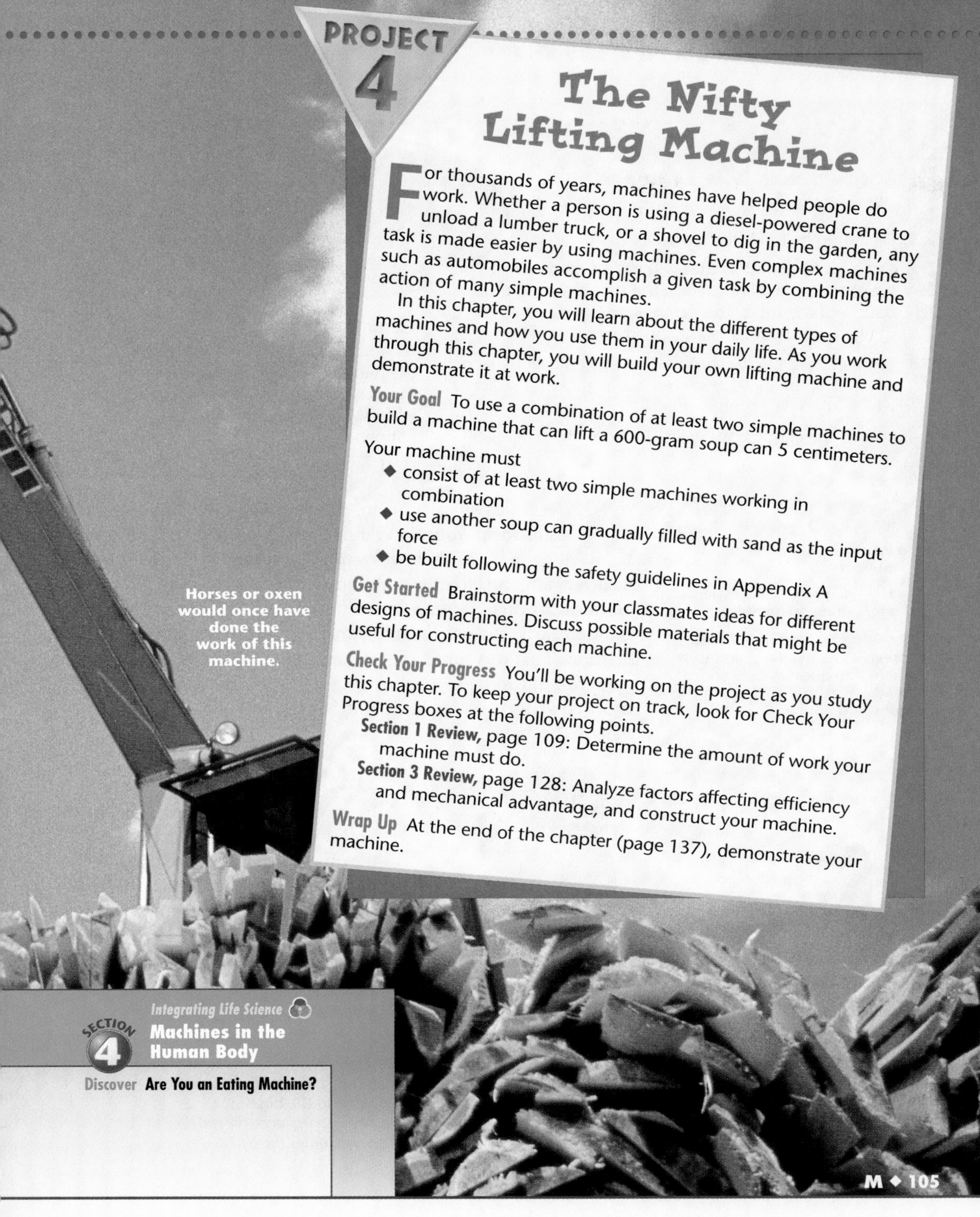

PROJECT 4

The Nifty Lifting Machine

For thousands of years, machines have helped people do work. Whether a person is using a diesel-powered crane to unload a lumber truck, or a shovel to dig in the garden, any task is made easier by using machines. Even complex machines such as automobiles accomplish a given task by combining the action of many simple machines.

In this chapter, you will learn about the different types of machines and how you use them in your daily life. As you work through this chapter, you will build your own lifting machine and demonstrate it at work.

Your Goal To use a combination of at least two simple machines to build a machine that can lift a 600-gram soup can 5 centimeters.

Your machine must

- ◆ consist of at least two simple machines working in combination
- ◆ use another soup can gradually filled with sand as the input force
- ◆ be built following the safety guidelines in Appendix A

Get Started Brainstorm with your classmates ideas for different designs of machines. Discuss possible materials that might be useful for constructing each machine.

Check Your Progress You'll be working on the project as you study this chapter. To keep your project on track, look for Check Your Progress boxes at the following points.

Section 1 Review, page 109: Determine the amount of work your machine must do.

Section 3 Review, page 128: Analyze factors affecting efficiency and mechanical advantage, and construct your machine.

Wrap Up At the end of the chapter (page 137), demonstrate your machine.

Horses or oxen would once have done the work of this machine.

Integrating Life Science

SECTION 4 **Machines in the Human Body**

Discover **Are You an Eating Machine?**

Allow students to read the description of the project in their text and the Chapter Project Overview on pages 94–95 in Teaching Resources. Then encourage discussions on simple machines, how one might build a machine, how one could combine two machines into one, materials that could be used, and any initial questions students may have. Pass out copies of the Chapter 4 Project Worksheets on pages 96–97 in Teaching Resources for students to review.

Launching the Project To introduce the project and stimulate student interest, load an empty soup can with sand until its mass is 600 g. Show students how the input force to lift this load can be reduced using a meter stick as a lever and a chalkboard eraser as a fulcrum. Invite students to lift the can with and without the lever. You may also with to use an incline plane and/or a set of pulleys to lift the load.

Program Resources

- ◆ **Teaching Resources** Chapter 4 Project Teacher Notes, pp. 92–93; Chapter 4 Project Overview and Worksheets, pp. 94–97; Chapter 4 Project Scoring Rubric, p. 98

Performance Assessment

The Chapter 4 Project Scoring Rubric on page 98 in Teaching Resources will help you evaluate how well students complete the Chapter 4 Project. Students will be assessed on

- ◆ the clarity, simplicity, and completeness of their designs;
- ◆ the progress they make when constructing their devices;
- ◆ how well their written explanations of how their devices work exhibit an understanding of the machines involved;
- ◆ How well their devices perform during the demonstration.

By sharing the Chapter 4 Project Scoring Rubric with students at the beginning of the project, you will make it clear to them what they are expected to do.

SECTION 1 What Is Work?

Objectives

After completing the lesson, students will be able to

- ◆ identify when work is done on an object;
- ◆ calculate the work done on an object.

Key Terms work, joule

1 Engage/Explore

Activating Prior Knowledge

Ask a volunteer to hold a book in his or her hand while standing perfectly still. Ask another volunteer to lift a book from the floor and place it on a table. Ask: **Which volunteer is exerting force?** *(both)* Ask another volunteer to open a book and look at the pages. Ask: **Is this person exerting force?** *(yes)* Challenge students to recall the definition of force. Ask: **But which student is doing the work?** *(the lifter, not the stander)*

DISCOVER ACTIVITY

Skills Focus developing hypotheses
Materials *mug, thin rubber band*
Time 10 minutes
Tips Students should fill the mug halfway with water so that it will not turn over when it is pulled. Provide paper towels to clean up any spills. Students can use sand instead of water or place a book on top of the mug if they want to use more weight.
Think It Over The pull in which the halves of elastic were held parallel was more effective. Students may say it was more effective because the force was in the same direction as the motion of the mug. Students may also say that if they increased the angle, they would have to pull harder to get the mug to move because, much of the pull does not help move the mug.

SECTION 1 What Is Work?

DISCOVER ACTIVITY

What Happens When You Pull at an Angle?

1. Fill a mug half full with water.
2. Cut a rubber band so that you have a medium-weight piece of elastic. Loop the elastic through the handle of the mug. You can pull on the elastic to move the mug at constant speed across a table.
3. You can hold the two halves of elastic parallel to each other or at an angle to each other as shown. Predict which way will be more effective in moving the mug.
4. Pull on the elastic both ways. Observe any differences.

Think It Over
Developing Hypotheses Which of the two pulls was more effective in moving the mug? Can you explain why? What do you think would happen if you increased the angle?

GUIDE FOR READING

- ◆ When is work done on an object?
- ◆ How do you calculate the work done on an object?

Reading Tip **Before you read, preview the headings and turn them into questions. As you read, write brief answers to the questions.**

After a heavy snowstorm, a neighbor's car gets stuck in a snowdrift. You shovel some snow away from the car, and then try to push it backward. The spinning tires whine as the driver attempts to move. Although you try as hard as you can, the car just won't budge. After 10 minutes of strenuous pushing, you are nearly exhausted. Unfortunately, the car is still lodged in the snow. That was sure hard work, wasn't it? You exerted a lot of force. You did some work shoveling the snow. But you might be surprised to discover that in scientific terms you didn't do any work at all on the car!

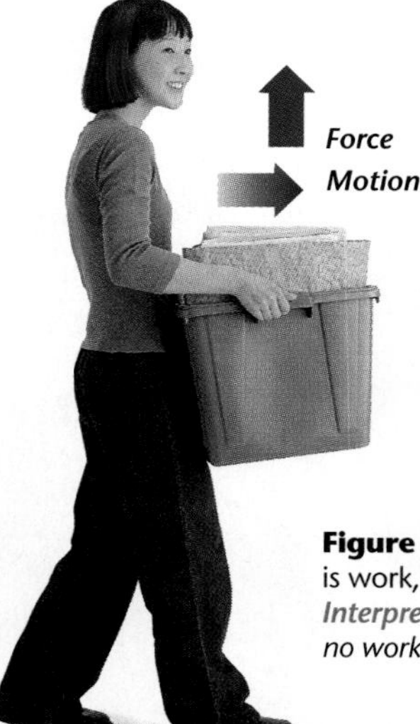

Figure 1 Lifting a bin full of newspapers is work, but carrying the bin is not. *Interpreting Photos Why does the girl do no work when she carries the bin?*

The Meaning of Work

In science you do **work** on an object when you exert a force on the object that causes the object to move some distance. If you push a child on a swing, for example, you are doing work on the child. If you pull your books out of your

READING STRATEGIES

Reading Tip Ask students to rewrite the headings as questions. Remind them to begin their questions with words such as *What, How,* and *Why*. After students write their questions, but before they read the section, have them meet with a study partner to compare questions and discuss possible answers. After students read the section, have partners discuss what they learned from their reading.

Study and Comprehension Before students read the section, remind them of these strategies for breaking down information to make it easier to understand:

- ◆ Read the title, headings, subheadings, and captions to get an overview.
- ◆ Read one section of text at a time, line by line. Reread parts you did not understand.
- ◆ Jot down unfamiliar words. Try to figure out their meanings or look the words up in a dictionary.

book bag, you do work on the books. If you lift a bag of groceries out of a shopping cart, you do work on the bag of groceries.

No Work Without Motion So why didn't you do work when trying to push the car out of the snow? The car didn't move. **In order for you to do work on an object, the object must move some distance as a result of your force.** If the object does not move, no work is done no matter how much force is exerted.

There are many situations in which you exert a force but don't do any work. Suppose, for example, you are asked to hold a piece of wood while you are helping on a construction project. You definitely exert a force to hold the wood in place, so it might seem as if you do work. But because the force you exert does not make the wood move, you are not doing any work on it.

Figure 2 You may be making a great effort, but if the car doesn't move, you do no work.

Only Force in the Same Direction How much work do you do when you carry your heavy books to school? You may think you do a lot of work, but actually you don't. **In order to do work on an object, the force you exert must be in the same direction as the object's motion.** When you carry an object at constant velocity, you exert an upward force to hold the object so that it doesn't fall to the ground. The motion of the object, however, is in the horizontal direction. Since the force is vertical and the motion is horizontal, you don't do any work on the object as you carry it.

How much work do you do when you pull a sled? When you pull a sled, you pull on the rope at an angle to the ground. Therefore your force has both a horizontal part (to the right) and a vertical part (upward). When you pull this way, only part of your force does work—the part in the same direction as the motion of the sled. The rest of your force does not help pull.

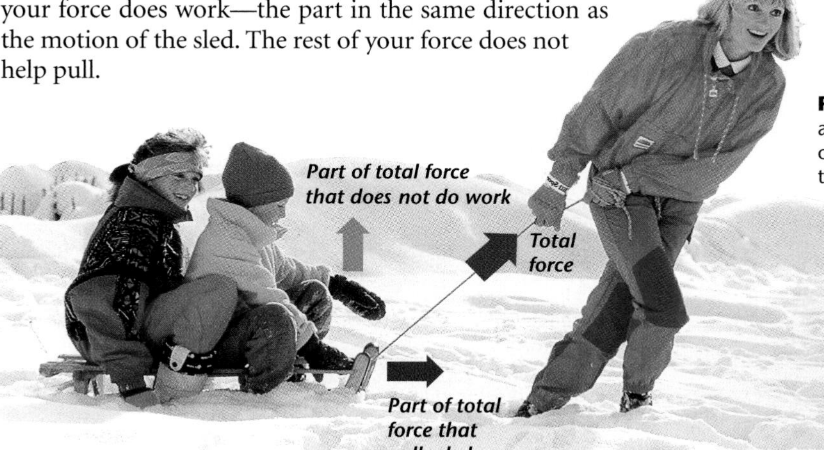

Figure 3 When you pull a sled with a rope, not all of your force does work to move the sled.

2 Facilitate

The Meaning of Work

Including All Students

To assist students who are still mastering English, have all students assemble several pictures that illustrate the various meanings of the word *work*. For example, in Figure 1, one picture shows the girl exerting a force to do work, and the other picture shows the girl exerting a force but doing no work. Ask students to indicate which pictures reflect the scientific definition of work. *(Students should indicate pictures in which an object is moved by a force acting in the direction of the motion.)* **limited English proficiency**

Using the Visuals: Figure 3

As students examine the photograph, have them point to the forces that are exerted on the sled. *(Some force pulls the sled upward and some force pulls the sled forward.)* Have students consider how much work it takes to move the sled. Explain that whatever direction the woman pulls, only the portion of the force in the direction of motion does work. Ask: **What could the woman do to increase the part of the force that does work on the sled?** *(She could pull the rope horizontally.)* **learning modality: visual**

Program Resources

◆ **Teaching Resources** 4-1 Lesson Plan, p. 99; 4-1 Section Summary, p. 100

Media and Technology

 **Audiotapes** English-Spanish Summary 4-1

Answers to Self-Assessment

Caption Question

Figure 1 When she carries the bin, the girl exerts a force on the bin. However, because none of the force is in the same direction as the bin is moving, no work is done.

Ongoing Assessment

Drawing Have students draw two diagrams that show a person exerting force on a ball. In one diagram, the person should do work on the ball; in the other the person should *not* do work on the ball.

Students can save their diagrams in their portfolios.

The Meaning of Work, continued

Sharpen your Skills

Inferring

Time 10 minutes

Tips No work is done by Earth on the satellite because the force is always at right angles to the motion. Diagrams should indicate the satellite's motion (tangential to Earth) and the force of gravity (down toward the center of Earth).

Extend Ask students: **When an object speeds up or slows down, is work being done? Why?** *(Yes, because force is in the same direction as motion.)*

Calculating Work

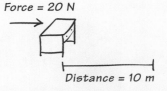

Integrating Mathematics

Materials *spring scale; meter stick; three objects of different weights*

Time 15 minutes

Tips Pair students and have them find the force necessary to lift several objects a distance of 1 meter. Students should then calculate the amount of work done when each object is lifted and record the answer in joules. Ask: **What happens to the amount of work done when the force needed to lift up an object increases?** *(The amount of work increases.)* **learning modality: logical/mathematical**

Sample Problem

Encourage good problem solving techniques by making sure students always write the formula first, substitute known values, then solve.

Practice Problems

1. 12,000 N × 2 m = 24,000 J
2. 0.2 N × 1.5 m = 0.3 J

Sharpen your Skills

Inferring

You do work when you drag your family's trash cans out to the curb. You exert a force and the trash cans move. Does this mean that work is always done on an object if the object is moving? Recall how a satellite orbits Earth. Is work done on the satellite as it orbits? Draw a diagram to support your answer.

If you did the Discover activity, you know that your effort will be more effective when you reduce the angle at which you push or pull an object. That is, exert as much of your force as possible in the direction of the object's motion. Keep this in mind the next time you rake a pile of leaves or vacuum a floor.

✓ *Checkpoint* *How can you determine if work is done on an object?*

Calculating Work

Which do you think involves more work: lifting a 100-newton potted tree a meter off the ground or lifting a 200-newton tree to the same height? Is it more work to lift a tree from the ground to a wheelbarrow or from the ground floor to the top story of a building? Your common sense may suggest that lifting a heavier object, which demands a greater force, requires more work than lifting a lighter object. And moving an object a greater distance requires more work than moving the object a shorter distance. Both of these are true.

The amount of work you do depends on both the amount of force you exert and the distance the object moves:

Work = Force × Distance

The amount of work done on an object can be determined by multiplying force times distance.

Sample Problem

To help rearrange the furniture in your classroom, you exert a force of 20 N to push a desk 10 m. How much work do you do?

Analyze. You know the force exerted on the desk and the distance the desk moved. You want to find the amount of work done. Draw a diagram similar to the one shown to help you.

Write the formula. *Work = Force × Distance*

Substitute and solve. *Work = 20 N × 10 m*

Work = 200 N·m, which is 200 J

Force = 20 N

Distance = 10 m

Think about it. The answer tells you that the work you do on the desk is 200 J.

Practice Problems

1. A hydraulic lift raises a 12,000-N car 2 m. How much work is done on the car?
2. You exert a force of 0.2 N to lift a pencil off the floor. How much work do you do if you lift it 1.5 m?

Background

History of Science The metric unit *joule* is named after James Prescott Joule (1818–1889). Joule was born in Salford, England. After training as a scientist Joule built a laboratory in his father's house and used it to conduct experiments and try out new inventions. Among other important discoveries, he calculated the amount of electrical work needed to produce a unit of heat. By performing increasingly precise experiments with many different materials, he was able to show that the same amount of mechanical or electrical work always produced the same amount of heat. This is usually called the "mechanical equivalent of heat."

INTEGRATING MATHEMATICS When force is measured in newtons and distance is measured in meters, the SI unit of work is the newton × meter (N•m). This unit is also called a joule (JOOL) in honor of James Prescott Joule, a physicist who studied work in the middle 1800s. One **joule** (J) is the amount of work you do when you exert a force of 1 newton to move an object a distance of 1 meter.

With the work formula, you can compare the amount of work you do to lift the trees. When you lift an object at constant speed, the upward force you exert must be equal to the object's weight. To lift the first tree, you would have to exert a force of 100 newtons. If you were to raise it 1 meter, you would do 100 newtons × 1 meter, or 100 joules of work. To lift the heavier tree, you would have to exert a force of 200 newtons. So the amount of work you do would be 200 newtons × 1 meter, or 200 joules. Thus you do more work to move the heavier object.

Now think about lifting the tree higher. You did 100 joules of work lifting it 1 meter. Suppose an elevator lifted the same tree to the top floor of a building 40 meters tall. The elevator would exert the same force on the tree for a greater distance. The work done would be 100 newtons × 40 meters, or 4,000 joules. The elevator would do 40 times as much work as you did.

Figure 4 These students are doing work as they transplant a tree. ***Inferring*** *How much work would they do if the tree weighed twice as much? If they had to lift it four times as far?*

Section 1 Review

1. If you exert a force, do you always do work? Explain your answer.
2. What is the formula for calculating work?
3. Compare the amount of work done when a force of 2 N moves an object 3 meters with the work done when a force of 3 N moves an object 2 meters.
4. **Thinking Critically** **Applying Concepts** You need to move five one-gallon cans of paint from the basement to the second floor of a house. Will you do more work on the cans of paint if you take them up all at once (if possible) or if you take them up individually? Explain.

CHAPTER PROJECT 4

Check Your Progress

Determine the amount of work that your machine must do to lift a 600-g soup can 5 cm. Draw a diagram showing the forces involved and the direction of those forces. Jot down some suggestions for accomplishing this work. Brainstorm with classmates about what materials you could use to build your machine.

3 Assess

Section 1 Review Answers

1. No. Force must cause motion that is in the same direction as the force.
2. Work = Force × Distance
3. The same amount of work is done because work is the product of force and distance. Both equal 6 J of work.
4. You will do the same amount of work whether you take the cans up all at once or individually. The total force and the total distance are the same.

CHAPTER PROJECT 4

Check Your Progress

In order to determine the amount of work their machine must do, students will need to convert 600 g to newtons, and 5 cm to m *(6.0 N, 0.05 m)*. Remind students of the difference between weight and mass (Chapter 2), and show them how to do the conversion.

600 g / 1,000 g/kg = 0.6 kg
0.6 kg × 9.8 m/s^2 = 5.88 N
5.88 N × 0.05 m = 0.29 J

To draw diagrams with force arrows, students will need to consider the direction of the force and whether force is applied to their machine from the top, side, or bottom. Once they have decided what simple machine to use to lift the soup can, they can choose another simple machine to apply force to the first.

Program Resources

- **Teaching Resources** 4-1 Review and Reinforce, p. 101; 4-1 Enrich, p. 102

Media and Technology

Interactive Student Tutorial CD-ROM M-4

Transparencies "Work and Force," Transparency 9

Answers to Self-Assessment

Caption Question

Figure 4 If the tree weighed twice as much, they would do twice as much work. If they lifted it four times as far, they would do four times as much work.

☑ Checkpoint

The object moves some distance in the direction of the force that you exerted on it.

Performance Assessment

Oral Presentation Have students work in groups of three. One student performs an activity, such as holding a book, walking around while holding a book, moving a book across a table, or lifting a book from the floor. The second student states whether work is being done. The third students either agrees or disagrees, and explains why.

Section 2 Mechanical Advantage and Efficiency

Objectives

After completing the lesson, students will be able to

- explain what machines do and how they make work easier;
- identify the difference between actual and ideal mechanical advantage;
- calculate the efficiency of a machine.

Key Terms machine, input force, output force, mechanical advantage, efficiency, actual mechanical advantage, ideal mechanical advantage

1 Engage/Explore

Activating Prior Knowledge

Show the class a kitchen spoon, a whisk, and an egg beater. Ask: **Which tool do you think is the best one to use to mix cake batter? Why?** *(Most students will infer that all the tools can be used, but that the egg beater makes the work easier, particularly if the batter is heavy.)*

Discover Activity

Skills Focus forming operational definitions

Materials *objects that are machines—pliers, corkscrew, blunt knife, can opener, screwdriver, broom; objects that are not machines—eraser, pencil, chalk, paper, ruler, ball, book*

Time 20 minutes

Tips Assign students to small groups and give them a few objects to examine. Once a group has classified an object, they should pass it along to another group. Make sure students list the criteria they used to classify the objects. Allow students to classify machines based on their own criteria.

Think It Over Students may say that objects that were machines could do work or make work easier. Or they may say a machine helps you to exert force.

Section 2 Mechanical Advantage and Efficiency

Discover Activity

Is It a Machine?

1. Your teacher will give you an assortment of objects. Examine each object closely.
2. Sort the objects into those that you think are machines and those you think are not machines.
3. Determine how each object that you have identified as a machine functions. Explain each object to another student.

Think It Over

Forming Operational Definitions Why did you decide certain objects were machines while other objects were not?

Guide for Reading

- **How do machines make work easier?**
- **What is the difference between actual and ideal mechanical advantage?**
- **How can you calculate the efficiency of a machine?**

Reading Tip **As you read, use the headings to make an outline showing what machines do.**

A truckload of mulch for your new garden has just arrived. The only problem is that the pile of mulch has been dumped 10 meters from where it belongs. What can you do? You could move the mulch by handfuls, but that would take a very long time. You could use a shovel and a wheelbarrow, which would make the job much easier. Or you could have a bulldozer move it. That would make the job easier still.

What Is a Machine?

Shovels and bulldozers are examples of machines. A **machine** is a device with which you can do work in a way that is easier or more effective. You may be used to thinking of machines as complex gadgets that run on electricity, but a machine can be as simple as a shovel or even a ramp.

Perhaps you think that a machine decreases the amount of work that is done. But it doesn't. Moving the pile of mulch, for example, will involve the same amount of work no matter how you do it. Similarly, you have to do the same amount of work to lift a piano whether you lift it by hand or push it up a ramp.

Reading Strategies

Reading Tip Write the following outline guide on the board. Review each item with students before they create outlines that show what machines do.

I. First Main Idea
  A. First supporting idea or fact.
    1. detail or example
    2. detail or example
  B. Second supporting idea or fact.
II. Second Main Idea (outline will continue)

Vocabulary Lead a discussion of the terms *input force* and *output force.* Then have students name other uses of *input* and *output* with which they are familiar.

Study and Comprehension Assign each of three students in a group one of the Guide for Reading questions. Allow time for students to reread the section to make notes on the answer to their question. Then have students present their answers to the group.

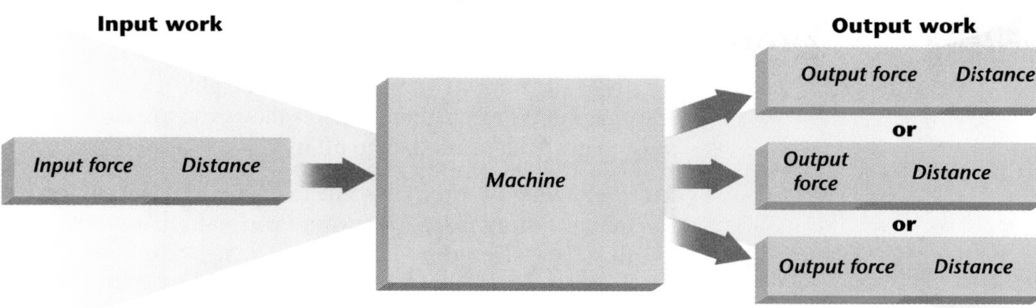

Figure 5 A machine can make a task easier in one of three ways. *Interpreting Diagrams How does the output force compare to the input force in each type of machine?*

What the shovel and the ramp do is to change the way in which you do the work. **A machine makes work easier by changing the amount of force you exert, the distance over which you exert your force, or the direction in which you exert your force.** You might say that a machine makes work easier by multiplying either force or distance, or by changing direction.

When you do work with a machine, you exert a force over some distance. For example, you exert a force on the handle when you use a shovel to lift mulch. The force you exert on the machine is called the **input force,** or sometimes the effort force. The machine then does work, by exerting a force over some distance. The shovel, in this case, exerts a force to lift the mulch. The force exerted by the machine is called the **output force.** Sometimes the term resistance force is used instead, because the machine must overcome some resistance.

Multiplying Force In some machines, the output force is greater than the input force. How can you exert a smaller force than is necessary for a job if the amount of work is the same? Remember the formula for work: Work = Force × Distance. If the amount of work stays the same, a decrease in force must mean an increase in distance. So if a machine allows you to use less force to do some amount of work, you must apply the input force over a greater distance. In the end, you do as much work with the machine as you would without the machine, but the work is easier to do.

What kind of device might allow you to exert a smaller force over a longer distance? Think about a ramp. Suppose you have to lift a piano onto the stage in your school auditorium. You could try to lift it vertically, or you could push it up a ramp. If you use

Figure 6 The input force exerted on the shovel is greater than the output force exerted by the shovel.

2 Facilitate

What Is a Machine?

Using the Visuals: Figure 5

Have students compare the total amount of input work with the total amount of output work. Ask students: **How does the total input work compare to the total output work in each type of machine?** *(The same)* **How do the distances compare?** *(different for the top two machines, the same for the bottom machine, where only the direction of the force changes)* Ask: **If you wanted to exert more force, which machine should you use?** *(The machine with the smaller distance)* Reinforce that a machine does not change the amount of work required—only force, distance, or direction. **learning modality: visual**

Building Inquiry Skills: Interpreting Illustrations

To help students understand the difference between input and output force, give them five pictures of machines taken from magazines or newspapers. Pair students and have them label the pictures with a marker, identifying the machine, the input force, and the output force. To further challenge students, ask them to infer whether the machine multiplies the input force, multiplies the distance over which the input force is exerted, or changes the direction of the input force. **learning modality: logical/mathematical**

Program Resources

- **Teaching Resources** 4-2 Lesson Plan, p. 103; 4-2 Section Summary, p. 104
- **Interdisciplinary Exploration Series** "Mill Life in the 1840s," pp. 10-11

Media and Technology

 **Audiotapes** English-Spanish Summary 4-2

Answers to Self-Assessment

Caption Question

Figure 5 In the top machine, output force is greater than input force. In the middle machine, output force is less than input force. In the bottom machine, output force is equal to input force.

Ongoing Assessment

Oral Presentation Ask students to explain how a snow shovel makes clearing a sidewalk easier. Students' explanations should use the terms input force and output force. *(The snow shovel takes the input force exerted on the handle and multiplies it to lift and move the snow.)*

What is a Machine?, continued

Including All Students

ACTIVITY

Some students may need extra help with understanding what happens when a machine multiplies force. Allow students to work in pairs to build a ramp with a board and a wooden block. Have students measure the length of their ramps and the height of their blocks. Ask: **Which measurement is greater?** *(The length of the ramp)* Fasten a string around a book and give students a spring scale to weigh the book. Then ask students to predict whether they would use more force lifting the book or pulling it up a ramp. *(Lifting it)* Allow students to test their predictions. Guide them to conclude that a ramp allows them to use less input force to do the work; thus, it multiplies the input force. **learning modality: kinesthetic**

Inquiry Challenge

ACTIVITY

Materials *meter stick, ruler, 2-cm stack of newspapers, desk or table*

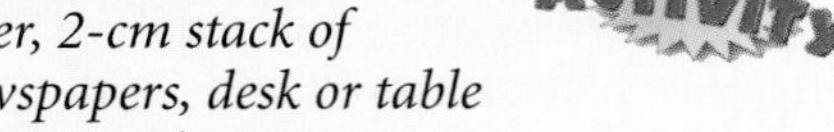

Time 15 minutes

Tips In this activity, students compare the mechanical advantage of two machines by making observations about the force needed to operate each. Organize students in small groups. To carry out the activity, have students place a 2-cm stack of newspapers on the edge of a desk or table. Students should slip a ruler under the stack so that 15 cm of the ruler is resting on the table. Then they can lift the stack of newspapers by pressing down on the end of the ruler with one finger. Next have students repeat the procedure with the meter stick. Ask: **Which lifter has the greater mechanical advantage?** *(The meter stick.)*

Extend Challenge students to design a method to calculate the output force, input force, and mechanical advantage for the ruler and meter stick. **cooperative learning**

the ramp, the distance over which you must exert your force is greater than if you lift the piano directly. This is because the length of the ramp is greater than the height of the stage. The advantage of the ramp, then, is that it allows you to exert a smaller force to push the piano than to lift it.

Multiplying Distance In some machines, the output force is less than the input force. Why would you want to use a machine like this? The advantage of this kind of machine is that it allows you to exert your input force over a shorter distance than you would without the machine. For you to apply a force over a shorter distance, you need to apply a greater force.

When do you use this kind of machine? Think about taking a shot with a hockey stick. You move your hands a short distance, but the other end of the stick moves a greater distance to hit the puck. The hockey puck moves much faster than your hands. What happens when you fold up a sheet of paper and wave it back and forth to fan yourself? You move your hand a short distance, but the other end of the paper moves a longer distance to cool you off on a warm day. And when you ride a bicycle in high gear, you apply a large force to the pedals over a short distance. The bicycle, meanwhile, moves a much longer distance.

Changing Direction Some machines don't multiply either force or distance. What could be the advantage of these machines? Well, think about raising the sail in Figure 7. You could raise the sail by climbing the mast of the boat and pulling up on the sail with a rope. But it is much easier to stand on the deck and pull down than to lift up. By running a rope through the top of the mast as shown, you can raise the sail by pulling down on the rope. This rope system is a machine that makes your job easier by changing the direction in which you exert your force.

***Checkpoint* What are three ways in which a machine can make work easier?**

Figure 7 One, two, three, pull! Up goes the sail. This sailor pulls down on the rope in order to hoist the sail into position. *Applying Concepts Why is the rope system considered a machine?*

Background

Facts and Figures Many machines make work easier because of automation—they are automatically controlled by mechanical or electronic devices.

Unlike machines such as shovels, axes, or even hockey sticks, automated machines usually don't require human effort, other than the initial effort required to turn them on. Today, machines such as dishwashers, washing machines, bread machines, video recorders, and CD players are controlled by tiny computers called microprocessors. All the operator has to do is to program the controller to carry out the function of the machine.

However automated they are, machines are still machines. They do not change the amount of work to be done, they just make the work easier.

Figure 8 Chop, chop, chop. A knife is a machine that makes your work easier when you prepare a tasty meal.

Mechanical Advantage

If you compare the input force to the output force, you can determine the advantage of using a machine. **A machine's mechanical advantage is the number of times a force exerted on a machine is multiplied by the machine.** Finding the ratio of output force to input force gives you the **mechanical advantage** of a machine.

$$\text{Mechanical advantage} = \frac{\text{Output force}}{\text{Input force}}$$

Mechanical Advantage of Multiplying Force For a machine that multiplies force, the mechanical advantage is greater than 1. That is because the output force is greater than the input force. For example, consider a manual can opener. If you exert a force of 20 newtons on the opener, and the opener exerts a force of 60 newtons on a can, the mechanical advantage of the can opener is 60 newtons ÷ 20 newtons, or 3. The can opener tripled your force! Or suppose you would have to exert 3,200 newtons to lift a piano. If you use a ramp, you only need to exert 1,600 newtons. The mechanical advantage of the ramp is 3,200 newtons ÷ 1,600 newtons, or 2. The ramp doubles the force that you exert.

Mechanical Advantage of Multiplying Distance For a machine that multiplies distance, the output force is less than the input force. So in this case, the mechanical advantage is less than 1. If, for example, you exert an input force of 20 newtons and the machine produces an output force of 10 newtons, the mechanical advantage is 10 newtons ÷ 20 newtons, or 0.5. The output force of the machine is half your input force, but the machine exerts that force over a longer distance.

Mechanical Advantage of Changing Direction What can you predict about the mechanical advantage of a machine that changes the direction of the force? If only the direction changes, the input force will be the same as the output force. The mechanical advantage will be 1.

Going Up ACTIVITY

Does a rope simply turn your force upside down? Find out!

1. Tie a piece of string about 50 cm long to an object, such as an empty cooking pot. Make a small loop on the other end of the string.
2. Using a spring scale, slowly lift the pot 20 cm. Note the reading on the scale.
3. Now loop the string over a pencil and pull down on the spring scale to lift the pot 20 cm. Predict the reading on the scale. Were you correct?

Developing Hypotheses How did the readings on the spring scale compare? If the readings were different, suggest a reason why. What might be an advantage to using this system?

Media and Technology

Transparencies "Machines," Transparency 10

Exploring Physical Science Videodisc Unit 3, Side 1, "Work, Work, Work"

Chapter 7

Answers to Self-Assessment

Caption Question

Figure 7 The rope system is considered a machine because it changes the direction of force to make work easier.

☑ Checkpoint

Machines can make work easier by multiplying input force, by increasing the output distance, or by changing the direction of the input force.

Mechanical Advantage

Addressing Naïve Conceptions

Some students may incorrectly assume that a machine with a mechanical advantage less than 1 is not a useful machine. Ask students to name a machine that makes work easier by multiplying the distance over which the input force acts. *(Sample: baseball bat, wooden spoon, bicycle)* Then ask them to describe the mechanical advantage of a machine that increases distance. *(Less than 1)* Help students conclude that a machine with an mechanical advantage of less than 1 may still be a useful machine. **learning modality: logical/mathematical**

TRY THIS

Skills Focus developing hypotheses
Materials *small cooking pot, 50-cm string or twine, 20-N spring scale, pencil*
Time 15 minutes
Tips Pair students. Before the activity, invite students to infer what they think will happen with the rope system. Students should find that it takes about 3 N to lift the pot directly with the spring scale, and about 6 N to lift the pot by looping the string over the pencil. Help students analyze their results by asking them to compare the amount of friction on the string in Steps 2 and 3.
Developing Hypotheses The reading on the spring scale was higher when the pot was lifted by a string looped over a pencil. Students may say that the readings were different because additional force was needed to overcome the friction between the pencil and the string in order to lift the pot in Step 3. The advantage to using the pencil is that it is easier to pull down than to pull up.
Extend Have students find the force needed to raise another pot when a pulley is used, then compare their results with the first activity. **learning modality: visual**

Ongoing Assessment

Skills Check Have students find the mechanical advantage of a lever if they exert 10 N to push it down and it exerts a force of 30 N to raise a box. *(3)*

Efficiency of Machines

Including All Students

Students whose native language is not English may have difficulty pronouncing the term *efficiency.* Provide all students with a phonetic spelling, such as *e FI shuhn see.* **limited English proficiency**

Integrating Mathematics

Guide students in interpreting the equation for efficiency. Ask: **Will the fraction output work/input work ever equal a value higher than 1? Why or why not?** *(No, output work is always less than input work because some work is always used to overcome friction.)* Then ask students to analyze the following machine: When the machine is properly maintained, it has an output work of 12 J for every 24 J of input work. When the machine is not properly maintained (needs to sharpened, lubricated, cleaned, etc.), the machine has an output work of 8 J. Ask: **How efficient is the machine when it is properly maintained? When it is not properly maintained?** *(properly maintained = (12/24) × 100% = 50%; not properly maintained: = (8/24) × 100% = 33%)* **learning modality: logical/mathematical**

Sample Problem

Be sure students are careful to divide the output work by the input work, otherwise they will calculate efficiencies over 100%. Reemphasize writing the formula first before substituting values. Some students may need a brief refresher in the meaning of percent and why the fraction is multiplied by 100.

Practice Problems

1. Efficiency = (825/1,500) × 100% = 55%
2. 40%

Efficiency of Machines

So far you have learned that the work you put into a machine (input work) is exactly equal to the work done by the machine (output work). In an ideal situation, this is true. In real situations, however, the output work is always less than the input work. If you have ever tried to cut something with scissors that barely open and close, you know that a large part of your work is wasted overcoming the tightness, or friction, between the parts of the scissors.

In any machine, some work is wasted overcoming friction. The less friction there is, the closer the output work is to the input work. The **efficiency** of a machine compares the output work to the input work. Efficiency is expressed as a percent. The higher the percent, the more efficient the machine is.

If the tight scissors described above have an efficiency of 60%, a little more than half of the work you do goes into cutting the paper. The rest is wasted overcoming the friction in the scissors. A machine that has an efficiency of 95% loses very little work. An ideal machine would have an efficiency of 100%.

Sample Problem

You cut the lawn with a hand lawn mower. You do 250,000 J of work to move the mower. If the work done by the mower in cutting the lawn is 200,000 J, what is the efficiency of the lawn mower?

Analyze. You are given the input work and the output work. You are asked to find the efficiency.

Write the formula. $\text{Efficiency} = \frac{\text{Output work}}{\text{Input work}} \times 100\%$

Substitute and solve. $\text{Efficiency} = \frac{200{,}000}{250{,}000} \times 100\%$

$\text{Efficiency} = 0.8 \times 100\% = 80\%$

Think about it. An efficiency of 80% means that 80 out of every 100 joules of work went into cutting the lawn. This answer makes sense, because most of the input work is converted to output work.

Practice Problems

1. You do 1,500 J of work in using a hammer. The hammer does 825 J of work on a nail. What is the efficiency of the hammer?
2. Suppose you left your lawn mower outdoors all winter. It's now rusty. Of your 250,000 joules of work, only 100,000 go to cutting the lawn. What is the efficiency of the lawn mower now?

Background

History of Science For many years, inventors and scientists were fascinated with the idea of a perpetual motion machine, which is a machine that runs continually with no input work. In 1150, a Hindu mathematician described a wheel that spun continually as weights swung outward on one side and inward on the other. Although many tried to build such a machine, it always failed. A perpetual motion machine of this kind will not work because all machines have efficiencies of less than 100%. Some work is always wasted in overcoming friction.

In the 18th century, James Cox designed a self-winding clock that used a barometer to drive the clockworks. It appeared to be a perpetual motion machine, but it actually received additional power from changes in the atmosphere.

Calculating Efficiency If you know the input work and output work for a machine, you can calculate a machine's efficiency. **To calculate the efficiency of a machine, divide the output work by the input work and multiply the result by 100 percent.** This is summarized by the following formula.

INTEGRATING MATHEMATICS

$$Efficiency = \frac{Output\ work}{Input\ work} \times 100\%$$

Actual and Ideal Mechanical Advantage The mechanical advantage that a machine provides in a real situation is called the **actual mechanical advantage.** You can only determine the actual mechanical advantage by measuring the true input and output forces. It cannot be determined in advance because the actual values depend on the efficiency of the machine.

You cannot predict the actual mechanical advantage of a machine. But you can predict a quantity related to the actual mechanical advantage if you ignore losses due to friction. In other words, you can consider the machine under ideal conditions. **The mechanical advantage of a machine without friction is called the ideal mechanical advantage of the machine.** The more efficient a machine is, the closer the actual mechanical advantage is to the **ideal mechanical advantage.** By keeping a machine clean and well lubricated, you can make its operation closer to the ideal. In this way you can increase the machine's efficiency and make your own work easier.

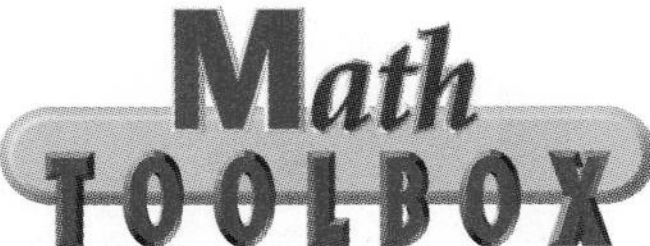

Percents

When you compare a number to 100, you are finding a percent. For example, 25 out of 100 can be written as 25 ÷ 100 or 25%.

Any ratio can be written as a percent by multiplying the fraction by 100 ÷ 1 and expressing the answer with a percent symbol. For example,

$$\frac{11}{20} \times \frac{100}{1} = 55\%$$

$$\frac{3}{4} \times \frac{100}{1} = 75\%$$

The efficiency of a machine is compared to an ideal machine, which would be 100% efficient.

Section 2 Review

1. Explain how machines make work easier if they do not decrease the amount of work you need to do.
2. Why is the actual mechanical advantage of a machine different from a machine's ideal mechanical advantage?
3. What do you need to know to calculate the efficiency of a machine?
4. Can a machine increase both force and distance? Explain why or why not.
5. **Thinking Critically Comparing and Contrasting** Make a comparison table for two machines: one that increases force and one that increases distance. For each machine, compare input and output force, input and output distance, and input and output work.

Science at Home

Have a family member examine hand-powered devices around your home. You might pick a hand tool such as a shovel, hammer, or screwdriver, or a kitchen utensil such as a knife or egg beater. Explain the idea of input and output forces. Then have him or her identify the input and output forces for the device you picked.

Math TOOLBOX

Explain to students that *percent* comes from the Latin words meaning "by the hundreds." Point out that students can find the percent of a number written as a decimal by moving the decimal two places to the right. **learning modality: logical/mathematical**

3 Assess

Section 2 Review Answers

1. Machines change the amount of an input force required or the direction of a force.
2. Some work is used to overcome friction.
3. Output work and input work.
4. No, if one is increased the other is decreased.
5.

Sample Answer Table

For a machine that	Force	Distance	Work
increases force	input less than output	input greater than output	input greater than output
increases distance	input greater than output	input less than output	input greater than output

Science at Home

Sample answers: You exert input force on a hammer when you swing it; the hammer exerts output force when it hits a nail.

Program Resources

- **Interdisciplinary Exploration Series** "Mill Life in the 1840s," p. 29
- **Teaching Resources** 4-2 Review and Reinforce, p. 105; 4-2 Enrich, p. 106

Media and Technology

Interactive Student Tutorial CD-ROM M-4

Performance Assessment

Writing Have students imagine that they are engineering consultants for a lawn-mower manufacturer. They must explain why the actual mechanical advantage of their latest lawnmower is only 80% of its ideal mechanical advantage.

Skills Lab

Controlling Variables

Seesaw Science

Preparing for Inquiry

Key Concept Distance from the pivot point and the amount of input force play equal roles in determining the effect of the force on each side of a seesaw ($w_1d_1 = w_2d_2$).

Skills Objective Students will be able to
- control variables to determine the effect of a particular variable;
- make predictions about where to place a load to balance a seesaw;
- draw conclusions about how various factors affect a seesaw.

Time 30 minutes

Advance Planning Gather meter sticks, masking tape, pennies (or washers, hex nuts, or other standard sized objects), 50-g masses, and dowels or other cylindrical objects for pivot point.

Guiding Inquiry

Invitation Ask students: **What happens when an adult gets on one end of a seesaw and a child on the other?** Model this for students using a meter stick. Place the dowel at 50 cm for the pivot point. Put ten pennies on one end of the meter stick and five pennies on the other. Then ask students: **What can we do to make the meter stick balance?** Students may suggest that you could move the ten pennies closer to the dowel. Do this, then ask students if there is another way to balance the meter stick. They may suggest moving the pivot point closer to the ten pennies.

Introducing the Procedure

- Have the students read the procedure. Then ask them what variables are being changed and what variables are being held constant. *(Changed—number of pennies; held constant—pivot point, position of eight pennies)*

Troubleshooting the Experiment

- Students should position the meter stick so that the pivot point is on the center of the dowel. The meter stick will tend to move as it is used, and should be readjusted before each trial.

Skills Lab

Controlling Variables

Seesaw Science

In this lab, you will use the skill of controlling variables as you investigate the properties of seesaws.

Problem

What is the relationship between distance and weight for a balanced seesaw?

Materials

meter stick
masking tape
28 pennies, post-1982
small object, mass about 50 g
dowel or other cylindrical object for pivot point, about 10 cm long and 3 cm in diameter

Procedure

1. Begin by using the dowel and meter stick to build a seesaw. Tape the dowel firmly to the table so that it does not roll.
2. Choose the meter stick mark that will rest on the dowel from the following: 55 cm, 60 cm, 65 cm, 70 cm, or 75 cm. Record your choice. Position your meter stick so that it is on your chosen pivot point with the 100-cm mark on your right.
3. Slide the 50-g mass along the shorter end of the meter stick until the meter stick is balanced, with both sides in the air. (This is called "zeroing" your meter stick.)
4. Copy the data table into your notebook.
5. Place a stack of 8 pennies exactly over the 80-cm mark. Determine the distance, in centimeters, from the pivot point to the pennies. Record this distance in the "Distance to Pivot" column for the left side of the seesaw.
6. Predict where you must place a stack of 5 pennies in order to balance the meter stick. Test your prediction and record the actual position in the "Position of Pennies" column for the right side of the seesaw.

DATA TABLE

Your group's pivot point position: _____ cm

Trial #	Side of Seesaw	# of Pennies or Weight of Pennies (pw)	Position of Pennies (cm)	Distance to Pivot (cm)	# of Pennies × Distance
1	right				
	left				
2	right				
	left				
3	right				

- Students should measure the position of the center of the stack of pennies to the nearest tenth of a centimeter.

Expected Outcome

- Students' data should illustrate that a large weight close to the pivot point can be compensated by a small weight far from the pivot point (and vice versa).

Analyze and Conclude

1. Manipulated variable—the weight on the left side of the pivot point, because it is the variable which is being changed in each trial; responding variable—distance of that weight from the pivot point needed to achieve balance, because it changes as a result of the change in weight
2. As the number of pennies on the left increases, the distance must be decreased to balance the see saw.
3. For a balanced seesaw, the product of weight and distance from the pivot point on the left is equal to the product of weight and distance

7. Determine the distance, in centimeters, from the pivot point to the left stack of pennies. Record this distance in the "Distance to Pivot" column for the right side of the seesaw.
8. If you use an imaginary unit of weight, the pennyweight (pw), then one penny weighs 1 pw. Multiply the weight of each stack of pennies by the distance to the pivot point. Record the result in the last column of the data table.
9. Predict how the position of the pennies in Step 6 would change if you used 7, 12, 16, and 20 pennies instead of 5 pennies. Test your predictions.

Analyze and Conclude

1. In this experiment, what is the manipulated variable? The responding variable? How do you know which is which?
2. As you increase the number of pennies on the right, what happens to the distance at which you must place the stack in order to balance the meter stick?
3. What conclusion can you draw about the relationship between distances and weights needed to balance a seesaw?
4. Why was it important to zero the meter stick with the 50-g mass?
5. Compare your results with the other groups. How do different positions of the pivot point affect the results?
6. **Think About It** Name two other variables that could be manipulated in this experiment.

Design an Experiment

Suppose you have a seesaw with a movable pivot. You want to use it with a friend who weighs half what you weigh. You and your friend want to sit on the two ends of the seesaw. Make a hypothesis about where you should position the pivot point. Explain how you could modify the pennies experiment to see if you are right.

from the pivot point on the right ($w_1d_1 = w_2d_2$). Weight and distance have equal importance in balancing the seesaw.
4. To ensure that the meter stick is balanced before you begin
5. For all groups, ($w_1d_1 = w_2d_2$). Different positions of the pivot point do not affect the result.
6. Accept any two: the distance of the weight on the left, the pivot point, the weight on the right, the distance on the left.

Design an Experiment
Students should hypothesize that the distance of the smaller student from the pivot point should be twice the distance of the larger student from the pivot point. For example, for a seesaw 3 m long, the distance of the smaller student from the pivot point should be 2 m, and the distance of the larger student from the pivot point should be 1 m. One way the student could modify the experiment to test his or her hypothesis is to place five weights at 95 cm, ten weights at 5 cm, and the pivot point at 35 cm.

Sample Data Table

Your group's pivot point position: 55 cm

Trial #	Side of Seesaw	# of Pennies	Position of Pennies	Distance to Pivot
1	right	8	80	25
	left	5	40	15
2	right	8	80	25
	left	7	28.6	26.4
3	right	8	80	25
	left	12	16.7	38.3
4	right	8	80	25
	left	16	12.5	42.5
5	right	8	80	25
	left	20	10.0	45

Program Resources

Teaching Resources Chapter 4 Skills Lab, pp. 115–117

SECTION 3 Simple Machines

Objectives

After completing the lesson, students will be able to

- ◆ describe the six types of simple machines;
- ◆ calculate the ideal mechanical advantage of four types of simple machines;
- ◆ define compound machines.

Key Terms inclined plane, wedge, screw, lever, fulcrum, wheel and axle, pulley, compound machine, gears

1 Engage/Explore

Activating Prior Knowledge

From a selection of ordinary household objects, such as chopsticks, table knives, screwdrivers, and so on, show students examples of each kind of simple machine. Have students describe how each machine works and how it differs from the others.

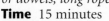

DISCOVER ACTIVITY

Skills Focus predicting
Materials *2 broomsticks or dowels, long rope*
Time 15 minutes
Tips After students have pulled the broom sticks together using the rope, ask: **What did the rope do to the force?** *(It multiplied the force exerted on the rope.)* Encourage students to test the predictions they make in Think It Over.
Expected Outcome Students should find it extremely difficult, if not impossible, to bring the students together by pulling on the broomsticks. They will be able to bring the brooms together by pulling on the rope.
Think It Over Wrapping the rope several more times will increase the force exerted on the broomsticks.

SECTION 3 Simple Machines

DISCOVER ACTIVITY

How Can You Increase Your Force?

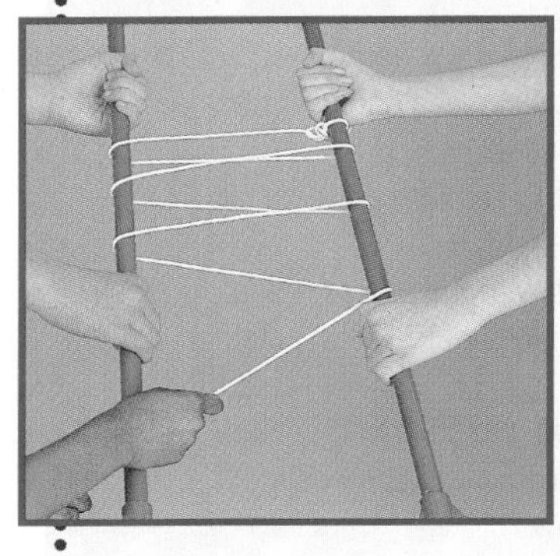

1. Working with two partners, wrap a rope around two broomsticks as shown.
2. Your two partners should try to hold the brooms apart with the same amount of force throughout the activity. For safety, they should hold firmly, but not with all their strength.
3. Try to pull the two students together by pulling on the broomsticks. Can you do it?
4. Can you pull them together by pulling on the rope?

Think It Over
Predicting What do you think will be the effect of wrapping the rope around the broomstick several more times?

GUIDE FOR READING

- ◆ What are the six kinds of simple machines?
- ◆ How can you calculate the mechanical advantage of simple machines?

Reading Tip As you read, make a list of the six kinds of simple machines. Describe each one in your own words.

Look at the objects shown on these pages. Which of them would you call machines? Would it surprise you to find out that each is an example of a simple machine? As you learned in the last section, a machine helps you do work by changing the amount or direction of the force you need to apply.

There are six basic kinds of simple machines: the inclined plane, the wedge, the screw, the lever, the wheel and axle, and the pulley. In this section you will learn how the different types of simple machines help you.

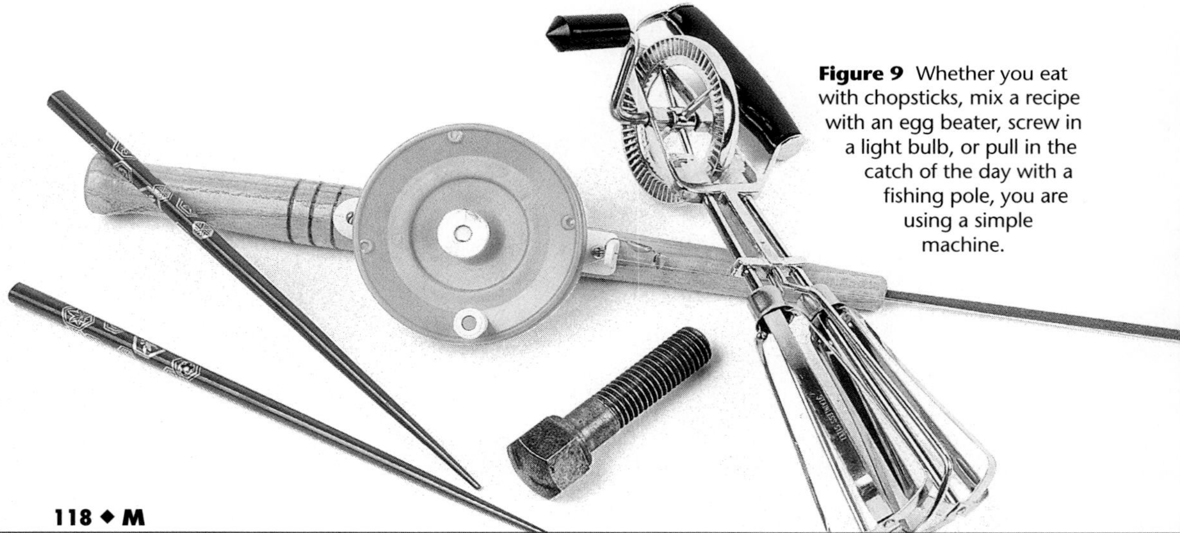

Figure 9 Whether you eat with chopsticks, mix a recipe with an egg beater, screw in a light bulb, or pull in the catch of the day with a fishing pole, you are using a simple machine.

READING STRATEGIES

Reading Tip Give each student six notecards. After students read the second paragraph, have them write the name of one type of simple machine on each notecard. As students read the section, instruct them to use their own words to write a description of each type of machine on the back of the card and at least one example of the machine. Pair students and have partners use the cards to quiz each other.

Study and Comprehension Before students read the section, have them preview each figure and caption. Suggest they answer these questions for each figure:

- ◆ What is being shown in this picture?
- ◆ What is the main idea of the picture?
- ◆ How does the information in the caption relate to what I already know?
- ◆ What new information did I learn from the caption?

Inclined Plane

Have you ever faced the task of lifting something from a lower level to a higher level? You probably know that the job is much easier if you have a ramp. For example, a ramp makes it much easier to push a grocery cart over a curb or a cart into a truck. A ramp is an example of a simple machine called an inclined plane. An **inclined plane** is a flat, slanted surface.

An inclined plane allows you to exert your input force over a longer distance. The input force necessary will then be less than the output force. The input force that you use on an inclined plane is the force with which you push or pull an object. The output force is the force that you would need to lift the object without the inclined plane. This force is equal to the weight of the object.

Figure 10 Although the amount of work is the same whether you lift the loaded cart or push it up the ramp to the truck, you need less force when you use an inclined plane.
Relating Cause and Effect What happens to the distance over which you exert your force?

Advantage of an Inclined Plane **You can determine the ideal mechanical advantage of an inclined plane by dividing the length of the incline by its height.**

$$\textit{Ideal mechanical advantage} = \frac{\textit{Length of incline}}{\textit{Height of incline}}$$

Suppose you are loading a truck that is 1 meter high and you set up a ramp 3.0 meters long, as shown in Figure 11. The ideal mechanical advantage of this inclined plane is 3.0 meters ÷ 1 meter, or 3.0. This inclined plane multiplies your input force three times.

What can you conclude about how the length of the inclined plane affects the ideal mechanical advantage? If the height of the incline does not change, increasing the length of the incline causes the ideal mechanical advantage to increase. So the longer the incline (the less steep the incline), the less input force you need to push or pull an object.

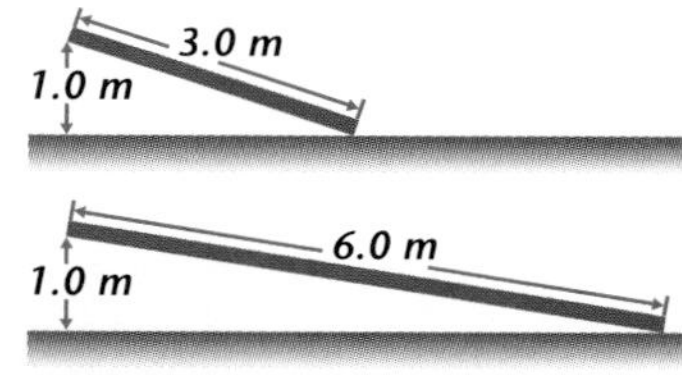

Figure 11 If you double the length of a ramp and leave its height unchanged, you double the mechanical advantage.

Efficiency of an Inclined Plane Even though an inclined plane has no moving parts, work is lost due to friction just as it is in any machine. The friction in this case is between the object and the inclined plane. For example, if you pull a crate up an

2 Facilitate

Inclined Plane

Real-Life Learning

Time 20 minutes

ACTIVITY

Inform students that professional furniture movers often use ramps when they move heavy objects onto a truck or up steps into a house. Group students and challenge them to design on paper a model ramp that could be used to move a piano from a driveway into a house. Make sure the design includes control of variables. Have students calculate the ideal mechanical advantage of their ramps and prepare drawings that show where the ramp would be installed as well as its dimensions. Then have them summarize and report on their design. As a follow-up to the activity, ask: **How does increasing the length of the ramp make it easier to move the piano into the house?** *(The longer the ramp, the less effort it takes to move an object, such as a piano, up the ramp.)* **learning modality: logical/mathematical**

Portfolio Students can save their drawings in their portfolios.

Building Inquiry Skills: Problem Solving

Have students identify ways to increase the efficiency of an inclined plane. *(Sample: Put the object on wheels, put a lubricant between the plane and the object, build the inclined plane out of a smooth material)* Then ask: **Does reducing friction on an inclined plane always make it more useful?** *(Sample: No, if there is too little friction on a ramp, a person walking on the ramp may slip and fall.)* **learning modality: verbal**

Program Resources

◆ **Teaching Resources** 4-3 Lesson Plan, p. 107; 4-3 Section Summary, p. 108

Media and Technology

Audiotapes English-Spanish Summary 4-3

Answers to Self-Assessment

Caption Question

Figure 10 The distance increases.

Ongoing Assessment

Drawing Tell students to draw several different inclined planes and calculate the mechanical advantage for each plane. Drawings should include the length and height of the incline.

Wedge

Demonstration

Help students understand how a wedge can make work easier by demonstrating that a can opener is an effective machine. Begin by showing students a large, unopened juice can. Then show students the following tools: a hammer, butter knife, nail, and a hand-held can opener. Ask: **Which of these tools are wedges?** *(Nail, can opener, butter knife, claw part of hammer)* If students do not recognize the can opener as a wedge, show them the sharp-edged wheel and explain why it is a wedge. Ask: **Which tool should we use to open the can?** Ask students to describe how the wedge on the can opener uses your input force to puncture the can. *(The input force exerted on the handle of the can opener is multiplied by the wedge. The larger output force from the thin edge punctured the can.)* **learning modality: visual**

Building Inquiry Skills: Predicting

Materials *3 chisels of different sizes, metric ruler*
Time 10 minutes
Tips Challenge students to predict which chisel requires the least input force to achieve a desired result. After they observe the length and width of each chisel head, ask them to predict which chisel uses input force most efficiently and explain their reasoning. *(The chisel head that is the longest in length and the thinnest in width; accuracy of predictions may vary.)* **learning modality: logical/mathematical**

Figure 12 A large force is required to split a log in two. But with the use of a wedge, a small force is multiplied to do the job.

incline, friction acts between the bottom of the crate and the surface of the incline. You can increase the efficiency of an inclined plane by decreasing this friction. There would be less friction, for example, if you put the crate on a dolly with wheels and rolled it up the inclined plane instead of sliding it.

Wedge

If you've ever sliced an apple with a knife or seen someone chop wood with an ax, you are familiar with another simple machine known as a wedge. A **wedge** is a device that is thick at one end and tapers to a thin edge at the other end. It might be helpful to think of a wedge as an inclined plane (or two inclined planes back to back) that can move. As in the case of the inclined plane, the longer and thinner a wedge is, the less input force is required to do the same work.

In a wedge, instead of an object moving along the inclined plane, the inclined plane itself moves. For example, when someone uses an ax to split wood, the person applies an input force to the ax handle. The ax handle exerts a force on the thicker end of the wedge. That force pushes the wedge down into the wood. The wedge in turn exerts an output force that pushes down through the wood, splitting it in two.

A zipper is another device that depends on the wedge. Have you ever tried to interlock the two sides of a zipper with your hands? It is almost impossible to create enough force with your fingers to join the two rows of teeth. But when you close a zipper, the part that you pull contains small wedges that multiply your input force. The result is a strong output force that either closes or separates the two sides of the zipper.

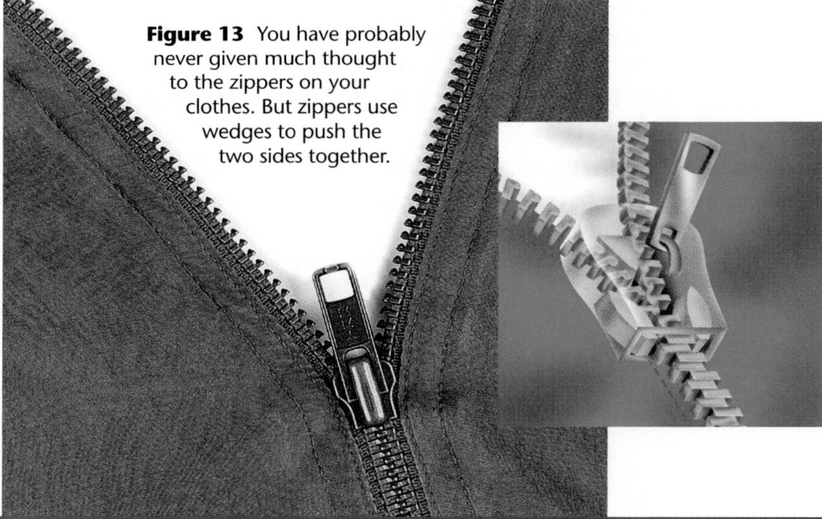

Figure 13 You have probably never given much thought to the zippers on your clothes. But zippers use wedges to push the two sides together.

Background

Facts and Figures The first tool thought to be made and used by human beings was a wedge. This tool, called a pebble tool, or chopper, dates back to the beginning of the Paleolithic, over 2.5 million years ago. The chopper was used for almost 2 million years, until the development of the hand axe.

When Neanderthals evolved about 110,000 years ago, they used many different hand axes, as well as the first knives and spears. About 40,000 years ago, the first modern humans invented another wedged tool called a burin, or graver. The graver could make narrow cuts into bone, and the Cro-Magnons used it to manufacture needles, hooks, and darts for spears and arrows.

Ground tools, including axe heads and chisels, appeared during the Neolithic Period, which began about 7000 B.C.

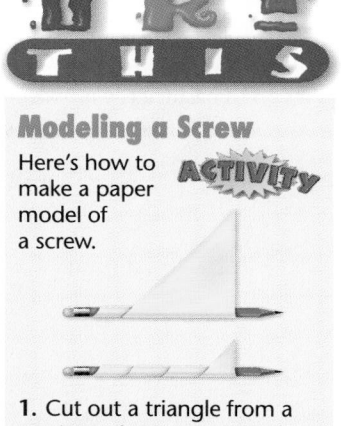

Figure 14 These screws multiply force by increasing the distance over which you exert your force. The smaller the distance between threads, the greater the distance the screw travels, and the less force you have to exert. *Relating Cause and Effect* *How does the distance between threads affect mechanical advantage?*

Screws

Like a wedge, a screw is a simple machine that is related to the inclined plane. A **screw** can be thought of as an inclined plane wrapped around a cylinder. This spiral inclined plane forms the threads of the screw.

When you use a screwdriver to twist a screw into a piece of wood, you exert an input force on the screw. As the threads of the screw turn, they exert an output force on the wood. If the threads of a screw are close together, you need to turn the screw many times in order to screw it into something. In other words, you apply your input force over a long distance. As with all machines, this increased distance results in an increased output force. The closer together the threads are, the greater is the mechanical advantage.

There are many other devices besides ordinary screws that take advantage of this principle. Examples include bolts, faucets, and jar lids. Think about a jar lid for a moment. You exert a relatively small input force when you turn the lid, but this force is greatly increased because of the screw threads on the lid (which fit into matching threads on the jar). The result is that the lid is pulled against the top of the jar with a strong enough output force to make a tight seal.

☑ *Checkpoint* *How are wedges and screws related?*

Levers

Have you ever ridden on a seesaw or pried open a paint can with an opener? If so, then you are already familiar with another simple machine called a lever. A **lever** is a rigid bar that is free to pivot, or rotate, about a fixed point. The fixed point that a lever pivots around is called the **fulcrum.**

TRY THIS

Modeling a Screw

ACTIVITY

Here's how to make a paper model of a screw.

1. Cut out a triangle from a piece of paper.
2. Tape the wide end of the triangle to a pencil. Then wind the paper around the pencil.

Making Models How does this model represent a real screw? Can you think of a way to calculate the ideal mechanical advantage of your model screw?

Screws

Using the Visuals: Figure 14

Guide students in analyzing which characteristics allow input force to be used most efficiently. Ask: **Which screw appears to have the largest diameter (requires the largest hole)? The smallest diameter (requires the smallest hole)?** *(Large screw on the lower right; screw on the top left)* Then ask: **Which screw appears to have the largest distance between threads? The smallest distance?** *(Screw at the top right; screw at the top left)* Remind students that the input force is used most efficiently when the diameter of the screw is large and the distance between the threads is small. **learning modality: visual**

TRY THIS

ACTIVITY

Skills Focus making a model

Materials *sheet of paper, long pencils, scissors, markers, ruler, tape, string*

Time 10 minutes

Tips Be sure students use right triangles. Keep the short sides of the triangles the same length. The short sides should be about the same length as the pencil. Have students mark the diagonal edge of the triangle with a marker. This will make the edge easier to see. As students examine paper triangles of different shapes, they should draw the conclusion that triangles with small angles and longer edges form model screws with tighter threads.

Making a Model The paper edge forms a spiral around the pencil, just like a real screw. To calculate ideal mechanical advantage, divide length of long side of paper triangle by length of side of paper parallel to pencil. **learning modality: kinesthetic**

Program Resources

◆ **Integrated Science Laboratory Manual** M-4 "Pulleys as Simple Machines"

Answers to Self-Assessment

Caption Question

Figure 14 The smaller the distance between the threads, the greater the mechanical advantage.

☑ *Checkpoint*

Both wedges and screws are related to inclined planes. A wedge is an inclined plane that moves. A screw is an inclined plane wrapped around a central cylinder.

Ongoing Assessment

Oral Presentation Ask students to explain why a lid that requires eight twists to seal a jar requires less input force than a similar lid that requires four twists. *(The first jar lid exerts the output force over a longer distance, so it requires a lower input force.)*

Using the Visuals: Figure 15

Calder trained as a mechanical engineer before beginning a career in art. Thus, he understood how simple machines work. As students examine the picture of Calder's mobile, ask them to point out one fulcrum and one lever. Ask: **What would happen if you pressed down on one end of the lever?** *(The other end of the lever will rise and exert a force on a connected lever; the whole mobile will begin to move.)* **learning modality: visual**

Visual Arts CONNECTION

Materials *construction paper, string, wire hanger*
Time 20 minutes

Students may need assistance constructing their mobile. Students will have more success working from the bottom up. It may be helpful to have students first sketch the mobile. Stress creativity and imagination in design.

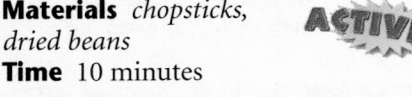

In Your Journal Make sure students include a description of how the mobile was constructed and balanced.

Portfolio Students can save their sketches or mobiles in their portfolios.

Cultural Diversity

Materials *chopsticks, dried beans*
Time 10 minutes

Identify the chopsticks in Figure 9. Discuss how these are used. *(One chopstick is held still while the other is moved back and forth.)* Ask: **What simple machine is used here?** *(lever)* Encourage students with experience using chopsticks to demonstrate how they are used by picking up the beans. Challenge students to identify the fulcrum, the source of the input force, and direction of the output force. *(fulcrum: finger on which moving chopstick rests; input force: pointer finger; output force: the tip of the moving chopstick closing down on the bean)* Ask: **What kind of lever is this? How do you know?** *(third-class lever; both forces are on one side of the fulcrum, with the input force between the output force and the fulcrum)* **learning modality: kinesthetic**

Visual Arts CONNECTION

Imagine creating a new form of art. Alexander Calder (1898–1976) did just that! Calder developed the art of mobiles. "A mobile is a piece of poetry that dances with the joy of life," he once said.

Calder combined his artistic flair with his knowledge of levers to express beauty through mobiles. You can, too.

In Your Journal

Make a mobile using construction paper, string, and a wire hanger. Write a description of your mobile and explain how you balanced it. Point out any adjustments you made to your design to balance the mobile.

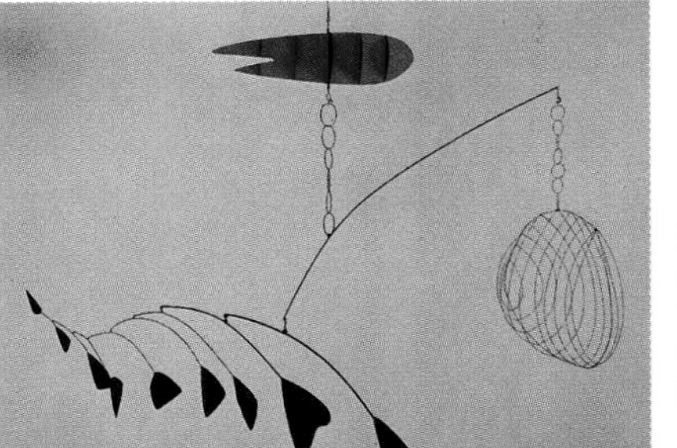

Figure 15 This Calder mobile, entitled "Lobster Trap and Fish Tail," is in the Museum of Modern Art in New York City.

To understand how levers work, think about using a paint can opener. The opener acts as a lever. The opener rests against the edge of the can, which acts as the fulcrum. The tip of the opener is under the lid of the can. When you push down, you exert an input force on the handle and the opener pivots about the fulcrum. As a result, the tip of the opener pushes up, thereby exerting an output force on the lid.

The lever helps you in two ways. First, it increases the effect of your input force. Second, the lever changes the direction of your input force. You push down and the lid is pried up.

Different Types of Levers When a paint can opener is used as a lever, the fulcrum is located between the input and output forces. But this is not always the case. There are three different types of levers, classified according to the location of the fulcrum relative to the input and output forces. Examples are described in *Exploring the Three Classes of Levers.*

Advantage of a Lever When you used the paint can opener, you had to push the handle for a long distance in order to move the lid a short distance. However, you were able to apply a smaller force than you would have without the opener.

You can calculate the ideal mechanical advantage of a lever using the distances between the forces and the fulcrum.

$$\text{Ideal mechanical advantage} = \frac{\text{Distance from fulcrum to input force}}{\text{Distance from fulcrum to output force}}$$

Output distance

Input distance

Figure 16 The mechanical advantage of this lever is greater than 1.

Remember the case of the paint can opener. The distance from the fulcrum to the input force was greater than the distance from the fulcrum to the output force. This means that the ideal mechanical advantage was greater than 1. A typical ideal mechanical advantage for a paint can opener is 16 centimeters ÷ 0.8 centimeter = 20. That's a big advantage!

☑ *Checkpoint* *What point on a lever does not move?*

Background

Facts and Figures Archimedes, a scientist and philosopher who lived in ancient Greece, is believed to have said this about the lever, a simple machine, "Give me a place to stand and I will move the Earth." Whether or not he actually said this, Archimedes clearly understood that a lever could be used to multiply force.

It is hard to think of a machine of any kind that does not involve levers. Some automobiles engines use levers to activate the valves. Some automobile clutches work with levers. The arms of construction cranes are levers, and lift immense loads. Pianos have levers for keys and pedals. The jaws of some vises open and close with levers. Some organs use levers to control the flow of air to the pipes.

EXPLORING the Three Classes of Levers

The three classes of levers differ in the positions of the fulcrum, input force, and output force. Note the locations of the labels in each example.

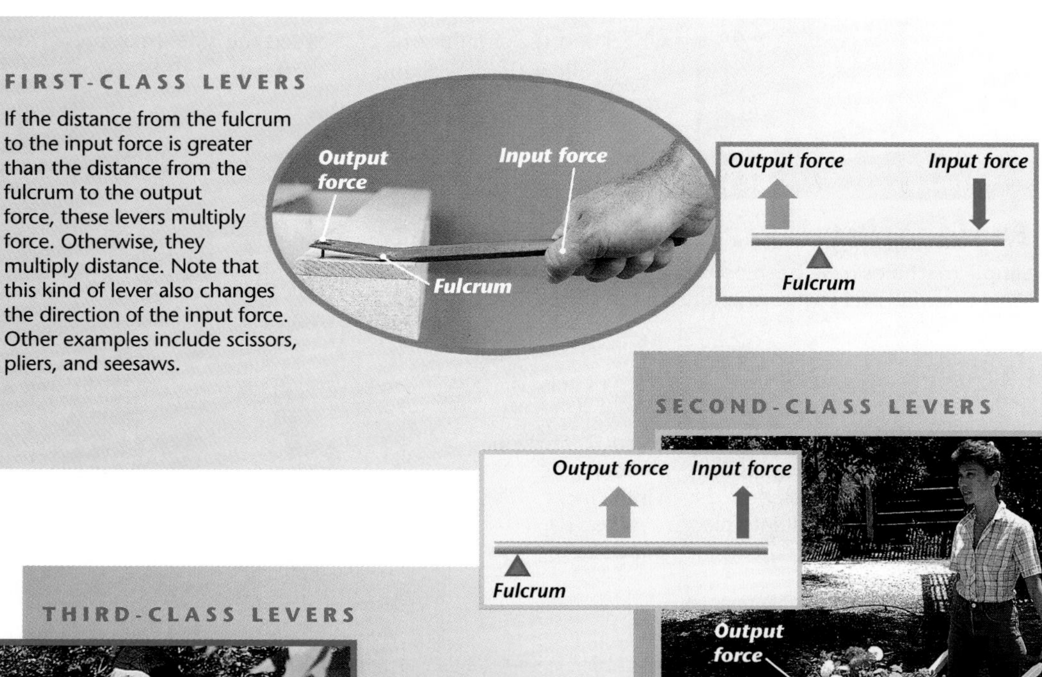

FIRST-CLASS LEVERS If the distance from the fulcrum to the input force is greater than the distance from the fulcrum to the output force, these levers multiply force. Otherwise, they multiply distance. Note that this kind of lever also changes the direction of the input force. Other examples include scissors, pliers, and seesaws.

SECOND-CLASS LEVERS These levers always multiply force. They do not, however, change the direction of the input force. Other examples include doors, nutcrackers, and bottle openers.

THIRD-CLASS LEVERS These levers multiply distance, but do not change the direction of the input force. Other examples include fishing poles, shovels, and baseball bats.

Program Resources

◆ **Interdisciplinary Exploration Series** "Wagons West," p. 21

Media and Technology

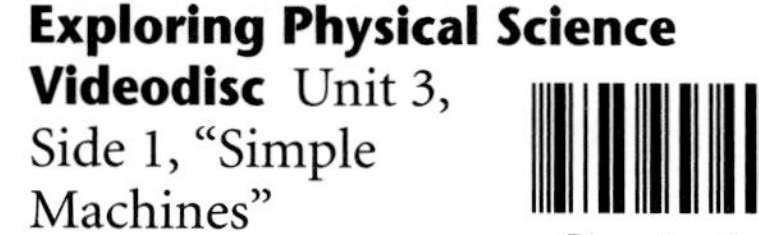

Exploring Physical Science Videodisc Unit 3, Side 1, "Simple Machines"

Chapter 8

Answers to Self-Assessment

☑ *Checkpoint*

The point touching the fulcrum

EXPLORING

The Three Classes of Levers

Materials *plastic spoons, raisins* ACTIVITY

Time 10 minutes

To compare the three classes of levers, students can model each one using plastic spoons and raisins. Organize students in pairs. Have one student place an index finger flat down on a table and balance the spoon on the finger. Another student can place a raisin in the bowl of the spoon and demonstrate how pressing on the spoon handle allows them to lift the raisin. Ask each group to identify the location of the input force, output force, and fulcrum. *(Input force—spoon handle, output force—bowl of spoon, fulcrum—finger)* Ask: **Did this first-class lever multiply force or distance?** *(Force—the students probably had to place their finger closer to the bowl than to the handle.)* Next, have one group member place the bowl of the spoon on the table and balance a raisin on the middle of spoon's handle. Another can carefully lift the edge of the handle. Ask: **How is this a second-class lever?** *(The fulcrum is at one end, the output force is in the middle, and the input force is at the other end of the lever.)* Finally, challenge groups to create a model of a third-class lever. Ask: **Where is the input force, output force, and fulcrum located in this lever?** *(Input force—in the center of the spoon handle, output force—at the bowl of the spoon, fulcrum—at the top of the spoon's handle.)*

Extend Challenge students to design and construct other models to demonstrate the 3 kinds of levers. **cooperative learning**

Ongoing Assessment

Skills Check Have students prepare compare/contrast tables that analyze the three classes of levers.

Wheel and Axle

Building Inquiry Skills: Measuring

Materials *plastic lid from coffee can, piece of cardboard or poster board, long pencil, scissors, measuring tape, marker, white paper* **ACTIVITY**

Time 15 minutes

Tips In this activity, students explore the relationship between a wheel and axle by designing cardboard wheels. Have students trace the coffee-can lid onto the cardboard and cut out the circle. Then have them make a hole in the center of the circle with scissors, and insert the pencil through the hole. Have students measure the circumference of the cardboard circle (wheel) and the pencil (axle) with the measuring tape. This equals the distance that the wheel and axle travel during one rotation. Ask: **How does the distance traveled by the wheel compare to that traveled by the axle?** *(It is greater.)* Then ask: **Based on your measurements, what will happen to an input force exerted on the wheel? On the axle?** *(An input force exerted on the wheel will cause the output force to be greater. An input force exerted on the axle will cause the distance that the force travels to be multiplied.)* **learning modality: kinesthetic**

Wheel and Axle

Could you insert a screw into a piece of wood using nothing more than your fingers? You would find it almost impossible. But with a screwdriver, you can turn the screw with ease.

A screwdriver makes use of a simple machine known as the wheel and axle. A **wheel and axle** is a simple machine made of two circular or cylindrical objects that are fastened together and that rotate about a common axis. The larger object is called the wheel and the smaller object is called the axle. In a screwdriver, the handle is the wheel and the shaft is the axle.

Engineering Marvels

Simple machines have been used to create some of the most beautiful and useful structures in the world.

2550 B.C. Great Pyramid, Giza, Egypt

Workers used wooden wedges to cut 2.3 million blocks of stone to build the pyramid. At the quarry, the wedges were driven into cracks in the rock. The rock split into pieces. Workers hauled the massive blocks up inclined planes to the tops of pyramid walls.

2000 B.C. **1000 B.C.** **A.D. 1**

500 B.C. Theater at Epidaurus, Greece

Instead of ramps, the Greeks relied on a crane powered by pulleys to lift the stone blocks to build this theater. The crane was also used to lower actors to the stage during performances.

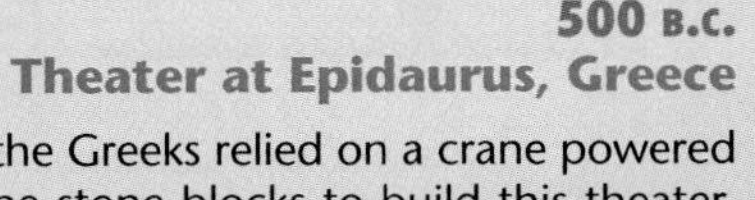

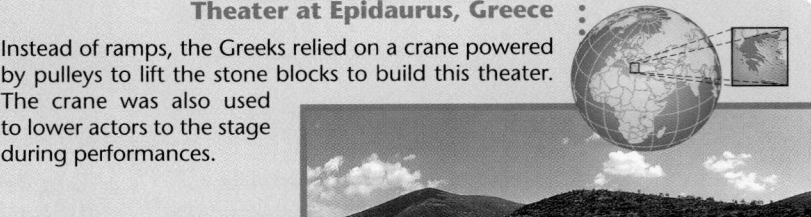

Background

Facts and Figures

- The wheel was most likely invented in Mesopotamia during the Bronze Age, around 3500 B.C.
- The spinning wheel was probably invented in India, but reached Europe in the Middle Ages.
- The first practical four-wheeled roller skates were designed in 1863 by James Plimpton, who lived in Massachusetts.
- The kinetoscope, the predecessor to the motion-picture projector, was invented in 1891 by Thomas Edison and William Dickson. The viewer looked through peephole in front of a spinning wheel with a narrow slit that acted as a shutter.
- The world's first true automobile, a steam-powered tricycle, was invented in France in 1869 by Nicolas-Joseph Cugnot.

Every time you turn a doorknob, you are using a wheel and axle. The knob is the wheel and the shaft is the axle. The water wheel of a mill, the steering wheel of a car, and the handle of an eggbeater are also examples of a wheel and axle.

Advantage of a Wheel and Axle How does a wheel and axle make work easier? You apply an input force to turn the wheel, which is larger than the axle. As a result, the axle rotates and exerts an output force to turn something such as a screw. The wheel and axle multiplies your force, but you must exert your force over a longer distance—in this case a circular distance.

Imagine that you are the person who first thought of using a simple machine at one of the construction sites in the time line. Write out your proposal. You'll need to research the time and place. Explain to the people in charge why the simple machine you suggest will give workers a mechanical advantage.

A.D. 1056

Yingxian Pagoda, China

Slanted wooden beams called *ang* act as first-class levers to hold up the roof of this pagoda. The weight of the center of the roof presses down on one end of the beam. The other end of the beam swings up to support the outer edge of the roof.

A.D. 1000 **A.D. 2000**

A.D. 1000

Brihadeshrava Temple, India

The temple's tower at Thanjavur rises to a height of more than 60 meters. Workers dragged the dome-shaped capstone, a mass of over 70,000 kilograms, to the top of the structure along an inclined plane several kilometers long.

A.D. 1994

The Chunnel, United Kingdom to France

Special drilling equipment was built to tunnel under the English Channel. Opened in May of 1994, the tunnel is 50 kilometers long. It carries only railway traffic.

Media and Technology

Transparencies "Exploring the Three Classes of Levers," Transparency 11

List some simple machines on the board. Then ask student volunteers to read the description of each engineering marvel shown in the time line. After each paragraph, ask a volunteer to name the simple machines used in the construction of the structure. Write the name of the structure beneath the name of that machine on the board. Then ask students to speculate on the tools that might be used to build similar structures today. *(Samples: jackhammers instead of a wooden wedges, motor-driven cranes in place of a hand-powered pulley or a ramp)*

In Your Journal Encourage students to prepare their journal entries as formal letters to the architects and construction leaders of particular projects. When they explain why the simple machine gives workers a mechanical advantage, students should mention how the machine makes work easier by multiplying input force, multiplying the distance the force is exerted, or changing the direction of the force.

Students can save their letters in their portfolios. **learning modality: verbal**

Extend Ask students to list common hand tools that they have used. *(hammers, pliers, screwdrivers, crow bars, etc.)* Discuss how these tools are used. (Remind them that a hammer can be used to pull out nails as well as hammer them in.) Ask the students to identify the simple machines these tools represent.

Ongoing Assessment

Writing Have students prepare magazine advertisements for a museum exhibit called *Ancient Engineering.* Students should describe at least three simple machines in their advertisements.

Wheel and Axle, continued

Addressing Naïve Conceptions

Some students may confuse the radius of a circle with its diameter or circumference. While any of these three may be used to calculate mechanical advantage of a wheel and axle, using the radius assures consistency. Draw a large circle on the board. Invite volunteers to draw in the radius, circumference, and diameter. Ask: **What is the relationship between the radius and diameter?** *(The radius is one half the diameter.)* Draw a large diagram of a wheel and axle on the board. Have students measure the radii and calculate the ideal mechanical advantage. **learning modality: visual**

Pulley

Building Inquiry Skills: Interpreting Diagrams

ACTIVITY

Materials *2 pulleys, rope, 1-kg mass, spring scale*
Time 30 minutes
Tips Allow pairs of students to assemble the pulleys shown in Figure 18. You may wish to provide a clothesline, wire, or wooden dowel between two chairs for students to hang their pulleys. For each set-up, students should raise the mass using a spring scale, record the force needed to lift it, and record the ideal mechanical advantage. Ask:

- **In which set-ups did you change the direction of force?** *(A and C)*
- **In which set-up did you have to exert the least input force to raise the pulley?** *(D)*

Encourage students to form hypotheses about the number of sections of rope supporting the mass and the ideal mechanical advantage of a pulley system. Allow them to test their hypotheses. *(Sample hypothesis: If the number of sections supporting the mass increases, the mechanical advantage will increase.)* **learning modality: kinesthetic**

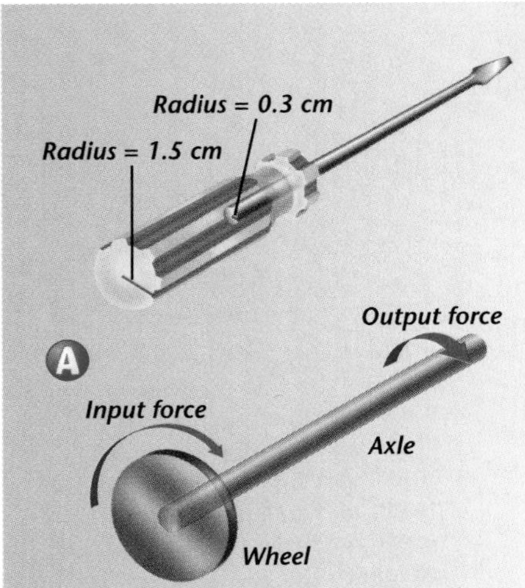

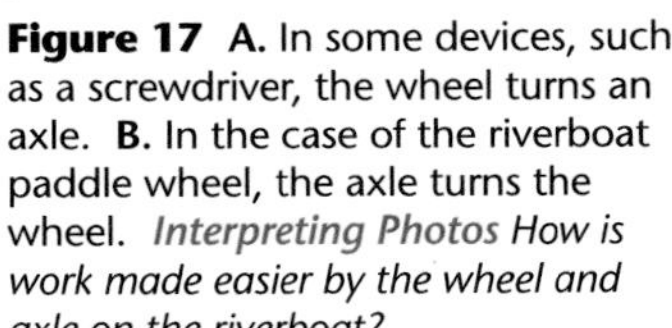

Figure 17 A. In some devices, such as a screwdriver, the wheel turns an axle. B. In the case of the riverboat paddle wheel, the axle turns the wheel. *Interpreting Photos How is work made easier by the wheel and axle on the riverboat?*

You can calculate the ideal mechanical advantage of a wheel and axle using the radius of the wheel and the radius of the axle. (Each radius is the distance from the outside to the common center of the wheel and axle.)

$$\text{Ideal mechanical advantage} = \frac{\text{Radius of wheel}}{\text{Radius of axle}}$$

For a screwdriver, a typical ideal mechanical advantage would be 1.5 centimeters ÷ 0.3 centimeter, or 5.

A Variation on the Wheel and Axle What would happen if the input force were applied to the axle rather than the wheel? For the riverboat in Figure 17, the force of the engine is applied to the axle of the large paddle wheel. The large paddle wheel in turn pushes against the water. In this case, the input force is exerted over a short distance while the output force is exerted over a long distance. So when the input force is applied to the axle, a wheel and axle multiplies distance. This means that the ideal mechanical advantage of the paddle wheel is less than 1.

☑ *Checkpoint* *How does a doorknob work?*

Pulley

When you raise or lower a flag on a flagpole or open and close window blinds, you are using a simple machine known as a pulley. A **pulley** is a grooved wheel with a rope (or a chain, or even a steel cable) wrapped around it. You use a pulley by pulling on the rope. As a result, you can change the amount and direction of your input force.

126 ◆ M

Background

Facts and Figures Many kinds of cranes use pulley systems to lift heavy objects and shift them horizontally.

Derricks are one class of crane. Derrick cranes consist of a boom called a jib, along which runs a pulley system. The cables or chains of the pulley system are wound and unwound around a drum at the base of the jib. The drum is turned by a motor. One type of derrick crane, a floating crane, is built onto a barge and used for constructing bridges or salvaging sunken objects. The *Musachi,* a floating crane built in Japan in 1974, can lift 3,000 tons.

Derrick is actually the name for the combination of a flexible rope or cable and pulleys used in cranes. The derrick was named after a famous seventeenth-century hangman in Tyburn, England.

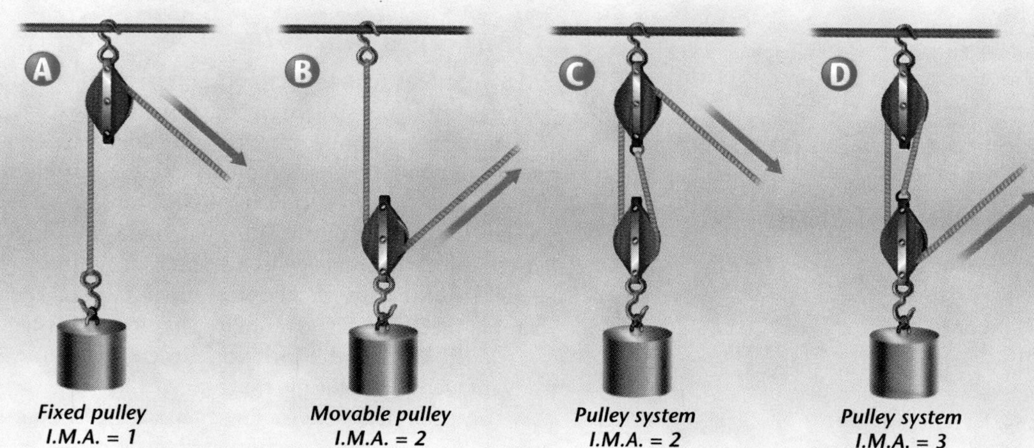

Figure 18 **A.** A fixed pulley changes the direction of your force. **B.** A movable pulley multiplies your force. **C, D.** You can combine fixed and movable pulleys to increase the mechanical advantage.

Fixed Pulleys A pulley that you attach to a structure is called a fixed pulley. A single fixed pulley, as shown in Figure 18A, does not change the amount of force you apply. Instead it changes the direction of the input force. The ideal mechanical advantage of a single fixed pulley is 1. A single fixed pulley can be used to raise a sail, as you read in the previous section.

Movable Pulleys If you attach a pulley to the object you wish to move, then you are using a movable pulley. As you see in Figure 18B, the object is then supported by each side of the rope that is looped around the pulley. As a result, the ideal mechanical advantage of a movable pulley is 2. The output force on the object is twice the input force that you exert on the rope. You can also see that you must exert your force over a greater distance. For every meter you lift the object with a movable pulley, you need to pull the rope two meters.

Notice that with the movable pulley, your input force is in the same direction as the output force. A movable pulley is especially useful when you are lifting an object from above. Large construction cranes often work with a movable pulley. A hook fastened to the pulley carries the building materials.

Pulley Systems If you combine fixed and movable pulleys, you can make a pulley system. Such a pulley system is also called a "block and tackle." The pulley system pictured in Figure 18C has an ideal mechanical advantage of 2. The pulley system in Figure 18D has an ideal mechanical advantage of 3. **The ideal mechanical advantage of a pulley system is equal to the number of sections of the rope that support the object.** (Don't include the rope on which you pull downward, because it does not support the object.)

Classifying ACTIVITY

Even though levers and pulleys may seem very different, pulleys can be classified as levers.

When you pull down on a fixed pulley, the object rises. In other words, the pulley changes the direction of your input force. This is what happens with a first-class lever. Instead of a bar, you apply your force to a rope. The center of the pulley acts like the fulcrum of the lever.

Draw a diagram showing how a single fixed pulley is like a first-class lever. Why is the mechanical advantage 1?

Sharpen your Skills

Classifying

Materials *first-class lever, single fixed pulley* ACTIVITY
Time 10 minutes
Tips Provide students with a first-class lever and a single fixed pulley to observe. Have them diagram both the pulley and the lever and label the diagrams to indicate the location and direction of input and output forces.
Expected Outcome Students should conclude that a single fixed pulley changes only the direction of the force, so the input and output forces are the same and the ideal mechanical advantage equals 1.
Extend Have students suggest why single fixed pulleys have an actual mechanical advantage less than 1. *(Some effort is used to overcome friction.)*

Students can save their diagrams in their portfolios.

Compound Machines

Inquiry Challenge

Materials *2 or 3 bicycles* ACTIVITY
Time 15 minutes

Students can investigate how a compound machine works by observing simple machines in a multi-speed bicycle. Group students and have the groups identify and report on the number of simple machines they find in each bicycle. Encourage students to label drawings showing the different simple machines and how the machines are connected to the bicycle. **cooperative learning**

Program Resources

- **Teaching Resources** 4-3 Review and Reinforce, p. 109; 4-3 Enrich, p. 110

Media and Technology

Interactive Student Tutorial CD-ROM M-4

Transparencies "Pulleys," Transparency 12

Answers to Self-Assessment

Caption Question

Figure 17 The input force is exerted over a short distance and the output force is exerted over a long distance, so turning the paddle is easier.

☑ Checkpoint

You apply an input force to the knob, or wheel, which causes the shaft, or axle, to rotate.

Ongoing Assessment

Oral Presentation Have students compare and contrast a single fixed pulley with a single moveable pulley.

3 Assess

Section 3 Review Answers

1. Sample answer: Inclined plane—ramp; wedge—knife; screw—jar lid; lever—see-saw; wheel and axle—doorknob; pulley—clothesline
2. inclined plane: length of incline/height of incline; lever: distance from fulcrum to input force/distance from fulcrum to output force; wheel and axle: radius of wheel/radius of axle; pulley: number of sections of rope that support the object
3. A flip-top opener is a first-class lever. You lift up on the metal tab (input force), the flip-top rotates around the point where it is connected to the can (fulcrum) and pushes in on the part of the top of the can where it is partially pre-cut (output force).
4. A machine with a mechanical advantage less than 1 allows you to increase the distance over which the input force acts. This is useful for a paddle wheel on a steamboat.

CHAPTER PROJECT 4

Check Your Progress

Measurements to make for calculating actual mechanical advantage are the weight of the load can (5.88 N) and the amount of input force needed to lift the load. Discuss how lengthening a lever, adding a pulley, or changing the angle of an inclined plane increases ideal mechanical advantage. Note that the ideal mechanical advantage of a compound machine is the product of the ideal mechanical advantages of its components.

Performance Assessment

Drawing Have students draw blueprints for a design of a compound machine that allows them to open their bedroom door while still lying in bed.

Figure 19 Both a pencil sharpener and a clock are examples of compound machines that use gears. ***Applying Concepts*** *What is a compound machine?*

Compound Machines

Many devices that you can observe around you do not resemble the six simple machines you just read about. That is because more complex machines consist of combinations of simple machines. A machine that utilizes two or more simple machines is called a **compound machine.** To calculate the ideal mechanical advantage of a compound machine, you need to know the mechanical advantage of each simple machine. The overall mechanical advantage is the product of the individual ideal mechanical advantages of the simple machines.

A mechanical pencil sharpener is a good example of a compound machine. When you turn the handle, you are using a wheel and axle to turn the mechanism inside the sharpener. The two cutting wheels inside are screws that whittle away at the end of the pencil until it is sharp.

Inside the pencil sharpener in Figure 19 is an axle that turns **gears.** The gears then turn the cutting wheels. A system of gears is a device with toothed wheels that fit into one another. Turning one wheel causes another to turn. Gears form a compound machine with one wheel and axle linked to another wheel and axle. Sometimes this link is direct, as in the gears shown in Figure 19. In other devices, such as a bicycle, this link is through a chain.

Section 3 Review

1. List and give an example of each of the six kinds of simple machines.
2. Explain how to find the ideal mechanical advantage of four types of simple machines.
3. What kind of lever is the flip-top opener on a soda can? Explain your answer with the help of a diagram.
4. **Thinking Critically Making Generalizations** Some machines give a mechanical advantage less than 1. Explain why you might want to use such a machine.

CHAPTER PROJECT 4

Check Your Progress

Think about whether force or distance is multiplied by each simple machine in your design. Consider how making levers longer, adding pulleys, or changing the angle of your inclined planes will affect the mechanical advantage. What measurements will you need to know to calculate the ideal mechanical advantage of your lifting machine? Finalize your design, and build your machine. As you build, consider how you can use lubrication or polishing to improve its efficiency.

Background

Facts and Figures Micromachines range in size from half a micron to 500 microns. Usually made from silicon, these machines are often simple gears and levers built at a tiny scale. Scientists envision one micromachine that could attack viruses in blood cells; such a machine might have gears the size of a protein molecule. Equipped with tiny sensors, micromachines may improve the manufacturing of all kinds of products.

Answers to Self-Assessment

Caption Question

Figure 19 A compound machine is a machine that uses two or more simple machines to do work.

Science and Society

Automation in the Workplace—Lost Jobs or New Jobs?

Workers 150 years ago spent long days stitching clothes by hand. In a modern American factory, a worker makes a shirt with a sewing machine and much less effort. Since ancient times, people have invented machines to help with work. Today, factories can use automated machines to perform jobs that are difficult, dangerous, or even just boring. Like science-fiction robots, these machines can do a whole series of different tasks.

But if a machine does work instead of a person, then someone loses a job. How can society use machines to make work easier and more productive without having some people lose their chance to work?

The Issues

What Are the Effects of Automation? New machines replace some jobs, but they also can create jobs. Suppose an automobile factory starts using machines instead of people to paint cars. At first, some workers may lose their jobs. But the factory may be able to produce more cars. Then it may need to hire more workers—to handle old tasks as well as some new ones. New jobs are created for people who are educated and skilled in operating and taking care of the new machines.

Still, some workers whose skills are no longer needed lose their jobs. Some are forced to work in different jobs for less money. Others may be unable to find new jobs. The challenge to society is to provide workers who have lost jobs with the skills needed for good new jobs.

What Can People Do? Education programs can train young people for new jobs and give older workers new skills. Those who learn how to use computers and other new machines can take on new jobs. Learning how to sell or design a product can also prepare workers for new jobs. Workers who have lost jobs can train for very different types of work—work that cannot be done by machines. A machine, for example, cannot replace human skill in day care or medical care.

Who Should Pay? Teaching young people how to work in new kinds of jobs costs money. So do training programs for adult workers who have lost jobs. What is the fairest way to pay these costs? Businesses might share some of the costs. Some businesses give workers full pay until they are retrained or find new work. The government might provide unemployment pay or training for the unemployed. Then all taxpayers would share the costs.

You Decide

1. **Identify the Problem**
   Describe in your own words the benefits and drawbacks of workplace automation.
2. **Analyze the Options**
   List ways society could deal with the effects of automation. For each plan, give the benefits and drawbacks and tell how it would be paid for.
3. **Find a Solution**
   The owner of the pizza shop in your neighborhood has bought an automated pizza-making system. Make a plan for the shop to use the system without having to fire workers.

You Decide

- Students' responses to Identify the Problem and Analyze the Options should be based on the concepts and issues presented in the text and in the class presentation. In response to Find a Solution, students may discuss issues raised in the debates.
- Make sure students understand that there are no "correct" opinions or solutions. As with many complex issues in our society, there are no easy answers.

Extend Have students contact and interview representatives from local industries about how much automation has affected their business. Students can ask if workers were displaced, and if so, whether the industries retrained displaced workers.

Science and Society

Automation in the Workplace—Lost Jobs or New Jobs?

Purpose

To provide students with an understanding of the problems created by worker dislocations as a result of increased automation in industry.

Debate

Time one class period for research and preparation, 30 minutes to conduct the debate

- Begin a discussion by asking students if they know anyone who has had to change jobs as a result of automation in the workplace. (Use caution. This may be a sensitive subject!) Work through an example of automation-induced changes with students. For example, in the automobile industry, robots now do most of the body welding formerly done by individual workers.
- Explain to students that they will be debating the proposition that "It is the responsibility of the local, state, or federal government to fund retraining for workers displaced by automation." Inform them that a debate is not an argument. In a debate, two groups discuss a proposition by presenting reasons that support their position.
- Separate the class into two groups: one to support the proposition, the other to oppose it. Have groups review and investigate the issue from their respective points of view.
- Both groups should critically and constructively support their viewpoints. Encourage students in the group supporting government-funded training to explore ideas such as who else could ultimately pay for worker retraining. Encourage students in the other group to consider the consequences if workers are not retrained, as well as alternatives to government training.

Real-World Lab

You and Your Community

Angling for Access

Preparing for Inquiry

Key Concept The actual and ideal mechanical advantages of an inclined plane, such as a wheelchair-access ramp, vary with steepness.

Skills Objective Students will be able to
- model a wheelchair ramp and relate it to a real ramp;
- measure distances and forces;
- calculate ideal and actual mechanical advantages.

Time 55 minutes

Advance Planning Gather boards for inclined planes, wooden blocks with eye hooks, spring scales, metric rulers, and markers. Any board about half a meter in length will do for an inclined plane. Make sure enough books are available, or ask students to bring some from home.

Alternative Materials A ballistic cart, which you may be able to borrow from the physics department, can be substituted for the wooden block. The forces needed to pull the cart and block are comparable because the cart has less friction, but generally is much heavier. You can use a 20-N spring scale to weigh the cart, or find its mass in grams with a balance scale and multiply by 0.01.

Real-World Lab

You and Your Community

ANGLING FOR ACCESS

You and your friends have volunteered to help build a wheelchair-access ramp for the local public library. The design of the ramp has not been decided upon yet, so you need to build a model inclined plane. The model will help you determine what the steepness of the ramp should be.

Problem

How does the steepness of a wheelchair-access ramp affect its usefulness?

Skills Focus

making models, measuring, calculating

Materials

board, at least 10 cm wide and 50 cm long
wooden block with eye-hook
spring scale, 0–5 N
4 books, about 2 cm thick
metric ruler
marker

Procedure

1. Preview the following steps that describe how you can construct and use a ramp. Then copy the data table into your notebook.
2. The output force with an inclined plane is equal to the weight of the object. Lift the block with the spring scale to measure its weight. Record this value in the data table.
3. Make a mark on the side of the board about 3 cm from one end. Measure the length from the other end of the board to the mark and record it in the data table.
4. Place one end of the board on top of a book. The mark you made on the board should be even with the edge of the book.

DATA TABLE

Number of Books	Output Force (N)	Length of Incline (cm)	Height of Incline (cm)	Input Force (N)	Ideal Mechanical Advantage	Actual Mechanical Advantage
1						
2						
3						
4						

Guiding Inquiry

Invitation Have the boards, spring scales, and blocks or carts in the room so that the students will notice them. Ask the students if they have seen or used a wheelchair ramp. Then ask them how they might make a model to investigate these ramps using materials in the room. Let students brainstorm things they might investigate using the model. Ask: **What variables can you manipulate?** *(Weight of the block or cart, steepness of the ramp, type of material the ramp is made of, height of the ramp, length of the ramp)* Then ask: **What are some responding variables?** *(Force needed to pull the block or cart up the ramp, amount of friction)* In this experiment, the manipulated variable will be the steepness of the ramp and the responding variable will be the force needed to pull the block or cart up the ramp at constant speed.

Introducing the Procedure
- If necessary, show students how to use and zero a spring scale. Stress the importance of pulling the spring scale parallel to the inclined plane to prevent inaccurate readings.
- Be sure that the students are clear what distances to measure. They are measuring from the table to the bottom of the ramp instead of the top to compensate for the fact that the top of the ramp doesn't go all the way to the table.

Troubleshooting the Experiment
- If the spring scale is calibrated in grams, the students can multiply by 0.01 to obtain a reading in newtons.
- Be sure students pull the block or cart at a slow, constant speed to measure the pulling force. The force needed to get the block or

5. Measure the vertical distance in centimeters from the top of the table to where the underside of the incline touches the book. Record this value in the data table as "Height of Incline."
6. Lay the block on its largest side and use the spring scale to pull the block straight up the incline at a slow, steady speed. Be sure to hold the spring scale parallel to the incline, as shown in the photograph. Measure the force needed and record it in the data table.
7. Predict how your results will change if you repeat the investigation using two, three, and four books. Test your predictions.
8. For each trial, calculate the ideal mechanical advantage and the actual mechanical advantage. Record the calculations in your data table.

Analyze and Conclude

1. How did the ideal mechanical advantage and the actual mechanical advantage compare each time you repeated the experiment? Explain your answer.
2. Why do you write ideal and actual mechanical advantage without units?
3. What happens to the mechanical advantage as the inclined plane gets steeper? On the basis of this fact alone, which of the four inclined planes models the best steepness for a wheelchair-access ramp?
4. What other factors, besides mechanical advantage, should you consider when deciding on the steepness of the ramp?
5. **Apply** Suppose the door of the local public library is 2 m above the ground and the distance from the door to the parking lot is 15 m. How would these conditions affect your decision about how steep to make the ramp?

Getting Involved

Find actual ramps that provide access for people with disabilities. Measure the heights and lengths of these ramps and calculate their ideal mechanical advantages. Find out what the requirements are for access ramps in your area. Should your ramp be made of a particular material? Should it level off before it reaches the door? How wide should it be? How does it provide water drainage?

Sample Data Table

Number of Books	Output Force (N)	Length of Incline (cm)	Height of Incline (cm)	Input Force (N)	Ideal Mech. Adv.	Actual Mech. Adv.
1	3.0	47	3.5	1.6	13.4	1.9
2	3.0	47	6.4	1.9	7.3	1.6
3	3.0	47	9.6	2.1	4.9	1.4
4	3.0	47	13.0	2.4	3.6	1.3

Program Resources

- **Teaching Resources** Chapter 4 Real-World Lab, pp. 118–119

cart started will be more than this and should not be used.

Expected Outcome

- Students data should show that the actual mechanical advantage is always less than the ideal mechanical advantage, and the actual advantage decreases with increasing height of the incline.
- If both carts and blocks are used, the actual mechanical advantages for the cart will be much higher than for the block.

Analyze and Conclude

1. The ideal mechanical advantage is always more than the actual mechanical advantage because of the friction between the block or cart and the incline.
2. Ideal mechanical advantage is obtained by dividing the length of incline by the height of incline. The units of distance (cm) cancel out. Actual mechanical advantage is obtained by dividing the output force by the input force. The units of force (newtons) cancel out.
3. The mechanical advantage decreases as the ramp gets steeper. On this basis alone, one would choose the least steep ramp.
4. Answers may vary. Sample: If the ramp is too gradual it may be too long to be feasible. If the ramp is too steep, it will be dangerous.
5. Unless the ramp doubled back on itself, the shallowness of the ramp would be limited by those conditions. The best possible ideal mechanical advantage would be 15/2 = 7.5.

Extending the Inquiry

Getting Involved Students may have difficulty measuring the length and height of their ramps. Explain that only the ratio of length to height determines the ideal mechanical advantage, and that this ratio is the same for all or part of the ramp. Students can work with only part of the ramp if that is more feasible. When interviewing people who use access ramps, students should prepare a series of questions in advance. Students should explain what they are doing and why, so that people will be more inclined to respond to their requests for an interview.

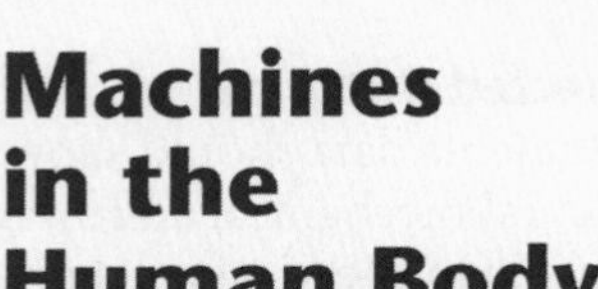

Machines in the Human Body

Objectives

After completing the lesson, students will be able to

- ◆ explain how the body uses levers and wedges.

Key Term tendons

1 Engage/Explore

Activating Prior Knowledge

Have two student volunteers kick a soccer ball back and forth. Ask: **Is work being done? How can you tell?** *(Yes; the ball is moving and changing direction.)* Then ask: **What is doing the work on the ball?** *(The student's feet and legs)* Challenge students to infer how legs are related to simple machines. Explain that legs can be considered to be levers.

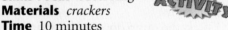

DISCOVER

Skills Focus observing
Materials *crackers*
Time 10 minutes
Tips Tell students to take a bite of the cracker using their front teeth, rather than placing the entire cracker into their mouths at one time. Allow students to repeat the exercise until they are sure they can determine how their jaws move. If your school has one, a model of the jaw would be helpful.
Expected Outcome Students should not have difficulty recognizing that their front teeth are wedges. The recognition that their jaws are levers may be more difficult. But by opening their mouths wide so that the front of the jaw moves down, students should be able to feel the back of the jaw move up.
Think It Over The jaw is a lever; the teeth are wedges.

SECTION 4 Machines in the Human Body

DISCOVER ACTIVITY

Are You an Eating Machine?

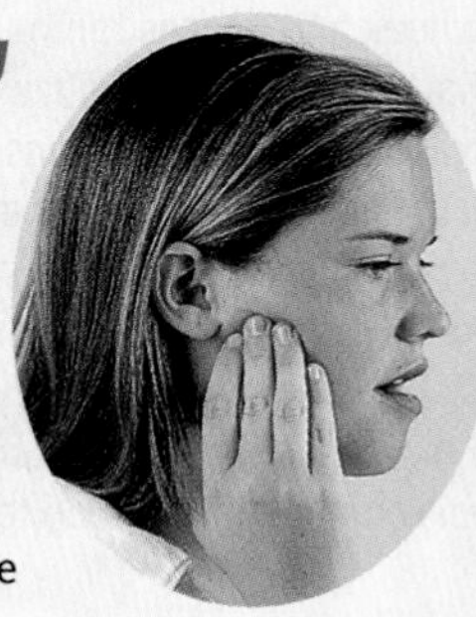

1. Using your front teeth, bite off a piece of a cracker. As you bite, observe how your teeth are breaking the cracker. Also think about the shape of your front teeth.
2. Now chew the cracker. Pay attention to how your lower jaw moves. Touch your jaw below your ear, as shown in the photo. As you chew, push in slightly there so that you can feel how your jaw moves. If the structure is still not clear, try opening your mouth wide while you feel the back of the jaw.

Think It Over
Observing When you bite and chew, your teeth and jaws serve as two kinds of machines. What are they?

GUIDE FOR READING

- ◆ How does the body use levers and wedges?

Reading Tip **Before you read, preview the illustrations and predict how simple machines are related to the human body.**

It's Saturday night, and you and your friends are taking a well-deserved break from your school work. You're watching a great movie, happily eating popcorn from a big bowl. Are you doing any work? Surprisingly, you are!

Every time you reach for the popcorn, your muscles exert a force that causes your arm to move. And when you chew on the popcorn, breaking it into bits that you can easily swallow, you are again doing work.

How are you able to do all this work without even noticing? The answer is machines! You probably don't think of the human body as being made of machines. But believe it or not, machines are involved in much of the work that your body does.

Living Levers

Most of the machines in your body are levers that consist of bones and muscles. Every time you move, you use a muscle. Your muscles are attached to your bones by tough connective tissue called **tendons.** Tendons and muscles pull on bones, making them work as levers. The joint, near where the tendon is attached to the bone, acts as the fulcrum of the lever. The muscles produce the input force. The output force is used for everything from lifting your hand to swinging a hammer.

READING STRATEGIES

Reading Tip Have partners work together to preview the illustrations and predict ways that simple machines are related to the human body. Suggest that they return to Section 3 for a quick review of simple machines. Encourage students to imitate the actions being shown in the illustrations as they make their predictions.

Compare/Contrast Tables Have students make compare/contrast tables which indicate the characteristics of levers and wedges and give examples of human-made machines and of machines in the body.

Compare/Contrast

	Levers	Wedges
Characteristics	bar that pivots about a fulcrum	tapered, inclined plane
Examples	scissors, pliers, neck, arm, foot	axe, zipper, teeth

A muscle by itself cannot push; it can only pull. When a muscle contracts, or becomes shorter, it pulls the bone to which it is attached. So how can you bend your arm as shown in *Exploring Levers in the Body?* The answer is that most muscles work in pairs. For example, when your biceps muscle (on the front of the upper arm) contracts, it exerts a force on the bone in your forearm. The result is that you arm bends at the elbow joint, which in this case is the fulcrum of the lever. When the triceps muscle (on the back of the upper arm) contracts, it opens the elbow joint.

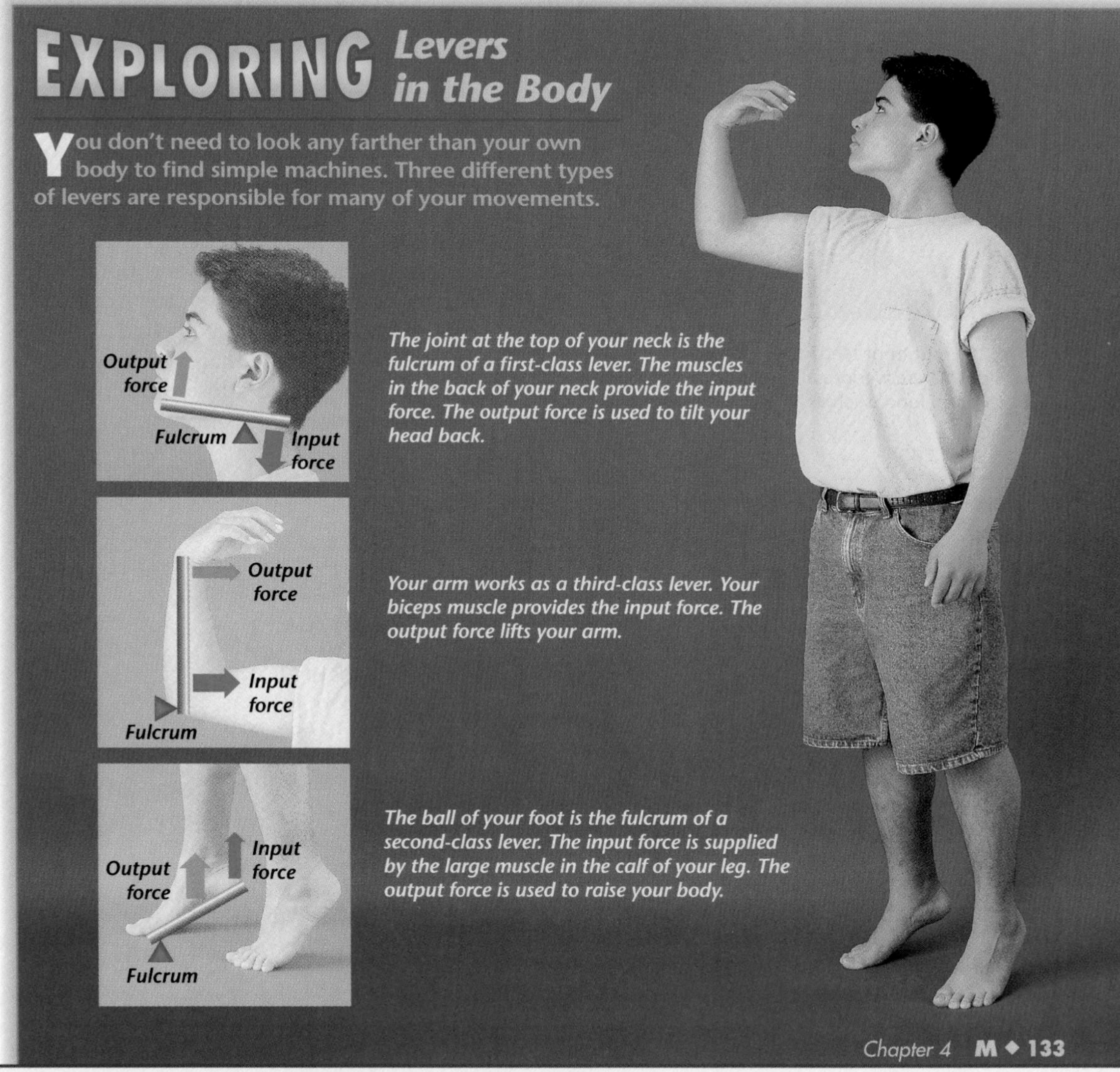

EXPLORING Levers in the Body
You don't need to look any farther than your own body to find simple machines. Three different types of levers are responsible for many of your movements.
Output force
Fulcrum
Input force
The joint at the top of your neck is the fulcrum of a first-class lever. The muscles in the back of your neck provide the input force. The output force is used to tilt your head back.
Output force
Input force
Fulcrum
Your arm works as a third-class lever. Your biceps muscle provides the input force. The output force lifts your arm.
Output force
Input force
Fulcrum
The ball of your foot is the fulcrum of a second-class lever. The input force is supplied by the large muscle in the calf of your leg. The output force is used to raise your body.
Chapter 4 M ◆ 133

2 Facilitate

Living Levers

Building Inquiry Skills: Observing

Materials *skinned chicken wings, antibacterial wipes*
Time 20 minutes
CAUTION: Make sure students use antibacterial wipes or wash their hands with antibacterial soap after handling the chicken wings. Have students diagram the wings, label the muscles, tendons, and bones, and label the input force, output force, and fulcrum of one lever in the wing. After the activity, have students properly dispose of the wings. **learning modality: kinesthetic**

EXPLORING Levers in the Body

Have students copy motions shown in the photos. Pair students and allow each to feel their partner's muscles contract as force is applied. As they look at the first photo, one student can place a hand on the back of his or her partner's neck. Ask: **What do you feel as your partner lowers and raises his or her head?** *(The muscles tighten and contract)* As students examine the photo of the arm and move their arms as shown, ask: **What other joints work as third-class levers?** *(knuckles, knees)*
Extend Challenge students to draw a diagram or construct a model that shows how the motion of the arm would be affected if a tendon was injured. **learning modality: visual**

Program Resources

◆ **Teaching Resources** 4-4 Lesson Plan, p. 111; 4-4 Section Summary, p. 112

Science Explorer Series *Human Biology and Health,* Chapter 2, covers bones and muscles.

Media and Technology

Audiotapes English-Spanish Summary 4-4

Exploring Life Science Videodisc Unit 4, Side 1, "Muscles and Bones"

Chapter 2

Ongoing Assessment

Oral Presentation Have students describe how their arms function as simple machines when they raise light dumbbells. *(The arm is a lever. The biceps provide the input force, the elbow is the fulcrum, and the lower hand and arm provide the output force to move the barbell.)*

Working Wedges

Including All Students

Suggest that all students use their tongue to feel the shape of their teeth. Then provide students with a model of human jaw and teeth. Allow them to feel the difference between the wedge-shaped incisors and the broad back teeth. Ask: **How would you find the mechanical advantage of the incisors?** *(Divide the length of the tooth by the width of the tooth at the point where it is attached to the jaw.)* **learning modality: kinesthetic**

3 Assess

Section 4 Review Answers

1. The bones are levers. The muscles exert the input force.
2. Some teeth are wedges. They are used to bite into foods.
3. The fulcrum is at the base of the index finger, where the finger meets the hand. The input force is the contraction of a muscle attached partway up the finger. The finger is a third-class lever.
4. You use the triceps muscle to straighten your arm. It is a third-class lever.

Performance Assessment

Drawing Have students trace their hands onto a piece of paper. They should identify all the levers in the hand, then label the fulcrums, output forces, and input forces.

Figure 20 Your front teeth are shaped like wedges. These wedges allow you to cut through food, such as an apple.

Look again at the different levers in *Exploring Levers in the Body*. You will see that you can find a lever in your neck and another lever in your leg and foot. Just as you found with shovels, wheelbarrows, and fishing poles, the type of lever you find in the human body depends on the locations of the fulcrum, input force, and output force.

Working Wedges

Have you ever paid attention to the shape of your teeth? Some of your teeth are wedge-shaped, others are pointed, and still others are relatively flat. This is because they have different uses.

When you bite into an apple, you use your sharp front teeth, called incisors. These teeth are shaped to enable you to bite off pieces of food. What simple machine do these teeth resemble? **Your incisors are shaped like wedges.** When you bite down on something, the wedge shape of your front teeth produces enough force to break it in half, just as an ax is used to split a log. Your rear teeth, or molars, are more flat. These teeth are used to grind your food into pieces that are small enough to be swallowed and digested.

There's a lot more to chewing than you may have realized. The next time you take a bite of a crunchy apple, think about the machines in your mouth!

Section 4 Review

1. In what way do your bones and muscles operate as levers?
2. Where in your body can you identify wedges? What role do they play in you daily life?
3. Point your left index finger (your pointing finger) in front of you. Then move it to the right. Where is the fulcrum? Where is the input force? What kind of lever is your finger?
4. **Thinking Critically Inferring** Make a motion as if you were going to throw a ball. What muscle do you think you use to straighten out your arm when you throw? What kind of lever are you using?

Science at Home

Have a family member place a wooden toothpick between the ends of his or her fingers as shown in the upper photograph. Ask that person to try to break the toothpick by pressing down with the first and third fingers. Now repeat the procedure, but this time have the person hold the toothpick as shown in the lower photograph. Explain to your family why the toothpick was easier to break on the second try. How were the positions of the forces and fulcrum different in each case?

Background

Integrating Science Many animals have adaptations that are wedges. A woodpecker's bill functions as a wedge when it drills into the bark of trees. Carnivores such as lions have sharply pointed teeth that help them pierce the flesh of prey. Similarly, the pointed talons of eagles and other birds of prey also function as wedges when they sink into the bodies of prey.

Program Resources

- **Teaching Resources** 4-4 Review and Reinforce, p. 113; 4-4 Enrich, p. 114

Media and Technology

Transparencies "Exploring Levers in the Body," Transparency 13

Section 1 What Is Work?

Key Ideas

- Work is done on an object when a force causes that object to move some distance.
- The amount of work done on an object is equal to the force on the object in the direction of its motion multiplied by the distance the object moves.

$$Work = Force \times Distance$$

Key Terms

work
joule

Section 2 Mechanical Advantage and Efficiency

Key Ideas

- A machine makes work easier by changing the direction or amount of force needed to accomplish a task.
- The efficiency of a machine is the percentage of the input work that is changed to output work.

$$Efficiency = \frac{Output\ work}{Input\ work} \times 100\%$$

- The mechanical advantage of a machine is obtained by dividing the output force by the input force.

$$Mechanical\ advantage = \frac{Output\ force}{Input\ force}$$

- The ideal mechanical advantage of a machine is the mechanical advantage that it would have if there were no friction.

Key Terms

machine
input force
output force
mechanical advantage
efficiency
actual mechanical advantage
ideal mechanical advantage

Section 3 Simple Machines

Key Ideas

- There are six basic kinds of simple machines: the inclined plane, the wedge, the screw, the lever, the wheel and axle, and the pulley.
- A compound machine is a machine that is made from two or more simple machines.

Key Terms

inclined plane
wedge
screw
lever
fulcrum
wheel and axle
pulley
compound machine
gears

Section 4 Machines in the Human Body

INTEGRATING LIFE SCIENCE

Key Ideas

- Most of the machines in your body are levers that consist of bones with muscles attached to them.
- When you bite into something, your front teeth use the principle of the wedge.

Key Term

tendon

Science at Home

Materials *wooden toothpick*

Tips The muscles of the hand move the fingers as a third-class lever. The knuckle serves as the fulcrum, the toothpick is moved by the output force, and the input force is exerted between the knuckle and the toothpick (roughly around the joint). The mechanical advantage is the input distance divided by the output distance. The longer the distance from the output force to the fulcrum (knuckle to toothpick) as compared to the distance from the input force to the fulcrum (joint to knuckle), the less the mechanical advantage of the lever. The mechanical advantage increases as you slide the toothpick toward the hand, and so the toothpick is easier to break.

Program Resources

- **Teaching Resources** Chapter 4 Project Scoring Rubric, p. 98; Chapter 4 Performance Assessment Teacher Notes, pp. 207–208; Chapter 4 Performance Assessment Student Worksheet, p. 209; Chapter 4 Test, pp. 210–213

Media and Technology

Interactive Student Tutorial CD-ROM M-4

Computer Test Bank M-4 Test

CHAPTER 4 REVIEW

Reviewing Content: Multiple Choice

1. b **2.** b **3.** a **4.** d **5.** c

True or False

6. true **7.** true **8.** efficiency
9. screw **10.** wedge

Checking Concepts

11. No, because he does not move the Earth, he only holds it. There is no work without motion.
12. The longer ramp has a greater ideal mechanical advantage (6 as opposed to 3) because ideal mechanical advantage = length of incline ÷ height.
13. A wheel and axle
14. 15 N (input force × actual mechanical advantage.)
15. 50%
16. Answers may vary. Students might suggest the lower leg is a lever, with the knee as the fulcrum and the thigh muscle supplying the input force.
17. Students' responses should be creative and should incorporate what they learn in this chapter .

Thinking Visually

18. Sample compare/contrast table:

Simple Machine	Mechanical Advantage	Example
Inclined Plane	Length of incline ÷ height of incline	Ramp
Lever	Distance from fulcrum to input force ÷ distance from fulcrum to output force	Seesaw, crowbar, fishing pole, wheelbarrow
Wheel and Axle	Distance from center of wheel to outside of wheel ÷ distance from center of axle to outside of axle	Hand-mixer, screwdriver, doorknob, steering wheel
Pulley	Number of sections of rope supporting the load	Block and tackle, flag-pole lifting

Applying Skills

19. Ideal mechanical advantage = distance from fulcrum to input force ÷ distance from fulcrum to output force = 60 cm ÷ 20 cm = 3
20. 1; 2; 4

CHAPTER 4 REVIEW

Reviewing Content

For more review of key concepts, see the Interactive Student Tutorial CD-ROM.

Multiple Choice

Choose the letter of the answer that best completes each statement.

1. The amount of work done on an object is obtained by multiplying
a. input force and output force.
b. force and distance.
c. time and force.
d. efficiency and work.

2. One way a machine can make work easier for you is by
a. decreasing the amount of work you do.
b. changing the direction of your force.
c. increasing the amount of work required for a task.
d. decreasing the friction you encounter.

3. The output force is greater than the input force for a
a. nutcracker.
b. fishing pole.
c. single fixed pulley.
d. rake.

4. An example of a second-class lever is a
a. seesaw. **b.** shovel.
c. paddle. **d.** wheelbarrow.

5. An example of a compound machine is a
a. screwdriver. **b.** crowbar.
c. bicycle. **d.** ramp.

True or False

If the statement is true, write true. If it is false, change the underlined word or words to make the statement true.

6. If none of the force on an object is in the direction of the object's motion, no work is done.
7. Friction reduces the efficiency of a machine.
8. The comparison between output work and input work is ideal mechanical advantage.
9. A pulley can be thought of as an inclined plane wrapped around a central cylinder.
10. Your front teeth act as a fulcrum when you bite into something.

Checking Concepts

11. The mythical god Atlas was supposed to hold the stationary Earth on his shoulders. Was Atlas performing any work? Explain your answer.
12. Which has a greater ideal mechanical advantage, a ramp that is 12 m long and 2 m high or a ramp that is 6 m long and 2 m high? Explain your answer.
13. When you let water into a bathtub, what kind of machine helps you open the tap?
14. The actual mechanical advantage of a machine is 3. If you exert an input force of 5 N, what output force is exerted by the machine?
15. Suppose that you do 1,000 joules of work when you operate an old can opener. However, the can opener does only 500 joules of work in opening the can. What is the efficiency of the can opener?
16. Describe a lever in your body. Locate the input force, output force and fulcrum.
17. Writing to Learn You are a brilliant inventor. Recently you completed your most outstanding project—an odd-looking, but very important machine. Write an explanation describing your machine, how you built it, what it is made of, and what it does. You may wish to illustrate your explanation.

Thinking Visually

18. Compare/Contrast Table Complete a compare/contrast table similar to the one shown below. For each of three other basic types of simple machines, you should show how to calculate the ideal mechanical advantage and give an example. (For more on compare/contrast tables, see the Skills Handbook.)

Simple Machine	Mechanical Advantage	Example
Inclined Plane	*Length of incline ÷ Height of incline*	*Ramp*

136 ◆ M

21. The graph describes the line $y = (1/20)x$.
22. The ideal mechanical advantage increases as the distance between the fulcrum and input force increases. They are directly proportional.

Thinking Critically

23. A door is a lever. The hinge is a fulcrum. The distance between the fulcrum and the output force remains the same. So if you decrease the distance between the effort force and the fulcrum (by pushing in the center of the door rather than the edge), you decrease the mechanical advantage.
24. A pulley
25. As friction increases, efficiency decreases.
26. Sharpening a knife makes the mechanical advantage greater by reducing friction and by making the narrow edge of the wedge thinner.

Applying Skills

Use the illustration to answer Questions 19–22.

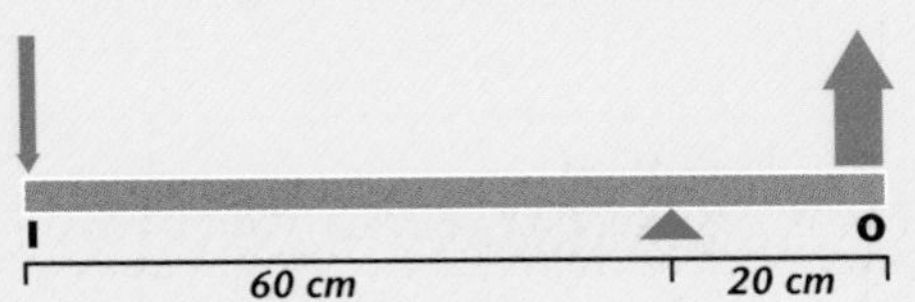

19. Calculating The figure shows the distance from the fulcrum to the input force (point I) and from the fulcrum to the output force (point O). Use the distance to calculate the ideal mechanical advantage of the lever.

20. Predicting What would the ideal mechanical advantage be if the distance from the fulcrum to the input force were 20 cm, 40 cm, or 80 cm?

21. Graphing Use your answers to questions 19 and 20 to graph the distance from the fulcrum to the input force on the *x*-axis and the ideal mechanical advantage of the lever on the *y*-axis.

22. Interpreting Data What does your graph show you about the relationship between the ideal mechanical advantage of a first-class lever and the distance between the fulcrum and the input force?

Thinking Critically

23. Applying Concepts To open a door, you push on the part farthest from the hinges. Why would it be harder to open the door if you pushed on the center?

24. Classifying What type of simple machine would be used to lower an empty bucket into a well and then lift the bucket full of water?

25. Relating Cause and Effect Describe the relationship between friction and the efficiency of a machine.

26. Inferring Why would sharpening a knife or ax blade improve its mechanical advantage?

CHAPTER 4 REVIEW

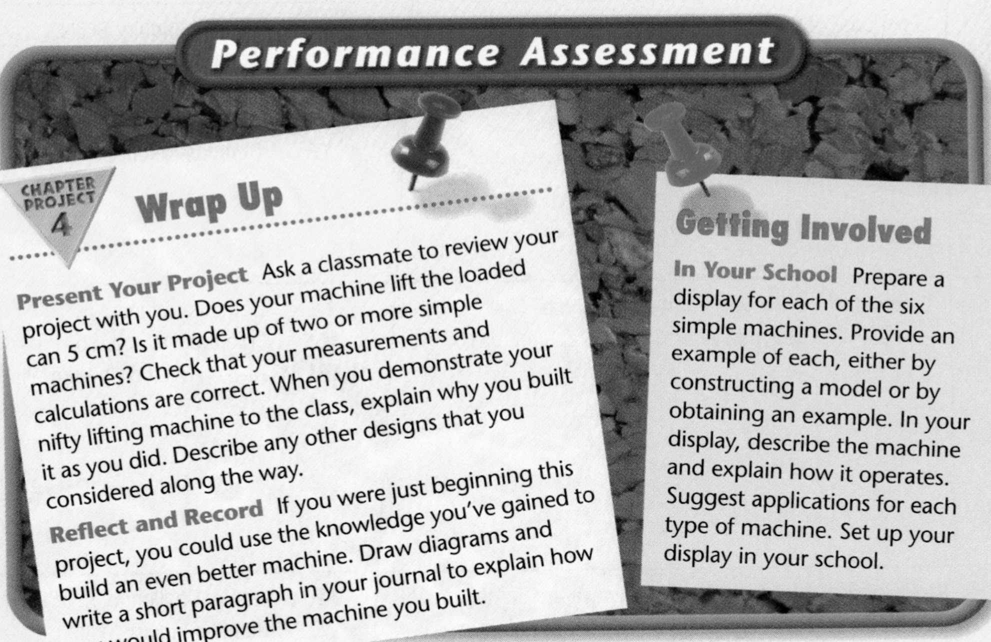

Performance Assessment

CHAPTER PROJECT 4

Wrap Up

Present Your Project Ask a classmate to review your project with you. Does your machine lift the loaded can 5 cm? Is it made up of two or more simple machines? Check that your measurements and calculations are correct. When you demonstrate your nifty lifting machine to the class, explain why you built it as you did. Describe any other designs that you considered along the way.

Reflect and Record If you were just beginning this project, you could use the knowledge you've gained to build an even better machine. Draw diagrams and write a short paragraph in your journal to explain how you would improve the machine you built.

Getting Involved

In Your School Prepare a display for each of the six simple machines. Provide an example of each, either by constructing a model or by obtaining an example. In your display, describe the machine and explain how it operates. Suggest applications for each type of machine. Set up your display in your school.

Performance Assessment

CHAPTER PROJECT 4

Wrap Up

Present Your Project Review the rules with students the day before presentations to prevent students from missing their goals because they overlooked a restriction of the project. For instance, students may not remember that their machines must lift the load at least 5 cm because they were so focused on the mechanical advantage of their devices.

Any student who reached any level of success is indeed successful. A cooperative climate makes this project a positive experience for more students than does a competitive climate. You can set the example by stressing each student's success rather than comparing students' results.

Reflect and Record This step, sometimes called feedback, is an essential part of any design process. Encourage students to use their knowledge to improve their designs, not to just design another machine.

Program Resources

◆ **Inquiry Skills Handbook** Provides teaching and review of all inquiry skills

Getting Involved

In Your School You might want to accumulate a collection of pictures from magazines, posters, and other sources. Students can find a good selection of simple machines in the classroom or in the school.

CHAPTER 5

Energy and Power

Sections	Time	Student Edition Activities	Other Activities	
CHAPTER PROJECT 5 **Roller Coaster!** p. 139	Ongoing (2 weeks)	Check Your Progress, pp. 145, 157, 162 Wrap Up, p. 165	**TE**	Chapter 5 Project Notes, pp. 138–139
1 The Nature of Energy pp. 140–147 ◆ Relate work and energy. ◆ Define and calculate potential and kinetic energy. ◆ List different forms of energy.	4 periods/ 2 blocks	**Discover** How High Does a Ball Bounce?, p. 140 **Skills Lab: Controlling Variables** Soaring Straws, pp. 146–147	**TE** **TE** **TE** **TE** **TE** **IES**	Including All Students, p. 141 Inquiry Challenge, p. 141 Demonstration, p. 143 Addressing Naive Conceptions, p. 144 Real-Life Learning, p. 144 "Mill Life in the 1840s," pp. 12–13
2 Energy Conversion and Conservation pp. 148–153 ◆ Identify and describe conversions from one type of energy to another. ◆ State the law of conservation of energy.	3 periods/ $1\frac{1}{2}$ blocks	**Discover** What Would Make a Card Jump?, p. 148 **Try This** Pendulum Swing, p. 151	**TE** **TE** **TE**	Building Inquiry Skills: Applying Concepts, p. 149; Predicting, p. 150 Including All Students, p. 151 Demonstration, p. 152
3 *INTEGRATING EARTH SCIENCE* **Energy Conversions and Fossil Fuels** pp. 154–157 ◆ Identify the source of energy stored in fossil fuels. ◆ Explain how energy is converted when fossil fuels are used.	2 periods/ 1 block	**Discover** What Is a Fuel?, p. 154 **Sharpen Your Skills** Graphing, p. 155	**TE** **IES** **ISLM**	Demonstration, p. 155 "Metropolis," pp. 35–36 M-5, "Winding Up With Wind"
4 Power pp. 158–162 ◆ Define and calculate power. ◆ Compare energy and power.	2–3 periods/ 1 block	**Discover** Is Work Always the Same?, p. 158 **Real-World Lab: Careers in Science** Can You Feel the Power?, pp. 160–161	**TE** **TE** **IES** **IES**	Inquiry Challenge, p. 159 Building Inquiry Skills: Observing, p. 159 "Back to the Thirties," pp. 38–39 "Fate of the Rain Forest," pp. 17–19
Study Guide/Chapter Review pp. 163–165	1 period/ $\frac{1}{2}$ block		**ISAB**	Provides teaching and review of all inquiry skills

For Standard or Block Schedule The Resource Pro® CD-ROM gives you maximum flexibility for planning your instruction for any type of schedule. Resource Pro® contains Planning Express®, an advanced scheduling program, as well as the entire contents of the Teaching Resources and the Computer Test Bank.

CHAPTER PLANNING GUIDE

Program Resources	Assessment Strategies	Media and Technology
TR Chapter 5 Project Teacher Notes, pp. 120–121 **TR** Chapter 5 Project Overview and Worksheets, pp. 122–125 **TR** Chapter 5 Project Scoring Rubric, p. 126	**SE** Performance Assessment: Chapter 5 Project Wrap Up, p. 165 **TE** Check Your Progress, pp. 145, 157, 162 **TE** Performance Assessment: Chapter 5 Project Wrap Up, p. 165 **TR** Chapter 5 Project Scoring Rubric, p. 126	Science Explorer Internet Site
TR 5-1 Lesson Plan, p. 127 **TR** 5-1 Section Summary, p. 128 **TR** 5-1 Review and Reinforce, p. 129 **TR** 5-1 Enrich, p. 130 **TR** Chapter 5 Skills Lab, pp. 143–145 **SES** Book L, *Chemical Interactions,* Chapter 1	**SE** Section 1 Review, p. 145 **SE** Analyze and Conclude, p. 147 **TE** Ongoing Assessment, pp. 141, 143 **TE** Performance Assessment, p. 145 **TR** 5-1 Review and Reinforce, p. 129	Audiotapes: English-Spanish Summary 5-1 Transparency 14, "Kinetic Energy" Interactive Student Tutorial CD-ROM, M-5
TR 5-2 Lesson Plan, p. 131 **TR** 5-2 Section Summary, p. 132 **TR** 5-2 Review and Reinforce, p. 133 **TR** 5-2 Enrich, p. 134 **SES** Book E, *Environmental Science,* Chapter 6 **SES** Book O, *Sound and Light,* Chapter 4	**SE** Section 2 Review, p. 153 **TE** Ongoing Assessment, pp. 149, 151 **TE** Performance Assessment, p. 153 **TR** 5-2 Review and Reinforce, p. 133	Exploring Physical Science Videodisc, Unit 3 Side 1, "Energy" Audiotapes: English-Spanish Summary 5-2 Transparency 15, "Energy Conversions" Transparency 16, "The Pendulum" Interactive Student Tutorial CD-ROM, M-5
TR 5-3 Lesson Plan, p. 135 **TR** 5-3 Section Summary, p. 136 **TR** 5-3 Review and Reinforce, p. 137 **TR** 5-3 Enrich, p. 138 **SES** Book I, *Inside Earth,* Chapter 5	**SE** Section 3 Review, p. 157 **TE** Ongoing Assessment, p. 155 **TE** Performance Assessment, p. 157 **TR** 5-3 Review and Reinforce, p. 137	Exploring Earth Science Videodisc, Unit 6 Side 2, "Power for the People" Audiotapes: English-Spanish Summary 5-3 Transparency 17, "Exploring Energy Conversions" Interactive Student Tutorial CD-ROM, M-5
TR 5-4 Lesson Plan, p. 139 **TR** 5-4 Section Summary, p. 140 **TR** 5-4 Review and Reinforce, p. 141 **TR** 5-4 Enrich, p. 142 **TR** Chapter 5 Real-World Lab, pp. 146–147 **SES** Book N, *Electricity and Magnetism,* Chapter 3	**SE** Section 4 Review, p. 162 **SE** Analyze and Conclude, p. 161 **TE** Ongoing Assessment, p. 159 **TE** Performance Assessment, p. 162 **TR** 5-4 Review and Reinforce, p. 141	Audiotapes: English-Spanish Summary 5-4 Interactive Student Tutorial CD-ROM, M-5
TR Chapter 5 Performance Assessment pp. 214–216 **TR** Chapter 5 Test, pp. 217–220	**SE** Chapter Review, pp. 163–165 **TR** Chapter 5 Performance Assessment: pp. 214–216 **TR** Chapter 5 Test, pp. 217–220 **CTB** Test M-5	Computer Test Bank, Test M-5 Interactive Student Tutorial CD-ROM, M-5

Key: **SE** Student Edition
CTB Computer Test Bank
ISAB Inquiry Skills Activity Book
TE Teacher's Edition
SES Science Explorer Series Text
PTA Product Testing Activities by *Consumer Reports*
TR Teaching Resources
ISLM Integrated Science Laboratory Manual
IES Interdisciplinary Explorations Series

Meeting the National Science Education Standards and AAAS Benchmarks

National Science Education Standards	Benchmarks for Science Literacy	Unifying Themes
Science as Inquiry (Content Standard A) ◆ **Design and conduct a scientific investigation** Students examine how to alter power while doing exercise. *(Real-Life Lab)* ◆ **Use mathematics in all aspects of scientific inquiry** Students calculate kinetic and potential energy and power. *(Sections 1,4; Skills Lab; Real-Life Lab)* **Physical Science** (Content Standard B) ◆ **Transfer of energy** Energy is transferred in many ways and energy changes form. Energy cannot be created or destroyed. The sun's energy is stored as different forms on Earth. *(Sections 1, 2, 3; Chapter Project; Skills Lab)* **Science and Technology** (Content Standard E) ◆ **Design a solution or a product** Students design a roller coaster powered by potential energy. *(Chapter Project)* ◆ **Implement a proposed design** Roller coaster designs are tested. *(Chapter Project)* Students investigate how gravitational potential energy and elastic potential energy are related in a rubber band launcher. *(Skills Lab)* ◆ **Understandings about science and technology** The reciprocal nature of science and technology are explored as students learn about Watt's steam engine and the value of horsepower. *(Section 4)*	**1B Scientific Inquiry** Students control variables as they build a roller coaster and investigate the relationship between the height reached by a rocket and the amount of stretch in a rubber band launcher. *(Chapter Project; Skills Lab)* **3B Design Systems** Students design a roller coaster to detailed specifications. *(Chapter Project)* **4B The Earth** Gravity gives objects gravitational potential energy. Some of Earth's resources, including fossil fuels, are limited and can be depleted. *(Sections 2, 3)* **4E Energy Transformations** Energy is conserved. When work is done or change takes place, energy is transferred and transformed. Energy appears in many different forms. *(Sections 1, 2, 3; Chapter Project; Skills Lab)* **5E Flow of Matter and Energy** The sun produces electromagnetic energy that plants and animals store as chemical energy. Fossil fuels are the result of energy stored millions of years ago. *(Sections 2, 3)* **8C Energy Sources and Use** Energy changes form; some energy is converted to thermal energy. Electrical energy can be produced from different energy sources, including fossil fuels. *(Sections 1, 2, 3)* **9B Symbolic Relationships** Equations can be used to calculate energy and power. *(Sections 2, 4; Skills Lab, Real-World Lab)* **10J Harnessing Power** James Watt created the unit horsepower to describe the energy used by machines. *(Section 4)*	◆ **Energy** Energy is defined as the ability to do work or cause change. Energy conversions occur when work is done or energy is transformed. Power is the rate at which energy is transferred or converted. *(Sections 1, 2, 3, 4; Chapter Project; Skills Lab; Real-World Lab)* ◆ **Patterns of Change** Energy converts from one form to another when work is done or energy is transferred. Kinetic energy can be stored as potential energy and potential energy can be released as kinetic energy. *(Sections 1, 2, 3; Chapter Project; Skills Lab; Real-World Lab)* ◆ **Systems and Interactions** An object that has energy can do work. Work is the transfer of energy from one object to another or transforming energy from one form to another. *(Sections 1–4; Chapter Project; Skills Lab)* ◆ **Unity and Diversity** Energy has many different forms. Any form of energy can be converted to another form. *(Sections 1, 2, 3; Chapter Project; Skills Lab)*

Media and Technology

Exploring Physical Science Videodisc

◆ **Section 2** "Energy" models the difference between kinetic and potential energy.

Exploring Earth Science Videodisc

◆ **Section 3** "Power for the People" shows the advantages and disadvantages of fossil fuels and explores the use of alternate power sources.

Interactive Student Tutorial CD-ROM

◆ **Chapter Review** Interactive questions help students to self-assess their mastery of key chapter concepts.

Student Edition Connection Strategies

◆ **Section 1** **Math Toolbox,** p. 142

◆ **Section 2** **Visual Arts Connection,** p. 152
Integrating Environmental Science, p. 153

◆ **Section 3** **Integrating Earth Science,** p. 154 

◆ **Section 4** **Integrating Technology,** p. 162 

www.science-explorer.phschool.com

Visit the Science Explorer Internet site to find an up-to-date activity for Chapter 5 of *Motion, Forces, and Energy.*

Student Edition Activities Planner

ACTIVITY	Time (minutes)	Materials *Quantities for one work group*	Skills
Section 1			
Discover, p. 140	10	**Nonconsumable** meter stick, tennis ball	Observing
Skills Lab, pp. 146–147	40	**Consumable** 3 plastic straws, empty toilet paper tube, rubber band, masking tape **Nonconsumable** scissors, marker, balance, meter stick, metric ruler	Controlling Variables
Section 2			
Discover, p. 148	10	**Consumable** 3 x 5 index card **Nonconsumable** rubber band, scissors	Forming Operational Definitions
Try This, p. 151	15	**Nonconsumable** washers or rubber stoppers, string, ring stand, 2 clamps, meter stick	Observing
Section 3			
Discover, p. 154	20	**Consumable** water, wooden coffee stirrer, matches **Nonconsumable** flask, ring stand, clamp, thermometer, small aluminum pan, safety goggles	Forming Operational Definitions
Sharpen your Skills, p. 155	15	**Consumable** graph paper **Nonconsumable** compass, protractor	Graphing
Section 4			
Discover, p. 158	10	**Nonconsumable** pinwheel, hair dryer with two settings	Inferring
Real-World Lab, pp. 160–161	45	**Nonconsumable** calculator; meter stick; stopwatch or clock with a second hand; board, about 2.5 cm x 30 cm x 120 cm; 8–10 books, each about 2 cm thick	Measuring, Calculating, Interpreting Data

A list of all materials required for the Student Edition activities can be found on pages T14–T15. You can order Materials Kits by calling 1-800-828-7777 or by accessing the Science Explorer Internet site at **www.science-explorer.phschool.com.**

CHAPTER PROJECT 5

Roller Coaster

Students may not realize that all motion can be described in terms of energy. This project will provide students with an opportunity to evaluate motion in terms of kinetic and potential energy.

Purpose In this project, students will have the opportunity to create a roller coaster so that they can gain hands-on experience with the conversion of potential energy into kinetic energy. Students will be able to use energy conversions as criteria for modifying the designs of their models.

Skills Focus After completing the Chapter 5 project, students will be able to

- ◆ create working models of roller coasters in accordance with the specifications;
- ◆ control variables as they experiment with different hill heights and add turns and loops to their roller coasters;
- ◆ evaluate their models in terms of kinetic energy, potential energy, and the law of conservation of energy.

Project Time Line This project will take approximately two weeks to complete. During the first week, students will begin experimenting with different materials to determine how they will construct their tracks and vehicles. Once they determine what materials to use, students may begin to build the tracks, experimenting with hills of different heights. During the second week, students should modify their tracks to include turns and/or vertical loops. They should apply key terms such as friction, kinetic energy, potential energy, acceleration, and velocity to their descriptions of the roller coasters. Finally, students will present their roller coasters to the class. Before beginning the project, see the Chapter 5 Project Teacher Notes on pages 120–121 in Teaching Resources for more details on carrying out the project. Also distribute the Students' Chapter 5 Project Overview and Worksheets and Scoring Rubric on pages 122–126 in Teaching Resources.

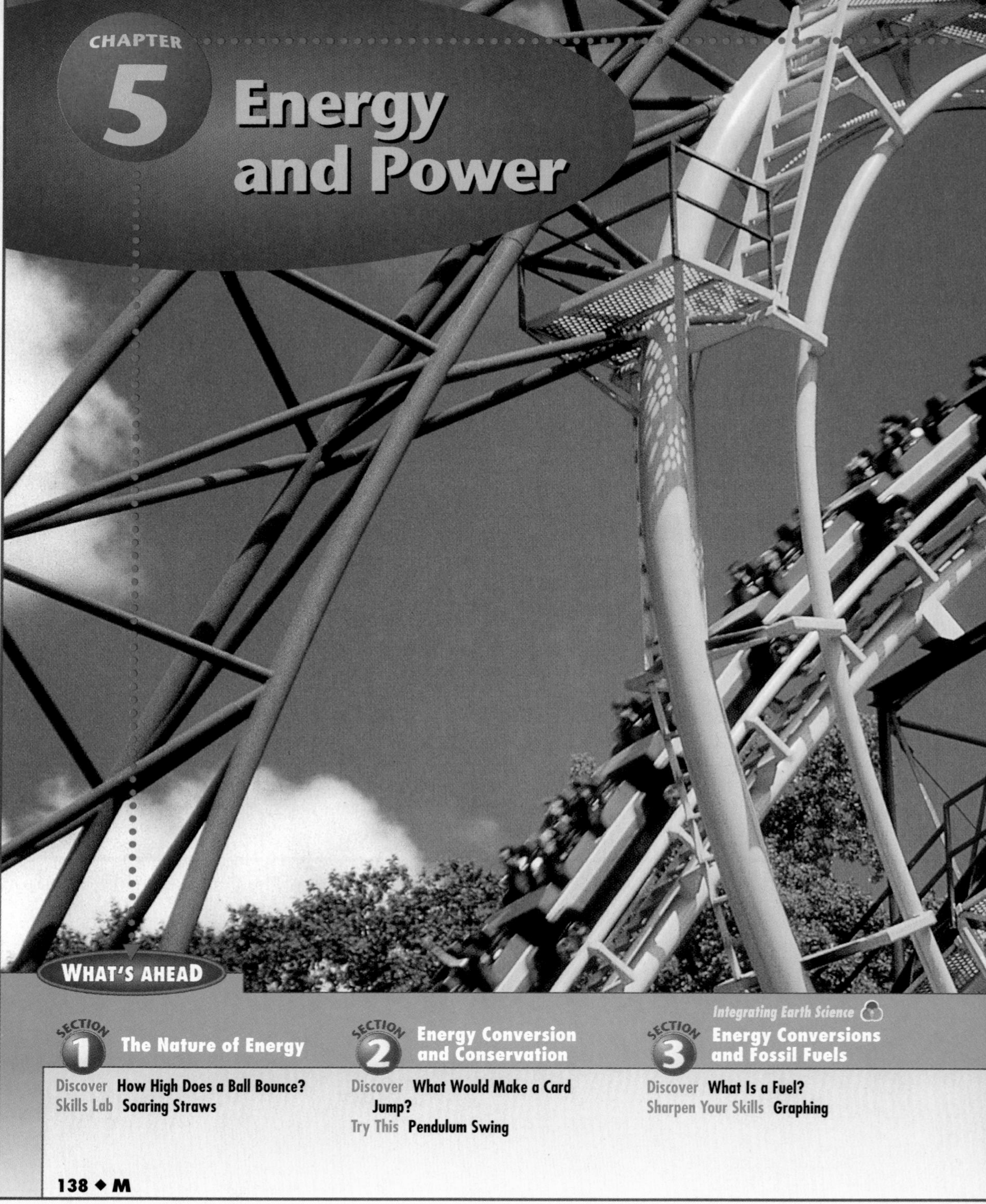

CHAPTER 5
Energy and Power
WHAT'S AHEAD
SECTION 1 The Nature of Energy
Discover How High Does a Ball Bounce?
Skills Lab Soaring Straws
SECTION 2 Energy Conversion and Conservation
Discover What Would Make a Card Jump?
Try This Pendulum Swing
Integrating Earth Science
SECTION 3 Energy Conversions and Fossil Fuels
Discover What Is a Fuel?
Sharpen Your Skills Graphing
138 ◆ M

Possible Materials Students may use cardboard, posterboard, garden hoses, rubber or vinyl tubing, foam pipe insulation, drinking straws, or other materials. Marbles, ball bearings, rubber balls, or toy cars can be used as vehicles. Students may also need additional materials including string, tape, glue, paper clips, bricks, shoe boxes, blocks of wood, stopwatches, cups, or buckets. Encourage students to suggest and use other materials as well, but make sure that they choose materials that are readily available.

Launching the Project To introduce the project, begin a class discussion about roller coasters. Ask students: **Have you ever ridden a roller coaster?** Have them describe their experiences. Did they feel fear or excitement? Why? What happened as the roller coaster rushed down a hill, climbed a hill, or went around a corner? Did it speed up or slow down? Why? Get them involved in a discussion about the hills, speed, and turns of a roller

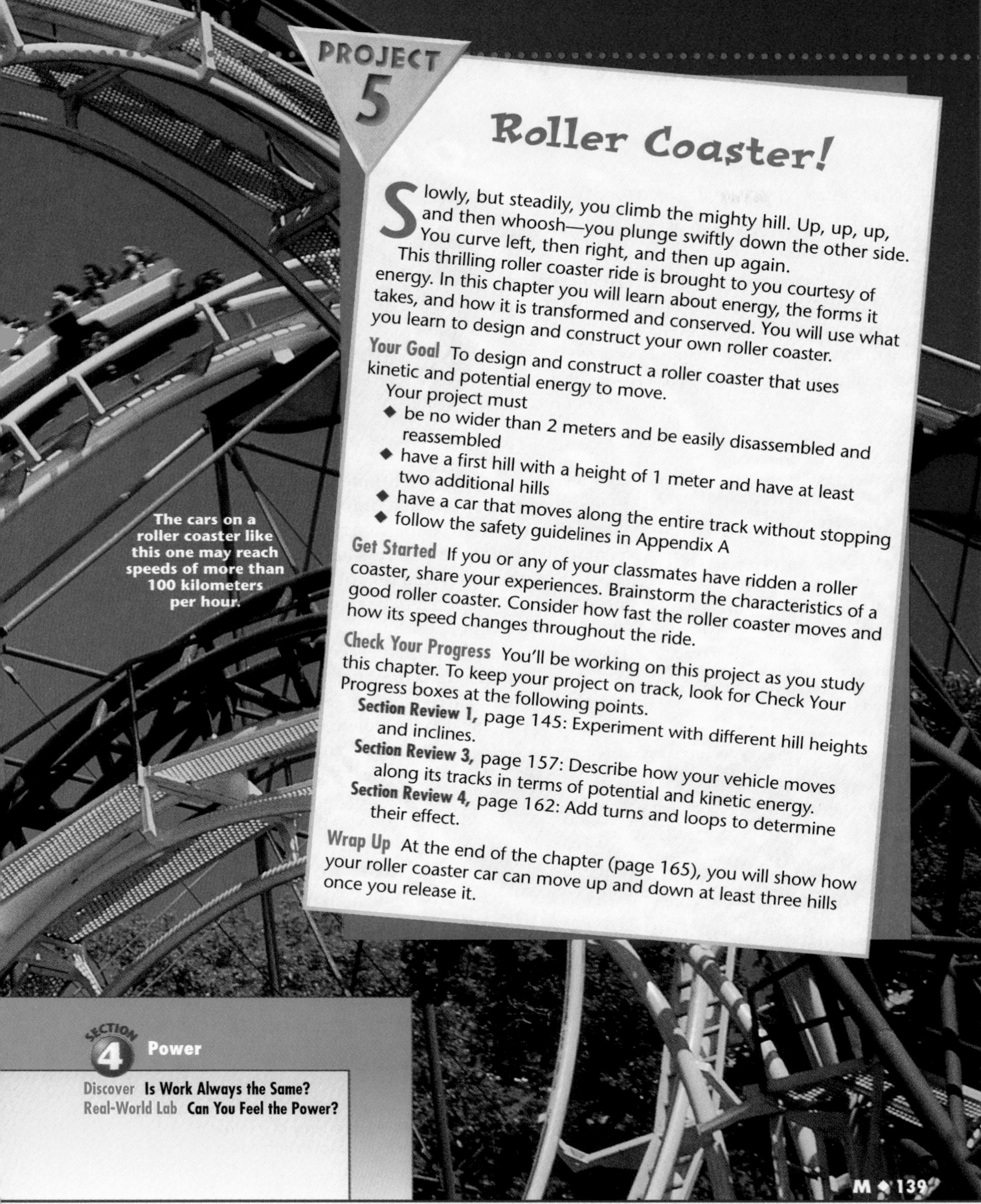
PROJECT 5

Roller Coaster!

Slowly, but steadily, you climb the mighty hill. Up, up, up, and then whoosh—you plunge swiftly down the other side. You curve left, then right, and then up again.

This thrilling roller coaster ride is brought to you courtesy of energy. In this chapter you will learn about energy, the forms it takes, and how it is transformed and conserved. You will use what you learn to design and construct your own roller coaster.

Your Goal To design and construct a roller coaster that uses kinetic and potential energy to move.

Your project must

- ◆ be no wider than 2 meters and be easily disassembled and reassembled
- ◆ have a first hill with a height of 1 meter and have at least two additional hills
- ◆ have a car that moves along the entire track without stopping
- ◆ follow the safety guidelines in Appendix A

Get Started If you or any of your classmates have ridden a roller coaster, share your experiences. Brainstorm the characteristics of a good roller coaster. Consider how fast the roller coaster moves and how its speed changes throughout the ride.

Check Your Progress You'll be working on this project as you study this chapter. To keep your project on track, look for Check Your Progress boxes at the following points.

Section Review 1, page 145: Experiment with different hill heights and inclines.

Section Review 3, page 157: Describe how your vehicle moves along its tracks in terms of potential and kinetic energy.

Section Review 4, page 162: Add turns and loops to determine their effect.

Wrap Up At the end of the chapter (page 165), you will show how your roller coaster car can move up and down at least three hills once you release it.

The cars on a roller coaster like this one may reach speeds of more than 100 kilometers per hour.

SECTION 4 **Power**

Discover **Is Work Always the Same?**
Real-World Lab **Can You Feel the Power?**

M ◆ 139

coaster. Ask students: **What features of a roller coaster would you include if you were going to build one? What materials and knowledge would you need?**

Allow time for students to read the description of the project in the text and the Chapter Project Overview on pages 122–123 in Teaching Resources. Then encourage students to discuss potential and kinetic energy as they relate to a roller coaster. Distribute copies of the Chapter 5 Project Worksheets on pages 124–125 in Teaching Resources for students to review.

Program Resources

- ◆ **Teaching Resources** Chapter 5 Project Teacher's Notes, pp. 120–121; Chapter 5 Project Overview and Worksheets, pp. 122–125; Chapter 5 Project Scoring Rubric, p. 126

Performance Assessment

The Chapter 5 Project Scoring Rubric on page 126 of Teaching Resources will help you evaluate how well students complete the Chapter 5 Project. Students will be assessed on whether

- ◆ their roller coaster is no wider than 2 meters and has three hills, the first of which is 1 meter high; and the vehicle successfully completes the entire track without stopping;
- ◆ modifications are made to the roller coaster based on the results of experiments and the application of concepts involving energy conversions;
- ◆ they are able to apply concepts such as kinetic energy, potential energy, and the law of conservation of energy to the description of their roller coaster;
- ◆ their presentation and written analysis are thorough and well-organized.

By sharing the Chapter 5 Scoring Rubric with students at the beginning of the project, you will make it clear to them what they are expected to do.

SECTION 1 The Nature of Energy

Objectives

After completing the lesson, students will be able to

- relate work and energy;
- define and calculate potential and kinetic energy;
- list different forms of energy.

Key Terms energy, kinetic energy, potential energy, elastic potential energy, gravitational potential energy, mechanical energy, thermal energy, chemical energy, electrical energy, electromagnetic energy, nuclear energy

1 Engage/Explore

Activating Prior Knowledge

Use a croquet ball and mallet, a tennis ball and racquet, or a golf ball and putter. Place the ball on the floor or hold it up for the class to see. Ask students what you would have to do to change the ball's position. Encourage them to describe how you could make the ball move quickly or slowly.

DISCOVER ACTIVITY

Skills Focus observing
Materials *meter stick, tennis ball*
Time 10 minutes
Tips Students should work in pairs or small groups. Suggest that students perform several trials at each position and find the average height. Encourage students to use the same method of observation in every trial.
Expected Outcome The ball bounces the highest when it is dropped from the greatest height.
Think It Over The greater the height from which the ball is dropped, the higher the ball bounces.
Extend Have students repeat the experiment using several different balls, such as hard rubber balls, golf balls, and baseballs.

SECTION 1 The Nature of Energy

DISCOVER ACTIVITY

How High Does a Ball Bounce?

1. Hold a meter stick vertically, with the zero end on the ground.
2. Drop a tennis ball from the 50-centimeter mark and record the height to which it bounces.
3. Drop the tennis ball from the 100-centimeter mark and record the height to which it bounces.
4. Predict how high the ball will bounce if dropped from the 75-centimeter mark. Test your prediction.

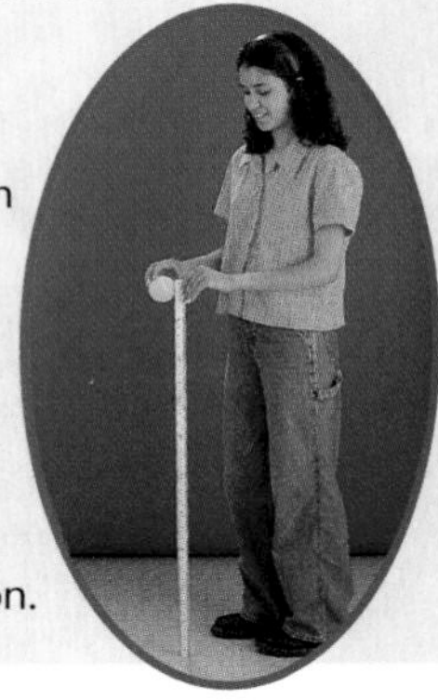

Think It Over
Observing How does the height from which you drop the ball relate to the height to which the ball bounces?

GUIDE FOR READING

- How are work and energy related?
- What are the two basic kinds of energy?
- What are some of the different forms of energy?

Reading Tip Before you read, list several familiar examples of energy. Add to your list as you read the section.

Brilliant streaks of lightning flash across the night sky. The howl of the wind and the crashing of thunder drown out the sound of falling rain. Then a sound like a railroad locomotive approaches. As the sound grows louder, a small town experiences the power and fury of a tornado. Whirling winds of more than 250 kilometers per hour blow through the town. Roofs are lifted off of buildings. Cars are thrown about like toys. Then, in minutes, the tornado is gone.

The next morning, as rescuers survey the damage, a light breeze delicately carries falling leaves past the debris. How strange it is that the wind is violent enough to destroy buildings one night and barely strong enough to carry a leaf the next morning. Wind is just moving air, but it possesses energy. As you read on, you'll find out what energy is.

Figure 1 The energy of a tornado can devastate a town in minutes.

What Is Energy?

When wind moves a leaf, or even a house, it causes a change. In this case, the change is in the position of the object. Recall that work is done when a force moves an object through a distance. The ability to do work or cause change is called **energy.** So the wind has energy.

READING STRATEGIES

Reading Tip Before they read the section, have students list examples of energy. Have them review their lists to see if the examples can be arranged in categories. Ask students to write the categories as column headings on a new sheet of paper and place items in the categories. As students read the section, have them place more examples in the categories and rename or add categories as necessary.

Study and Comprehension Instruct students to write a brief definition of each form of energy in their own words and to include examples from their experience.

Concept Mapping Have students create concepts maps to organize information about the six major forms of energy presented in the section.

Figure 2 A bowling ball can do work because it is moving. *Applying Concepts What is the ability to do work called?*

When an object or organism does work on an object, some of its energy is transferred to that object. **You can think of work, then, as the transfer of energy.** When energy is transferred, the object upon which the work is done gains energy. Energy is measured in joules—the same units as work.

Kinetic Energy

There are two general kinds of energy. **The two kinds of energy are kinetic energy and potential energy.** Whether energy is kinetic or potential depends on whether the energy is being transferred or stored.

The examples you have read about so far have involved things that were moving. A moving object can collide with another object and move it some distance. In that way, the moving object does work. For example, a bowling ball knocks over a bowling pin.

Because the moving object can do work, it must have energy. The energy of motion is called **kinetic energy.** The word kinetic comes from the Greek word *kinetos,* which means "moving."

Mass and Velocity The kinetic energy of an object depends on both its mass and its velocity. Think about rolling a golf ball and a bowling ball so that they travel at the same velocity. Which ball would you have to roll more forcefully? You would have to exert a greater force on the bowling ball because it has more mass than the golf ball.

Since energy is transferred during work, the more work you do, the more energy you give to the ball. So a bowling ball has more kinetic energy than a golf ball traveling at the same velocity. Kinetic energy increases as mass increases.

What would you have to do to make the bowling ball move faster? You would have to throw it harder, or use a greater force.

2 Facilitate

What Is Energy?

Including All Students

Materials *sponge, balloon, tuning fork, wood block*
Time 10 minutes

Have small groups of students, including those who are visually impaired, perform these activities and identify the energy source.

- ◆ blow up a balloon *(energy source—diaphragm and chest muscles)*
- ◆ strike a tuning fork on a table *(energy source—hand or arm)*
- ◆ compress a large soft sponge with a brick or wood block *(energy source—weight of the brick)*

learning modality: kinesthetic

Kinetic Energy

Inquiry Challenge

ACTIVITY

Materials *2 skateboards or toy trucks, meter stick, 3 heavy books, large rubber ball, stopwatch*
Time 20 minutes

Arrange the class into cooperative groups. Ask groups to hypothesize how increasing the mass of a moving object affects the distance the object can move. Students should design an experiment to test their hypothesis. Remind students that, in a controlled experiment, only one variable should change. After you approve their plans, students should carry them out. **cooperative learning.**

Program Resources

- ◆ **Teaching Resources** 5-1 Lesson Plan, p. 127; 5-1 Section Summary, p. 128

Media and Technology

Audiotapes English-Spanish Summary 5-1

Answers to Self-Assessment

Caption Question

Figure 2 The ability to do work is called energy.

Ongoing Assessment

Writing Have students list three examples where energy is transferred or stored. For each example, have them explain whether the energy involved is kinetic, potential, or both.

Kinetic Energy, continued

Building Inquiry Skills: Calculating

Have students find the kinetic energy for the following wagons: a 10-kg wagon moving at 5 m/s *(125 kg•m²/s²)*, a 10-kg wagon moving at 10 m/s *(500 kg•m²/s²)*, and a 20-kg wagon moving at 5 m/s *(250 kg•m²/s²)*. Visual learners may benefit from having the wagons drawn on the board to show the difference in their sizes, with arrows to show their velocities. Ask: **Which has the greatest kinetic energy?** *(The 10-kg wagon moving at 10 m/s)* Then ask students to infer how to increase a moving object's kinetic energy. *(Increase its velocity, or its mass)* **learning modality: logical/mathematical**

Math TOOLBOX

Ask students: **What is the exponent in the number 9^2?** *(2)* **What is the value of 9^2?** *(81)* If students incorrectly give the value as 18 (9 × 2), clarify that the square of a number is the number multiplied by itself. Have students write the numbers 1 through 20 on flash cards with their squares on the back. Pair students and have them take turns testing each other. **learning modality: logical/mathematical**

Potential Energy

Building Inquiry Skills: Classifying

Ask students to find, describe, and classify two things with gravitational and two things with elastic potential energy. **learning modality: verbal**

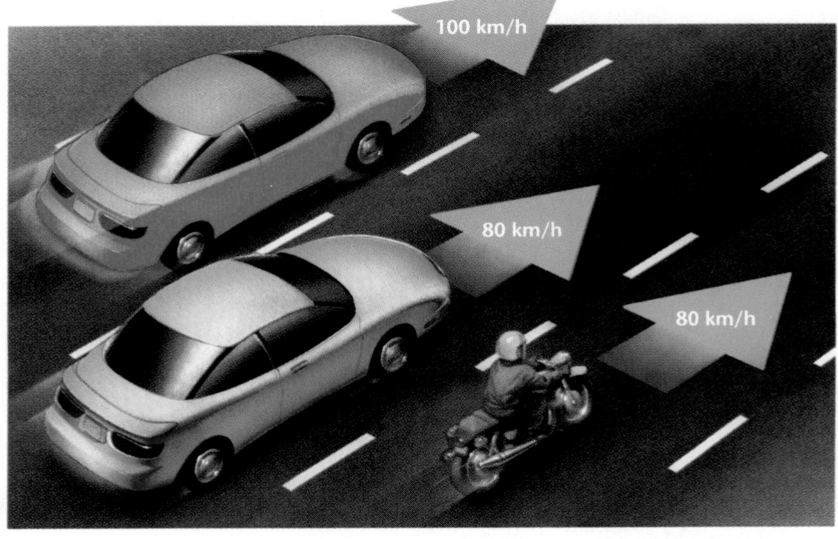

Figure 3 Kinetic energy increases as mass and velocity increase. *Interpreting Diagrams List the three vehicles in order of increasing kinetic energy.*

In other words, you have to do more work on the bowling ball to give it a greater velocity. Kinetic energy increases when velocity increases.

Calculating Kinetic Energy Kinetic energy depends on both mass and velocity. The mathematical relationship between kinetic energy, mass, and velocity is written as follows.

$$\text{Kinetic energy} = \frac{\text{Mass} \times \text{Velocity}^2}{2}$$

Do changes in velocity and mass have the same effect on kinetic energy? No—changing the velocity of an object will have a greater effect on its kinetic energy than changing its mass. This is because velocity is squared in the energy equation. For instance, doubling the mass of an object will double its kinetic energy. But doubling its velocity will quadruple its kinetic energy.

Math TOOLBOX

Squared Numbers

A squared number is written with an exponent of 2. For example, you can write 2^2, 3^2, or 4^2. To find the value of a squared number, multiply the number by itself.

$2^2 = 2 \times 2 = 4$

$3^2 = 3 \times 3 = 9$

$4^2 = 4 \times 4 = 16$

Notice how fast the squared numbers increase. For example, although the numbers 2 and 3 only differ by one, their squares differ by five.

✓ *Checkpoint* *What is kinetic energy?*

Potential Energy

Sometimes when you transfer energy to an object, you change its position or shape. For example, you lift a book up to your desk or you compress a spring to wind a toy. Unlike kinetic energy, which is the energy of motion, potential energy is stored. It might be used later on when the book falls to the floor or the spring unwinds. Energy that is stored and held in readiness is called **potential energy.** This type of energy has the *potential* to do work.

Background

Integrating Science As the sun warms Earth's land and water, water evaporates and stores thermal energy. When this stored thermal energy is released , it causes violent storms. The thermal energy is released when warm air cools and condenses, forming liquid water. An average thunderstorm releases about 36 terajoules of energy. Severe storms can release up to 100 times more energy.

The thermal energy stored in warm air also forms tornadoes and hurricanes. A tornado may have wind speeds as high as 800 km per hour. Hurricanes, which are much larger than tornadoes, release even more energy. They form over warm ocean waters where evaporation takes place. Winds near the eye may be as high as 300 kilometers per hour, and a hurricane may be over 2,000 km in diameter.

An archer gives potential energy to a bow by pulling it back. The stored energy can send an arrow whistling to its target. The potential energy associated with objects that can be stretched or compressed is called **elastic potential energy.**

You give a different type of potential energy to an object when you lift it. Potential energy that depends on height is **gravitational potential energy.**

The gravitational potential energy an object has is equal to the work done to lift it. Remember that Work = Force × Distance. The force is the force you use to lift the object, or its weight. The distance is the distance the object moves, or its height. This gives you the following formula.

Gravitational potential energy = Weight × Height

When weight is measured in newtons and height is measured in meters, the unit of energy is the newton-meter. This unit is also known as the joule (J). Recall from Chapter 4 that a joule is the amount of work you do when you exert a force of 1 newton to move an object a distance of 1 meter. Work and energy share the same unit because energy and work are so closely related.

Once you know weight and height, you can calculate gravitational potential energy. Suppose that a hiker climbs 40 meters up a hill and that he weighs 680 newtons. The hiker has gained 27,200 joules (680 newtons × 40 meters) of gravitational potential energy at the top of the climb.

The greater the weight of an object or the greater the height it is lifted, the greater its gravitational potential energy. The hiker would gain more gravitational potential energy by climbing to a greater height or by increasing weight, maybe by wearing a backpack.

What if you know the mass of an object instead of its weight? Then you multiply the mass of the object by the acceleration of gravity (9.8 m/s^2) to find its weight in newtons. In this way you can write a second equation for gravitational potential energy.

Gravitational potential energy = Mass × Gravitational acceleration × Height

Again, the unit of measure is the joule.

Figure 4 A rock poised for a fall has potential energy. *Inferring How did the rock get its potential energy?*

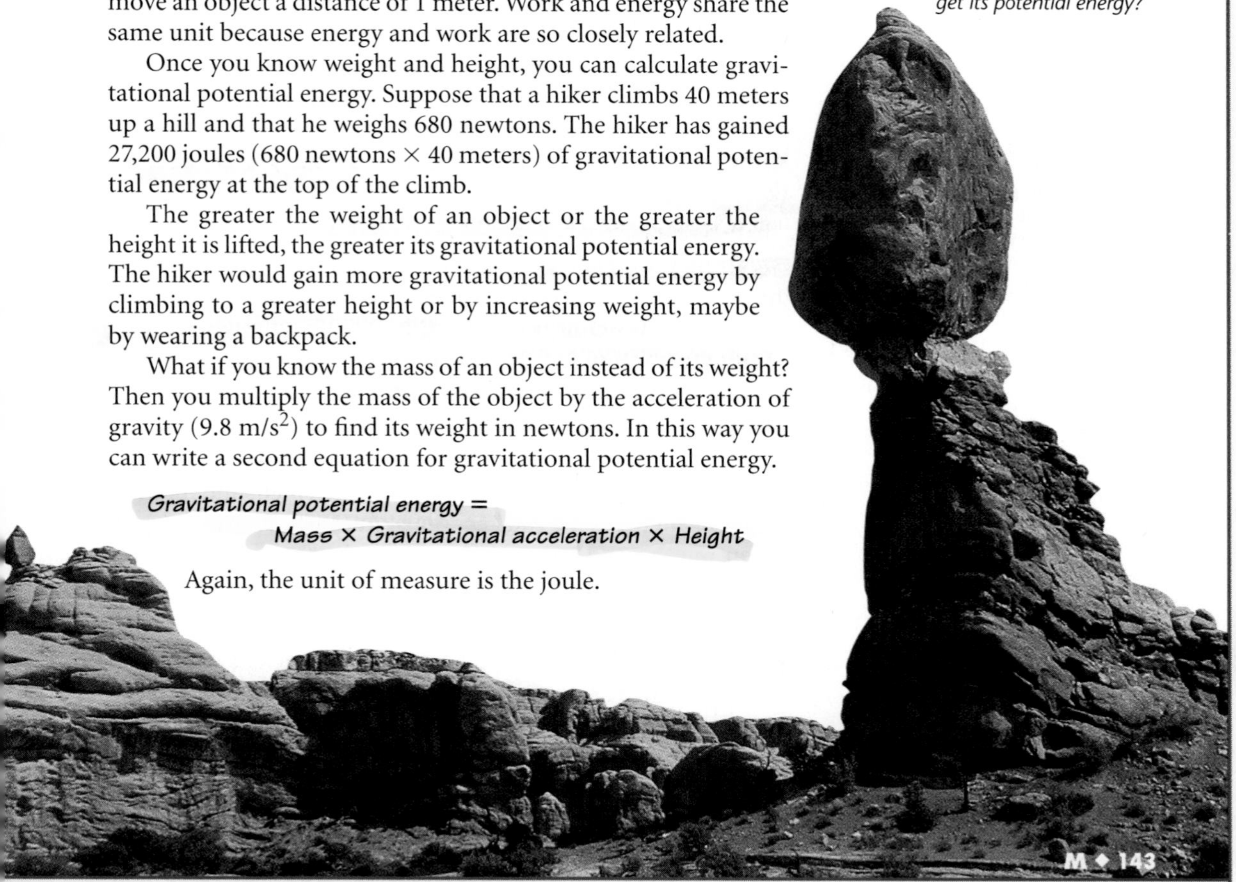

Including All Students

There are many new and confusingly similar terms in these sections: energy, potential, kinetic, chemical, elastic, gravitational. Have students who are still mastering English compile a list of these terms with definitions written out in their own words. **limited English proficiency**

Demonstration

ACTIVITY

Materials *4 identical aluminum pans such as disposable pie pans, 4 marbles of different masses, meter stick, metric ruler, balance. five sheets of corrugated cardboard*
Time 15 minutes

Determine the mass of each marble and record the mass in a data table on the board. Place an aluminum pan on a stack of five sheets of corrugated cardboard. Explain that you are going to test the hypothesis that gravitational potential energy depends on mass and that you will be determining energy by measuring the size of the dent produced in the pan. Ask: **What variable must be controlled?** *(The height)* CAUTION: Have students wear safety goggles or stand clear. Drop the marbles one at a time from a height of 1 m. After each drop, pick up the pan, turn it over, and measure the depth of the dent. Record this in the table. Replace the pans as necessary. Ask: **Which marble had the most energy?** *(The one that made the deepest dent)* Discuss with students whether the hypothesis was verified. *(Yes, the marble with the most mass made the deepest dent.)* **learning modality: visual**

Program Resources

◆ **Interdisciplinary Exploration Series** "Mill Life in the 1840s," pp. 12–13

Media and Technology

Transparencies "Kinetic Energy," Transparency 14

Answers to Self-Assessment

Caption Question

Figure 3 The motorcycle, the car moving at 80 km/h, then the car moving at 100 km/h.
Figure 4 Erosion of land around the rock left the rock in a position to fall. Its potential energy depends on its weight and height.

✓ Checkpoint

Kinetic energy is the energy of motion.

Ongoing Assessment

Skills Check Ask students to explain which has the greatest kinetic energy: a motorcycle moving at 30 km/h, a four-door car moving at 30 km/h. or a truck sitting on top of a hill. *(A four-door car moving at 30 km/h has more kinetic energy than the motorcycle because it has more mass. The truck has no kinetic energy because it is not moving.)*

Different Forms of Energy

Addressing Naive Conceptions

Some students may believe that energy cannot change form. Show students a flashlight with the batteries next to it. Ask them to identify the form of energy stored in the batteries. *(chemical or potential)* Then place the batteries in the flashlight and turn it on. Ask: **What form of energy do you see?** *(electromagnetic)* Allow students to place their hands near the bulb of the flashlight. Ask: **What form of energy do you feel?** *(thermal)* **learning modality: kinesthetic**

Building Inquiry Skills: Applying Concepts

Encourage students to describe each type of energy in their own words. Challenge students to think of one or two examples of each type of energy. **limited English proficiency**

Real Life Learning

ACTIVITY

Materials *wintergreen candies, small mirrors*
Time 15 minutes

Not all wintergreen candies work. Test different brands to see which do work.

CAUTION: *Since small pieces of candy can stick in the throat, give students access to a water fountain. Some students may find the wintergreen flavor unpleasant.* Pass out candies to each student. Darken the room. (Note: The room must be very dark and time must be allowed for eyes to adjust.) Have students chew the candies with their lips open as they watch themselves in the mirrors. As each piece of candy is crushed, they will see tiny flashes of white or bluish-white light. Ask: **What kind of energy did the mints have?** *(chemical)* **What kind of energy did your teeth add?** *(mechanical)* **What kind of energy did you see?** *(electromagnetic)* Explain that this is an example of triboluminescence, luminescence induced by friction. **learning modality: visual**

Figure 5 Energy is all around you in many different forms. The leaping frog is an example of mechanical energy, and the melting ice is an example of thermal energy. *Observing Which forms of energy are shown in the photographs of the sparkler, the sun, and the lightning?*

Different Forms of Energy

The examples of energy you have read about so far involve objects being moved or physically changed. But both kinetic energy and potential energy have a variety of different forms. **Some of the major forms of energy are mechanical energy, thermal energy, chemical energy, electrical energy, electromagnetic energy, and nuclear energy.**

Mechanical Energy The school bus you ride in, a frog leaping through the air, and even the sounds you hear all have mechanical energy. **Mechanical energy** is the energy associated with the motion or position of an object. Mechanical energy can occur as kinetic energy or potential energy.

Thermal Energy All matter is made up of small particles, called atoms and molecules. These particles have both potential energy and kinetic energy due to their arrangement and motion. **Thermal energy** is the total energy of the particles in an object. When the thermal energy of an object increases, its particles move faster, making it feel warm to the touch. Ice cream melts when its thermal energy increases.

Chemical Energy Chemical compounds, such as chocolate, wood, and wax, store **chemical energy.** Chemical energy is potential energy stored in chemical bonds that hold chemical compounds together. Chemical energy is stored in the foods you eat and in a match that is used to light a candle. Chemical energy is even stored in the cells of your body.

Background

Integrating Science Energy is stored as chemical energy in the foods we eat. While energy is often measured in joules, stored food energy is generally measured in kilocalories. Kilocalories are commonly called Calories (with a capital "C"), so that if a serving of skim milk has 86 Calories, it really has 86 kilocalories. The caloric content of a food depends on the quantity of fat, protein, and carbohydrate. A gram of fat provides 9 kcal of energy, a gram of protein provides 4 kcal, and a gram of carbohydrate provides 4 kcal. Whether from fat, protein, or carbohydrate, one calorie represents the same amount of food energy.

For proper nutrition, scientists recommend that less than 30% of kilocalories come from fat, about 15% come from protein, and about 60% come from carbohydrate.

Electrical Energy When you receive a shock from a metal doorknob, you experience electrical energy. Moving electric charges produce electricity, or **electrical energy.** You rely on electrical energy from batteries or power lines to run electrical devices such as radios, lights, and computers.

Electromagnetic Energy The light that you see each day is a form of **electromagnetic energy.** Electromagnetic energy travels in waves. These waves have some electrical properties and some magnetic properties. In addition to visible light, ultraviolet radiation, microwaves, and infrared radiation are all examples of electromagnetic energy.

Nuclear Energy Another type of potential energy, called **nuclear energy,** is stored in the core, or nucleus, of an atom. One kind of nuclear reaction occurs when a nucleus splits (nuclear fission). Another kind occurs when nuclei fuse, or join together (nuclear fusion). These reactions release tremendous amounts of energy. Nuclear power plants use fission reactions to produce electricity. Nuclear fusion occurs in the sun and other stars.

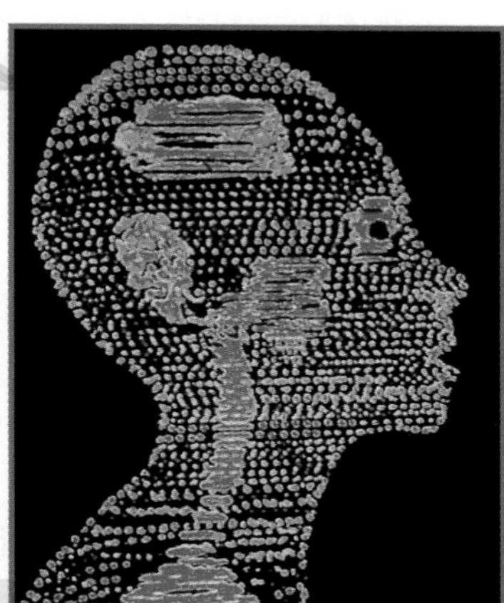

Figure 6 Electromagnetic energy is used to take a CT scan.

Section 1 Review

1. Are energy and work the same thing? Explain.
2. How are kinetic and potential energy different?
3. List the forms of energy and give an example of each.
4. **Thinking Critically Problem Solving** A boulder that weighs 200 N is poised at the edge of a 100-meter cliff. What is its gravitational potential energy? Draw a diagram showing how its potential energy changes as it falls to 50 m, 20 m, and 10 m.

Check Your Progress

CHAPTER PROJECT 5

Some materials that you can use to build a roller coaster track and car include marbles, rubber tubing, cardboard, and string. Experiment with different hill heights and inclines. (*Hint:* See how high you can make the second and third hills before the roller coaster car can no longer climb up the hills.) Think about how you can explain the types of energy involved as the roller coaster car moves.

Program Resources

◆ **Teaching Resources** 5-1 Review and Reinforce, p. 129; 5-1 Enrich, p. 130

Science Explorer Series *Chemical Interactions,* Chapter 1

Media and Technology

Interactive Student Tutorial CD-ROM M-5

Answers to Self-Assessment

Caption Question

Figure 5 Sparkler—chemical, thermal, electromagnetic; sun—nuclear, thermal, electromagnetic; lightning—electrical, thermal, electromagnetic

3 Assess

Section 1 Review Answers

1. Work and energy are not the same thing, even though they are measured in the same units. Energy is the ability to do work. As work is done, energy is transferred from one object to another.
2. Kinetic energy is the energy of motion. Potential energy is stored energy; it has the potential to do work.
3. Mechanical—riding a bicycle; thermal—hot water; chemical—food energy; electrical—batteries; electromagnetic energy—sunlight; nuclear energy—fusion in a star
4. Gravitational potential energy = 200 N × 100 m = 20,000 J. At 50 m, 10,000 J. At 20 m, 4,000 J. At 10 m, 2,000 J. Diagrams should be labeled with correct values.

Check Your Progress

CHAPTER PROJECT 5

You may wish to show students a simple model of a roller-coaster track with one hill. When students have selected their materials, they should begin to experiment by trying different hills. Students should understand that the roller coaster car has the greatest potential energy at the top of the hill. As the car moves down the hill, potential energy is gradually converted into kinetic energy.

Performance Assessment

Drawing Have students draw a sketch or diagram of playground equipment and label positions where a child would have potential energy and kinetic energy. Diagrams may include a slide, a merry-go-round, a see-saw, climbing equipment, or a swing.

Portfolio Students can keep their diagrams in their portfolios.

Skills Lab

Controlling Variables

Soaring Straws

Preparing for Inquiry

Key Concept As the amount of stretch (related to elastic potential energy) in a rocket launcher increases, the subsequent height that the rocket attains (related to gravitational potential energy) increases.

Skills Objective Students will be able to

- control variables in an experiment to find the relationship between elastic potential energy and gravitational potential energy.

Time 40 minutes

Advance Planning Collect sufficient toilet paper tubes or ask students to bring them from home. Purchase rubber bands and straws if necessary.

Alternative Materials Any short tube will do for a launcher, for example, a 10 cm–15 cm piece of 5-cm diameter plastic or PVC pipe. Any size rubber bands can be used.

Guiding Inquiry

Invitation Shoot a straw into the air with the launcher. The students will immediately want to try it themselves. Tell them that they can try it if they can describe what just occurred in terms of energy. *(The potential energy of the rubber band was transformed into the kinetic energy and then the gravitational potential energy of the rocket.)*

Introducing the Procedure

- Demonstrate the construction of the rocket and launcher using the instructions provided.

Troubleshooting the Experiment

- For accurate and repeatable results, the straw rocket should be put on the rubber band the same way each time, centered along the elastic and perpendicular to it. The ends of the straws must be kept parallel when the straw rocket is pulled down.
- If a toilet paper tube is used, it may begin to collapse slightly with repeated stretches and affect the results. Offer students a fresh tube if this happens.
- Warn students not to twist the straw rocket as they read the stretch markings. Instead, they should rotate the entire launcher and rocket assembly to see the marks.

Skills Lab

Controlling Variables

SOARING STRAWS

In this lab you will use the skill of controlling variables. You will investigate the relationship between the height reached by a rocket and the amount of stretch in a rubber band.

Problem

How does the gravitational potential energy of a straw rocket depend on the elastic potential energy of the rubber band launcher?

Materials

scissors
3 plastic straws
marker
balance
empty toilet paper tube
rubber band
meter stick
metric ruler
masking tape

Procedure 

1. Construct the rocket and launcher following the instructions below. Use a balance to find the mass of the rocket in grams. Record the mass.
2. Hold the launcher in one hand with your fingers over the ends of the rubber band. Load the launcher by placing the straw rocket on the rubber band and pulling down from the other end as shown in the photograph. Let go and launch the rocket straight up. **CAUTION:** *Be sure to aim the straw rocket into the air, not at classmates.*
3. Have your partner hold a meter stick, or tape it to the wall, so that its zero end is even with the top of the rocket launcher. Measure the height, in meters, to which the rocket rises. If the rocket goes higher than a single meter stick, use two meter sticks.
4. In your notebook, make a data table similar to the one on the next page.
5. You can measure the amount of stretch of the rubber band by noting where the markings on the rocket line up with the bottom of the launching cylinder. Launch the rocket using three different amounts of stretch. Record your measurements.

Making a Rocket and Launcher

A. Cut a rubber band and tape it across the open end of a hollow cylinder, such as a toilet paper tube. The rubber band should be taut, but only stretched a tiny amount. This is the launcher.
B. Cut about 3 cm off a plastic straw.
C. Lay 2 full-length straws side by side on a flat surface with the 3-cm piece of straw between them. Arrange the straws so that their ends are even.
D. Tape the straws together side by side.

E. Starting from the untaped end, make marks every centimeter on one of the long straws. This is the rocket.

Safety

Warn students not to point or shoot their rockets at another person. Students should wear safety goggles at all times. A straw rocket is usually harmless, but a direct hit in the eye could do considerable harm. Review the safety guidelines in Appendix A.

Program Resources

- **Teaching Resources** Chapter 5 Skills Lab, pp. 143–145

DATA TABLE

Amount of Stretch (cm)	Height (Trial 1) (m)	Height (Trial 2) (m)	Height (Trial 3) (m)	Average Height (m)	Gravitational Potential Energy (mJ)

6. For each amount of stretch, find the average height to which the rocket rises. Record the height in your data table.
7. Find the gravitational potential energy for each amount of stretch:

   Gravitational potential energy =
   Mass × Gravitational acceleration × Height

   You have measured the mass in grams. So the unit of energy is the millijoule (mJ), which is one thousandth of a joule. Record the results in your data table.

Analyze and Conclude

1. Which variable in your data table is the manipulated variable? The responding variable? How do you know?
2. Graph your results. Show gravitational potential energy on the vertical axis and amount of stretch on the horizontal axis.
3. What measurement is related to the elastic potential energy in this experiment?
4. Look at the shape of the graph. What conclusions can you reach about the relationship between the gravitational potential energy of the rocket and the elastic potential energy of the rubber band?
5. How do you think the amount of energy before the rocket was released compares to the amount of energy after the rocket was released? Account for any losses.
6. **Think About It** Besides the amount of stretch, what other variables might affect the height to which the straw rocket rises? Have you been able to control these variables in your experiment? Explain why or why not.

More to Explore

Use your launcher to investigate launches at angles other than straight up. Instead of manipulating the amount of stretch, hold that variable constant and manipulate the angle of launch. Measure both the heights and distances of the rocket. **CAUTION:** *Be careful not to aim the rocket near any of your classmates.*

Sample Data Table

Mass of rocket : 1.4 g

Elastic Stretch (cm)	Height (Trial 1) (m)	Height (Trial 2) (m)	Height (Trial 3) (m)	Average Height (m)	Gravitational Potential Energy (mJ)
1.0	0.18	0.23	0.17	0.193	2.6
2.0	0.52	0.46	0.55	0.51	7.0
3.0	0.96	0.94	1.13	1.01	14.1
4.0	1.90	2.12	1.88	1.967	27.0
5.0	2.25	2.44	2.19	2.293	31.5

Expected Outcome
As the elastic potential energy of the rubber band increases, the subsequent gravitational potential energy of the rocket increases. However, the relationship between the two is complex. If the band is stretched very tight, more stretching may have a progressively smaller effect.

Analyze and Conclude
1. Manipulated variable—the amount of stretch of the elastic; responding variable—the height that the rocket reached. The elastic was stretched to various lengths and the height was measured in response to the stretch.
2. The curve should point up and to the right.
3. Amount of stretch
4. As the elastic potential energy of the rubber band increases, the gravitational potential energy increases.
5. Before the rocket was released, elastic potential energy was stored in the stretched rubber band. That energy was converted into a combination of kinetic energy and gravitational potential energy as the rocket moved. Some of the energy was converted to kinetic energy of the rubber band and some was converted to thermal energy of the rubber band by friction. Taking all of these into account, the total amount of energy before the rocket was released equals the total amount of energy after.
6. The height is also affected by the weight of the rocket, the type of rubber band, the diameter of the tube, the air drafts in the room, and the angle of launch. Most of these variables were controlled by performing every trial the same way.

Extending the Inquiry

More to Explore The expected results are that the maximum distance occurs at 45° and the maximum height occurs at 90°. However, air resistance and the aerodynamic characteristics of the rocket will affect the results for maximum distance.

Energy Conversion and Conservation

Objectives

After completing the lesson, students will be able to
- ◆ identify and describe conversions from one type of energy to another;
- ◆ state the law of conservation of energy.

Key Terms energy conversion, law of conservation of energy

1 Engage/Explore

Activating Prior Knowledge

Ask students: **What happens when you rub your hands together?** *(They feel warm.)* Ask: **When you're cold, what are some other ways you can get warm?** *(Jump up and down, stay in heated areas, use electric blankets, stand in the sunlight.)*

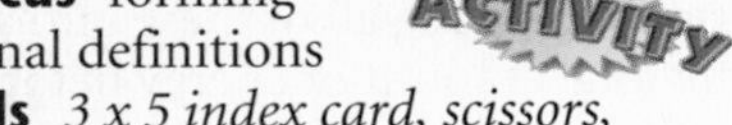

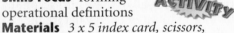

Skills Focus forming operational definitions

ACTIVITY

Materials *3 x 5 index card, scissors, rubber band*

Time 10 minutes

Tips Make sure students use a rubber band just large enough to stretch out when the card is flattened. Make sure students wear safety goggles during this activity.

Think It Over As students push down on the card, they stretch the rubber band and give it potential energy. When they release the card, the potential energy changes into kinetic energy as the rubber band snaps back and pulls the card with it.

Extend Ask students to describe any other observations they made during the activity and to identify what kind of energy was involved in each. *(Sample: When the rubber band snapped back, it vibrated and made a sound, an example of mechanical energy.)*

SECTION 2

Energy Conversion and Conservation

DISCOVER ACTIVITY

What Would Make a Card Jump?

1. Fold an index card in half as shown.
2. In the edge opposite the fold, cut two slits that are about 2 cm long and 2 cm apart.
3. Open the card a little, and loop a rubber band through all four slits. Keeping the fold upward, flatten the card and hold it flat as shown.
4. Predict what will happen to the card if you let go. Then test your prediction.

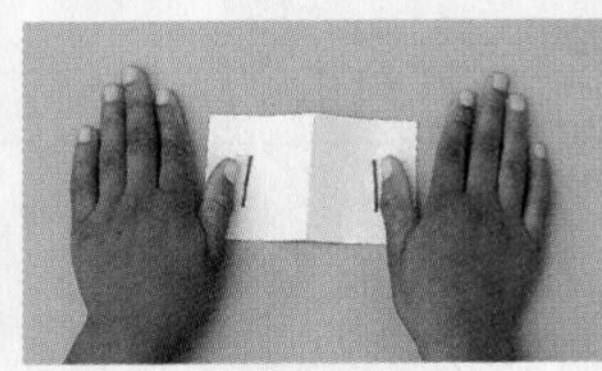

Think It Over

Forming Operational Definitions Describe what happened to the card. Define potential and kinetic energy in terms of the card and the rubber band.

GUIDE FOR READING

- ◆ How are different forms of energy related?
- ◆ What is the law of conservation of energy?

Reading Tip **As you read, draw a flowchart to show each example of energy conversions.**

The spray of water bounces off your raincoat as you look up at the millions of liters of water plunging toward you. The roar of water is deafening. You hold on to the rail as you are rocked back and forth by the rough waves. Are you doomed? Fortunately not—you are on a sightseeing boat at the foot of the mighty Niagara Falls, located on the border between the United States and Canada. The waterfall carries the huge amount of water that drains from the upper Great Lakes. It is an awesome sight that has attracted visitors from all over the world for hundreds of years.

What many visitors don't know, however, is that Niagara Falls serves as much more than just a spectacular view. The waterfall is the center of a network of electrical power lines. The falling water is used to generate electricity for much of the neighboring region.

Figure 7 Niagara Falls is more than 50 meters high.

READING STRATEGIES

Reading Tip Draw a flowchart on the board. As a class, complete the chart for the example of the energy conversion involved in juggling. Then have students work on their own to complete flowcharts for the remaining examples.

Energy Conversion in Juggling

As the orange rises, it slows down.
↓ Kinetic energy decreases and potential energy increases;
Orange stops moving.

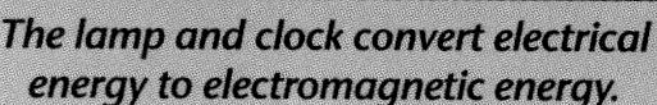

The lamp and clock convert electrical energy to electromagnetic energy.

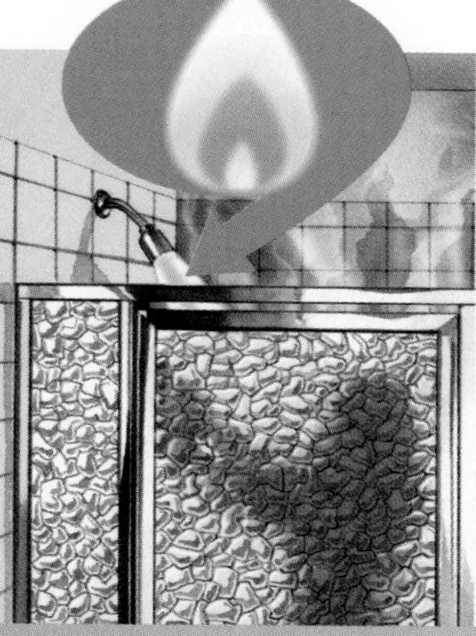

A water heater converts chemical energy in natural gas to thermal energy.

The student's body converts chemical energy in food to mechanical energy.

Figure 8 In just the first few minutes of the morning, this student experiences numerous energy conversions. Imagine how many more can be identified throughout the course of a single day!

Conversions Between Forms of Energy

What does water have to do with electricity? You may already know that the mechanical energy of moving water can be converted, or transformed, into electrical energy. A change from one form of energy to another is called an **energy conversion,** or an energy transformation. **Any form of energy can be converted into any other form.**

You encounter energy conversions frequently. A toaster, for example, converts electrical energy to thermal energy. In an electric motor, electrical energy is converted to mechanical energy that can be used to run a machine.

Your body converts the chemical energy in the food you eat to the mechanical energy you need to move your muscles. Chemical energy in food is also converted to the thermal energy your body uses to maintain its temperature. Chemical energy is even converted to the electrical energy your brain uses to think.

Often a series of energy conversions is needed to do a task. Strike a match, for example, and the mechanical energy used to move the match is converted to thermal energy. The thermal energy causes the match to release stored chemical energy, which is converted to thermal energy and to the radiant energy you see as light.

In a car engine another series of conversions occurs. Electrical energy produces a hot spark. The thermal energy of the spark releases chemical energy in the fuel. When the fuel burns, this chemical energy in turn becomes thermal energy. Thermal energy is converted to mechanical energy used to move the car, and to electrical energy that produces more sparks.

☑ *Checkpoint* *Give an example of an energy conversion.*

2 Facilitate

Conversions Between Forms of Energy

Building Inquiry Skills: Applying Concepts

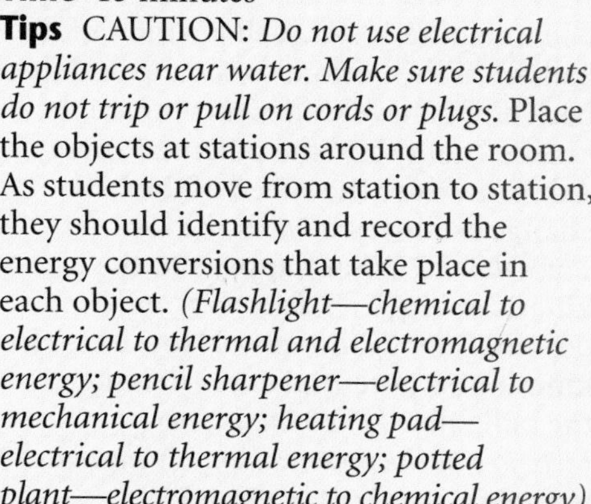

Materials *flashlight, electric pencil sharpener, heating pad, potted plant*
Time 15 minutes
Tips CAUTION: *Do not use electrical appliances near water. Make sure students do not trip or pull on cords or plugs.* Place the objects at stations around the room. As students move from station to station, they should identify and record the energy conversions that take place in each object. *(Flashlight—chemical to electrical to thermal and electromagnetic energy; pencil sharpener—electrical to mechanical energy; heating pad—electrical to thermal energy; potted plant—electromagnetic to chemical energy)* **learning modality: kinesthetic**

Building Inquiry Skills: Applying Concepts

Help students recognize the variety and number of energy conversions taking place around them. Assign each student an everyday activity, such as cooking dinner, playing ball, riding a bicycle, doing homework, or washing dishes. Students should then give brief oral presentations and describe the energy conversions that took place during the activity. **learning modality: verbal**

Program Resources

- **Teaching Resources** 5-2 Lesson Plan, p. 131; 5-2 Section Summary, p. 132

Media and Technology

Audiotapes English-Spanish Summary 5-2

Transparencies "Energy Conversions," Transparency 15

Answers to Self-Assessment

☑ *Checkpoint*

Sample: An electric stove converts electrical energy to thermal energy.

Ongoing Assessment

Drawing Ask students to draw or illustrate an example of one of these energy conversions: mechanical to thermal energy, radiant to thermal energy, or electrical to mechanical energy.

Students can save their drawings in their portfolios.

Kinetic and Potential Energy

Using the Visuals: Figure 10

Some students may not grasp that energy can be transformed from kinetic to potential. Raise an object above your head, and ask students to identify the kind of energy it has while you are moving it upward. *(Kinetic)* When it is at rest above your head, ask: **What happened to the kinetic energy?** *(It changed to potential energy.)* Have students trace the path of the moving ball in Figure 10. At each position of the ball, from the bottom to the top and then back down, have students compare the kinetic energy and the potential energy. Ask: **How does the speed of the ball change as moves toward the top?** *(It slows down.)* **What happens to the kinetic energy?** *(It decreases, and the potential energy increases.)* **How does the kinetic and potential energy change as the ball falls?** *(The kinetic energy increases as the potential energy decreases.)* **learning modality: visual**

Building Inquiry Skills: Predicting

Challenge students to compare potential energy and kinetic energy as they examine a windup toy. Ask them to predict how increasing the elastic potential energy stored in the toy's spring will affect the length of time the toy runs. Then have students test their predictions by comparing how long the toy runs when wound one, two, or three turns. Ask: **How do you increase the toy's potential energy?** *(Wind it more.)* **How does increased potential energy affect the toy's kinetic energy? How can you tell?** *(There is more potential energy to convert into kinetic energy. You can tell the toy had more potential energy because it ran longer.)* **limited English proficiency**

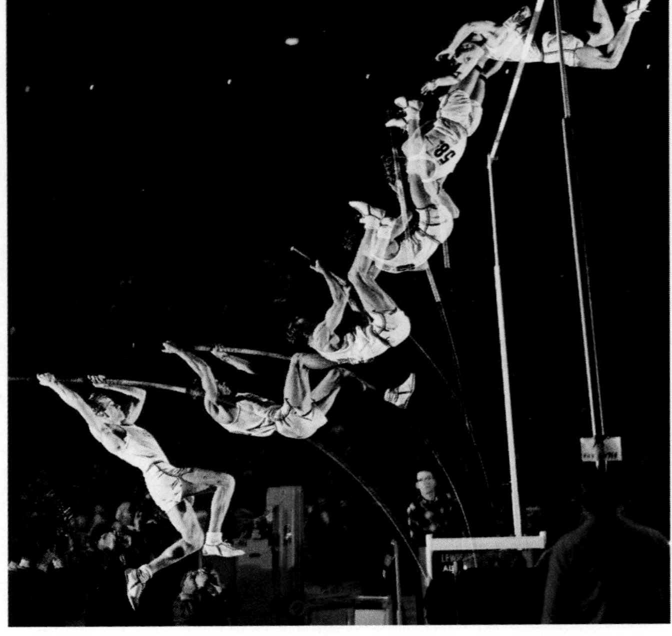

Figure 9 Energy conversions enable this athlete to vault more than six meters into the air. *Predicting What energy conversions will occur after the vaulter falls over the bar?*

Figure 10 When an object is tossed into the air, energy conversions take place.

Kinetic and Potential Energy

One of the most common conversions is the conversion of potential energy to kinetic energy. When you stretch a rubber band, you give it elastic potential energy. If you let it go, the rubber band flies across the room. When the rubber band is moving, it has kinetic energy. The potential energy of the stretched rubber band is converted to the kinetic energy of the moving rubber band.

Energy Conversion in Juggling Any object that rises or falls experiences a change in its kinetic and potential energy. Look at the orange tossed in the air in Figure 10. When it moves, the orange possesses kinetic energy. As it rises, it slows down. Its kinetic energy decreases. But because its height increases, its potential energy increases. At the highest point in its path, it stops moving. At this point, it no longer possesses kinetic energy, but it possesses potential energy. As the orange falls, the entire energy conversion is reversed—kinetic energy increases while potential energy decreases.

Energy Conversion in a Waterfall There is a conversion between potential and kinetic energy on a large scale at Niagara Falls, which you read about earlier. The water at the top of the falls has

Background

Facts and Figures Hydroelectric power plants convert the kinetic energy of falling water into electric current that can be used to power computers, televisions, and other appliances. One of the nation's best-known hydroelectric power plants is the Hoover Dam on the Colorado River between Nevada and Arizona. The water for the Hoover Dam is stored in Lake Mead, one of the world's largest artificial lakes. Falling water from the reservoir runs through pipes and spins turbines in generating stations on each side of the river. The turbines spin a shaft that turns a large electromagnet. The Hoover power plant generates enough electrical energy to serve 1.3 million people, over 4 billion kilowatt-hours per year. Communities in Arizona, California and Nevada—including Las Vegas—buy the electricity, and the money is used to maintain and operate the dam, reservoir, and electrical generating stations.

gravitational potential energy because it is higher than the bottom of the falls. But as the water falls, its height decreases and so it loses potential energy. At the same time, its kinetic energy increases because its velocity increases. Thus potential energy is converted into kinetic energy.

Energy Conversion in a Pole Vault As a pole vaulter runs, he has kinetic energy because he is moving. When he plants his pole to jump, the pole bends. His kinetic energy is converted to elastic potential energy in the pole. As the pole straightens out, the vaulter is lifted high into the air. The elastic potential energy of the pole is converted to the gravitational potential energy of the pole vaulter. Once over the bar, the vaulter's gravitational potential energy is converted into kinetic energy as he falls to the safety cushion below.

Energy Conversion in a Pendulum A continuous conversion between kinetic energy and potential energy takes place in a pendulum. At the highest point in its swing, the pendulum in Figure 11 has only gravitational potential energy. As the pendulum starts to swing downward, it speeds up and its gravitational potential energy changes to kinetic energy. At the bottom of its swing, all its energy is kinetic energy. Then, as it swings to the other side and slows down, it regains gravitational potential energy, and at the same time loses kinetic energy. At the top of its swing on the other side it again has only gravitational potential energy. And so the pattern of energy conversion continues.

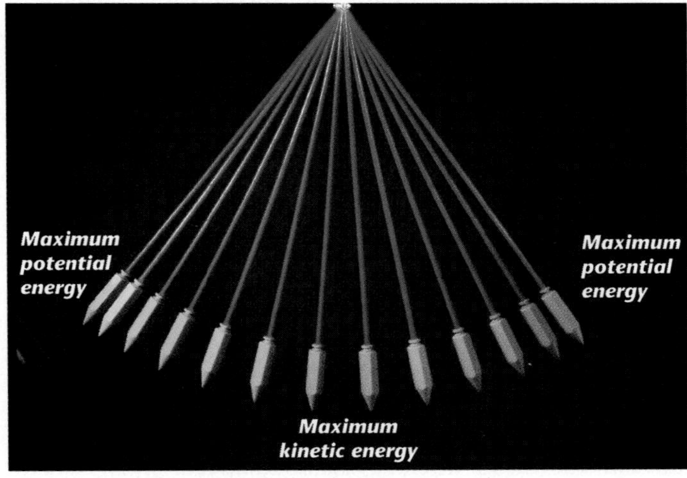

Figure 11 Conversions between kinetic energy and potential energy take place in a pendulum. *Interpreting Diagrams At what two points is potential energy greatest?*

Pendulum Swing

ACTIVITY

1. Set up a pendulum using washers or a rubber stopper, string, a ring stand, and a clamp.
2. Pull the pendulum back so that it makes a 45° angle with the vertical. Measure the height of the stopper. Then set it in motion and observe the height to which it swings.
3. Use a second clamp to reduce the length of the pendulum as shown. The pendulum will run into the second clamp at the bottom of its swing.

4. Pull the pendulum back to the same height as you did the first time. Predict the height to which the pendulum will swing. Then set it in motion and observe it.

Observing How high did the pendulum swing in each case? Explain your observations.

Including All Students

ACTIVITY

Students who have difficulty connecting the photo with the text can build this small model to study how the pole stores energy during a pole vault. Provide students with a flexible plastic drinking straw and some modeling clay. Tell them to stick one end of the straw in the clay and then gently push down on the other end. Ask students to describe what happens to the straw. *(It bends.)* Then ask students what happens if they release the straw. *(It straightens.)* Help students recognize that the pole stores energy in the same way as the drinking straw. **learning modality: kinesthetic**

TRY THIS

ACTIVITY

Skills Focus Observing
Materials *washers or rubber stoppers, string, ring stand, 2 clamps, meter stick*
Time 15 minutes
Tips Suggest students practice several times so they can get an accurate measurement of the height.
Observing In Step 2, the pendulum swings to almost the same height it was released from. In Step 3, the pendulum will swing through a larger angle but will still reach almost the same height above the table it had when released. The gravitational potential energy is converted to kinetic energy at the bottom of the swing and back to gravitational potential energy.
Extend Have students test how increasing mass affects the swing of the pendulum. **learning modality: kinesthetic**

Program Resources

Science Explorer Series *Environmental Science*, Chapter 6

Media and Technology

Transparencies "The Pendulum," Transparency 16

Answers to Self-Assessment

Caption Question

Figure 9 Gravitational potential energy is converted to kinetic energy as the pole vaulter falls.
Figure 11 Potential energy is greatest at the far ends of the swing.

Ongoing Assessment

Oral Presentation Have students imagine that they are swinging on a swing. Have them describe the energy conversions that take place. *(Swinging upward—kinetic energy is converted to potential energy; top of the swing—maximum potential energy, kinetic energy is zero. Swinging down—potential energy is converted to kinetic energy.)*

Conservation of Energy

Demonstration

Materials *hammer, nail, wood block* 

Time 10 minutes

Tips Have students consider the law of conservation of energy as they predict what happens to the energy applied to a hammer when it hits a nail. Then allow them to observe as you hammer a nail into a wood block. Tell students to touch the top of the nail after you finish. Ask: **What form of energy do you feel?** *(Thermal)* Point out that the law of conservation of energy says in part that energy cannot be created. Ask: **Where did the thermal energy come from?** *(Some of the mechanical energy used to swing the hammer was converted into thermal energy.)* Then ask: **Where did the rest of the energy go?** *(It was used to do work on the nail by forcing it into the wood.)* **learning modality: kinesthetic**

Visual Arts CONNECTION

Have students look at the drawing and ask: **Where does the water have the maximum potential energy? Kinetic energy?** *(Students may answer that potential energy is greatest at the top of the fall and kinetic energy is greatest at the bottom of the fall.)* Now have students trace the path of the water with one finger. As they attempt to trace the path they should recognize the optical illusions Escher has created by distorting perspective. If perspective were followed correctly, the "top" of the waterfall would be at the same elevation as the "bottom."

In Your Journal Encourage students to use simple, precise terms to describe the drawing. Students should recognize that Escher's drawing does not follow the law of conservation of energy. **learning modality: visual**

Portfolio Students can save their descriptions in their portfolios.

Figure 12 M. C. Escher's print "Waterfall" was done in 1961.

Visual Arts CONNECTION

The Dutch artist M. C. Escher produced many intriguing illustrations. Escher, who lived from 1898 to 1972, was most recognized for his use of illusions and repeating geometric patterns.

In Your Journal

Look at Escher's "Waterfall." Then look again. In your journal, write a description of the illustration. Did you see anything in the art during your second look that you didn't see at first glance? Is the law of conservation of energy followed or violated in the art? Explain your answer.

Conservation of Energy

If you set a pendulum in motion, do you think it will remain in motion forever? No, it will not. Does that mean that energy is destroyed over time? The answer is no. The **law of conservation of energy** states that when one form of energy is converted to another, no energy is destroyed in the process. **According to the law of conservation of energy, energy cannot be created or destroyed.** So the total amount of energy is the same before and after any process. All energy can be accounted for.

Energy and Friction So what happens to the kinetic energy of the pendulum? As the pendulum moves, it encounters friction at the pivot of the string and from the air through which it moves. When an object experiences friction, the motion (and thus the kinetic energy) of the atoms or molecules increases. This means its thermal energy increases. So the mechanical energy of the moving pendulum is converted to thermal energy. The pendulum slows down, but its energy is not destroyed.

The fact that friction converts mechanical energy to thermal energy should not surprise you. After all, you take advantage of

Background

History of Science When he was 21, M.C. Escher was an architecture student at the School of Architecture and Decorative Arts in Haarlem, Holland. He decided to study graphic art instead of architecture, and he traveled throughout Europe, studying and creating strange landscapes.

In 1936, Escher visited the Alhambra in Spain to study the geometrical tiles used as decoration there and he began to study mathematical papers about geometry and symmetry. Escher corresponded with several mathematicians about his work. He developed a complex system of designing the figures in his art, using a mathematical style of notation that he invented. Escher's unique perspectives and designs have influenced the work of scientists, mathematicians, and cognitive psychologists, as well as interesting the general public.

such thermal energy when you rub your cold hands together to warm them up. The fact that energy is converted to thermal energy because of friction explains why no machine is 100 percent efficient. Recall from Chapter 4 that the work output of a machine is always less than the work input. Now you know that energy is converted to thermal energy in a machine.

Energy and Matter You might have heard of Albert Einstein's theory of relativity. Einstein's theory included a small change to the law of conservation of energy. He explained that energy can sometimes be created—by destroying matter! This process is not important for most of the energy conversions described in this chapter. But it is important in nuclear reactions, where huge amounts of energy are produced by destroying tiny amounts of matter. This discovery means that in some situations energy alone is not conserved. But scientists say that matter and energy together are always conserved. Just as different forms of energy can be converted to one another, matter and energy can be converted back and forth.

Figure 13 Albert Einstein published his theory of special relativity in 1905.

Conserving Energy

INTEGRATING ENVIRONMENTAL SCIENCE When you hear or read about conserving energy, don't get confused with the law of conservation of energy. Conserving energy means saving energy, or not wasting it. In other words, conserving energy means we should not waste fuels, such as gasoline, or our resources will be used up quickly. The law of conservation of energy in physical science, however, refers to a quantity that remains constant. In science, energy is always conserved because its total quantity does not change.

Section 2 Review

1. What is an energy conversion?
2. State the law of conservation of energy in your own words.
3. Describe the energy conversions that occur when a ball is dropped and bounces back up. Why do you think the ball bounces a little lower each time?
4. **Thinking Critically** Applying Concepts A roller coaster car with a mass of 500 kg is at the top of a hill that is 30 m high. Without friction, what would its kinetic energy be as it reached the bottom of the hill?

Science at Home

Straighten a wire hanger. Have your family members feel the wire and observe whether it feels cool or warm. Then hold the ends of the wire and bend it several times. **CAUTION:** *If the wire breaks, it can be sharp.* Do not bend it more than a few times. After bending the wire, have your family members feel it again. Ask them to explain how energy conversions can produce a change in temperature.

Integrating Environmental Science

Make sure students understand the difference between conservation of energy and conserving an energy resource. Ask students to name an energy resource and describe the conversions that take place when it is used. *(Gasoline—chemical energy from the fuel is converted into thermal and mechanical energy.)* Have students discuss what finally happens to all the energy released when a liter of gasoline is burned in an automobile engine and the car is subsequently brought to a stop. *(The energy is all converted to thermal energy.)* **learning modality: verbal**

3 Assess

Section 2 Review Answers

1. A change from one form of energy to another or an energy transformation
2. The total energy before a process is the same as the total energy after.
3. As it falls, potential energy changes to kinetic energy. As it bounces back up, kinetic energy is converted to potential energy. The ball does not bounce as high because some energy escapes as thermal energy or sound when the ball hits the ground.
4. Without friction, kinetic energy would be equal to the gravitational potential energy, $500 \text{ kg} \times 9.8 \text{ m/s}^2 \times 30 \text{ m} = 147{,}000 \text{ J}$.

Science at Home

Materials *wire hanger*
Tips Students should find that the wire feels warm after it has been bent. Some of the energy used to bend the wire is converted into thermal energy, so the wire feels warm.

Performance Assessment

Organizing Information Have students make flowcharts to show the energy conversions made by an electric fan.

Program Resources

- **Teaching Resources** 5-2 Review and Reinforce, p. 133; 5-2 Enrich, p. 134

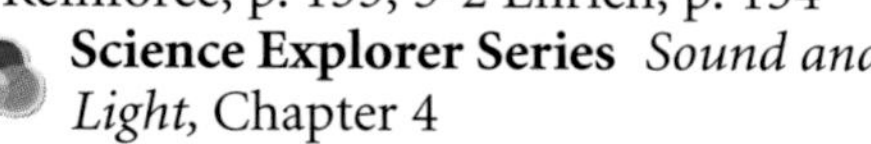

Science Explorer Series *Sound and Light,* Chapter 4

Media and Technology

Interactive Student Tutorial CD-ROM M-5

Exploring Physical Science Videodisc Unit 3, Side 1, "Energy"

Chapter 9

INTEGRATING EARTH SCIENCE

Energy Conversions and Fossil Fuels

Objectives

After completing the lesson, students will be able to

- identify the source of energy stored in fossil fuels;
- explain how energy is converted when fossil fuels are used.

Key Term fossil fuel

1 Engage/Explore

Activating Prior Knowledge

Show students a piece of coal. Ask: **What is this and what is it used for?** *(Coal: providing thermal energy)* Ask students to describe what happens when the coal is burned. *(The coal produces light and thermal energy.)* Ask: **What does this tell you about the coal?** *(Sample: It contains potential energy.)*

DISCOVER

Skills Focus forming operational definitions
Materials *flask, ring stand, clamp, thermometer, water, wooden coffee stirrer, small aluminum pan, matches, safety goggles*
Time 20 minutes
Tips Caution students to use care when using matches and to keep loose hair and clothing away from the burning wood. The flask will be hot.
Expected Outcome The temperature of the water is higher after the coffee stirrer is burned.
Think It Over A fuel is a substance that stores energy.

SECTION 3 Energy Conversions and Fossil Fuels

DISCOVER ACTIVITY

What Is a Fuel?

1. Put on your goggles. Attach a flask to a ring stand with a clamp. Then place a thermometer in the flask.
2. Add enough water to the flask to cover the thermometer bulb. Record the temperature of the water, and remove the thermometer.
3. Fold a wooden coffee stirrer in three places to look like a W.
4. Stand the bent coffee stirrer in a small aluminum pan so that the W is upright. Position the pan 4–5 cm directly below the flask.
5. Ignite the coffee stirrer at the center. **CAUTION:** *Be careful when using matches.*
6. When the coffee stirrer has stopped burning, find the temperature of the water again. Wait until the flask has cooled before cleaning up.

Think It Over

Forming Operational Definitions Gasoline in a car, kerosene in a lantern, and a piece of wood are all fuels. Based on your observations, what is a fuel?

GUIDE FOR READING

- What is the source of the energy stored in fossil fuels?
- How is energy converted when fossil fuels are used?

Reading Tip Before you read, preview *Exploring Energy Conversions.* Write down any questions that you may have. Then look for answers as you read.

Envision a lush, green, swampy forest. Ferns as tall as trees block the view as they rise up to 30 meters. Enormous dragonflies buzz through the warm, moist air. And huge cockroaches, some longer than your finger, crawl across the ground. Where is it? Actually, the question should be, When is it? The time is over 400 million years ago. That's even before the dinosaurs lived! What does this ancient forest have to do with you? You might be surprised to find out just how important this forest is to you.

Figure 14 The plants and animals in this painting of an ancient forest have become the fossil fuels you use today. *Applying Concepts What are fossil fuels?*

READING STRATEGIES

Reading Tip Have a volunteer read aloud the sentence that introduces the visual essay *Exploring Energy Conversions.* Before students look at the visual essay, ask volunteers to suggest what the statement might mean. *(Sample: The electrical energy for the toaster was converted from another source of energy that is millions of years old.)*

Program Resources

- **Teaching Resources** 5-3 Lesson Plan, p. 135; 5-3 Section Summary, p. 136
- **Science Explorer Series** *Inside Earth,* Chapter 5, has information on the formation of sedimentary rock
- **Integrated Science Laboratory Manual** M-5, "Winding Up With Wind"

Figure 15 Fossil fuels such as coal store chemical potential energy.
Predicting How do you think the stored energy is utilized?

Formation of Fossil Fuels

The plants of vast forests that once covered Earth provide you with energy you use today. This energy is stored in fuels. A fuel is a material that stores chemical potential energy. The gasoline used in your school bus, the propane used in a gas barbecue grill, and the chemicals used to launch a space shuttle are examples of fuels. Some of the fuels used today were formed hundreds of millions of years ago by geological processes. These fuels, which include coal, petroleum, and natural gas, are known as **fossil fuels.**

As you'll discover in *Exploring Energy Conversions* on page 156, coal was formed from the ancient forests you just read about. When ancient plants and animals died, they formed thick layers in swamps and marshes. Clay and sand sediments covered the plant and animal remains. Over time, more and more sediment piled up. The resulting pressure along with high temperatures turned the animal and plant remains into coal.

Energy is conserved. That means that fuels do not create energy. So if fossil fuels store energy, they must have gotten energy from somewhere else. But where did it come from? **Fossil fuels contain energy that came from the sun.** In fact, the sun is the major source of energy for all Earth's processes. Within the dense core of the sun, hydrogen atoms are moving at such high velocities that when they collide they join, or fuse, together to form helium atoms. During this process of nuclear fusion, nuclear energy is converted to electromagnetic energy. A portion of this energy reaches Earth.

When the sun's energy reaches Earth, plants, algae, and certain bacteria convert some of the light energy to chemical potential energy. This process is known as photosynthesis because the plants or bacteria synthesize, or make, complex chemicals. Some of this chemical energy is used for the plant's daily needs, and the rest is stored. Animals that eat plants convert some of the

Graphing ACTIVITY

The following list shows what percent of power used in a recent year in the United States came from each power source: coal, 23%; nuclear, 8%; oil, 39%; natural gas, 24%; water, 3%; and biofuels, 3%. Prepare a circle graph that presents these data. (See the Skills Handbook for more on circle graphs.)

What fuel source does the United States rely on most? What percent of total energy needs is met by coal, oil, and natural gas combined?

2 Facilitate

Formation of Fossil Fuels

Addressing Naive Conceptions

Some students may think that fossil fuels are made from fossils such as dinosaur bones. Explain that the term *fossil* refers to any remains of an organism from an earlier geological age formed through a geological process. Fossil fuels are made from the remains of plants or diatoms. **learning modality: verbal**

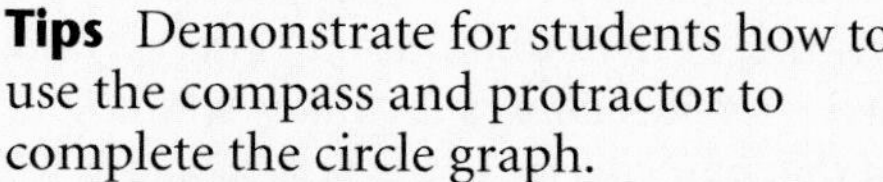

Graphing

Materials *graph paper, compass, protractor* ACTIVITY
Time 15 minutes
Tips Demonstrate for students how to use the compass and protractor to complete the circle graph.
Expected Outcome Students will find that the United States relies mostly on oil. Together, coal, oil, and natural gas meet 86% of the total energy needs.
Extend Ask students to find out what fuel resources provide the energy they use in their homes.

Demonstration

Materials *two seedlings, cups, water, potting soil* ACTIVITY
Time 5 minutes a day for several days

Place two similar seedlings in the classroom, one near a window where it receives ample light, and one in a dark corner. Observe the plants for several days. Ask students to explain any differences in terms of the energy from the sun. **learning modality: visual**

Media and Technology

Audiotapes English-Spanish Summary 5-3

Exploring Earth Science Videodisc Unit 6, Side 2, "Power for the People"

Chapter 2

Answers to Self-Assessment

Caption Question

Figure 14 Fossil fuels, such as coal, petroleum, and natural gas, are energy sources that store energy from the sun.
Figure 15 The chemical potential energy of coal is used to produce thermal and electrical energy.

Ongoing Assessment

Writing Have students write paragraphs to describe how ancient plants were converted into a fossil fuel.

Students can save their paragraphs in their portfolios.

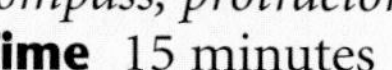

EXPLORING

Energy Conversions

Invite students to trace the flow of energy from the sun to the toaster; as they examine the picture, encourage them to find the source of electrical energy. Then guide their analysis further using the following questions: **What kind of energy is in coal? Where did it come from?** *(The chemical energy in coal is the stored chemical energy from plants and animals.)* **When is electromagnetic energy transferred to potential energy?** *(When plants and animals convert light into stored chemical energy)* **When is potential energy converted into electromagnetic energy?** *(When nuclear fusion occurs and the sun converts nuclear energy to electromagnetic energy; when chemical energy in coal is burned and converted to light and thermal energy, and when electrical energy is converted to light and thermal energy.)*

Extend Assign students a different process and challenge them to create a flowchart that shows the energy conversions starting with fusion in the core of the sun. **learning modality: visual**

Including All Students

For students who need additional challenges, ask: **Are fossil fuels a renewable or non renewable energy resource?** Have students find a definition for *renewable energy resource.* Organize the class into two teams. Have one team prepare an argument in favor of reducing U.S. dependence on fossil fuels while the other team prepares an opposing argument. The allow students to debate the issue. **learning modality: verbal**

EXPLORING *Energy Conversions*

The energy you use to toast your bread may have had a very long history—hundreds of millions of years worth.

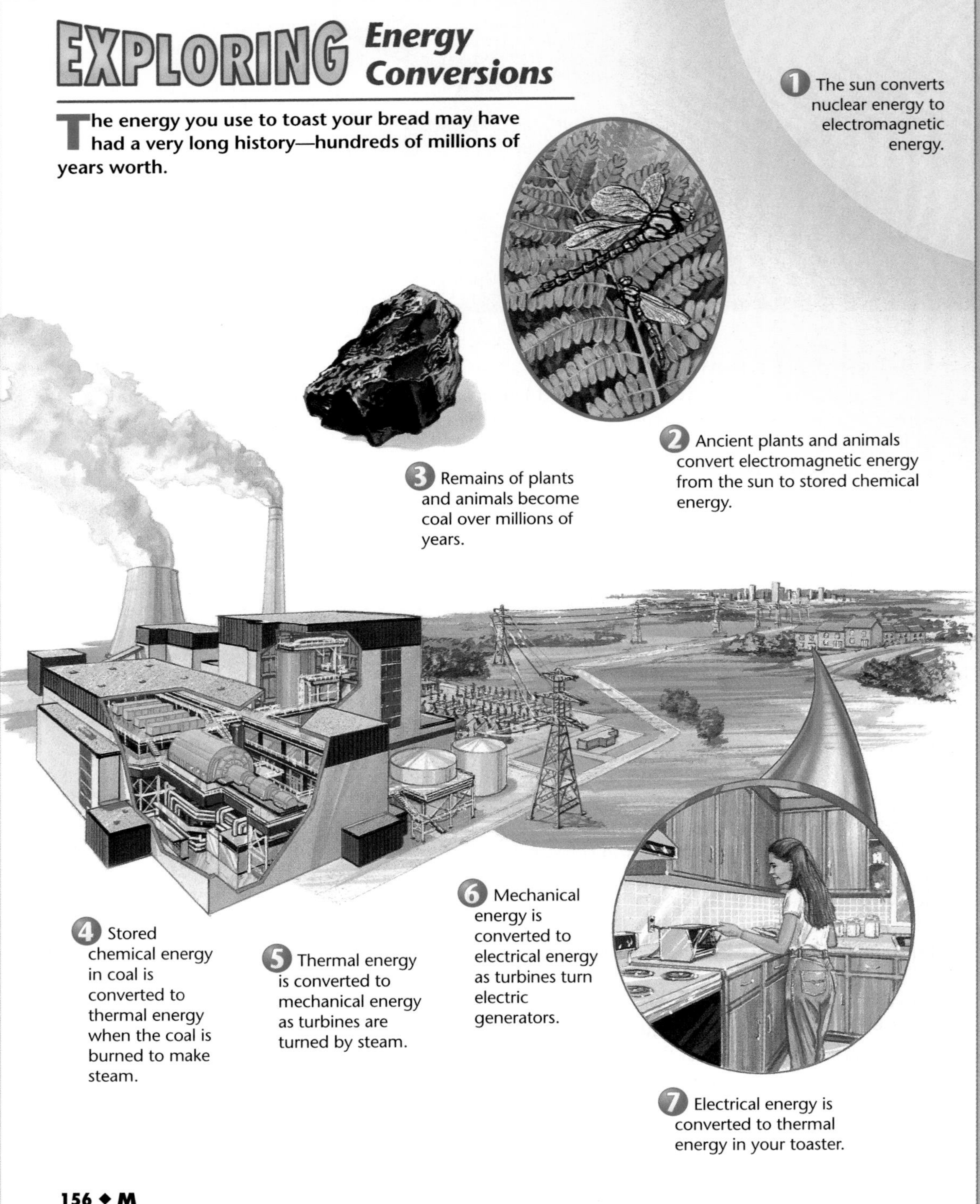

1 The sun converts nuclear energy to electromagnetic energy.
2 Ancient plants and animals convert electromagnetic energy from the sun to stored chemical energy.
3 Remains of plants and animals become coal over millions of years.
4 Stored chemical energy in coal is converted to thermal energy when the coal is burned to make steam.
5 Thermal energy is converted to mechanical energy as turbines are turned by steam.
6 Mechanical energy is converted to electrical energy as turbines turn electric generators.
7 Electrical energy is converted to thermal energy in your toaster.

156 ◆ M

Background

Facts and Figures Early fuels included wood, straw, dried dung, and dried peat. There are also a few references to early uses of coal. For example, Aristotle referred to "bodies which have more of earth than of smoke." He called these substances coal.

Archaeologists have found coal dust and coal cinders in Roman ruins in Europe dating back to A.D. 400. However, the first written record of coal mined in Europe was a document written by a monk in Liège about A.D. 1200 that included a reference to "black earth."

Coal mining exploded into prominence in the early 18th century when coke (almost pure carbon made from coal heated in the absence of air) was first used in blast furnaces to smelt iron and make steel. The invention of the steam engine and the beginnings of the industrial age created a huge demand for coal.

stored chemical energy to chemical energy that is stored in their own cells. The rest is converted to other forms of energy, such as mechanical energy used in movement or thermal energy used to maintain body temperature.

When ancient animals and plants died, the chemical potential energy they had stored was trapped within them. This is the chemical potential energy that is found in coal.

☑ *Checkpoint* *What is the process that produces the sun's energy?*

Use of Fossil Fuels

Fossil fuels can be burned to release the potential chemical energy stored millions of years ago. The process of burning fuels is known as combustion. During combustion, the fuel's chemical potential energy is converted to thermal energy. This thermal energy can be used to heat water until the water boils and produces steam.

In modern coal-fired power plants, the steam is raised to a very high tempeature in a boiler. When it leaves the boiler it has enough pressure to turn a turbine. A turbine is like a fan, with blades attached to a shaft. The pressure of the steam on the blades causes the turbine to spin very fast. In this process, the thermal energy of the steam is converted to the mechanical energy of the moving turbine. Turbines are in turn connected to generators. Generators are just electric motors made to run backward. When they are spun by turbines, they produce electricity. In other words, in a power plant mechanical energy is converted to electrical energy. This energy is then used to light your home and run other electrical devices, such as a toaster.

Section 3 Review

1. How is the chemical energy in fossil fuels related to the sun's energy?
2. How is the energy of coal released?
3. Describe the energy conversions involved in the formation of coal.
4. **Thinking Critically Making Judgments** What general statement can you make about the supply of fossil fuels, given what you know about their formation?

Check Your Progress

CHAPTER PROJECT 5

Experiment with different design ideas for your roller coaster vehicle. What variables affect how fast your vehicle moves? How do potential and kinetic energy change as you make modifications to your design? At what point does the vehicle have the greatest kinetic energy? The greatest potential energy? How does friction affect the performance of your roller coaster? How can you relate the law of conservation of energy to your design?

3 Assess

Section 3 Review Answers

1. Fossil fuels store the sun's energy. The sun's energy is first converted and stored in plants and in animals that eat plants. The remains of the plants and animals become fossil fuels over millions of years.
2. The energy of coal is released by combustion, when its potential chemical energy is converted to thermal energy.
3. Nuclear energy in the sun is converted into electromagnetic energy (sunlight). Plants and animals convert the sun's electromagnetic energy to stored chemical energy. When exposed to high pressures and temperatures over millions of years, the remains of the plants and animals become coal.
4. Because fossil fuels are formed much more slowly than we are using them, they may become increasingly scarce.

Check Your Progress

CHAPTER PROJECT 5

As you review students' designs, make sure they are practical and meet the guidelines established for this project. Encourage students to answer the questions in the text by pointing to specific examples from their design. For example, students should recognize that the car will have the greatest potential energy when it is at the top of the 1-m hill. The car probably has the greatest kinetic energy at the bottom of the first hill or at the lowest point on the track.

Program Resources

- **Teaching Resources** 5-3 Review and Reinforce, p. 137; 5-3 Enrich, p. 138
- **Interdisciplinary Exploration Series** "Metropolis," pp. 35–36

Media and Technology

Interactive Student Tutorial CD-ROM M-5

Answers to Self-Assessment

☑ *Checkpoint*

Nuclear fusion

Performance Assessment

Organizing Information Have students construct concept maps starting with the terms: *potential chemical energy, electromagnetic energy, ancient plants and animals, gasoline* and adding other terms of their own.

Power

Objectives

After completing the lesson, students will be able to

- ◆ define and calculate power;
- ◆ compare energy and power.

Key Term power

1 Engage/Explore

Activating Prior Knowledge

Ask students to brainstorm a list of people or things they describe as powerful. *(Samples: computers, car engines, a smell, an athlete's legs, stereo speakers, a superhero)* Ask students to think about what all these things have in common, and how they compare to less powerful things. Explain that the term power has a special meaning in science that is different from its meaning in everyday language.

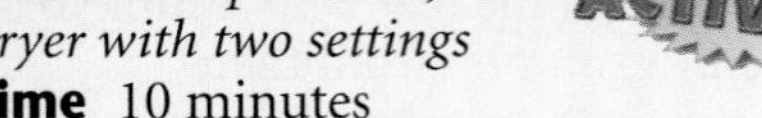

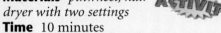

Skills Focus inferring
Materials *pinwheel, hair dryer with two settings*
Time 10 minutes
Tips CAUTION: *Make sure students' work areas are dry before they use the hair dryer.* Perform this activity as a demonstration if you do not have enough hair dryers for all students.
Expected Outcome The pinwheel spins faster when blown by a hairdryer at its highest setting.
Think It Over Work is done because a force is required to overcome air resistance and friction. Work is force times distance. It requires more force to make the pinwheel spin at a higher speed. Thus, more work is done at the higher setting.

Power

DISCOVER ACTIVITY

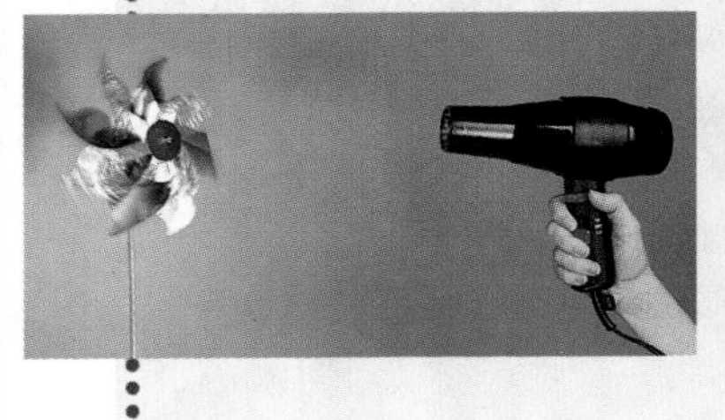

Is Work Always the Same?

1. Obtain a pinwheel and a hair dryer with at least two different power settings.
2. Set the dryer on its lowest setting. Use it to blow the pinwheel. Observe the pinwheel's motion.
3. Set the dryer on its highest setting. Again, use it to blow the pinwheel. Observe the pinwheel's motion.

Think It Over
Inferring Explain why work is done in spinning the pinwheel. What differences can you identify between the two situations? Is the amount of work greater for the high or low speed?

GUIDE FOR READING

- ◆ How do you calculate power?
- ◆ What is the difference between power and energy?

Reading Tip As you read, use your own words to describe the relationship among work, power, and energy.

The ad for a sleek new sports car catches your eye as you read a magazine. Its manufacturer boasts that the car can go from 0 to 100 km/h in 5 seconds because it has a 320-horsepower engine. But what does a car have to do with horses? You may find more than you think.

What Is Power?

A car does work to accelerate from rest. Some car engines do this work rapidly, while others do it more slowly. The faster an engine can do an amount of work, the more power the engine has. **Power** is the rate at which work is done or the amount of work done in a unit of time.

When you carry an object up some stairs, you do the same amount of work whether you walk or run up the stairs. (Work is the weight of the object times the height of the stairs.) But you exert more power when you run because you are doing the work faster.

You can think of power in another way. A device that is twice as powerful as another can do the same amount of work in half the time. Or it can do twice the work in the same time.

Calculating Power Whenever you know how fast work is done, you can calculate power. **Power is calculated by dividing the amount of work done by the amount of time taken to do the work.** This can be written as the following formula.

$$Power = \frac{Work}{Time}$$

READING STRATEGIES

Reading Tip Have students use their own words to write down notes about the relationships between work, power, and energy as they read the section. Then arrange students in groups of three. Assign each student in the group one of the three main headings in the section. In the order topics are presented in the section, have students use their reading notes to paraphrase aloud the information on their topic.

Study and Comprehension Encourage students to write a definition of the word power using their own words before they study the section. Have students consider the way they use this word in everyday situations. As they read, students should compare the descriptions in the section to their definitions to help them understand the scientific meaning of the word.

Since work is equal to force times distance, you can rewrite the equation for power as follows.

$$Power = \frac{Force \times Distance}{Time}$$

When work is measured in joules and time in seconds, the unit of power is the joule per second (J/s). This unit is also known as the watt (W), in honor of James Watt, who made great improvements to the steam engine. One watt of power is produced when one joule of work is done in one second. In other words, 1 watt = 1 J/s.

A watt is a relatively small unit of power. For example, you produce about one watt of power if you raise a glass of water to your mouth in one second. Because a watt is so small, power is often measured in larger units. One kilowatt (kW) equals 1,000 watts. A washing machine uses about one kilowatt when it is running. An electric power plant produces millions of kilowatts.

☑ *Checkpoint* *What is power?*

Sample Problem

A crane lifts an 8,000-N beam 75 m to the top of a building in 30 s. How much power does the crane use?

Analyze. The force needed to lift the beam will be equal to its weight, 8,000 N. The distance and time are given, so the formula for power can be used.

Write the formula. $Power = \frac{Force \times Distance}{Time}$

Substitute and solve. $Power = \frac{8,000\ N \times 75\ m}{30\ s}$

$Power = \frac{600,000\ N{\cdot}m}{30\ s}$ or $\frac{600,000\ J}{30\ s}$

$Power = 20,000\ J/s = 20,000\ W$ or $20\ kW$

Think about it. The answer tells you that the crane used 20,000 W to lift the beam. That equals 20 kW.

Practice Problems

1. A motor exerts a force of 10,000 N to lift an elevator 6 m in 5 s. What is the power produced by the motor?
2. A tow truck exerts a force of 9,000 N to pull a car out of a ditch. It moves the car a distance of 6 m in 25 s. What is the power of the tow truck?

Program Resources

- **Teaching Resources** 5-4 Lesson Plan, p. 139; 5-4 Section Summary, p. 140
- **Science Explorer Series** *Electricity and Magnetism*, Chapter 3 has information on electric power.

Media and Technology

Audiotapes English-Spanish Summary 5-4

Answers to Self-Assessment

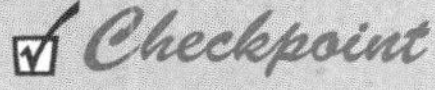

Power is the rate at which work is done, or the amount of work done in a unit of time.

2 Facilitate

What Is Power?

Inquiry Challenge

ACTIVITY

Materials *various objects that may be comfortably lifted, such as paint cans, small barbells*
Time 20 minutes

Have groups of students design experiments to test whether it is more tiring to do work quickly or slowly. CAUTION: *Review all plans for safety.* Ask: **How can you do the same work at different rates?** *(Lift or push the object at different speeds.)* Help students analyze their results. **cooperative learning**

Sample Problem

Be sure students include the proper units in their calculations. Point out that a newton × meter is a joule and that a joule per second is a watt.
So, $\frac{N \cdot m}{s} = \frac{J}{s} = W$

Practice Problems
1. $(10,000\ N \times 6\ m)/\ 5\ s = 12,000\ W$
2. $(9,000\ N \times 6\ m)/\ 25\ s = 2,160\ W$

Power and Energy

Building Inquiry Skills: Observing

Materials *15-W lamp, 40-W lamp, 100-W lamp*
Time 10 minutes

In a darkened room, have students record observations about the energy released by the light bulbs. Caution students not to touch the hot bulbs. Ask: **Why does the 15-W bulb look much dimmer than the 100-W bulb?** *(It converts less electrical energy per second.)* **learning modality: visual**

Ongoing Assessment

Skills Check Ask students what quantities they must measure to find the power of an elevator that travels to the top of a building 15 m tall.

Real-World Lab

Careers in Science

Can You Feel the Power?

Preparing for Inquiry

Key Concept Power is the rate of doing work and depends on force, distance and time.

Skills Objective Students will
- measure distance and time;
- calculate work and power;
- interpret data.

Time 45 minutes

Advance Planning Have boards, stopwatches, and meter sticks ready. Tell students to bring calculators and 2 cm-thick books to class on lab day. You may want to review using the calculator to calculate rates before the lab.

Alternative Methods If possible, try to borrow several aerobic "steps" to be used in the experiment. They will be easier to set up and be more stable. Aerobic steps are available in several heights.

Guiding Inquiry

Invitation Ask students if they are familiar with aerobics classes. Most will be at least familiar. Some may even take classes. Point out that in some classes students repeatedly step up onto a low platform to increase the effectiveness of the workout. Ask: **How does this increase the effectiveness?** *(By increasing the total distance, total work is increased. By increasing the speed of doing the exercise, power is increased.)*

Introducing the Procedure
- Divide the class into groups of three students each.
- Ask students why the body weights are given in newtons and why the distance is measured in meters. *(Work is measured in joules, which are newton-meters.)*

Troubleshooting the Experiment
- Students should recognize that the work done during the downward motion is done by gravity and cannot be counted as work done by the student. A complete up and down cycle is counted as one repetition, not two.

Power and Energy

Recall that work is the transfer of energy. Thus power can be defined in another way. **Power is the rate at which energy is transferred from one object to another or converted from one form to another.** For this reason, power is not limited to situations in which objects are moved. Power can be found whenever energy is being transferred or converted.

Real-World Lab

Careers in Science

Can You Feel the Power?

Imagine you are a physical therapist who wants to increase the power output of her patients. In this lab, you will simulate a simple exercise using a step.

Problem

How can you change how much power you expended while doing an exercise?

Skills Focus

measuring, calculating, interpreting data

Materials

calculator
meter stick
stopwatch or clock with a second hand
board, about 2.5 cm × 30 cm × 120 cm
8–10 books, each about 2 cm thick

Procedure 

1. Construct a step by making two identical stacks of books. Each stack should be about 20 cm high. Place a board securely on top of the stacks of books so that the ends of the board are even with the outside edges of the books. **CAUTION:** *Be sure to have your partners hold the board steady and level throughout the procedure.*
2. Copy the data table into your notebook.
3. You do work every time you take a step.
   Work = Weight × Height
   a. Assume your weight is 400 N and your partners' weights are 425 N and 450 N.
   b. Measure the vertical distance in centimeters from the floor to the top of the board. Convert to meters by dividing by 100 and record this height in the data table.
4. Calculate the work you do in stepping up onto the board once. Then calculate the work you do in stepping up onto the board 20 times. Record both answers in your data table.
5. Step up onto the board with both feet and then step backwards off the board onto the floor. This up and down motion is one repetition. Make sure you are comfortable with the motion.
6. Have one partner time how long it takes you to do 20 repetitions performed at a constant speed. Count out loud to help the timer keep track of the number of repetitions. Record the time in your data table.
7. Calculate the power you expended to do 20 repetitions. (Power = Work ÷ Time.) Predict how your results will change if you step up at different speeds.

Safety

Falling hazard Be sure partners hold the board steady and level throughout the investigation. Partners should "spot" for the steppers.

Program Resources

- **Teaching Resources** Chapter 5 Real-World Lab, pp. 146–147

You know that a 100-watt light bulb is much brighter than a 40-watt light bulb. The wattage printed on a light bulb tells you its power. The power of a light bulb is the rate at which electrical energy is converted into electromagnetic energy (light) and thermal energy. A 100-watt light bulb converts electrical energy at a rate of 100 joules each second. A 100-watt bulb is brighter because it gives off more energy per second than a 40-watt bulb.

DATA TABLE

	Weight (N)	Height of Board (m)	Time for 20 Repetitions (s)	Work for 1 Repetition (J)	Work for 20 Repetitions (J)	Power (W)
Student 1 Trial 1						
Student 1 Trial 2						

8. Repeat Steps 6 and 7, but climb the step more slowly than you did the first time. Record the new data in the Trial 2 row of your data table.
9. Switch roles with your partners and repeat Steps 3 through 8.

Analyze and Conclude

1. Compare the amount of work you did during your first and second trials.
2. Compare the amount of power you produced during your first and second trials.
3. Did you and your partners all do the same amount of work? Explain your answer.
4. Did you and your partners all produce the same power during your trials? Explain your answer.
5. **Apply** Suggest how a physical therapist could use music to change the power output of her patients. Why would a therapist want to change power outputs?

Design an Experiment

Design an experiment to test two other ways a physical therapist could change the power output of her patients. Get your teacher's approval before beginning your experiment.

Sample Data Table

	Weight (N)	Height of Board (m)	Time for 20 Repetitions (s)	Work for 1 Repetition (J)	Work for 20 Repetitions (J)	Power (W)
Student 1 Trial 1	400	0.2	20	80	1600	80
Student 1 Trial 2	400	0.2	30	80	1600	53.3

Expected Outcome

- Students' results should show that, for a given student, the work done for each repetition is the same because the step is the same height. However, slower repetitions mean lower power.
- Students' results should show that the student with a weight of 400 N does less work for each repetition.

Analyze and Conclude

1. The amount of work is the same.
2. The power is greater for the first trial, because it was faster.
3. No. Partners with greater weight do more work.
4. No. The power depended on the student's weight and how long it took to do 20 repetitions.
5. The beat of the music helps participants maintain the rate at which exercises are performed. Students who exercise to music with a faster beat will move faster and produce more power. By increasing the power of their workout, students will burn more calories and increase their overall strength and muscle tone.

Extending the Inquiry

Design an Experiment Other ways to change the power include using handheld or ankle weights, using higher steps, or increasing the speed. Students should test only one variable at a time and should never work unsupervised in the lab.

Horsepower

Integrating Technology

Have students find out the horsepower of a vehicle advertised in a newspaper or magazine. Then have them convert its horsepower to watts. **learning modality: logical/mathematical**

3 Assess

Section 4 Review Answers

1. Power = Work/Time
2. Power is the rate of doing work. Because work is the transfer of energy, power is the rate of transferring or converting energy from one form to another.
3. Work = 40 N × 18 m = 720 J; Power = 720 J ÷ 4 s = 180 J/s or 180 W
4. 24,000 J ÷ 60 s = 400 J/s or 400 W
5. The 40-horsepower engine consumes energy twice as fast as the 20-horsepower engine and it also produces energy twice as fast as a 20-horsepower engine.

Check Your Progress (Chapter Project 5)

Make sure students can describe how the results of their trials helped them find the best place for the features on their roller coasters. Some students may be having trouble with the performance of their roller coasters. Encourage them to simplify their designs until they find one that works, and then add more detail slowly. Students may have difficulty getting vertical loops to work properly.

Performance Assessment

Writing Have students write advertisements for James Watt's steam engine. They should include a definition of power and its relationship to work.

Figure 16 One of Watt's engines (next to the chimney) is shown at work at a coal mine.

Horsepower

INTEGRATING TECHNOLOGY When people talk about engines for automobiles, they use another power unit instead of the watt. This unit is the horsepower. One horsepower is equal to 746 watts. (The horsepower is not an SI unit.)

The word horsepower was used by James Watt to advertise the advantages of his improved steam engine of 1769. Watt decided to relate his engine to the common source of power in his day—horse power. He compared the amount of work his steam engine could do to the amount of work a horse could do hauling coal. He defined one horsepower as the amount of work a horse does to lift a 33,000-pound weight a distance of one foot in one minute.

Section 4 Review

1. State the formula for calculating power.
2. How are power and energy related?
3. Find the work you do when you exert a force of 40 N to run a distance of 18 m in 4 seconds. Then find the power you expend.
4. **Thinking Critically Problem Solving** The motor of an electric fan converts 24,000 J of electrical energy every minute (60 s). What is the power of the fan's motor?
5. **Thinking Critically Comparing and Contrasting** A 40-horsepower engine burns twice as much fuel each hour as a 20-horsepower engine. Explain this in terms of power and energy.

Check Your Progress (Chapter Project 5)

Add turns to the tracks on your roller coaster. What happens to the speed of the car as it rounds a turn? Are there certain locations along the tracks that are better for turns? Experiment with putting a vertical loop in the tracks. Where is the best place to put a loop? You can say that the roller coaster produces power because it converts gravitational potential energy to kinetic energy. At what point in the car's trip is this rate of conversion greatest?

Program Resources

- **Teaching Resources** 5-4 Review and Reinforce, p. 141; 5-4 Enrich, p. 142
- **Interdisciplinary Exploration Series** "Back to the Thirties," pp. 38–39
- **Interdisciplinary Exploration Series** "Fate of the Rain Forest," pp. 17–19

STUDY GUIDE

CHAPTER 5 REVIEW

Section 1 The Nature of Energy

Key Ideas

- Energy is the ability to do work or produce change.
- Energy is transferred from one object to another when work is done.
- Kinetic energy is the energy that an object has because of its motion. Potential energy is the energy an object has because of its position or condition.
- Six forms of energy are mechanical energy, thermal energy, chemical energy, electric energy, electromagnetic energy, and nuclear energy.

Key Terms

energy
kinetic energy
potential energy
elastic potential energy
gravitational potential energy
mechanical energy
thermal energy
chemical energy
electrical energy
electromagnetic energy
nuclear energy

Section 2 Energy Conversion and Conservation

Key Ideas

- An energy conversion or transformation occurs when energy changes from one form to another.
- In any process, no energy is lost. This is the law of conservation of energy.

Key Terms

energy conversion
law of conservation of energy

Section 3 Energy Conversions and Fossil Fuels

Integrating Earth Science

Key Ideas

- Energy from the sun is converted to chemical energy in plants and animals. Fossil fuels, such as coal and petroleum, were formed from the remains of ancient plants and animals.
- The energy in fossil fuels is released and transformed when the fuels are burned.

Key Term

fossil fuels

Section 4 Power

Key Ideas

- Power is the rate at which work is done, or the rate at which energy is transformed.
- Power is calculated by dividing the amount of work done (or energy converted) by the time it took. The unit of power is the watt: 1 W = 1 J/s.

Key Term

power

Program Resources

- **Teaching Resources** Chapter 5 Project Scoring Rubric, p. 126; Chapter 5 Performance Assessment Teacher Notes, pp. 214–215; Chapter 5 Performance Assessment Student Worksheet, p. 216; Chapter 5 Test, p. 217–220

Media and Technology

Interactive Student Tutorial CD-ROM M-5

Computer Test Bank M-5 Test

CHAPTER 5 REVIEW

Reviewing Content: Multiple Choice

1. b 2. b 3. c 4. a 5. c

True or False

6. energy 7. motion 8. true
9. chemical 10. true

Checking Concepts

11. Kinetic energy is the energy possessed by a moving object, while potential energy is stored energy, due to an object's position or condition. Potential energy can be converted into kinetic energy and vice versa.
12. Mechanical (kinetic energy and gravitational potential energy); thermal and chemical energy; elastic potential energy
13. On the perch, the eagle has gravitational potential energy. Halfway to the ground, half the gravitational potential energy has become kinetic energy. When it reaches its prey, all its mechanical energy is kinetic energy. The eagle also converts chemical energy from its food to mechanical energy when it flies.
14. As you climb the stairs, kinetic energy is converted to gravitational potential energy.
15. The energy is the same in both cases, but the power is double in the second case because the same energy transfer was done twice as fast.
16. Students' biographies should creatively demonstrate that energy is present in every aspect of life.

Thinking Visually

17. a. kinetic energy **b.** joules **c.** gravitational **d.** power

Applying Skills

18. The club has the greatest potential energy at B and D. It has the greatest kinetic energy at C.
19. At A, the club has no potential or kinetic energy. At B, it has maximum gravitational potential energy and no kinetic energy. At C, it has maximum kinetic energy and no potential energy. At D, it has maximum potential energy and no kinetic energy. At E, when it is brought to rest, it has no potential or kinetic energy.

CHAPTER 5 REVIEW

Reviewing Content

For more review of key concepts, see the Interactive Student Tutorial CD-ROM.

Multiple Choice

Choose the letter of the answer that best completes each statement.

1. Energy of motion is called
   a. elastic potential energy.
   b. kinetic energy.
   c. gravitational potential energy.
   d. chemical energy.
2. When you stretch a slingshot you give it
   a. kinetic energy.
   b. elastic potential energy.
   c. gravitational potential energy.
   d. power.
3. Whenever energy is transformed, some energy is converted to
   a. nuclear energy.
   b. electrical energy.
   c. thermal energy.
   d. mechanical energy.
4. Coal stores energy from the sun as
   a. chemical energy.
   b. electromagnetic energy.
   c. mechanical energy.
   d. electrical energy.
5. The rate at which work is done is called
   a. energy.
   b. efficiency.
   c. power.
   d. conservation.

True or False

If the statement is true, write true. If it is false, change the underlined word or words to make the statement true.

6. The SI unit of power is the Joule.
7. Kinetic energy is due to the position of an object.
8. Gravitational potential energy depends on weight and height.
9. Green plants convert the electromagnetic energy of the sun into mechanical energy.
10. A device that has three times the power of another can do the same amount of work in one third the time.

Checking Concepts

11. Describe the difference between kinetic energy and potential energy.
12. For each of the following, decide which forms of energy are present: a leaf falls from a tree; a candle burns; a rubber band is wrapped around a newspaper.
13. An eagle flies from its perch in a tree to the ground to capture its prey. Describe its energy transformations as it descends.
14. When you walk upstairs, how are you obeying the law of conservation of energy?
15. One chef places a pie in the oven at a low setting so that it is baked in one hour. Another chef places a pie in the oven at a high setting so that the pie bakes in half an hour. Is the amount of transformed energy the same in each case? Is the power the same?
16. **Writing to Learn** As you saw in the figures on pages 144 and 145, you can find different forms of energy all around you. Imagine you are writing your own biography. Pick three major events in your life. Write a paragraph about the form of energy that was most important in each event.

Thinking Visually

17. **Concept Map** Copy the concept map about energy onto a separate sheet of paper. Then complete it and add a title. (For more on concept maps, see the Skills Handbook.)

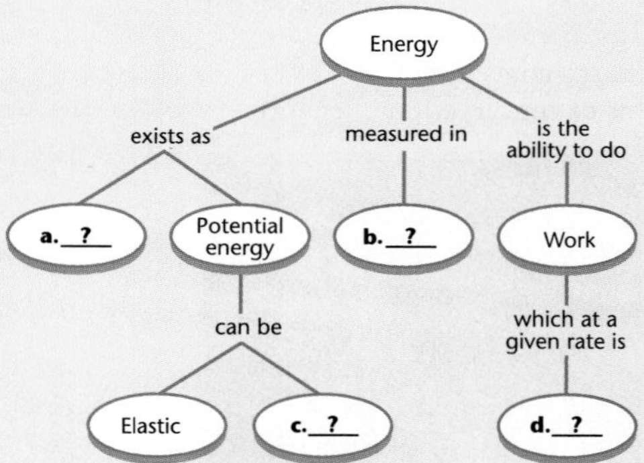

---

20. No. The man adds energy as he swings the club. Therefore, energy is conserved.

Thinking Critically

21. kinetic energy $= 0.5 \times 1300$ kg $\times$ $(11 \text{ m/s})^2 = 78{,}650$ J
22. Her final potential energy is less because she walked to a lower level. 500 N $\times$ (3 m) = 1500 J. So her potential energy decreased by 1500 J.
23. Electric energy is converted to mechanical energy to spin the fan blades and to thermal energy. The fan blades move air (kinetic energy) in a breeze toward you.
24. The motorcycle has the least kinetic energy, while the bus has the greatest kinetic energy. Kinetic energy = 1/2(mass $\times$ velocity^2). Kinetic energy increases as mass increases.

Applying Skills

Use the illustration of a golfer taking a swing to answer the Questions 18–20. The golf club starts at point A and ends at point E.

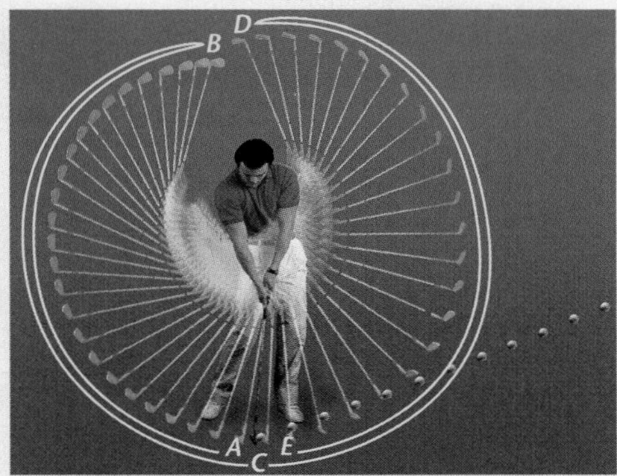

18. **Inferring** At which point(s) does the golf club have the greatest potential energy? At which point(s) does it have the greatest kinetic energy?

19. **Communication** Describe the energy conversions from point *A* to point *E*.

20. **Drawing Conclusions** The kinetic energy of the club at point *C* is more than the potential energy of the club at point *B*. Does this mean that the law of conservation of energy is violated?

Thinking Critically

21. **Calculating** A 1300-kg car travels at 11 m/s. What is its kinetic energy?

22. **Problem Solving** A 500-N girl walks down a flight of stairs so that she is 3 m below her starting level. What is the change in the girl's gravitational potential energy?

23. **Applying Concepts** You turn on an electric fan to cool off. Describe the energy conversions involved.

24. **Relating Cause and Effect** A motorcycle, an automobile, and a bus are all traveling at the same speed. Which has the least kinetic energy? The greatest kinetic energy? Explain your answer.

Performance Assessment

CHAPTER PROJECT 5

Wrap Up

Present Your Project Present your roller coaster to the class. Explain how you selected your materials, as well as the effect of hill height, incline, turns, and loops on the motion of the roller coaster. You should also explain how energy is converted as the roller coaster moves along the tracks. Point out an interesting feature of your roller coaster.

Reflect and Record In your journal, explain how you might improve your roller coaster. Think about what you knew about kinetic and potential energy before the project began, and what you know now. Which features would you change? Which would you keep the same?

Getting Involved

In Your Home Select a room in your home. Identify any device in the room that involves energy conversions, such as a clock, a radio, or exercise equipment. Also watch to see what activities are performed in the room, such as eating, sleeping, or cleaning. Make a poster showing photos or drawings of the devices and activities. Describe the energy conversions involved in each illustration.

Program Resources

- **Inquiry Skills Activity Book** Provides teaching and review of all inquiry skills.

Performance Assessment

CHAPTER PROJECT 5

Wrap Up

Present Your Project
Students should present their roller coasters to the class either in an oral presentation with demonstrations or as a class exhibit. An exhibit may allow students to interact and test each others' roller coasters. Ask the students to demonstrate how their roller coasters convert potential to kinetic energy.

Reflect and Record Encourage students to concentrate on ways to reduce air resistance and friction so that more gravitational potential energy is converted to kinetic energy.

Getting Involved

In Your Home Students should identify several energy conversions in their posters. Some students may want to trace all energy conversions back to the sun's energy. Encourage students to think about how they use energy in their everyday lives.

Thermal Energy and Heat

Sections	Time	Student Edition Activities	Other Activities
CHAPTER PROJECT 6 **In Hot Water** p. 167	Ongoing (2 weeks)	Check Your Progress, pp. 177, 190 Wrap Up, p. 193	**TE** Chapter 6 Project Notes, pp. 166–167
1 Temperature and Thermal Energy pp. 168–170 ◆ Define temperature and identify the three common temperature scales. ◆ Contrast temperature and thermal energy.	1–2 periods/ 1 block	**Discover** How Cold Is the Water?, p. 168	**TE** Building Inquiry Skills: Making Models, p. 169 **PTA** "Testing Popcorn," pp. 1–8
2 The Nature of Heat pp. 171–180 ◆ Describe how heat is related to thermal energy. ◆ Identify the three forms of heat transfer. ◆ Define and calculate the specific heat of a substance. ◆ Describe the movement of heat and how insulators and conductors affect heat transfer.	5 periods/ $2\frac{1}{2}$ blocks	**Discover** What Does It Mean to Heat Up?, p. 171 **Sharpen Your Skills** Inferring, p. 172 **Try This** Feel the Warmth, p. 174 **Skills Lab: Interpreting Data** Just Add Water, pp. 178–179	**TE** Inquiry Challenges, pp. 173, 174 **TE** Demonstrations, pp. 175, 176 **ISLM** M-6, "Combustion Heat of a Candle" **PTA** "Testing Bandages," pp. 1–8
3 *INTEGRATING CHEMISTRY* **Thermal Energy and States of Matter** pp. 181–186 ◆ Name the three states of matter and explain what causes changes of state. ◆ Relate expansion of matter to addition of thermal energy. ◆ Describe what takes place in solid-liquid and liquid-gas changes of state.	3 periods/ $1\frac{1}{2}$ blocks	**Discover** What Happens to Heated Metal?, p. 181 **Sharpen Your Skills** Observing, p. 184	**TE** Inquiry Challenge, p. 182 **TE** Language Arts Connection, p. 183 **TE** Demonstrations, pp. 183, 185 **IES** "Wagons West," pp. 31-32 **PTA** "Testing Disposable Cups," pp. 1–8
4 Uses of Heat pp. 187–190 ◆ Describe how engines convert thermal energy to mechanical energy. ◆ Describe how refrigerators transfer thermal energy from a cool area to a warm area.	2 periods/ 1 block	**Discover** What Happens at the Pump?, p. 187 **Try This** Shake It Up, p. 188	
Study Guide/Chapter Review pp. 191–193	1 period/ $\frac{1}{2}$ block		**ISAB** Provides teaching and review of all inquiry skills

For Standard or Block Schedule The Resource Pro® CD-ROM gives you maximum flexibility for planning your instruction for any type of schedule. Resource Pro® contains Planning Express®, an advanced scheduling program, as well as the entire contents of the Teaching Resources and the Computer Test Bank.

CHAPTER PLANNING GUIDE

Program Resources	Assessment Strategies	Media and Technology
TR Chapter 6 Project Teacher Notes, pp. 148–149 **TR** Chapter 6 Project Overview and Worksheets, pp. 150–153 **TR** Chapter 6 Project Scoring Rubric, p. 154	**SE** Performance Assessment: Chapter 6 Project Wrap Up, p. 193 **TE** Check Your Progress, pp. 177, 190 **TE** Performance Assessment: Chapter 6 Project Wrap Up, p. 193 **TR** Chapter 6 Project Scoring Rubric, p. 154	Science Explorer Internet Site
TR 6-1 Lesson Plan, p. 155 **TR** 6-1 Section Summary, p. 156 **TR** 6-1 Review and Reinforce, p. 157 **TR** 6-1 Enrich, p. 158	**SE** Section 1 Review, p. 170 **TE** Ongoing Assessment, p. 169 **TE** Performance Assessment, p. 170 **TR** 6-1 Review and Reinforce, p. 157	Exploring Physical Science Videodisc, Unit 4 Side 2, "What's Your Temperature" Audiotapes: English-Spanish Summary 6-1 Transparency 18, "Thermal Energy" Interactive Student Tutorial CD-ROM, M-6
TR 6-2 Lesson Plan, p. 159 **TR** 6-2 Section Summary, p. 160 **TR** 6-2 Review and Reinforce, p. 161 **TR** 6-2 Enrich, p. 162 **TR** Chapter 6 Skills Lab, pp. 171–173 **SES** Book I, *Weather and Climate,* Chapter 2 **SES** Book F, *Inside Earth,* Chapter 1 **SES** Book H, *Earth Waters,* Chapter 4	**SE** Section 2 Review, p. 177 **SE** Analyze and Conclude, p. 179 **TE** Ongoing Assessment, pp. 173, 175 **TE** Performance Assessment, p. 177 **TR** 6-2 Review and Reinforce, p. 161	Audiotapes: English-Spanish Summary 6-2 Exploring Physical Science Videodisc, Unit 4 Side 2, "As Hot As a Desert" Exploring Physical Science Videodisc, Unit 4 Side 2, "Hot Is Hot, Cold Is Not" Transparency 19, "Convection Currents in a Heating System" Interactive Student Tutorial CD-ROM, M-6
TR 6-3 Lesson Plan, p. 163 **TR** 6-3 Section Summary, p. 164 **TR** 6-3 Review and Reinforce, p. 165 **TR** 6-3 Enrich, p. 166 **SES** Book K, *Chemical Building Blocks,* Chapter 2 **SES** Book D, *Human Biology and Health,* Chapters 1 and 3	**SE** Section 3 Review, p. 186 **TE** Ongoing Assessment, pp. 183, 185 **TE** Performance Assessment, p. 186 **TR** 6-3 Review and Reinforce, p. 165	Audiotapes: English-Spanish Summary 6-3 Interactive Student Tutorial CD-ROM, M-6
TR 6-4 Lesson Plan, p. 167 **TR** 6-4 Section Summary, p. 168 **TR** 6-4 Review and Reinforce, p. 169 **TR** 6-4 Enrich, p. 170	**SE** Section 4 Review, p. 190 **TE** Ongoing Assessment, p. 189 **TE** Performance Assessment, p. 190 **TR** 6-4 Review and Reinforce, p. 169	Audiotapes: English-Spanish Summary 6-4 Transparency 20, "Exploring a Four-Stroke Engine" Interactive Student Tutorial CD-ROM, M-6
TR Chapter 6 Performance Assessment, pp. 221–223 **TR** Chapter 6 Test, pp. 224–227	**SE** Chapter Review, pp. 191–193 **TR** Chapter 6 Performance Assessment: pp. 221–223 **TR** Chapter 6 Test, pp. 224–227 **CTB** Test M-6	Computer Test Bank, Test M-6 Interactive Student Tutorial CD-ROM, M-6

Key: **SE** Student Edition
CTB Computer Test Bank
ISAB Inquiry Skills Activity Book
TE Teacher's Edition
SES Science Explorer Series Text
PTA Product Testing Activities by *Consumer Reports*
TR Teaching Resources
ISLM Integrated Science Laboratory Manual
IES Interdisciplinary Explorations Series

Meeting the National Science Education Standards and AAAS Benchmarks

National Science Education Standards	Benchmarks for Science Literacy	Unifying Themes
Science as Inquiry (Content Standard A) ◆ **Use appropriate tools and techniques to gather, analyze, and interpret data** Different temperature scales are described. Interpreting data is emphasized as students explore what happens when water of two different temperatures is added together. *(Section 1; Skills Lab)* **Physical Science** (Content Standard B) ◆ **Properties and changes of properties in matter** Substances have characteristic boiling and freezing points at which they change state. Matter can be described as solid, liquid, or gas. *(Sections 1, 3)* ◆ **Transfer of energy** Thermal energy can be measured. Heat moves through conduction, convection, and radiation. Insulators and conductors transfer heat at different rates. Thermal energy causes changes of state in matter. Thermal energy is transferred in heat engines and refrigerators. *(Sections 1, 2, 3, 4; Chapter Project; Skills Lab)* **Science and Technology** (Content Standard E) ◆ **Design a solution or a product** Students design an insulating device. *(Chapter Project)* **Science in Personal and Social Perspectives** (Content Standard F) ◆ **Personal health** Limiting indoor pollution in well-insulated buildings is discussed. *(Science and Society)*	**3B Design Systems** Specific criteria must be met in the design of an insulating device. *(Chapter Project)* **3C Issues in technology** Development of extremely efficient insulation in buildings has led to problems in cleaning and ventilating the air. *(Science and Society)* **4D The Structure of Matter** Particles of matter move more quickly when heated. Particles in solids, liquids, and gases move at different rates. *(Sections 1, 3; Skills Lab)* **4E Energy Transformation** Thermal energy moves from substances with hotter temperatures to substances with cooler temperatures. Heat moves by conduction, convection, or radiation. Insulators slow the transfer of heat and conductors allow heat to flow easily. Thermal energy is transferred in heat engines and refrigerators. *(Sections 2, 3, 4; Chapter Project; Skills Lab)* **8C Energy Sources and Use** Internal and external combustion engines convert stored chemical energy into thermal energy. The thermal energy is converted to mechanical energy. Changes of state and the transfer of thermal energy cool the inside of a refrigerator. *(Section 4)* **10J Harnessing Power** The external combustion engine powered the steam engine, which converted stored energy from coal into mechanical energy. *(Section 4)*	◆ **Energy** The measurement and transfer of thermal energy is described and analyzed. Devices that convert thermal energy to mechanical energy are discussed. *(Sections 1, 2, 3, 4; Chapter Project; Skills Lab; Science and Society)* ◆ **Patterns of Change** Matter changes state with loss or gain of thermal energy. *(Sections 3, 4)* ◆ **Stability** Thermal energy moves from a hotter substance to a cooler substance until both substances are the same temperature. *(Sections 2, 3, 4; Chapter Project; Skills Lab)* ◆ **Scale and Structure** Matter is made up of tiny particles. *(Sections 1–4)* ◆ **Systems and Interactions** When a fluid is heated unevenly, convection currents form. Convection currents are the source of winds and weather systems. *(Section 2)*

Media and Technology

Exploring Physical Science Videodisc

◆ **Section 1** "What's Your Temperature" looks at how thermometers work and the variety of temperature scales they use.

◆ **Section 2** "As Hot As a Desert" explains the properties of heat in a desert setting.

◆ **Section 2** "Hot Is Hot, Cold Is Not" defines heat as kinetic energy with examples of conduction, convection, and radiation.

Interactive Student Tutorial CD-ROM

◆ **Chapter Review** Interactive questions help students to self-assess their mastery of key chapter concepts.

Student Edition Connection Strategies

◆ **Section 2** **Integrating Earth Science,** p. 173

◆ **Section 3** **Integrating Chemistry,** p. 181
Language Arts Connection, p. 183
Integrating Health, p. 185

Visit the Science Explorer Internet site to find an up-to-date activity for Chapter 6 of *Motion, Forces, and Energy.*

Student Edition Activities Planner

ACTIVITY	Time *(minutes)*	Materials *Quantities for one work group*	Skills
Section 1			
Discover, p. 168	10	**Consumable** warm tap water, cold tap water, room temperature water, paper **Nonconsumable** 3 large bowls, markers	Observing
Section 2			
Discover, p. 171	15	**Consumable** frozen butter; hot water **Nonconsumable** glass beaker; utensils made of different materials, such as stainless steel, plastic, and wood	Observing
Sharpen Your Skills, p. 172	none	**Consumable** No special materials are required. **Nonconsumable** umbrella	Inferring
Try This, p. 174	10	**Nonconsumable** lamp with 60- or 75-W bulb, centimeter ruler, clock or stopwatch	Drawing Conclusions
Skills Lab, pp. 178–199	35	**Consumable** hot tap water **Nonconsumable** 4 plastic foam cups, scissors, beaker of water kept in an ice bath, 2 thermometers, balance, pencil	Interpreting Data
Section 3			
Discover, p. 181	15	**Consumable** matches **Nonconsumable** 1 m of thin metal wire, clamp, ring stand, 3 or 4 washers, candle, oven mitt	Inferring
Sharpen Your Skills, p. 184	10	**Consumable** water **Nonconsumable** teakettle, hot plate	Observing
Section 4			
Discover, p. 187	10	**Nonconsumable** bicycle pump, deflated basketball or soccer ball	Developing Hypotheses
Try This, p. 188	15	**Nonconsumable** dry sand, metal container such as a coffee can with a plastic lid, thermometer	Classifying

A list of all materials required for the Student Edition activities can be found on pages T14–T15. You can order Materials Kits by calling 1-800-828-7777 or by accessing the Science Explorer Internet site at **www.science-explorer.phschool.com.**

In Hot Water

Heat is the transfer of thermal energy. The thermogram of a house shows how heat is being lost from a house. Preventing heat loss means preventing the transfer of thermal energy from one object to another. In this project, students will investigate means of reducing the transfer of thermal energy by using insulation.

Purpose In this project, students will discover what is necessary to keep a can of hot water warm. The project allows students to reinforce the chapter content on heat transfer by applying it directly to a physical situation.

Skills Focus After completing the Chapter 6 project, students will be able to

- ◆ design and analyze an experiment to measure the insulating capabilities of several materials;
- ◆ apply these concepts to build and test an insulating device;
- ◆ communicate with other students concerning the insulating capabilities of different devices;

Project Time Line The project will take approximately eight to ten days. Class time should be set aside to allow students access to thermometers.

On the first day, introduce the project and have students brainstorm about heat and insulation. On the second and third day, have students design and perform experiments to measure the insulation ability of several materials. Students will need a few days to design and build their devices at home. It will take another day or two for students to test their devices with water of different temperatures. On the last day, students devices will be tested for their ability to keep hot water warm.

Before beginning the project, see Chapter 6 Project Teacher Notes on pages 148–149 in Teaching Resources for more details on carrying out the project. Also distribute the Students' Chapter 6 Project Overview and Worksheets and Scoring Rubric on pages 150–154 in Teaching Resources.

CHAPTER 6

Thermal Energy and Heat

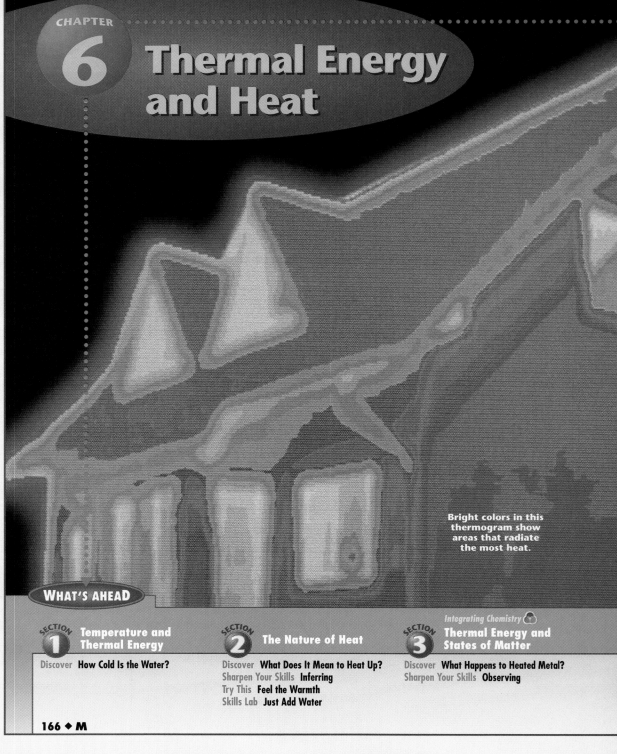

Bright colors in this thermogram show areas that radiate the most heat.

WHAT'S AHEAD

SECTION 1 Temperature and Thermal Energy
Discover **How Cold Is the Water?**

SECTION 2 The Nature of Heat
Discover **What Does It Mean to Heat Up?**
Sharpen Your Skills **Inferring**
Try This **Feel the Warmth**
Skills Lab **Just Add Water**

Integrating Chemistry
SECTION 3 Thermal Energy and States of Matter
Discover **What Happens to Heated Metal?**
Sharpen Your Skills **Observing**

166 ◆ M

Suggested Shortcuts Consider having students work in groups to come up with an experimental design and then have each student in a group test one or two materials using the design. Or, you may want to perform this project as a class. Have the whole class brainstorm ideas for designing the insulating device. Challenge students to select three or four designs to test against each other. Divide the class into small groups, and have each group build a device. Test the devices and compare them.

Possible Materials

- ◆ empty aluminum soda cans
- ◆ classroom thermometers
- ◆ funnels
- ◆ tongs or hot pads
- ◆ A wide variety of materials for insulation. For example: aluminum foil, newspaper, packing peanuts, cardboard, nylon cloth, canvas cloth, cotton balls, plastic wrap, foam board, and wood chips. Encourage students to suggest and use other materials as well.

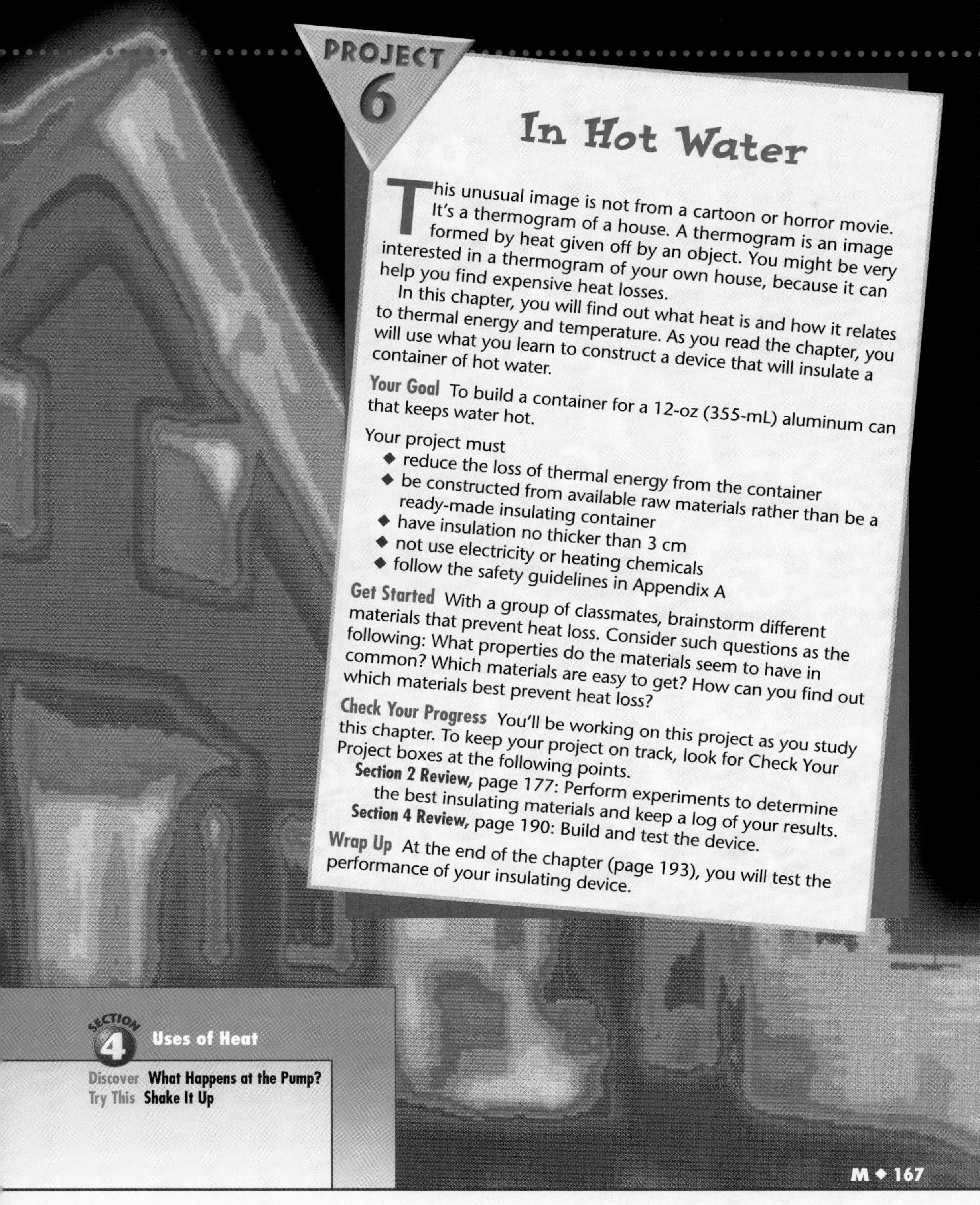

PROJECT 6

In Hot Water

This unusual image is not from a cartoon or horror movie. It's a thermogram of a house. A thermogram is an image formed by heat given off by an object. You might be very interested in a thermogram of your own house, because it can help you find expensive heat losses.

In this chapter, you will find out what heat is and how it relates to thermal energy and temperature. As you read the chapter, you will use what you learn to construct a device that will insulate a container of hot water.

Your Goal To build a container for a 12-oz (355-mL) aluminum can that keeps water hot.

Your project must
- reduce the loss of thermal energy from the container
- be constructed from available raw materials rather than be a ready-made insulating container
- have insulation no thicker than 3 cm
- not use electricity or heating chemicals
- follow the safety guidelines in Appendix A

Get Started With a group of classmates, brainstorm different materials that prevent heat loss. Consider such questions as the following: What properties do the materials seem to have in common? Which materials are easy to get? How can you find out which materials best prevent heat loss?

Check Your Progress You'll be working on this project as you study this chapter. To keep your project on track, look for Check Your Project boxes at the following points.

Section 2 Review, page 177: Perform experiments to determine the best insulating materials and keep a log of your results.

Section 4 Review, page 190: Build and test the device.

Wrap Up At the end of the chapter (page 193), you will test the performance of your insulating device.

SECTION 4 **Uses of Heat**

Discover **What Happens at the Pump?**
Try This **Shake It Up**

M ◆ 167

Launching the Project Introduce the project as a mystery to solve. Challenge students to find the best design to insulate the can of water.

Allow time for students to read the description of the project in their text and the Chapter Project Overview on pages 150–151 in Teaching Resources. Then encourage discussions on experimental design, such as controls and variable, other materials besides those that you have supplied that could be used, and any initial questions students may have. Pass out copies of the Chapter 6 Project Worksheets on pages 152–153 in Teaching Resources for students to review.

Students should measure the insulating ability of different materials to decide what materials to use in their containers and to be able to predict the insulating properties of other groups' containers. Remind students that they must also consider the design of the container. For example, students should consider whether it has a lid or a specific shape. Certain materials may make some container designs more difficult to build.

Program Resources

- **Teaching Resources** Chapter 6 Project Teacher's Notes, pp. 148–149; Chapter 6 Project Overview and Worksheets, pp. 150–153; Chapter 6 Project Scoring Rubric, p. 154

Performance Assessment

The Chapter 6 Project Scoring Rubric on page 154 of Teaching Resources will help you evaluate how well students complete the Chapter 6 Project. Students will be assessed on
- the experimental design proposed;
- whether students' experiments include controls;
- whether experiments test different materials and designs;
- how thoroughly they test their designs and how effective the completed devices are as an insulator;
- the accuracy of their predictions of the final temperatures of other students' devices;
- their participation in their groups (if students are assigned to work in groups).

By sharing the Chapter 6 Scoring Rubric with students at the beginning of the project, you will make it clear to them what they are expected to do.

SECTION 1 Temperature and Thermal Energy

Objectives

After completing the lesson, students will be able to

- ◆ define temperature and identify the three common temperature scales;
- ◆ contrast temperature and thermal energy.

Key Terms temperature, Fahrenheit scale, Celsius scale, Kelvin scale, absolute zero

1 Engage/Explore

Activating Prior Knowledge

Have students locate the daily high and low temperatures. Look for temperatures at other cities in other states. Invite students to describe the hottest temperature and the coldest temperature they have experienced. Ask: **When we say the temperature is 25°C, what is that a measure of?** List the answers and use them as a basis for assessing naive conceptions about temperature. Students may have a concept of temperature as heat or thermal energy.

DISCOVER

Skills Focus observing
Materials *3 large bowls, warm tap water, cold tap water, room temperature water, markers, paper*
Time 10 minutes
Tips Keep paper towels on hand to clean up any water spills. CAUTION: *Students should not use hot water that is uncomfortable to touch. Make sure the warm water is less than 45° C.*
Think It Over The water in the third bowl (room temperature water) feels warm to the hand that was in the cold water and cold to the hand that was in the warm water. The sense of temperature is relative.

SECTION 1 Temperature and Thermal Energy

DISCOVER ACTIVITY

How Cold Is the Water?

1. Fill a plastic bowl with cold water, another with warm water, and a third with water at room temperature. Label each bowl.
2. Line up the three bowls. Place your right hand in the cold water and your left hand in the warm water.
3. After about a minute, place both your hands in the third bowl at the same time.

Think It Over
Observing How did the water in the third bowl feel when you touched it? Did it feel the same on each hand? If not, can you explain why?

GUIDE FOR READING

- ◆ What are the three common temperature scales?
- ◆ How does temperature differ from thermal energy?

Reading Tip As you read, use the headings to make an outline about temperature and thermal energy. Leave space to add definitions as you read.

The radio weather report says that today's high temperature will be 25 degrees. What should you wear? Do you need a coat and a scarf to keep warm, or only shorts and a T-shirt? What you decide depends on the temperature scale. On one scale, 25 degrees is below freezing, while on another scale 25 degrees is quite comfortable.

Temperature

You don't need a science book to tell you that the word *hot* means higher temperatures or the word *cold* means lower temperatures. You wear different clothes on a hot day than on a cold day. When scientists think about temperature, however, they are considering the particles that make up matter.

Matter is made up of tiny particles called atoms and molecules. These particles are always in motion even if the object they make up isn't moving at all. As you recall, the energy of motion is called kinetic energy, so all particles of matter have kinetic energy. The faster particles move, the more kinetic energy they have. **Temperature** is a measure of the average kinetic energy of the individual particles in an object.

Figure 1 The particles of hot cocoa move faster than those of cold chocolate milk. *Applying Concepts Which drink has particles with greater average kinetic energy?*

READING STRATEGIES

Reading Tip After students read the information under the first heading, help them outline the topic.
I. Temperature is a measure of average kinetic energy of particles in an object.
A. If particles move faster, they have more kinetic energy and higher temperature.
B. If particles move more slowly, they have less kinetic energy and lower temperature.

Program Resources

- ◆ **Teaching Resources** 6-1 Lesson Plan, p. 155; 6-1 Section Summary, p. 156
- ◆ **Product Testing Activities by *Consumer Reports*** "Testing Popcorn," pp. 1–8

Look at the mug of hot cocoa and the glass of cold chocolate milk in Figure 1. The hot cocoa has a higher temperature than the cold chocolate. Its particles are moving faster, so they have greater average kinetic energy. If the chocolate milk is heated, its particles will move faster, so their kinetic energy will increase. This means that the temperature of the milk will rise.

Temperature Scales

If you did the Discover activity, you know that whether something feels hot or cold depends on what you compare it to. Walking into an air-conditioned building on a hot day can give you a chill. You need a few minutes to get comfortable with the indoor temperature. Since you can't rely on your sense of touch, you need a scale to measure temperature accurately. **The three common scales for measuring temperature are the Fahrenheit, Celsius, and Kelvin scales.**

Fahrenheit Scale In the United States, the most common temperature scale is called the **Fahrenheit scale.** On this scale, the number 32 is assigned to the temperature at which water freezes. The number 212 is assigned to the temperature at which water boils. The interval between these two temperatures is divided into 180 equal intervals called degrees Fahrenheit (°F).

Celsius Scale The temperature scale used in most of the world is the **Celsius scale.** On this scale, the number 0 is assigned to the temperature at which water freezes. The number 100 is assigned to the temperature at which water boils. The interval between freezing and boiling is divided into 100 equal parts, called degrees Celsius (°C).

Kelvin Scale The temperature scale commonly used in physical science is the **Kelvin scale.** Units on the Kelvin scale are the same size as those on the Celsius scale, and are called kelvins (K). Any

Figure 2 This illustration compares the three temperature scales. *Comparing and Contrasting How do the three temperature scales differ from one another?*

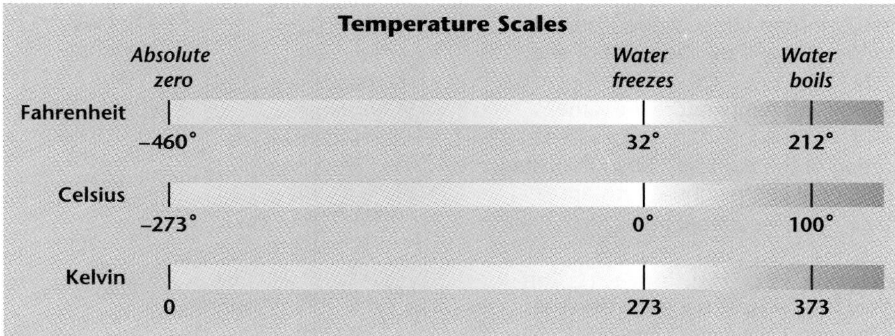

Media and Technology

Transparencies "Thermal Energy," Transparency 18

Exploring Physical Science Videodisc Unit 4, Side 2, "What's Your Temperature?"

Chapter 4

Answers to Self-Assessment

Caption Questions

Figure 1 The hot drink has particles with greater average kinetic energy.

Figure 2 The temperature scales differ in the intervals between degrees and in the numbers assigned to the freezing point of water and the boiling point of water.

2 Facilitate

Temperature

Building Inquiry Skills: Making Models

Materials *metal pie pan, plastic wrap, 10 marbles*
Time 10 minutes

Have students place 10 marbles in a pie pan and cover the pan tightly with plastic wrap, then gently shake the pan to model the movement of particles in a cold object. Ask: **What do the marbles represent?** *(Atoms and molecules)* Next, invite students to demonstrate what happens as an object heats. *(Students should shake the pans more vigorously.)* **learning modality: kinesthetic**

Temperature Scales

Using the Visuals: Figure 2

Direct students to look at the temperature scales and indicate what a comfortable room temperature would be in each. *(Sample: 75°F, 27°C, 300 K)* Tell students to place a finger on the left end of the temperature scales. Ask them to describe how the average kinetic energy of particles changes as they move their finger to the right. *(It increases.)* **learning modality: visual**

Cultural Diversity

Explain that in most countries, daily temperatures are given using the Celsius scale. Invite students who are not native to the United States to describe a typical weather report from their country of origin. **learning modality: verbal**

Ongoing Assessment

Writing Have students briefly describe the energy difference between the water particles in a pot of boiling water and in an ice cube tray. *(The particles in a pot of boiling water have a greater average kinetic energy than the particles in an ice cube tray.)*

Thermal Energy

Building Inquiry Skills: Comparing and Contrasting

To help students distinguish between average kinetic energy and thermal energy, ask: **If you go to the beach and get a cup of water out of the ocean, does the water in the cup have the same average kinetic energy as the ocean?** *(Yes, they are at the same temperature.)* **The same thermal energy?** *(No, the ocean is much larger so its total thermal energy is greater.)* **learning modality: verbal**

3 Assess

Section 1 Review Answers

1. Fahrenheit: 32°F, 212°F; Celsius: 0°C, 100°C; Kelvin: 273K, 373K
2. No. Thermal energy is the total energy of all the particles in an object. Temperature is a measure of the average kinetic energy of the particles.
3. As the thermal energy increases, the motion of particles increases.
4. Zero on the Kelvin scale is absolute zero, the point at which particles have no thermal energy.
5. Yes. A large container of cold water could have the same total energy (thermal energy) as a small container of hot water.

Science at Home

Encourage students to include situations in which temperature determines their actions, such as bringing pets inside on a cold night or deciding whether it is warm enough to go swimming. Businesses often have displays that include both Fahrenheit and Celsius temperatures.

Performance Assessment

Drawing Have students draw and label two containers of water, one freezing and one boiling. Students should show thermometers in the water and write captions describing the kinetic and thermal energy.

Figure 3 A large pot of hot cocoa can have the same temperature as a small cup of cocoa. *Comparing and Contrasting Do both containers have the same thermal energy?*

temperature on the Kelvin scale can be changed to Celsius degrees by adding 273 to it. So the freezing point of water on the Kelvin scale is 273 K and the boiling point is 373 K.

Why is the number 273 so special? Experiments have led scientists to conclude that −273°C is the lowest temperature possible. At this temperature, called **absolute zero,** no more energy can be removed from matter. The Kelvin scale is defined so that zero on the Kelvin scale is absolute zero.

✓ *Checkpoint* *What three points define the common temperature scales?*

Thermal Energy

The total energy of all of the particles in a substance is called thermal energy, or sometimes internal energy. Even if two samples of matter are at the same temperature, they do not necessarily have the same total energy.

The more particles a substance has at a given temperature, the more thermal energy it has. For example, 2 liters of hot cocoa at 75°C has more thermal energy than 0.15 liter at 75°C. **So temperature is a measure of the average kinetic energy of the individual particles. Thermal energy is the total energy of all of the particles.**

Thermal energy does not depend on just temperature and the number of particles in a substance. It also depends on how the particles are arranged. In Section 3 you will learn about how thermal energies differ for solids, liquids, and gases.

Section 1 Review

1. Name the three common temperature scales. Give the freezing point and boiling point of water for each.
2. Are thermal energy and temperature the same? Explain.
3. How is the motion of the particles within a substance related to the thermal energy of the substance?
4. Why are there no negative temperatures on the Kelvin scale?
5. **Thinking Critically** **Applying Concepts** Can a container of cold water have the same thermal energy as a container of hot water? Explain.

Science at Home

Ask your family members to look around your home for situations in which temperature is important. Perhaps the temperature in the oven is important—you might bake a cake at 350 degrees. Or you might set your air conditioning for 78 degrees. Make a table describing each situation. Your family members will probably use the Fahrenheit scale. Ask them to describe any situations they are familiar with that make use of the Celsius scale.

Program Resources

◆ **Teaching Resources** 6-1 Review and Reinforce, p. 157; 6-1 Enrich, p. 158

Media and Technology

Interactive Student Tutorial CD-ROM M-6

Audiotapes English-Spanish Summary 6-1

Answers to Self-Assessment

Caption Question

Figure 3 No. The large pot of cocoa has more thermal energy than the small cup of the same temperature.

✓ *Checkpoint*

The three reference points for the temperature scale are absolute zero, the freezing point of water, and the boiling point of water.

The Nature of Heat

DISCOVER — ACTIVITY

What Does It Mean to Heat Up?

1. Obtain several utensils made of different materials, such as silver, stainless steel, plastic, and wood.
2. Press a small gob of frozen butter on the handle of each utensil. Make sure that when the utensils stand on end, the butter is at the same height on each.
3. Stand the utensils in a beaker so that they do not touch each other.
4. Pour hot water into the beaker until it is about 6 cm below the butter. Watch the utensils for the next several minutes. What do you see happening?
5. The utensils will be greasy. Wipe them off and wash them in soapy water.

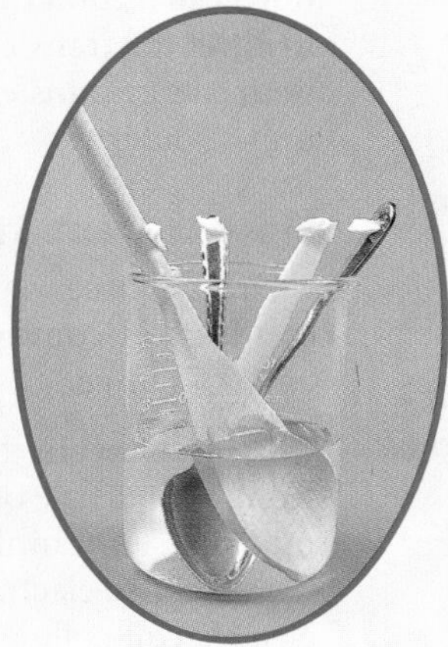

Think It Over

Observing What happened to the butter? Did the same thing happen on every utensil? How can you account for your observations?

Blacksmithing is hot work. A piece of iron held in the forge becomes warmer and begins to glow as thermal energy from the fire travels along it. At the same time, the blacksmith feels hot air rising from the forge. He also feels the glow of the fire directly on his face and arms. Each of these movements of energy is a form of heat. **Heat** is the movement of thermal energy from a substance at a higher temperature to another at a lower temperature.

GUIDE FOR READING

- How is heat related to thermal energy?
- What are the three forms of heat transfer?
- How is specific heat related to thermal energy?

Reading Tip **Before you read, define heat in your own words. Make any necessary corrections to your definition as you read the section.**

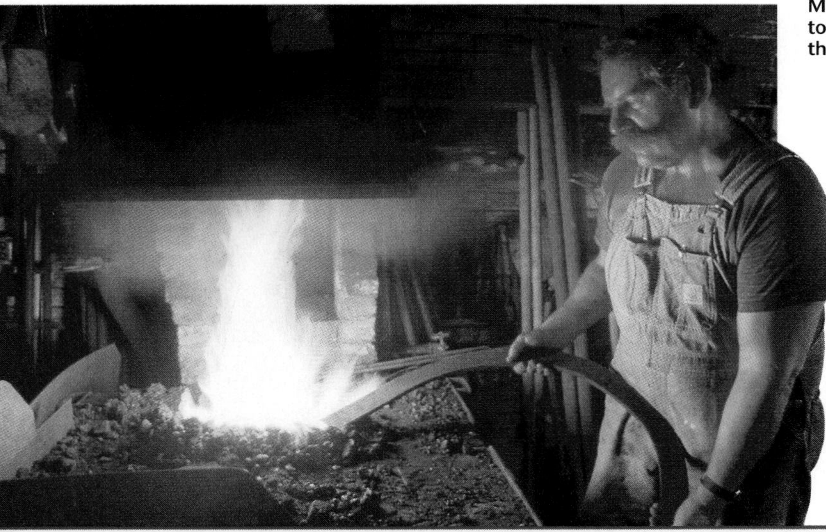

Figure 4 This blacksmith uses heat to soften a piece of iron before he hammers it into shape.

READING STRATEGIES

After students write their definitions of heat, prompt them to list three or more questions they have about the nature of heat. Pair students and direct them to share their definitions of heat and discuss possible answers to their questions. Students should next read the section, then meet again with their learning partners to see if their questions were answered as they read.

Program Resources

- **Teaching Resources** 6-2 Lesson Plan, p. 159; 6-2 Section Summary, p. 160

Media and Technology

Audiotapes English-Spanish Summary 6-2

Section 2 The Nature of Heat

Objectives

After completing the lesson, students will be able to

- describe how heat is related to thermal energy;
- identify the three forms of heat transfer;
- define and calculate the specific heat of a substance;
- describe the movement of heat and how insulators and conductors affect heat transfer.

Key Terms heat, conduction, convection, convection current, radiation, conductor, insulator, specific heat

1 Engage/Explore

Activating Prior Knowledge

Ask students to describe how to safely remove a tray of hot cookies from the oven. *(Sample: Hold the tray with an oven mitt.)* Ask: **What is the function of the oven mitt?** *(To keep the cookies and tray from burning your hands)* Tell students that in this section they will learn how the oven mitt protects their hand.

DISCOVER

Skills Focus observing

Materials *frozen butter, glass beaker, hot water, utensils made of different materials, such as stainless steel, plastic, and wood*

Time 15 minutes

Tips CAUTION: *Remind students to avoid touching the hot water and not to eat or taste anything in the lab.* Suggest that they keep a record of the order in which the butter melts on the utensils.

Think It Over The butter melted. It melted faster on metal utensils than on wooden or plastic. The heat from the water moved along the utensils, at a different rate for each material.

2 Facilitate

How Is Heat Transferred?

Including All Students

Students may need extra help to understand how the scientific meaning of heat differs from the everyday definition. Ask them to come up with examples of phrases that include heat such as "a heated debate," and "the heat in that jalapeño pepper." Ask: **Do any of these phrases involve the scientific definition of heat?** *(Sample: No, the scientific definition refers to the transfer of thermal energy.)* **limited English proficiency**

Sharpen your Skills

Inferring

ACTIVITY

Students should infer that the metal of the zipper conducts thermal energy better than the material of the jeans.

Extend Suggest students investigate how well different materials conduct heat. They can test samples of leather, cotton, wool, silk, and polyester. **learning modality: kinesthetic**

Addressing Naive Conceptions

Students hold many naive conceptions about the nature of heat. Some of these are fostered by everyday uses of the word that differ from scientific usage. List these terms along with their definitions on the board: Temperature—average kinetic energy of particles in a substance; heat—transfer of thermal energy; thermal energy: total energy of all the particles in an object. Now ask the students if an object can contain heat. *(No, heat is transfer of energy.)* **Can two objects have the same temperature but different amounts of thermal energy?** *(Yes, because thermal energy is the total energy.)* **learning modality: verbal**

Inferring

ACTIVITY

You pull some clothes out of the dryer as soon as they are dry. You grab your shirt without a problem, but when you pull out your jeans, you quickly drop them. The metal zipper is too hot to touch! What can you infer about which material in your jeans conducts thermal energy better? Explain.

Notice that the scientific definition of heat is different from its everyday use. In a conversation, you might hear someone say that an object contains heat. Matter, however, contains not heat but thermal energy. Only when thermal energy is transferred is it called heat. **Heat is thermal energy moving from a warmer object to a cooler object.** Recall from Chapter 5 that work also involves the transfer of mechanical energy. So work and heat are both energy transfers, and they are both measured with the same unit—joules.

How Is Heat Transferred?

There are three ways that heat can move. **Heat is transferred by conduction, convection, and radiation.** The blacksmith experienced all three.

Conduction In the process of **conduction,** heat is transferred from one particle of matter to another without the movement of matter itself. Think of a metal spoon in a pot of water being heated on an electric stove. The fast-moving particles of the hot electric coil collide with the slow-moving particles of the cool pot. Heat is transferred, causing the slower particles to move faster. Then the particles of the pot collide with the particles of the water, which in turn collide with the particles at one end of the spoon. As the particles move faster, the metal spoon becomes hotter. This process of conduction is repeated all along the metal until the entire spoon becomes hot.

In Figure 5, the horseshoes in a blacksmith's forge glow red as heat is transferred to the metal from the fire. This transfer of heat throughout the horseshoes is due to conduction.

Figure 5 The entire horseshoe becomes hot even though only its underside touches the hot coals. *Inferring By what method is heat transferred through the metal?*

Background

Integrating Science Convection currents in Earth's oceans and atmosphere cause major weather patterns. In the tropical Pacific, conditions known as El Niño and La Niña affect weather around the world.

During El Niño, which typically lasts for about a year, warm water flows eastward from the western tropical Pacific into the eastern Pacific, which is usually much colder. The thermal energy is transferred away from the equator by atmospheric convection cells, giant loops created by evaporating sea water. During the cooling phase of the cycle, La Niña, the atmosphere is less heated and convection occurs over a smaller and smaller area until temperatures in the eastern tropical Pacific are much colder than usual.

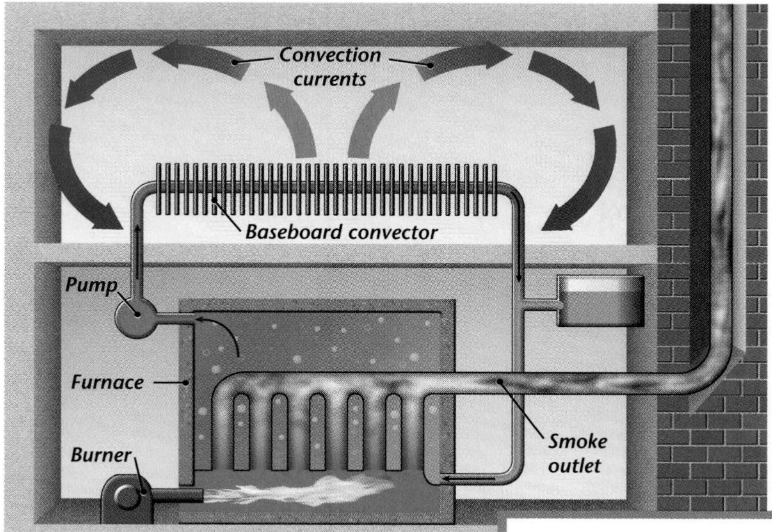

Figure 6 Just as convection currents move heat throughout the liquid in a pot, convection currents move heat from the baseboard throughout the room.

Convection If you watch a pot of hot water on a stove, you will see the water moving. **Convection** is the movement that transfers heat within the water. In convection, heat is transferred by the movement of currents within a fluid (a liquid or gas).

When the water at the bottom of the pot is heated, its particles move faster, and they also move farther apart. As a result, the heated water becomes less dense. Recall from Chapter 3 that a less dense fluid will float on top of a more dense one. So the heated water rises. The surrounding cooler water flows into its place. This flow creates a circular motion known as a **convection current,** as shown in Figure 6.

Convection currents are used to transfer heated air throughout a building. As the air near the baseboard heater in Figure 6 is heated, it becomes less dense and rises. When the warm air rises, the surrounding cool air flows into its place.

INTEGRATING EARTH SCIENCE Convection currents occur in the environment as well. A soaring bird, such as a hawk, takes advantage of this fact and rides updrafts where warm air rises. In fact, convection currents transfer air heated by the sun throughout Earth's atmosphere. They produce the global winds that form Earth's weather.

✓ Checkpoint *How does convection transfer heat?*

Inquiry Challenge

Materials *2 test tubes, test tube holder, 2 beakers, red and blue food coloring, cold water, hot water, large dropper*

ACTIVITY

Time 20 minutes

Tips Ask students to predict what will happen if hot water is placed on top of cold water and if cold water is placed on top of hot water. Students should work in small groups to record their predictions, compose hypotheses, and prepare a plan for your approval. Food coloring can be used to distinguish hot and cold water. Show students how to place one layer of water on top of another by gently squeezing a full dropper against the side of a test tube. Ask: **What happened when you placed hot water on top of the cold water?** *(The hot water floated on top. The layers of water did not mix.)* Have students infer why this occurred. *(Hot water is less dense than cold water.)* **learning modality: logical/mathematical**

Integrating Earth Science

Show students a globe. Ask: **Where is the Earth's atmosphere heated the most?** *(At the equator)* Ask students what happens to the heated air. *(It rises and cooler air flows in to replace it.)* Show them the latitude lines at 30° north and south. Explain that the heated air has cooled and this is where it sinks back to Earth's surface. Ask students to infer what happens to this air. *(It flows back to the equator, heats, and rises again.)* Explain that these areas of rising and falling air create convection currents in Earth's atmosphere. **learning modality: visual**

Media and Technology

Transparencies "Convection Currents in a Heating System," Transparency 19

Exploring Physical Science Videodisc Unit 4, Side 2, "Hot Is Hot, Cold Is Not"

Answers to Self-Assessment

Caption Question

Figure 5 Heat is transferred through the metal by conduction.

Convection transfers heat in currents within a fluid; the warm fluid rises and cooler fluid flows in to replace it. This creates a circular flow.

Ongoing Assessment

Drawing Have students draw a kettle of boiling water on a burner and label the convection currents and the path of heat conduction.

How Is Heat Transferred?, continued

Skills Focus drawing conclusions

Materials *lamp with a 60- or 75-W bulb, centimeter ruler, clock or stopwatch*

Time 10 minutes

Tips Caution students not to touch the light bulb and to withdraw their hands if they become uncomfortable.

Drawing Conclusions Students' palms should feel considerably warmer when held above the bulb. Many students may mention that air heated by the bulb is rising and that makes their hand feel warmer.

Extend Have students wrap a 2 cm × 2 cm piece of black paper around the base of a thermometer and tape it into place. Then repeat the experiment with the bulb of the thermometer held 10 cm away from the light. Increase the time if necessary. **learning modality: kinesthetic**

Heat Moves One Way

Inquiry Challenge

Materials *crushed ice, large beaker, small plastic film canisters, water at different temperatures, thermometer*

Time 30 minutes

Have groups of students design experiments to compare how temperature differences affect transfer of thermal energy. One procedure would be to float a small film canister with warm water into a large beaker with ice and water. Then measure how long it takes the temperature of water in the small canister to fall by 5°C. Repeat with other temperatures of warm water ranging from about 10°C to about 40°C. Graph the initial temperature versus time required for temperature to change. **learning modality: kinesthetic**

Figure 7 Radiation from the heat lamps above keeps food warm in a cafeteria.

Feel the Warmth

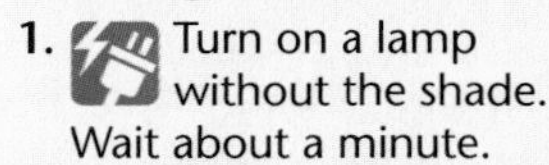

How is heat transferred from a light bulb?

1. Turn on a lamp without the shade. Wait about a minute.
2. Hold the palm of your hand about 10 cm from the side of the bulb for about 15 seconds. Remove it sooner if it gets too warm.
3. Now hold the palm of your hand about 10 centimeters above the top of the bulb for about 15 seconds.

Drawing Conclusions In which location did your hand feel warmer? Explain your observations in terms of heat transfer.

Radiation **Radiation** is the transfer of energy by electromagnetic waves. You can feel radiation from a bonfire or a heat lamp across a distance of several meters. And of course a blacksmith feels the glow of radiation from his forge. There is an important difference between radiation and the processes of conduction and convection. Radiation does not require matter to transfer thermal energy. All of the sun's energy that reaches Earth travels through millions of kilometers of empty space.

Heat Moves One Way

If two substances have different temperatures, heat will flow from the warmer object to the colder one. When heat flows into a substance, the thermal energy of the substance increases. As the thermal energy increases, its temperature increases. At the same time, the temperature of the substance giving off heat decreases. Heat will flow from one substance to the other until the two substances have the same temperature. A bowl of hot oatmeal cools to room temperature if you don't eat it quickly.

What happens to something cold, like ice cream? The ingredients used to make it, such as milk and sugar, are not nearly as cold as the finished ice cream. In an ice cream maker, the ingredients are put into a metal can that is packed in ice. You might think that the ice transfers cold to the ingredients in the can. But this is not the case. There is no such thing as "coldness." Instead, the ingredients grow colder as thermal energy flows from them to the ice. Heat transfer occurs in only one direction.

✓ ***Checkpoint*** *In what direction does heat move?*

Background

Facts and Figures In the early 1900s, settlers in Nebraska began to use straw bales to build houses because wood for lumber was scarce. Straw bale houses can withstand severe weather such as blizzards, wide temperature swings, and tornadoes. The thick straw bale walls also provide excellent insulation, keeping the house warm in winter and cool in summer. Because of this property, and also because straw bales are readily available and inexpensive, some builders are using straw bales instead of conventional wood-frame walls.

Building materials are assigned R-values according to how well they slow the transfer of heat. Materials with high R-values are good insulators. Straw bale walls can have an R-value as high as R-70. Walls made with 2 × 6 studs and fiberglass insulation have a thermal resistance rating of only about R-15.

Conductors and Insulators

Have you ever stepped from a rug to a tile floor on a cold morning? The tile floor feels colder than the rug. Yet if you measured their temperatures, they would be the same—room temperature. The difference between them has to do with how materials conduct heat.

A material that conducts heat well is called a **conductor.** Metals such as silver and stainless steel are good conductors. A metal spoon conducts heat faster than a wooden or plastic spoon. A material that does not conduct heat well is called an **insulator.** Wood, wool, straw, paper, and cork are good insulators. Gases, such as air, are also good insulators.

A good conductor, such as a tile floor, will feel cool to the touch because it transfers heat away from your skin easily. An insulator such as a rug, on the other hand, slows the transfer of heat from your skin, so it feels warmer.

Clothes and blankets are insulators that slow the transfer of heat out of your body. Mammals and birds have natural insulation. Birds have feathers that trap air under them, and mammals such as walruses have a layer of fat called blubber.

A well-insulated building is comfortable inside whether the weather is hot or cold outdoors. Insulation prevents heat from entering the building in hot weather and prevents heat from escaping in cold weather. Fiberglass is a common insulating material in buildings. It is made of a tangle of thin glass fibers that trap air. Air is a poor conductor of heat, and trapped air cannot transfer heat by convection. So fiberglass slows the transfer of heat through the walls or roof.

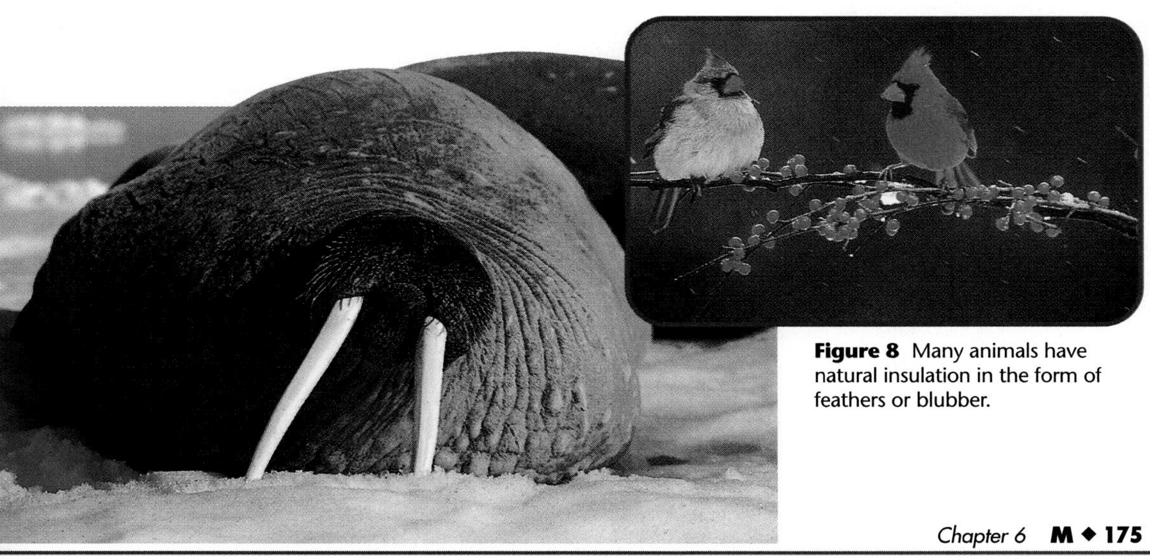

Figure 8 Many animals have natural insulation in the form of feathers or blubber.

Conductors and Insulators

Demonstration

ACTIVITY

Materials *plastic foam cup, paper cup, plastic cup, ceramic mug, aluminum can, five thermometers, 500 mL of hot tap water*
Time 20 minutes

Arrange the containers in the order listed in the materials. Pour 100 mL of hot tap water into each container and place a thermometer in each. Have volunteer students touch the outside of the containers and compare how warm they feel. Ask: **Which container felt the warmest?** *(Aluminum can)* **Which conducted the most thermal energy from the water to the outside?** *(Aluminum can)* Now allow the containers to cool for 10 minutes and have students read the thermometers. Ask which container cooled the fastest. *(The aluminum can)* Explain that the best conductor, aluminum, is also the worst insulator. **learning modality: kinesthetic**

Building Inquiry Skills: Applying Concepts

Challenge students to explain why a knit sweater, which has open spaces woven into the fabric, keeps you warm. *(Air is a poor conductor of heat, so the air trapped in the spaces of the sweater prevents the transfer of heat away from your body.)* Then ask: **Some animals have fur that traps a layer of air near their skin. How does this help them live in cold climates or swim in cold water?** *(The trapped air acts as an insulator.)* **learning modality: verbal**

Program Resources

- **Product Testing Activities by *Consumer Reports*** "Testing Bandages," pp. 1–8.
- **Integrated Science Laboratory Manual** M-6, "Combustion Heat of a Candle"
- **Science Explorer Series** *Weather and Climate,* Chapter 2; *Inside Earth,* Chapter 1; and *Earth's Waters,* Chapter 4

Answers to Self-Assessment

☑ Checkpoint

Heat moves from a substance of higher temperature to a substance of lower temperature.

Ongoing Assessment

Writing Have students explain why opening the windows of a car that has been parked in the sun causes the temperature of the air inside the car to drop. *(The heat from the air inside the car flows through convection toward the cooler air outside the car.)*

Conductors and Insulators, continued

Demonstration

Materials *clay flower pots, thermometers, water* ACTIVITY
Time 5 minutes to set up, 5 minutes to read temperatures

Inform students that people have used heat transfer to keep their homes comfortable since early times. For example, many homes in the southwestern United States are built with adobe bricks. Adobe bricks are made of clay and straw and are excellent insulators. To demonstrate the insulating properties of adobe, place a thermometer in a cup of water in a sunny location. Wet a large clay flower-pot, then turn the flowerpot over the cup. Place a second cup of water and thermometer about 10 cm away from the flowerpot. Explain that this cup is the control in the experiment. Ask students to predict what will happen to the temperature of the water in both cups after 30 minutes. Have volunteers check the temperatures at that time. Ask: **How do the temperatures compare?** *(The temperature of the water under the flowerpot is much cooler.)* Invite interested students to learn more about the construction of adobe houses and have them share their research with the class. **learning modality: visual**

Specific Heat

Using the Visuals: Figures 10 and 11

As students examine Figure 10, point out that the substance with the highest specific heat is water, at 4,180 J/(kg•K). Then ask them to identify the specific heat of sand. *(670 J/(kg•K))* Ask: **How does the difference in the abilities of sand and water to absorb thermal energy relate to Figure 11?** *(The same amount of thermal energy required to change the temperature of 1 kg of water by 1 K will change the temperature of 1 kg of sand by 6 K. So the water stays much cooler.)* **learning modality: logical/mathematical**

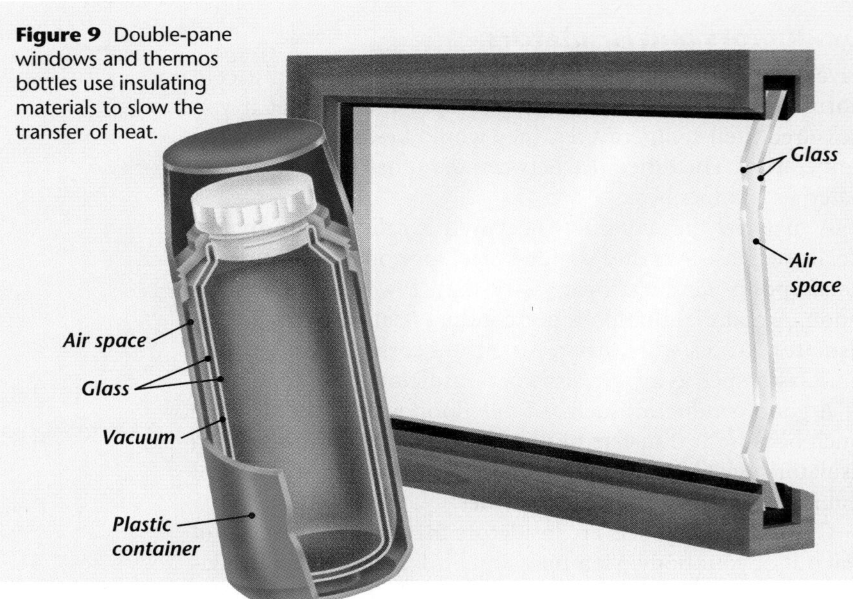

Figure 9 Double-pane windows and thermos bottles use insulating materials to slow the transfer of heat.

Much of the heat transfer in a house occurs through the windows. For this reason, insulating windows are made up of two panes of glass with a thin space of air between them. The air trapped between the glass panes does not transfer heat well. Thermos bottles use the same principle. They contain a vacuum, which is a better insulator than air.

Figure 10 This table lists the specific heats of several substances. *Problem Solving How much more energy is required to raise the temperature of 1 kg of iron than is needed to raise the temperature of 1 kg of copper by the same amount?*

Specific Heat of Common Substances

Substance	Specific Heat (J/(kg·K))
Aluminum	903
Brass	376
Copper	385
Glass	664
Ice	2,060
Iron	450
Sand	670
Silver	235
Water	4,180

Specific Heat

Imagine running across hot sand toward the ocean's edge. You run to the water's edge, but you don't go any farther—the water is too cold. How can the sand be so hot and the water so cold? After all, they were both heated by the sun. The answer is that water requires more heat to raise its temperature than sand does.

When an object is heated its temperature rises. But the temperature does not rise at the same rate for all objects. The amount of heat required to raise the temperature depends on the chemical makeup of the material. Different materials need more or less heat to change their temperature by the same amount.

Scientists have defined a quantity to measure the relationship between heat and temperature change. The amount of energy required to raise the temperature of 1 kilogram of a substance by 1 kelvin is called its **specific heat.** The unit of measure for specific heat is joules per kilogram-kelvin (J/(kg·K)). Look at the specific heats of the substances listed in Figure 10. Notice

Background

Facts and Figures To protect the shuttle from thermal energy generated by friction with the atmosphere, NASA has developed a thermal protection system made up of different materials covering the outside of the shuttle.

Materials to insulate a space shuttle must be low in weight and able to resist the high temperatures experienced during reentry.

The shuttle's leading wing edges and nose cap, where temperatures are the highest during reentry, are covered in a special material called reinforced carbon-carbon. This material protects against temperatures of about 1,200°C. Insulating tiles protect a large part of the shuttle's body, including its underside. These tiles are coupled with a special insulating blanket to protect the shuttle against temperatures that range between 648 and 1,260°C.

Figure 11 Bright summer sun has made the beach sand painfully hot. But a few meters away, the ocean water is still cool.

that the specific heat of water is quite high. One kilogram of water requires 4,180 joules of energy to raise its temperature 1 kelvin. Materials with a high specific heat can absorb a great deal of thermal energy without a great change in temperature.

The energy gained or lost by an object is related to the mass, change in temperature, and specific heat of the material. You can calculate thermal energy changes with the following formula.

Change in energy =
Mass × Specific heat × Change in temperature

How much heat is required to raise the temperature of 5 kilograms of water 10 kelvins?

Heat absorbed = (5 kg)(4,180 J/(kg·K))(10 K) = 209,000 J

You need to transfer 209,000 joules to the water to increase its temperature by 10 kelvins.

Section 2 Review

1. How does heat differ from thermal energy?
2. Describe the three kinds of heat transfer.
3. What is specific heat?
4. **Thinking Critically Problem Solving** How much energy is lost by 10 kg of silver if it is cooled from 35°C to 21°C?
5. **Thinking Critically Applying Concepts** Before homes were heated, people often placed hot water bottles in their beds at bedtime. Why is water a good choice?

Check Your Progress (Chapter Project 6)

Prepare a short summary of your experimental plan. How will you test insulating ability? (*Hint:* What variables do you want to keep constant? How can you make sure you control these?) Think about how you can design a fair test to compare the relative insulating abilities of each material. How often will you record the temperature? Then carry out your tests.

3 Assess

Section 2 Review Answers

1. Matter contains thermal energy. Thermal energy is called heat only when it is transferred from a warmer to a cooler object.
2. Conduction—transfer of heat from one particle of matter to another without the movement of the matter itself; convection—transfer of heat through currents in a fluid; radiation—transfer of energy through electromagnetic waves.
3. The amount of energy that must be added to raise the temperature of 1 kg of a substance by 1 K.
4. 32,900 J
5. Water is a good substance to store thermal energy because it has a high specific heat. The small amount of water in the hot water bottle can store a large amount of thermal energy.

Check Your Progress (Chapter Project 6)

Review the steps for designing an experiment in the Skills Handbook. Then help students brainstorm options for testing the best location of the insulation on the can and what insulation works best. The testing requires the use of thermometers, so you may wish to have students do the testing in class. Many experiments involve setting up the can at the beginning of class and then checking temperatures at the end. This can be done without sacrificing much of the class period.

Media and Technology

Interactive Student Tutorial CD-ROM M-6

Exploring Physical Science Videodisc Unit 4, Side 2, "As Hot As a Desert"

Program Resources

- **Teaching Resources** 6-2 Review and Reinforce, p. 161; 6-2 Enrich, p. 162

Answers to Self-Assessment

Caption Question

Figure 10 65 J more energy is required to raise the temperature of 1 kg iron by 1 K than is required to raise the temperature of 1 kg copper by the same amount

Performance Assessment

Writing Have students write a paragraph describing a situation in which heat is transferred by conduction, convection, and radiation.

Skills Lab

Interpreting Data

Just Add Water

Preparing for Inquiry

Key Concept Thermal energy is conserved when hot water and cold water are mixed.

Skills Objective Students will be able to
- predict how the amount of thermal energy lost by hot water is related to the amount gained by cold water;
- calculate the heat transferred from hot water to cold water in a calorimeter;
- draw conclusions about how thermal energy is conserved in a calorimeter.

Time 35 minutes

Advance Planning Obtain plastic foam cups (four cups are need for each student or team). Prepare an ice bath for the beakers of cold water. Provide sponges or paper towels to mop up spills.

Alternative Materials Any kind of disposable, insulated cup can be used instead of plastic foam cups.

Guiding Inquiry

Invitation Ask students what they would do if they got in a bath and found that the water was too hot. *(Add cold water)* Ask: **When you add cold water, what happens to the heat?** *(Heat is transferred from the hot water to the cold water. The cold water warms up as the hot water cools down. The transfer of thermal energy continues until the hot and cold water have the same temperature.)* Ask the students what factors affect how much thermal energy is transferred. *(It depends on the amounts of hot and cold water, their initial temperatures, and how much heat is lost to the surroundings.)*

Introducing the Procedure

- Describe the lab to the students, explaining that they will calculate the amount of heat transferred when hot and cold water are mixed.
- Set up and display a sample calorimeter. Ask students why the calorimeter uses a cup made of plastic foam. *(It is a good insulator.)*
- Help students understand how the equation for calculating the change in energy applies to this experiment. *(The heat transferred is equal to the change in thermal energy. Because the specific heat of water is known, the change in energy can be calculated using measurements of the mass and the change in temperature.)*

Troubleshooting the Experiment

- In the cold-water calorimeter, the level of liquid in the thermometer may be below the cover. Students can pull the thermometer up a bit to read it.
- Students should read the thermometers to the nearest half degree. They should round off their calculated results.
- In Step 8, students should wait a minute or two before recording the final temperature. Do not allow students to use thermometers to stir the water in the calorimeter.
- Remind students to use the final temperature to calculate the change in temperature for both the hot water and the cold water.

Skills Lab

Interpreting Data

Just Add Water

If you add hot water to cold water, what will happen? In this lab, you'll make a device that measures changes in thermal energy. It is called a calorimeter. You will use the skill of interpreting data to calculate the thermal energy transferred.

Problem

When hot and cold water are mixed, how much thermal energy is transferred from the hot water to the cold water?

Materials

4 plastic foam cups, hot tap water, scissors, beaker of water kept in an ice bath, 2 thermometers, balance, pencil

Procedure

1. Predict how the amount of thermal energy lost by hot water will be related to the amount of thermal energy gained by cold water.
2. Copy the data table into your notebook.
3. Follow the instructions in the box to make two calorimeters. Find the mass of each empty calorimeter (including the cover) on a balance and record each mass in your data table.

Making a Calorimeter

- **A.** Label a plastic foam cup with the letter C ("C" stands for cold water).
- **B.** Cut 2 to 3 cm from the top of a second plastic foam cup. Invert the second cup inside the first. Label the cover with a C also. The cup and cover are your cold-water calorimeter.
- **C.** Using a pencil, poke a hole in the cover large enough for a thermometer to fit snugly.
- **D.** Repeat Steps A, B, and C with two other plastic foam cups. This time, label both cup and cover with an H. This is your hot-water calorimeter.

4. From a beaker of water that has been sitting in an ice bath, add water (no ice cubes) to the cold-water calorimeter. Fill it about one-third full. Put the cover on, find the total mass, and record the mass in your data table.
5. Add hot tap water to the hot-water calorimeter. Fill it about one-third full. **CAUTION:** *Hot tap water can cause burns.* Put the cover on, find the total mass, and record the mass in your data table.

DATA TABLE

	Mass of Empty Cup (g)	Mass of Cup and Water (g)	Mass of Water (g)	Starting Temp. (°C)	Final Temp. (°C)	Change in Temp. (°C)
Cold Water Calorimeter						
Hot Water Calorimeter						

6. Calculate the mass of the water in each calorimeter. Record the results in your data table.
7. Put thermometers through the holes in the covers of both calorimeters. Wait a minute or two and then record the temperatures.
8. Remove both thermometers and covers. Pour the water from the cold-water calorimeter into the hot-water calorimeter. Put the cover back on the hot-water calorimeter, and insert a thermometer. Record the final temperature as the final temperature for both calorimeters.

Analyze and Conclude

1. What is the temperature change of the cold water? Record your answer in the data table.
2. What is the temperature change of the hot water? Record your answer in the data table.
3. Calculate the amount of thermal energy that enters the cold water by using the formula for the transfer of thermal energy. The specific heat of water is 4.18 J/(g·K), so you use the following formula.

   Thermal energy transferred =
   4.18 J/(g·K) × Mass of cold water × Temperature change of cold water

   Remember that 1°C is equal to 1 K.
4. Now use the formula to calculate the thermal energy leaving the hot water.
5. What unit should you use for your results for Questions 3 and 4?
6. Was your prediction from Step 1 confirmed? How do you know?
7. **Think About It** What sources of error might have affected your results? How could the lab be redesigned in order to reduce the errors?

Design an Experiment

How would your results be affected if you started with much more hot water than cold? If you used more cold water than hot? Make a prediction. Then design a procedure to test your prediction. Get your teacher's approval, and try your new procedure.

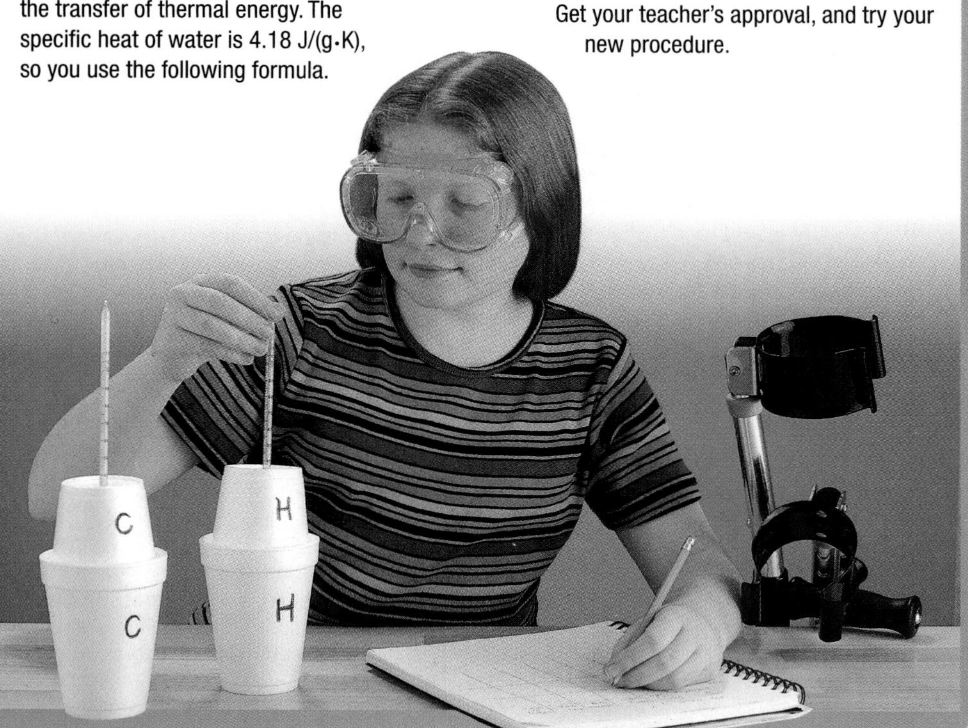

Expected Outcome

- The final temperature of the combined hot and cold water should be greater than the initial temperature of the cold water and less than the initial temperature of the hot water.
- The amount of thermal energy transferred to the cold water should be approximately equal to the thermal energy lost by the hot water, taking into account experimental error and heat lost to the surroundings during transfer.

Analyze and Conclude

1. Answers will vary. For sample data, change in temp. = 14.5°C.
2. Answers will vary. For sample data, change in temp. = 24.0°C.
3. Answers will vary. For sample data, thermal energy gained = 6300 J.
4. Answers will vary. For sample data, thermal energy lost = 6800 J.
5. The unit should be Joules (J).
6. Answers will depend on the initial predictions. Students should provide logical reasons for why their predictions were or were not confirmed, based on observations from the lab. A typical prediction could state that the thermal energy lost by the hot water will be nearly equal to the thermal energy gained by the cold water. Given experimental error, this prediction will probably be supported. Results usually reflect some difference due to heat lost to the surroundings during transfer.
7. Sources of error include loss of thermal energy in the form of heat through the sides or top of the cup, and misreading the thermometers or balances. Students may suggest using a thicker cup or a better insulating material, nesting two or more cups inside each other, or repeating the procedure several times and averaging the results.

Extending the Inquiry

Design an Experiment With more hot water, the mixture will end up hotter and with more cold water, the mixture will end up colder.

Sample Data Table

	Cold Water Calorimeter	Hot Water Calorimeter
Mass of Empty Cup (g)	3.1	3.3
Mass of Cup and Water (g)	107.0	71.5
Mass of Water (g)	103.9	68.2
Starting Temp. (°C)	3.0	41.5
Final Temp. (°C)	17.5	17.5
Change in Temp. (°C)	14.5	24.0

Program Resources

- **Teaching Resources** Chapter 6 Skills Lab, pp. 171–173

Safety

Caution students to be careful using thermometers. Thermometers must be placed in holders when not in the calorimeters. Review the safety guidelines in Appendix A.

SCIENCE AND SOCIETY

Insulation—And a Breath of Clean Air

Purpose

To investigate indoor air pollution.

Role-Play

Time 30 minutes first day, 45 minutes second day

Provide students with any additional materials needed to research their roles or tell them to base their role-playing on information in the textbook. Tell students that they will be playing the roles of individuals interested in the construction of a new building. A local accounting firm, Dewey Cheatem and Howe, is going to construct a new office building, They have hired a local construction company, Reckem & Ball. Ask students: **How do the owners of Dewey Cheatem and Howe benefit from energy-efficient buildings?** *(They spend less money on heating and cooling.)* **What problems can be caused for Dewey Cheatem and Howe by a poorly ventilated building?** *(If the employees get sick, they can't work.)* Assign students into groups of six. Two represent employees of Dewey Cheatem and Howe, two represent the owners of the company (Dewey and Cheatem), and two are representatives from Reckem & Ball. The two builders will answer questions regarding the relative costs of various building materials and ventilation designs. Dewey and Cheatem should present their concerns about how much money they have budgeted, how many people will work in the building when it is completed, and the cost of having a worker miss work due to illness. The employees should present their concerns regarding indoor air pollution. The groups of six will meet on the second day to discuss the issues for thirty minutes. Spend the rest of the time in a class discussion of the issues and possible solutions that were raised in each group.

SCIENCE AND SOCIETY

Insulation—And a Breath of Clean Air

People want to save money. They also want to conserve the fossil fuels—oil, coal, and natural gas—used to heat and cool buildings. So, since the 1970s, new homes, offices, and schools have been built to be energy-efficient. Builders have constructed large, square buildings with thick insulation, less outside wall space, and smaller, airtight windows. These features slow the transfer of thermal energy into and out of buildings.

Limiting the transfer of thermal energy, however, often means limiting the transfer of air. As a result, viruses, bacteria, and pollutants are not carried away by fresh outdoor air. People who live and work in these buildings sometimes develop illnesses. These illnesses cost billions of dollars a year in medical expenses and lost work.

The Issues

How Can Indoor Air Be Made Cleaner?

Limiting indoor pollutants—or getting rid of them altogether—is a major way of reducing building-related illness. Toward this end, builders can construct buildings with materials and insulation that do not pollute the air. They can use natural wood, for instance, instead of plastics and particle board, which give off irritating chemicals. Indoor air can be filtered. Walls, floors, and carpets can be cleaned frequently. Machines that give off irritating chemicals, such as copiers, can be placed in specially ventilated rooms. In this way, pollution can be kept out of the air that most people in the building breathe.

How Can Ventilation Be Improved?

Good ventilation requires at least 10 liters per second of fresh air for each person. If less fresh air comes in, some people may get illnesses or eye, nose, and throat irritations. There are several ways to increase ventilation. In some buildings, machines such as fans and blowers are used to move air in and out. People in those buildings must be careful not to block air vents with furniture or equipment. Special attention must be paid to ventilation during times of increased pollution, such as when a room is being painted.

Increasing air flow into buildings means using more energy for heating and air conditioning. So the energy savings from efficient buildings are reduced. To make up for this loss, people can wear heavier clothing in winter. They can set their thermostats lower and use less energy for heating. They can also wear lighter clothes in summer, and use less energy for air conditioning.

Another way to obtain clean air while conserving energy is called energy recovery ventilation. Heat is transferred from stale, but warm, indoor air to fresh, but cold, outdoor air. The air goes out but the energy stays inside.

You Decide

1. Identify the Problem
In your own words, describe the problem caused by thick layers of insulation.

2. Analyze the Options
List five different options for reducing building-related illnesses. How would each option affect the amount of fuel needed for heating?

3. Find a Solution
You're building a new school. Make a checklist of steps to take to prevent illness but still keep heating costs down.

You Decide

Students should discuss solutions that do not increase energy use, such as better filtration systems and increased frequency of cleaning. Students should realize that the cost of indoor air pollution can also be high when workers become sick and have to take time off, resulting in reduced productivity.

Issues raised during the role playing should be addressed when considering the construction of a new school.

Background

Studies by the Environmental Protection Agency have consistently shown indoor air pollution to be in the top five environmental risks to public health. In fact, the levels of certain pollutants in indoor air can be up to 100 times higher than outdoor levels. Because the symptoms can be similar to other illnesses such as colds or asthma, illness caused by indoor air pollution can be difficult to diagnose.

Section 3 Thermal Energy and States of Matter

DISCOVER ACTIVITY

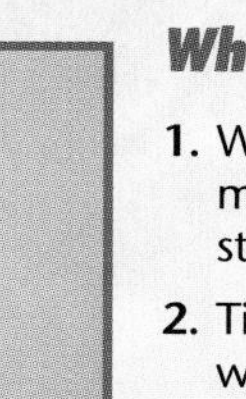

What Happens to Heated Metal?

1. Wrap one end of a one-meter-long metal wire around a clamp on a ring stand.
2. Tie the other end through several washers. Adjust the clamp so that the washers swing freely, but nearly touch the floor.
3. Light a candle. Hold the candle with an oven mitt, and heat the wire. **CAUTION:** *Be careful near the flame, and avoid dripping hot wax on yourself.* Predict how heat from the candle will affect the wire.
4. With your hand in the oven mitt, swing the wire. Observe any changes in the motion of the washers.
5. Blow out the candle and allow the wire to cool. After several minutes, swing the wire again and observe its motion.

Think It Over

Inferring Based on your observations, what can you conclude about the effect of heating a solid?

GUIDE FOR READING

- What causes matter to change state?
- Why does matter expand when it is heated?

Reading Tip As you read, take notes on how each illustration helps to explain the text.

Throughout the day, temperatures at an orange grove drop steadily. The anxious farmer awaits the updated weather forecast. The news is not good. The temperature is expected to fall even further during the night. Low temperatures could wipe out the entire crop. He considers picking the crop early, but the oranges are not yet ripe.

Instead, the farmer tells his workers to haul in long water hoses. He has them spray the orange trees with water. As the temperature drops, the water turns to ice. The ice keeps the oranges warm!

How can ice possibly keep anything warm? The answer has to do with how thermal energy is transferred as water becomes ice.

Figure 12 Imagine using ice to keep something warm! These oranges were sprayed with water because freezing temperatures threatened them.

READING STRATEGIES

Reading Tip Before students begin reading, focus their attention on the figures. For each figure, suggest the following questions, for students to either ask themselves or a partner: What does this picture show? What do the picture and caption together tell me? *(Figure 12: It shows oranges surrounded by ice. Ice can be used to prevent oranges from freezing.)* Then have students take notes on each figure.

Program Resources

- **Teaching Resources** 6-3 Lesson Plan, p. 163; 6-3 Section Summary, p. 164

 **Science Explorer Series** *Chemical Building Blocks,* Chapter 2

Media and Technology

Audiotapes English-Spanish Summary 6-3

INTEGRATING CHEMISTRY 

Thermal Energy and States of Matter

Objectives

After completing the lesson, students will be able to

- name the three states of matter and explain what causes changes of state;
- relate expansion of matter to addition of thermal energy;
- describe what takes place in solid-liquid and liquid-gas changes of state.

Key Terms state, change of state, melting, melting point, freezing, freezing point, vaporization, evaporation, boiling, boiling point, condensation, thermal expansion, thermostat, bimetallic strip

1 Engage/Explore

Activating Prior Knowledge

Show students a glass of water and ice cubes. Ask: **What kind of matter is in this glass?** *(water)* Then ask: **What forms of water are in this glass?** *(Liquid water and ice)* Ask students what will happen to the solid form of water if it sits at room temperature. *(It will melt and turn to liquid water.)*

DISCOVER

Skills Focus inferring

Materials *1 m of thin metal wire, clamp, ring stand, 3 or 4 washers, matches, candle, oven mitt*

Time 15 minutes

Tips CAUTION: *Students should keep loose hair and clothes away from the flame.* In Step 4, suggest that students swing the wire gently.

Expected Outcome As the metal wire is heated, its length increases and the washers drag on the floor. As it cools, the wire returns to its original length and the washers can swing.

Think It Over Students should infer that solids expand when heated and contract when cooled.

2 Facilitate

Three States of Matter

Using the Visuals: Figure 13

To help students understand the relative speeds of movement of the particles in the three states of matter, direct students to touch the picture of the mineral and move their fingers to represent the motion of particles in the mineral. *(Students should keep their fingers still or vibrating gently.)* Then have students repeat the procedure for the liquid metal. *(Students should move their fingers more quickly than before.)* Tell students to place their finger on the picture of the tube and demonstrate what would happen to the gas if the tube broke. *(Students should move their fingers away from the tube quickly.)* **learning modality: kinesthetic**

Changes of State

Inquiry Challenge

Materials *large beaker, hot plate, 250 mL of ice, thermometer, clock*
Time 30 minutes

To help them understand changes of state, small groups can design and carry out experiments that show the change in temperature as water turns from solid to liquid and liquid to gas. Each student in a group should have a specific task to perform. Check students' plans for accuracy and safety. In most experiments, students will fill the beaker with ice, heat it on the hot plate and take temperature readings at regular intervals while the ice melts, then heats to boiling. CAUTION: *All participants must secure long hair and loose clothing to keep them away from the heat source. All participants must use oven mitts and wear goggles.* Students can then prepare line graphs showing the change in temperature over time. Students should be able to indicate the beginning and ending points of each change of state. **cooperative learning**

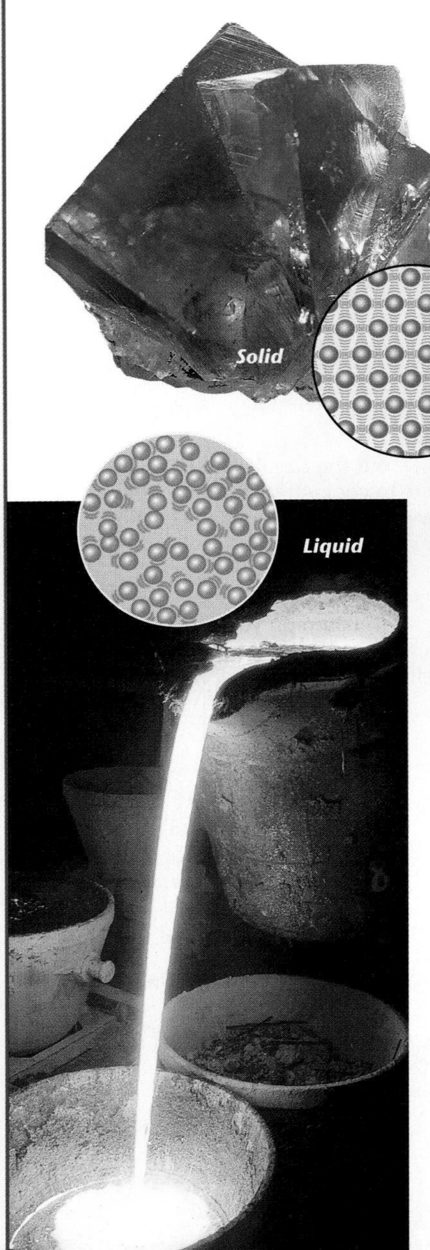

Figure 13 Matter exists in three states—solid, liquid, and gas. *Comparing and Contrasting How does the motion of the particles relate to the state of matter?*

Three States of Matter

What happens when you hold an ice cube in your hand? It melts. The solid and the liquid are both the same substance—water. Water can exist in three different forms. In fact, all matter exists in three **states**—solid, liquid, and gas. Although the chemical composition of a substance remains the same, the arrangement of the particles that make up the matter differ from one state to another.

Solids An ice cube, a coin, a book, and the crystal of fluorite shown above are all solids. The particles that make up a solid are packed together in relatively fixed positions. Particles of a solid cannot move out of their positions. They can only vibrate back and forth. This is why solids retain a fixed shape and volume.

Liquids Water, orange juice, and the molten steel shown at the left are all liquids. The particles that make up a liquid are close together, but they are not held together as tightly as those of a solid. Because liquid particles can move around, liquids don't have a definite shape. But liquids do have a definite volume.

Gases Air, helium, and the neon in the colored sign shown above are all gases. In a gas, the particles are moving so fast that they don't even stay close together. Gases expand to fill all the space available. They do not have a fixed shape or volume.

Changes of State

The physical change from one state of matter to another is called a **change of state.** A change of state occurs between the solid and liquid states, and between the liquid and gas states.

The state of a substance depends on the amount of thermal energy it possesses. The more thermal energy a substance has, the faster its particles move. Since a gas has more thermal energy

Background

Facts and Figures

- Nitrogen must be lowered to a temperature of –196°C (77.16 K) before it undergoes a change of state. Helium must be cooled to –268.90°C (4.26 K).
- In certain circumstances, a solid turns immediately into a gas through a process called sublimation. An example of sublimation can be seen in dry ice, which is frozen carbon dioxide. Dry ice forms at a temperature of –78.5°C. Instead of melting like ice made from frozen water, it immediately turns into vapor at room temperature. When added to hot water, dry ice produces a thick fog. Machines that use dry ice to produce fog are used for special effects in movies, theater, and amusement parks.

than a liquid, the particles of a gas move faster than the particles of the same substance in the liquid or solid state. Particles in a liquid move faster than particles in the solid state.

Matter will change from one state to another if thermal energy is absorbed or released. Figure 14 is a graph of changes of state. Thermal energy is shown on the horizontal axis and temperature is shown on the vertical axis. You can see that as thermal energy increases, a substance changes from a solid to a liquid and then to a gas. A substance changes from a gas to a liquid and then to a solid as thermal energy is removed from it.

The flat regions of the graph show conditions under which thermal energy is changing but temperature remains the same. Under these conditions matter is changing from one state to another. During a change of state, the addition or loss of thermal energy changes the arrangement of the particles. But the average kinetic energy of those particles does not change. Since temperature is average kinetic energy, the temperature does not change as a substance changes state.

Solid–Liquid Changes of State

On the lower left portion of the graph in Figure 14, matter goes through changes between the solid and liquid states of matter. These changes are known as melting and freezing.

Melting The change of state from a solid to a liquid is called **melting.** Melting occurs when a solid absorbs thermal energy. As the thermal energy of the solid increases, the rigid structure of its particles begins to break down. The particles become free to move around. The temperature at which a solid changes to a liquid is called the **melting point.**

☑ *Checkpoint* *What is a change of state?*

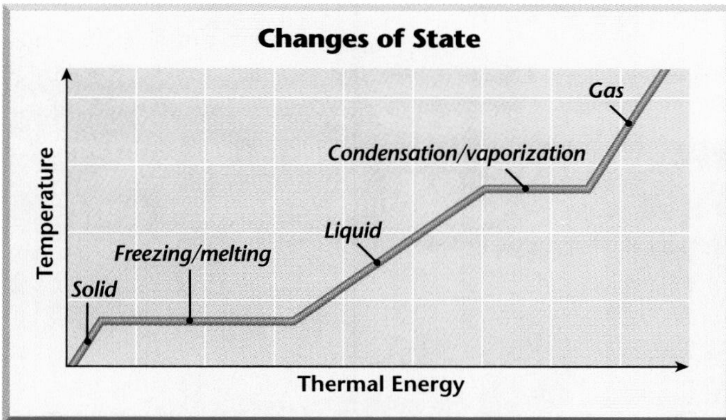

Figure 14 This graph shows how thermal energy and temperature change as a pure substance changes from one state to another.

Language Arts CONNECTION

All around you, you can observe substances in different states of matter. You can also observe matter changing from one state to another.

In Your Journal

Write a one-page description of a scene in which the state of matter changes. Here are some ideas: a glass of lemonade with ice cubes, a pond freezing in winter, a puddle of water on a hot pavement, water boiling on a stove, or rain falling on a desert. Write about how the scene would affect your senses of sight, smell, touch, taste, and hearing.

Answers to Self-Assessment

Caption Question

Figure 13 In a solid, particles vibrate back and forth in place. In a liquid, particles can move around. In a gas, particles move fast and fill the space they are in.

☑ *Checkpoint*

The physical change from one state of matter (solid, liquid, or gas) to another

Language Arts CONNECTION

ACTIVITY

Take students on a walking tour outside the classroom. Tell students to record three examples of each state of matter they observe and one example of a change of state.

In Your Journal Suggest students write their descriptions based on observations they recorded during the walking tour. Encourage students to use descriptive language. Allow them to explore a variety of literary forms, such as poems, songs, or dialogues. **learning modality: verbal**

Portfolio Students can save their descriptions in their portfolios.

Solid-Liquid Changes of State

Demonstration

Materials *hot plate, 2 blocks of paraffin, thermometer*
Time 30 minutes

Place the paraffin in a saucepan on a hot plate. CAUTION: *All participants must secure long hair and loose clothing to keep them away from the heat source. All participants must use oven mitts and wear safety goggles.* Gently warm the paraffin over low heat until it is completely melted. Remove the saucepan from the hot plate and turn it off. Place a thermometer into the liquid paraffin and record the temperature every minute until the paraffin is solid. Note the temperature at which the paraffin begins to solidify. Ask: **Is the freezing point of paraffin the same as water?** *(No, it is higher)* Freezing point is one of the characteristics of a substance. **learning modality: visual**

Ongoing Assessment

Skills Check Have students describe how the particles in a solid respond when thermal energy is added.

Liquid-Gas Changes of State

Sharpen your Skills

Observing

Time 10 minutes
Materials *teakettle, hot plate, water*

Students should recognize that the steam they see is condensation, a liquid. They should conclude that what is present but not visible is a gas, water vapor. **learning modality: visual**

Including All Students

Students who are still mastering English may have difficulty distinguishing the terms *vaporization, evaporation,* and *condensation.* Explain that the suffix *-tion* changes a verb, or action word, into a noun. The word *vaporize* means "to turn into a gas." The word *vaporization* thus means "the *process* of turning into a gas." Have students find the root verbs for the words *evaporation* and *condensation.* Students can then write definitions for the terms using their own words. **limited English proficiency**

Building Inquiry Skills: Comparing and Contrasting

Prompt students to compare and contrast evaporation and boiling. Then ask students to compare the temperatures at which each process takes place. *(Evaporation takes place at a much lower temperature than boiling.)* Guide students in designing experiments to compare the difference in time it takes for water to evaporate versus the time it takes for water to vaporize by boiling. Ask: **What variable would you need to control in this experiment?** *(The mass of water, rate of heating, amount of heat)* If possible, allow students to carry out their experiments. **learning modality: logical/mathematical**

Observing ACTIVITY

Put a teakettle on a stove or a lab burner, and bring the water to a boil. Look carefully at the steam coming out of the spout. **CAUTION:** *Steam and boiling water can cause serious burns.* What state of matter is the steam that you see? What is present, but not visible, in the small space between the steam and the spout?

Freezing The change of state from a liquid to a solid is called **freezing.** Freezing occurs when a substance loses thermal energy. The temperature at which a substance changes from a liquid to a solid is called its **freezing point.** For a given substance, the freezing point and the melting point are the same. The only difference between the two is whether the substance is gaining or releasing thermal energy.

The fact that freezing involves a release of energy explains why the farmer had his workers spray the orange trees with water. The liquid water released thermal energy as it froze. Some of this thermal energy was transferred to the oranges, and kept them from freezing.

Liquid–Gas Changes of State

The upper right portion of Figure 14 shows changes between the liquid and gas states of matter. These changes are known as vaporization and condensation.

Vaporization The process by which matter changes from the liquid to the gas state is called **vaporization.** During this process, particles in a liquid absorb thermal energy. This causes the particles to move faster. Eventually they move fast enough to escape the liquid, as gas particles.

If vaporization takes place at the surface of a liquid, it is called **evaporation.** At higher temperatures, vaporization can occur below the surface of a liquid as well. This process is called **boiling.** When a liquid boils, gas bubbles formed within the liquid rise to the surface. The temperature at which a liquid boils is called its **boiling point.**

Condensation You have seen that beads of water appear on the outside of a cold drinking glass or on the bathroom mirror after you take a shower. This occurs because water vapor that is

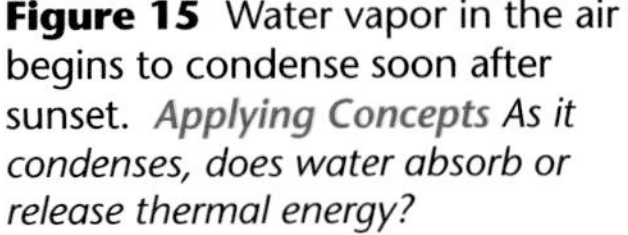

Figure 15 Water vapor in the air begins to condense soon after sunset. *Applying Concepts As it condenses, does water absorb or release thermal energy?*

Background

Integrating Science In the atmosphere, changes of state take place as part of the water cycle. Liquid water on Earth's surface absorbs thermal energy from the sun as it evaporates. The water vapor rises because it is warm. As the water vapor cools, it condenses and forms clouds of ice and water droplets. If these droplets are heavy enough, they fall to the ground as rain or snow.

Hail forms from ice droplets in a thundercloud. In a large thundercloud, masses of air move in updrafts. As ice droplets accumulate, they form larger ice pellets. These pellets can be carried from the bottom of the cloud back to the top by updrafts. As the ice pellets fall through the cloud, another layer of frozen water coats them; eventually they form large hail stones that are too heavy to be carried by the updraft, and they fall to the ground.

Figure 16 Joints on bridges and spaces in sidewalks allow for the expansion and contraction of matter. *Applying Concepts What happens to the spaces in the expansion joint as the bridge gets warmer?*

present in the air loses thermal energy when it comes in contact with the cold glass. When a gas loses a sufficient amount of thermal energy, it will change into a liquid. A change from the gas state to the liquid state is called **condensation.**

☑ *Checkpoint* ***What is the difference between boiling and evaporation of a liquid?***

Thermal Expansion

Have you ever loosened a tight jar lid by holding it under a stream of hot water? This works because the metal lid expands a little. Do you know why? **As the thermal energy of a substance increases, its particles spread out and the substance expands.** This is true even when the substance is not changing state. The expanding of matter when it is heated is known as **thermal expansion.**

When a substance is cooled, thermal energy is released. This means that the motion of the particles slows down and the particles move closer together. So as a substance is cooled, it contracts, or decreases in size.

Thermometers You are already familiar with one application of thermal expansion—a thermometer. In a common thermometer, a liquid such as mercury or alcohol is sealed within a glass tube. As the liquid is heated, it expands and climbs up the tube. As the liquid is cooled, it contracts and flows down in the tube.

Expanding Teeth Your teeth also expand and contract with changes in temperature. If you have a filling, the material used for the filling must expand and contract with your tooth. If it didn't, the filling could cause the tooth to crack, or the filling could loosen. So dentists use fillings that have the same expansion properties as teeth.

INTEGRATING HEALTH

Program Resources

- **Interdisciplinary Exploration Series** "Wagons West," pp. 31–32
- **Product Testing Activities by *Consumer Reports*** "Testing Disposable Cups," pp. 1–8.
- **Science Explorations Series** *Human Biology and Health,* Chapters 1 and 3

Answers to Self-Assessment

Caption Questions

Figure 15 Condensation releases energy.
Figure 16 The spaces in the expansion joint get smaller.

☑ *Checkpoint*

Boiling occurs when vaporization takes place beneath the surface of a liquid. Evaporation occurs when vaporization takes place at the liquid's surface.

Demonstration

ACTIVITY

Materials *metal eye screw, bolt or nail that fits snugly into the eye screw, wooden block, tongs, candle, oven mitt, large bowl of ice water*
Time 15 minutes

Firmly screw the eye screw into the wooden block. Demonstrate how the head of the bolt fits through the hole in the eye screw. See if students can predict what will happen when the bolt is heated. CAUTION: *All participants must secure long hair and loose clothing to keep them away from the candle. All participants must use oven mitts and wear safety goggles.* Using the tongs, hold the head of the bolt over the flame for a few minutes. Try to put the head of the bolt through the hole of the eye screw. Ask students to infer why the bolt no longer fits. *(It is too big. As the bolt was heated, its thermal energy increased, its particles spread out, and it expanded.)* Challenge students to test their inference by finding a way to fit the bolt back through the hole. *(Allow the bolt to cool and contract. It should then fit through the hole.)* Submerge the bolt in ice water for 2 minutes. Then demonstrate that the cooled bolt fits through the eye screw. **learning modality: visual**

Integrating Health

Some students may not know what a filling is. Explain that teeth can develop cavities, which are small holes caused by bacteria. A filling is material inserted into a cavity to seal it and protect the tooth. Have students create a list of other properties that the material used in fillings should have. *(Sample: durability, safety, hardness)* **learning modality: verbal**

Ongoing Assessment

Drawing Have students draw diagrams that compare the particles in two aluminum blocks, one held under cold water and one under hot water.

3 Assess

Section 3 Review Answers

1. Thermal energy must be added or removed from a solid to change its state. Changes in thermal energy change the motion of the particles. The motion determines the state.
2. Thermal expansion is the expansion of a substance as its thermal energy increases.
3. During a change of state, the temperature of a substance remains constant, while the thermal energy changes.
4. A thermostat contains a strip made of two metals (bimetallic strip). As the strip is heated, the metals expand at different rates, and the strip curls. As the strip curls and uncurls, it controls a switch.
5. Because matter expands when heated, the potato and water inside the potato skin expand when they are baked. Without holes to give the water and water vapor a place to escape, the potato may explode

Science at Home

Materials *2 medium-sized balloons, measuring tape, freezer*
Tips Suggest students mark the location of the measuring tape on the balloons so they can measure the same part of the balloon each time. Do not use mylar balloons. Students should explain that the particles of the gas in the balloon in the freezer lose thermal energy. This causes the balloon to contract, so that its circumference gets smaller.

Performance Assessment

Drawing Have students draw diagrams that show the different changes of state of a container of water that starts cold, then is heated until it boils and vaporizes. Students' diagrams should include captions and pictures of thermometers or water molecules.

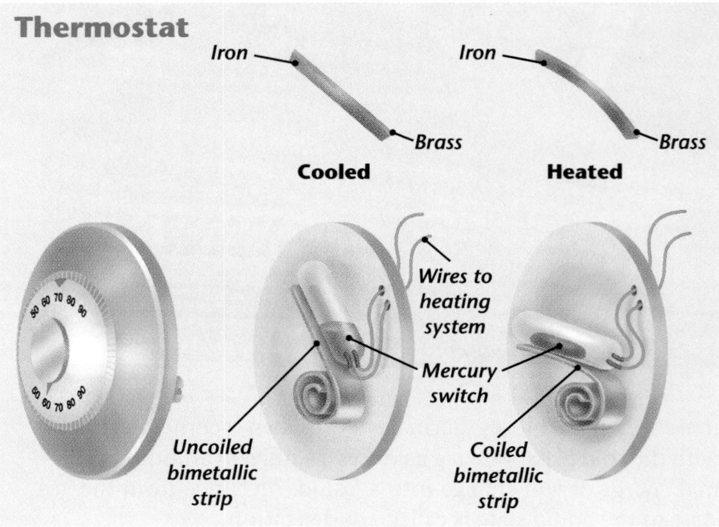

Figure 17 A bimetallic strip is an important part of many thermostats. When the temperature drops, the strip uncoils and closes a switch that starts a heating system. *Relating Cause and Effect What causes the bimetallic strip to coil and uncoil?*

Thermostats Thermal expansion is used in **thermostats,** or heat-regulating devices. Many thermostats contain **bimetallic strips,** which are strips of two different metals joined together. Different metals expand at different rates. When the bimetallic strip is heated, one side expands more than the other. This causes the strip to bend into a curve.

The movement of the strip operates a switch. If the switch is connected to a furnace or other heating system, the thermostat will turn the heating system on and off. In addition to home heating systems, thermostats are used on such devices as air conditioners, ovens, toasters, and electric blankets.

Section 3 Review

1. How does thermal energy produce a change from one state of matter to another?
2. What is thermal expansion?
3. What happens to the temperature of a substance during a change of state? What happens to thermal energy during a change of state?
4. How does a thermostat make use of thermal expansion?
5. **Thinking Critically** **Applying Concepts** Why do cookbooks recommend that you poke holes in a potato before baking it?

Science at Home

Blow up two medium-sized balloons so that they are the same size. Have a family member use a measuring tape to measure the circumference of the balloons. Then ask them to place one of the balloons in the freezer for fifteen to twenty minutes. Remove the balloon from the freezer and measure both balloons again. Explain how changes in thermal energy cause the change in circumference.

Program Resources

Teaching Resources 6-3 Review and Reinforce, p. 165; Enrich, p. 166

Media and Technology

Interactive Student Tutorial CD-ROM M-6

Answers to Self-Assessment

Caption Question

Figure 17 Addition or loss of thermal energy from air in the room causes the metals of the strip to expand or contract. Because the metals expand and contract at different rates, the bimetallic strip coils or uncoils.

Uses of Heat

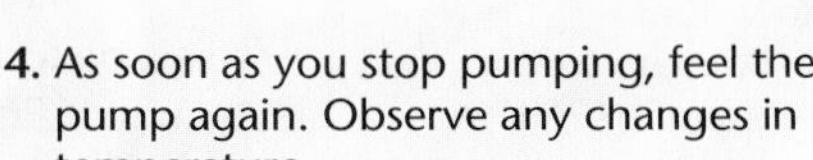

DISCOVER

What Happens at the Pump?

1. Obtain a bicycle pump and a deflated basketball or soccer ball.
2. Feel the pump with your hand. Note if it feels cool or warm.
3. Use the pump to inflate the ball to the recommended pressure.
4. As soon as you stop pumping, feel the pump again. Observe any changes in temperature.

Think It Over

Developing Hypotheses Propose an explanation for any changes that you observed.

GUIDE FOR READING

- **How is thermal energy related to heat engines and refrigerators?**

Reading Tip **Before you read, preview the illustrations showing how engines work. Write down any questions you have, and answer them as you read.**

For more than 100 years, the steam locomotive was a symbol of power and speed. It first came into use in the 1830s, and was soon hauling hundreds of tons of freight faster than a horse could gallop. Yet today, trains are pulled by diesel locomotives that are far more efficient. You will probably only see a coal-burning locomotive as a tourist attraction.

Heat Engines

To power a steam locomotive, a fireman shovels coal into a roaring fire. Heat is then transferred from the fire to water in the boiler. But how can heat move a train?

The thermal energy of the coal fire must be converted to the mechanical energy, or energy of motion, of the moving train. You already know about the reverse process, the conversion of mechanical energy to thermal energy. It happens when you rub your hands together to make them warm.

The conversion of thermal energy to mechanical energy requires a device called a **heat engine.** Heat engines usually make use of combustion. **Combustion** is the process of burning a fuel, such as coal or gasoline. During combustion, chemical energy that is stored in fuel is converted to thermal energy. **Heat engines convert thermal energy to mechanical energy.** Heat engines are classified according to whether combustion takes place outside the engine or inside the engine.

READING STRATEGIES

Reading Tip Provide each student with four or five note cards. As students preview the drawings in the section, instruct them to write their questions on the note cards, one question per card. Collect the cards and direct students to read the section. After all students have finished reading, have a volunteer select a card and read the question aloud. Challenge students to answer the question. Repeat with the remaining cards.

Program Resources

- **Teaching Resources** 6-4 Lesson Plan, p. 167; 6-4 Section Summary, p. 168

Media and Technology

Audiotapes English-Spanish Summary 6-4

Uses of Heat

Objective

After completing the lesson, students will be able to

- describe how engines convert thermal energy to mechanical energy;
- describe how refrigerators transfer thermal energy from a cool area to a warm area.

Key Terms heat engine, combustion, external combustion engine, internal combustion engine

1 Engage/Explore

Activating Prior Knowledge

Ask students to describe how it feels when you place your hand on the hood of a car that has just been driven. *(The hood feels hot.)* Ask: **Where does that heat come from?** *(Combustion in the engine releases thermal energy which is converted to mechanical energy by the engine.)*

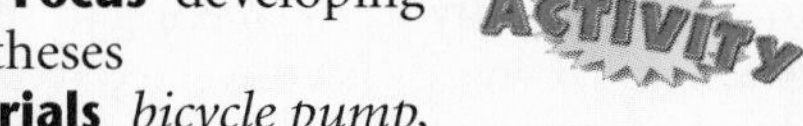

Skills Focus developing hypotheses
Materials *bicycle pump, deflated basketball or soccer ball*
Time 10 minutes
Tips Caution students to avoid over-inflating the ball, which could cause it to burst. Make sure students recognize that the bicycle pump is using mechanical energy to inflate the ball.
Expected Outcome Students should find that the temperature of the pump and the ball increases after pumping.
Think It Over Mechanical work and friction can convert mechanical energy to thermal energy.

2 Facilitate

Heat Engines

Using the Visuals: Figure 18

Ask students to trace the path of steam from the top of the engine until it leaves the cylinder. Ask: **When does the steam do work?** *(When it pushes the piston)* Ask: **When the piston is pushed toward the left, what happens to the connecting rod and the wheel?** *(The rod moves and spins the wheel.)* Ask students to infer what happens to the steam after it pushes the piston. *(The steam is pushed out of the engine by the next stroke of the piston.)* **learning modality: visual**

TRY THIS

ACTIVITY

Skills Focus classifying
Materials *dry sand, metal container such as a coffee can with a plastic lid, thermometer*
Time 15 minutes
Tips Caution students not to force the thermometer into the sand. Remind students that some thermal energy escapes when they open the lid to check the temperature.
Classifying The sand's temperature increases slightly from shaking it, thus mechanical energy is converted to thermal energy.
Extend Challenge students to find a way to reduce heat loss when the temperature is checked. *(Insert the thermometer into the lid.)* **learning modality: kinesthetic**

Shake It Up

How does work relate to temperature?

1. Place a handful of dry sand in a metal container that has a cover.
2. Measure the temperature of the sand with a thermometer.
3. Cover the can and shake it vigorously for a minute or two.
4. Predict any change in the temperature of the sand. Was your prediction correct?

Classifying Identify any energy conversions and use them to explain your observations.

External Combustion Engines In an **external combustion engine,** the fuel is burned outside the engine. A steam engine is an example of an external combustion engine. The combustion of wood, coal, or oil heats water in a boiler outside the engine. As its thermal energy increases, the water turns to water vapor, or steam. The steam is then passed through a valve into the engine where it pushes against a metal plunger called a piston. The piston moves back and forth in a tube called a cylinder.

Figure 18 shows how steam can do work, such as moving the wheels of a locomotive. Steam enters at the right end of the cylinder, pushing the piston to the left. Steam then enters at the left end of the cylinder and pushes the piston back. This type of external combustion engine can also move the propellers of a steamship. Modern steam engines are more efficient than old-fashioned piston steam engines. But in both types of engine, thermal energy is converted to mechanical energy.

Internal Combustion Engines In an **internal combustion engine,** the fuel is burned in cylinders inside the engine. Diesel and gasoline engines, which power most automobiles, are both examples of internal combustion engines. A piston inside a cylinder moves up and down, turning a crankshaft. The motion of the crankshaft is transferred to the wheels of the car.

Each up or down movement by a piston is called a stroke. Most diesel and gasoline engines are four-stroke engines, as shown in *Exploring a Four-Stroke Engine.* Automobile engines usually have four, six, or eight cylinders. The four-stroke process occurs in each cylinder, and is repeated many times each second.

☑ *Checkpoint* *What happens during the process of combustion?*

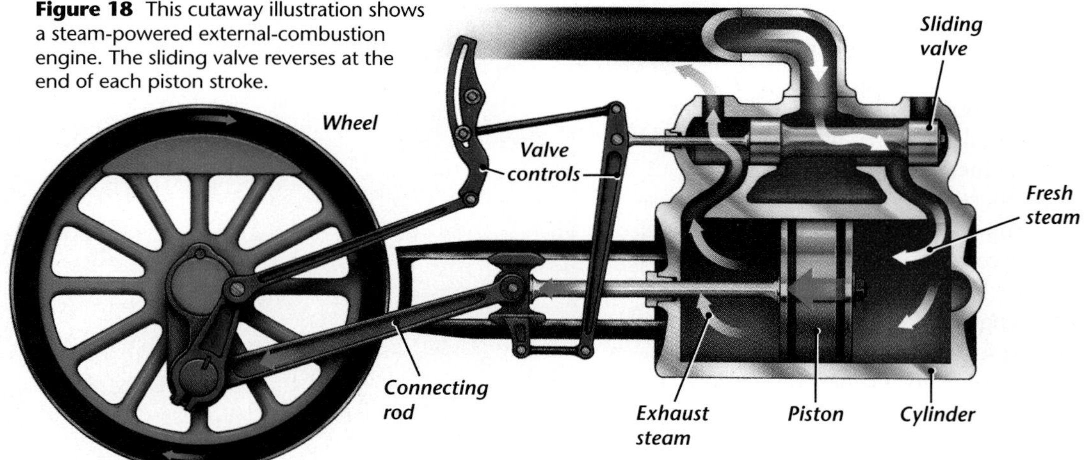

Figure 18 This cutaway illustration shows a steam-powered external-combustion engine. The sliding valve reverses at the end of each piston stroke.

Background

History of Science In the 1700s, scientists thought that heat was an invisible, caloric fluid that flowed from hotter objects to colder ones. In 1798, an American scientist named Benjamin Thompson, who lived in England and was made Count Rumford by the Elector of Bavaria, challenged the caloric theory. Count Rumford noticed that when holes were drilled in cannon barrels, the barrels and the drills became hot. He used this observation to design an experiment in which he placed a cannon barrel in a box filled with water. After drilling for several hours, the water boiled. It kept boiling for as long as the drilling continued. Count Rumford concluded that heat was released as a result of the drilling—not from the flow of caloric.

EXPLORING a Four-Stroke Engine

Most automobiles use four-stroke heat engines. These four strokes occur repeatedly in each cylinder in the engine.

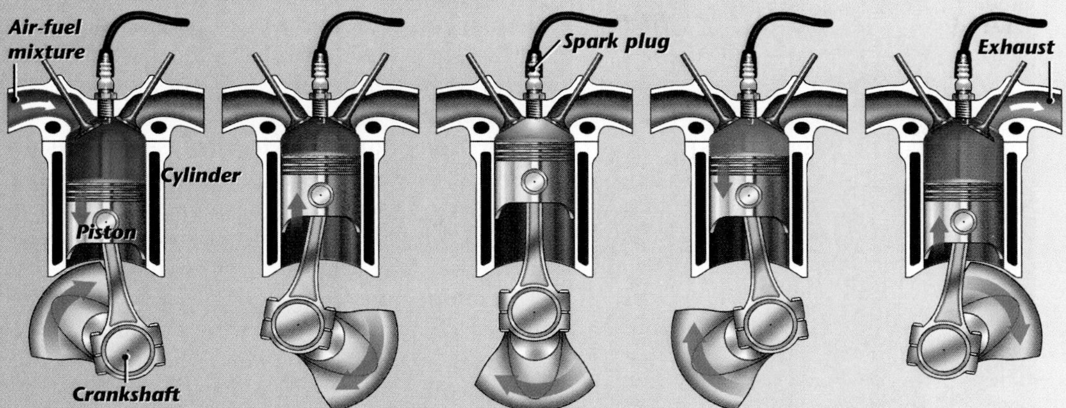

Intake Stroke A mixture of fuel and air is drawn into the cylinder as the piston moves down.

Compression Stroke The mixture is squeezed, or compressed, into a smaller space as the piston moves back up.

Ignition When the piston is almost at the top of the cylinder, a spark plug ignites the mixture. Stored chemical energy is converted to thermal energy, which heats the gas.

Power Stroke As the heated gas expands, it pushes the piston down. The piston, in turn, moves the crankshaft. Thus thermal energy is converted to mechanical energy.

Exhaust Stroke The piston moves back up, pushing the heated gas out. This makes room for new fuel and air, so that the cycle can be repeated.

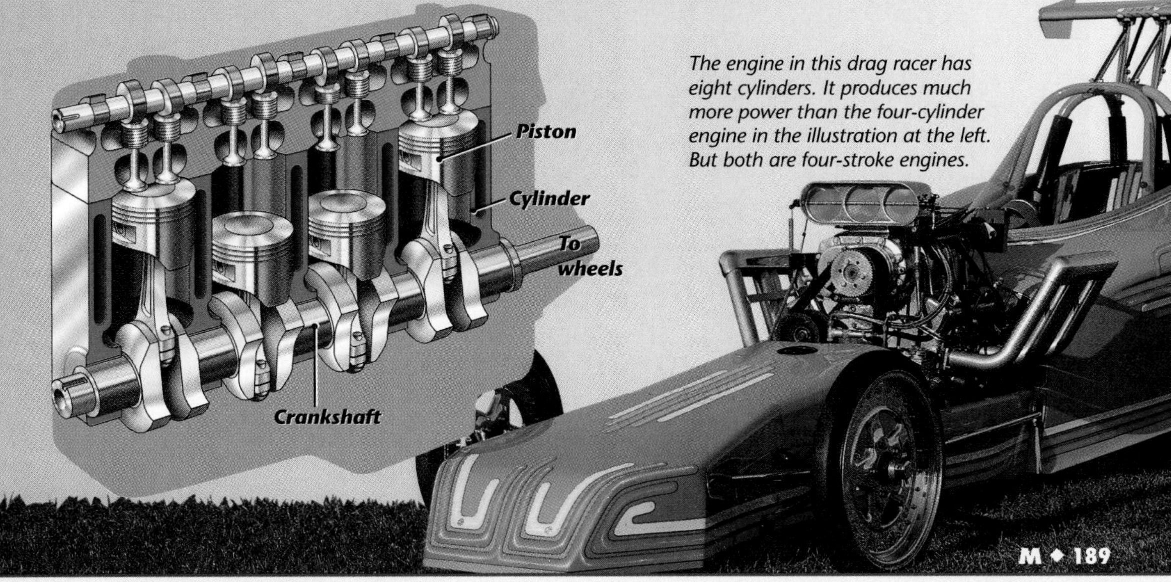

The engine in this drag racer has eight cylinders. It produces much more power than the four-cylinder engine in the illustration at the left. But both are four-stroke engines.

EXPLORING
a Four-Stroke Engine

Direct students attention to the Exploring feature on p. 189 and allow students plenty of time to examine it. Make sure students understand a stroke is one trip up or down in the cylinder. Have students identify which valves are open or closed on which stroke. Lead students in a discussion of each of the components shown in the figure: piston—pushed down by heated gas; cylinder—contains the heated gas; crankshaft—converts linear motion of piston into rotary motion; spark plug—ignites the fuel-air mixture.

You may wish to have students organize the information presented in the visual essay into a table. This could be done as a whole-class discussion, in groups, or individually. The terms *Intake Stroke, Compression Stroke, Ignition, Power Stroke,* and *Exhaust Stroke* could be written in a horizontal row across the top of the table and the names of engine parts, Piston, Spark Plug, Crankshaft, Intake Valve, Exhaust Valve, could be written in a vertical column at the left. Then students can fill in the table with information from the essay. **learning modality: logical/mathematical**

Media and Technology

Transparencies "Exploring a Four-Stroke Engine," Transparency 20

Answers to Self-Assessment

Checkpoint

During combustion, fuel is burned, releasing thermal energy. The thermal energy released is converted to work by the engine.

Ongoing Assessment

Skills Check Ask students to predict what will happen in a four-stroke engine if a spark plug does not fire. *(The fuel-air mixture will not be ignited and the heated gas will not push down on the piston.)*

Refrigerators

Building Inquiry Skills: Organizing Information

Have students organize the information about refrigeration into a flowchart or diagrams. Ask: **Inside the refrigerator, how is thermal energy transferred?** *(From warmer food item to the colder refrigerant gas)* **Outside the refrigerator, how is thermal energy transferred?** *(From warmer refrigerant gas to the cooler air in the kitchen.)* Point out that the end result is a transfer of thermal energy from a cool area to a warm area. **learning modality: verbal**

3 Assess

Section 4 Review Answers

1. A device that converts thermal energy to mechanical energy
2. A refrigerator removes thermal energy from a cold area and transfers it to a warm area.
3. Intake stroke, compression stroke, power stroke, exhaust stroke
4. Internal and external; both convert thermal energy to mechanical energy; internal—fuel is burned inside cylinder of engine, external—fuel is burned outside engine.

Check Your Progress

CHAPTER PROJECT 6

Tell students when they will be able to test their designs in class. You may wish to make the room available at other than regular class times. Make sure students are working on a device.

Performance Assessment

Writing Ask students to write advertisements for an air conditioning system which describe what happens in a hot room when the air conditioner is turned on.

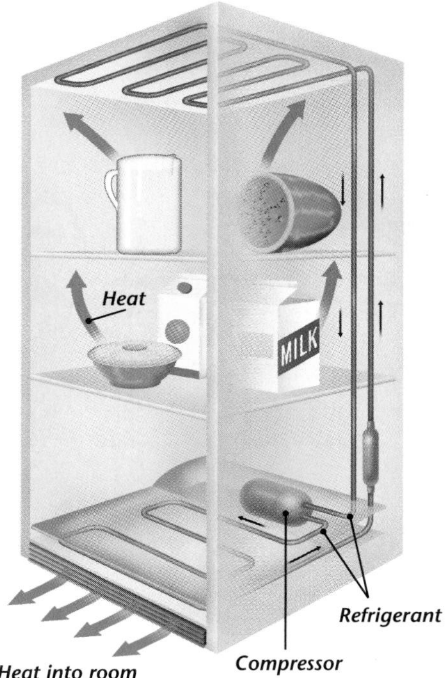

Figure 19 This diagram shows the basic parts of a refrigerator. *Interpreting Diagrams How are changes of state used to cool food?*

Refrigerators

Energy conversion can also be used to keep food cool. Does that seem surprising? After all, heat naturally flows from a warm body to a cold body—not the other way around. So how can you refrigerate food? A refrigerator transfers thermal energy from the cold space inside to the warm room outside. Perhaps you have felt this energy in the warm air blown out at the bottom of a refrigerator.

A refrigerator is a device that uses an outside energy source to transfer thermal energy from a cool area to a warm area. In your refrigerator, that energy is provided by an electric motor, powered by the electricity coming to your home.

A refrigerator also requires a refrigerant substance. The refrigerator motor compresses the refrigerant in the gas state, which causes its pressure and its temperature to rise. When this happens, the gas gives off thermal energy. This heat is transferred to the outside air. As the gas loses thermal energy, it changes from a gas to a liquid. The liquid is then allowed to evaporate. As it evaporates, it cools. The cold gas is then pumped through tubes inside the walls of the refrigerator. There the gas absorbs heat from inside the refrigerator. And so thermal energy is transferred from the space inside the refrigerator to the gas. The gas then returns to the compressor motor, and the whole cycle begins again.

An air conditioner operates in the same way. But it cools the area inside a building and transfers thermal energy to the air outdoors.

Section 4 Review

1. What is a heat engine?
2. Describe the process that occurs in a refrigerator.
3. What are the parts of the four-stroke cycle?
4. **Thinking Critically Comparing and Contrasting** What are the two types of heat engines? How are they alike? How are they different?

Check Your Progress

CHAPTER PROJECT 6

Build and test your container. Remember that you need to be able to get to the aluminum can at the beginning of the test so that hot water can be poured into it. You must also be able to measure the temperature of the water at the end of the test.

Program Resources

◆ **Teaching Resources** 6-4 Review and Reinforce, p. 169; 6-4 Enrich, p. 170

Answers to Self-Assessment

Caption Question

Figure 19 A refrigerant in the gas state is compressed so that it gives off thermal energy. As the refrigerant gas loses thermal energy, it changes from a gas to a liquid. The liquid evaporates and cools, and the cold gas is pumped through tubes in the refrigerator, where it absorbs thermal energy and cools the food.

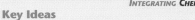

Section 1 Temperature and Thermal Energy

Key Ideas

- Temperature is a measure of the average kinetic energy of each particle within an object.
- Three temperature scales are Fahrenheit, Celsius, and Kelvin.
- Thermal energy is the total energy of the particles that make up an object.

Key Terms

temperature
Fahrenheit scale
Celsius scale
Kelvin scale
absolute zero

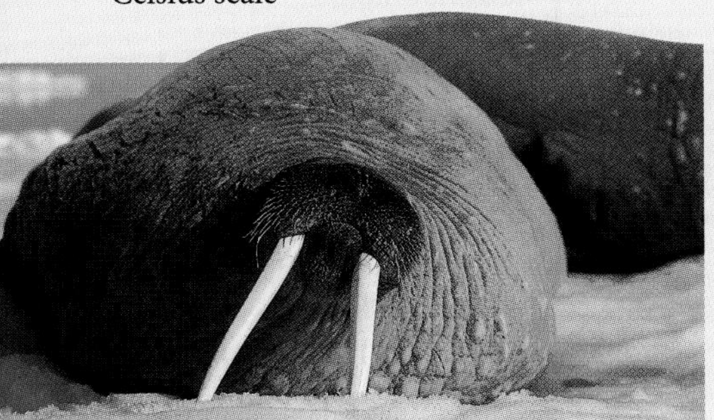

Section 2 The Nature of Heat

Key Ideas

- Heat is a transfer of thermal energy from an object at a higher temperature to an object at a lower temperature.
- Heat is transferred by conduction, convection, and radiation.
- A conductor transfers heat well, whereas an insulator does not.
- The amount of heat necessary to raise a given mass of a substance by a specific unit of temperature is called the specific heat.

Key Terms

heat
conduction
convection
convection current
radiation
conductor
insulator
specific heat

Section 3 Thermal Energy and States of Matter

INTEGRATING CHEMISTRY

Key Ideas

- Matter can exist in three states: solid, liquid, or gas. Matter can undergo a change of state when thermal energy is added or removed.
- When a substance is changing state, the temperature of the substance remains constant even though its thermal energy is changing.
- In general, matter expands when it is heated and contracts when it is cooled.

Key Terms

state
change of state
melting
melting point
freezing
freezing point
vaporization
evaporation
boiling
boiling point
condensation
thermal expansion
thermostat
bimetallic strip

Section 4 Uses of Heat

Key Ideas

- A heat engine converts thermal energy to mechanical energy that can be used to do work.
- Heat engines are classified as external or internal combustion engines depending on where the fuel is burned.
- A refrigerator transfers thermal energy from a cool region to a warm region.

Key Terms

heat engine
combustion
external combustion engine
internal combustion engine

Program Resources

- **Teaching Resources** Chapter 6 Project Scoring Rubric, p. 154; Chapter 6 Performance Assessment Teacher Notes, pp. 221–222; Chapter 6 Performance Assessment Student Worksheet, p. 223; Chapter 6 Test, pp. 224–227

Media and Technology

Interactive Student Tutorial CD-ROM M-6

Computer Test Bank M-6 Test

CHAPTER 6 REVIEW

Reviewing Content: Multiple Choice

1. b **2.** d **3.** b **4.** d **5.** c

True or False

6. true **7.** insulator **8.** remains the same **9.** Kelvin **10.** internal

Checking Concepts

11. The particles move faster and move farther apart.
12. The water near the heat source is warmed. The warm water expands and rises while cool water sinks into its place. This circular flow is a convection current.
13. During a change of state, thermal energy increases while temperature stays the same.
14. Thermal energy is released.
15. The metals in a bimetallic strip inside the thermostat expand and contract at different rates as the temperature changes. This causes the strip to curve and allows it to control a switch connected to the heating or cooling system.
16. No. Air has a much lower specific heat than water. Loss of the same amount of thermal energy by the water will result in a smaller temperature drop.
17. Make sure each line has the proper number of syllables. Look for creativity.

Thinking Visually

18. a. thermal energy **b.** conduction **c.** radiation

Applying Skills

19. The average motion of the molecules is greater at greater temperatures. The average motion is the same for the two containers on the left and greater for the container on the right.
20. The total thermal energy in the middle container is twice the thermal energy in the container on the left because it has twice as many molecules at the same temperature. The thermal energy of the container on the right is greater than in the middle container. It has the same number of molecules, but the average energy of each molecule is greater.
21. Heat = Specific heat × mass × temperature change (a change of 1 K is the same as a change of 1°C)
Left: 4.18 J/(kg•K) × 0.100 kg × 1 K = 0.418 J
Middle: 4.18 J/(kg•K) × 0.200 kg × 1 K = 0.836 J
Right: 4.18 J/(kg•K) × 0.200 kg × 1 K = 0.836 J

Thinking Critically

22. As the tires heat up the particles move faster and farther apart, producing greater pressure.
23. The wooden stick, because it would not conduct heat as easily.
24. 140 J/(kg•K) × 0.002 kg × 15 K = 4.2 J
25. The wire expands in summer and contracts in winter. If it did not sag, it would contract and pull away from the poles during cold winters.
26. Inside the open refrigerator, the system is transferring thermal energy from the air to the refrigerant. Outside the open refrigerator, the system is transferring that same amount of thermal energy from the refrigerant back to the room.

CHAPTER 6 REVIEW

Reviewing Content

For more review of key concepts, see the Interactive Student Tutorial CD-ROM.

Multiple Choice

Choose the letter of the answer that best completes each statement.

1. The average kinetic energy of the particles of an object is its
   a. heat content. b. temperature. c. specific heat. d. thermal energy.
2. If you want to know the amount of heat needed to raise the temperature of 2 kg of steel by 10°C, you need to know steel's
   a. temperature. b. thermal energy. c. heat content. d. specific heat.
3. The process by which heat moves from one end of a solid to the other is called
   a. convection. b. conduction. c. radiation. d. insulation.
4. The change of state that occurs when a gas becomes a liquid is called
   a. evaporation. b. boiling. c. freezing. d. condensation.
5. Heat engines convert thermal energy to
   a. chemical energy.
   b. electrical energy.
   c. mechanical energy.
   d. radiant energy.

True or False

If the statement is true, write true. If it is false, change the underlined word or words to make the statement true.

6. Heat transfer by <u>radiation</u> can occur in a vacuum.
7. In order to decrease the amount of thermal energy that moves from one place to another, you would use a <u>conductor</u>.
8. When a substance melts, the temperature of the substance <u>increases</u>.
9. The temperature reading of zero on the <u>Celsius</u> scale is equal to absolute zero.
10. In an <u>external</u> combustion engine, the fuel is burned inside the cylinder.

Checking Concepts

11. What happens to the particles of a solid as the thermal energy of the solid increases?
12. When you heat a pot of water on the stove, a convection current is formed. Explain how this happens.
13. How can you add thermal energy to a substance without increasing its temperature?
14. When molten steel becomes solid, is energy absorbed or released by the steel?
15. Describe how a thermostat controls the temperature in a building.
16. When night falls on a summer day, the air temperature drops by 10°C. Will the temperature of the water in a nearby lake change by the same amount? Explain why or why not.
17. **Writing to Learn** Haiku is a form of poetry that began in Japan. A haiku has three lines. The first and third lines have five syllables each. The second line has seven syllables. Write a haiku describing how you might feel on a frosty winter morning or a sweltering summer afternoon.

Thinking Visually

18. **Concept Map** Copy the thermal energy concept map onto a separate sheet of paper. Then complete it and add a title. (For more on concept maps, see the Skills Handbook.)

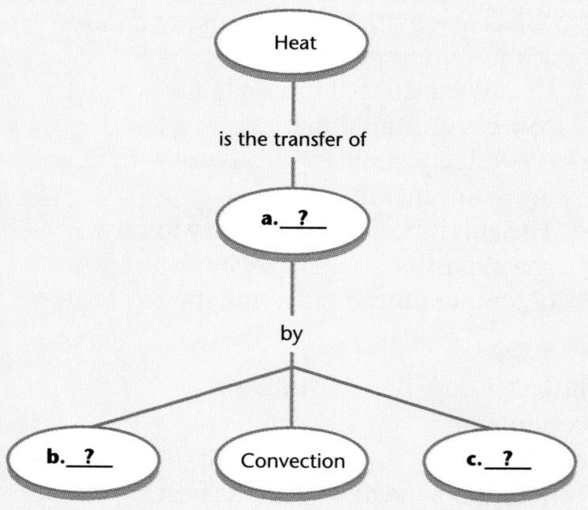

Applying Skills

Use the drawing of three containers of water to answer Questions 19–21.

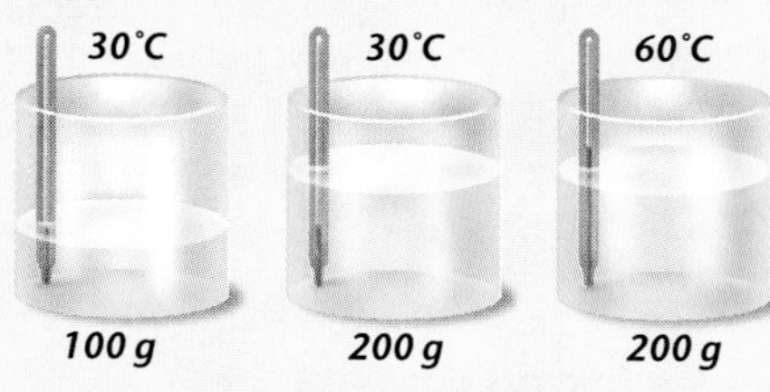

19. **Interpreting Data** Compare the average motion of the molecules in the three containers. Explain your answer.
20. **Drawing Conclusions** Compare the total amount of thermal energy in the three containers. Explain your answer.
21. **Calculating** Determine how much heat you would need to raise the temperature of each container by 1°C. (See Figure 10 on page 176.) Show your work.

Thinking Critically

22. **Relating Cause and Effect** Why is the air pressure in a car's tires different before and after the car has been driven for an hour?
23. **Applying Concepts** Suppose you need to move a log in a burning campfire. Would it be better to use a metal rod or a wooden stick? Explain why.
24. **Problem Solving** Suppose a mercury thermometer contains 2 grams of mercury. If the thermometer's reading changes from 25°C to 40°C, how much heat was needed? The specific heat of mercury is 140 J/(kg·K).
25. **Applying Concepts** Telephone lines are allowed to sag when they are hung. Can you think of a reason why?
26. **Relating Cause and Effect** A refrigerator is running in a small room. The refrigerator door is open, but the room does not grow any cooler. Use the law of conservation of energy to explain why the temperature does not drop.

Performance Assessment

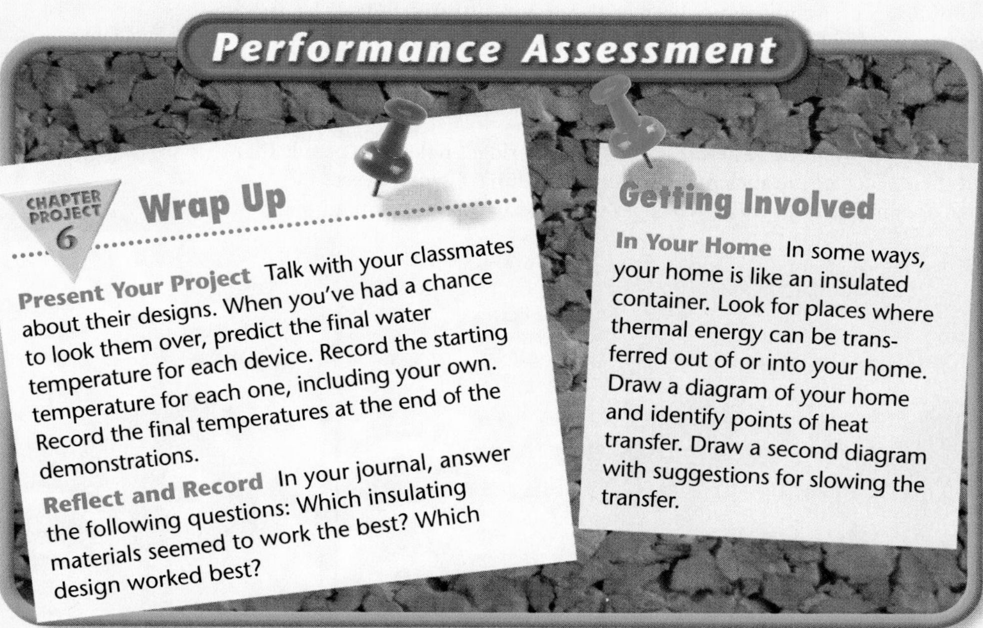

Wrap Up

CHAPTER PROJECT 6

Present Your Project Talk with your classmates about their designs. When you've had a chance to look them over, predict the final water temperature for each device. Record the starting temperature for each one, including your own. Record the final temperatures at the end of the demonstrations.

Reflect and Record In your journal, answer the following questions: Which insulating materials seemed to work the best? Which design worked best?

Getting Involved

In Your Home In some ways, your home is like an insulated container. Look for places where thermal energy can be transferred out of or into your home. Draw a diagram of your home and identify points of heat transfer. Draw a second diagram with suggestions for slowing the transfer.

Program Resources

◆ **Inquiry Skills Handbook** Provides teaching and review of all inquiry skills

Performance Assessment

Wrap Up

CHAPTER PROJECT 6

Present Your Project Students' predictions should be based on what they have learned throughout the unit. Encourage them to explain their designs and why they chose the materials they did. They should look for similarities between their designs. For example, does the device have a lid? While the class is waiting for the final temperatures, predictions can be posted. Ask students to explain the reasoning behind their predictions.

Reflect and Record Students should explain how their experimental results helped them choose the best design. Encourage students to compare their designs to the best-insulated designs in the class.

Getting Involved

In Your Home Before students make their diagrams, challenge the class to brainstorm some of the most likely places where energy transfer can occur. Encourage students to plan their diagrams so they include windows, doors, and other features. Students should think of ways to test whether heat transfer is occurring at a given place. Encourage students to talk to their families about implementing their plans to slow the heat transfer.

Bridges from Vines to Steel

This interdisciplinary feature presents the central theme of bridges by connecting four different disciplines: science, social studies, mathematics, and language arts. The four explorations are designed to capture students' interest and help them see how the content they are studying in science relates to other school subjects and to real-world events. The unit is particularly suitable for team teaching.

1 Engage/Explore

Activating Prior Knowledge

Help students recall what they learned in Chapter 2, Section 1, Balanced and Unbalanced Forces and Section 4, Action and Reaction, by asking questions such as: **What does Newton's third law say about action and reaction forces?** *(For every action force, there is an equal and opposite reaction force.)* and **If the weight of a truck pushes down on a bridge, what is the reaction force?** *(The bridge pushes up on the truck.)* Invite students to sketch on the board outlines of bridges they have seen.

Introducing the Unit

A bridge can save you from having to make a very long journey around an obstacle or from having to take a boat. Ask students the basic purposes of a bridge. Point out that bridges must be strong enough to support the weight of vehicles. Many bridges cross rivers used by water craft, so the design of the bridge must allow the craft to pass under the bridge. Refer students to the picture of the arch bridge. Ask: **What is holding this bridge up in the center of the arches?** *(Accept all reasonable responses.)*

Ask: **How do bridges encourage trade?** *(Write all reasonable responses on the board. Sample: The bridge makes it easier to transport goods.)*

INTERDISCIPLINARY EXPLORATION

BRIDGES FROM VINES TO STEEL

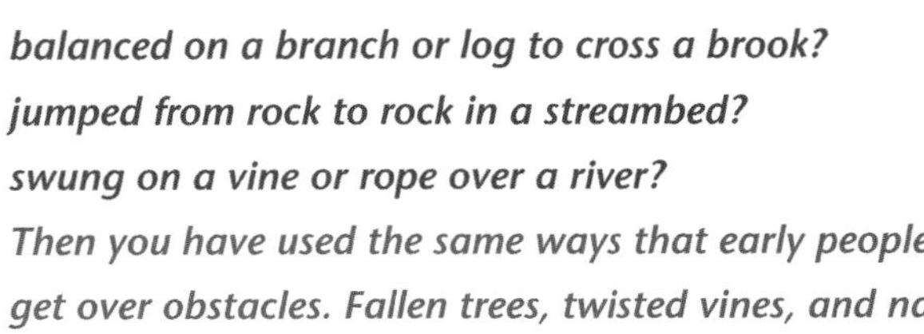

HAVE YOU EVER . . .

balanced on a branch or log to cross a brook?

jumped from rock to rock in a streambed?

swung on a vine or rope over a river?

Then you have used the same ways that early people used to get over obstacles. Fallen trees, twisted vines, and natural stones formed the first bridges.

Bridges are easy ways of getting over difficult obstacles. For thousands of years, bridges have also served as forts for defense, scenes of great battles, and homes for shops and churches. They have also been sites of mystery, love, and intrigue. They span history—linking cities, nations, and empires and encouraging trade and travel.

But bridges have not always been as elaborate as they are today. The earliest ones were made of materials that were free and plentiful. In deep forests, people used beams made from small trees. In tropical regions where vegetation was thick, people wove together vines and grasses, then hung them to make walkways over rivers and gorges.

No matter what the structures or materials, bridges reflect the people that built them. Each of the ancient civilizations of China, Egypt, Greece, and Rome designed strong, graceful bridges to connect and control its empire.

The Roman arch bridge Ponte Sant'Angelo in Rome

Program Resources

- **Teaching Resources** Interdisciplinary Explorations, Science, pp. 174-176; Social Studies, pp. 177-179; Language Arts, pp. 180-182; Mathematics, pp. 183-185

The Balance of Forces

What keeps a bridge from falling down? How does it support its own weight and the weight of people and traffic on it? Builders found the answers by considering the various forces that act on a bridge.

The weight of the bridge and the traffic on it are called the *load.* When a heavy truck crosses a beam bridge, the weight of the load forces the beam to curve downward. This creates a tension force that stretches the bottom of the beam. At the same time, the load also creates a compression force at the top of the beam.

Since the bridge doesn't collapse under the load, there must be upward forces to balance the downward forces. In simple beam bridges, builders attached the beam to the ground or to end supports called abutments. To cross longer spans or distances, they construct piers under the middle span. Piers and abutments are structures that act as upward forces—reaction forces.

Another type of bridge, the arch bridge, is strong in compression. A heavy load on a stone arch bridge squeezes or pushes the stones together, creating compression throughout the structure. Weight on the arch bridge pushes down to the ends of the arch. The side walls and abutments act as reaction forces.

Early engineers discovered that arch bridges made of stone could span wider distances than simple beam bridges. Arch bridges were also stronger and more durable. Although the Romans were not the first to build arch bridges, they perfected the form in their massive, elegant structures. Early Roman arch bridges were built without mortar or "glue." The arch held together because the stones were skillfully shaped to work in compression. After nearly 2,000 years, some of these Roman arch bridges are still standing.

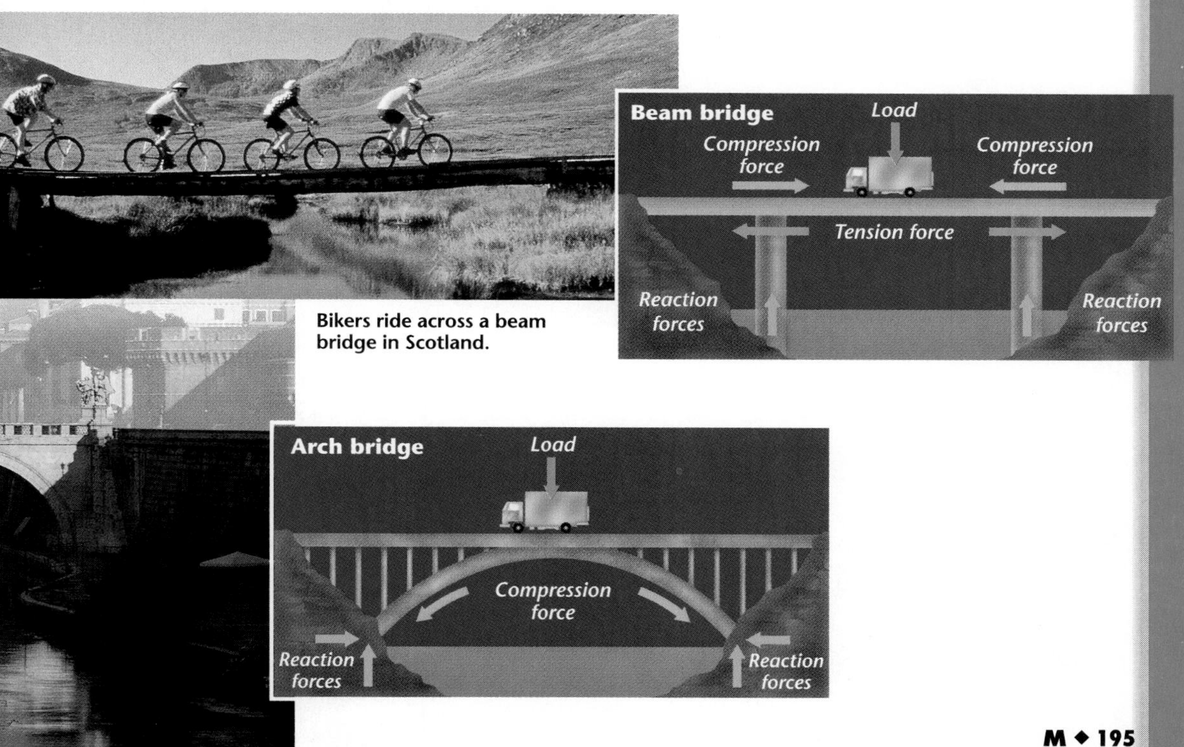

Bikers ride across a beam bridge in Scotland.

Background

Facts and Figures The oldest bridge still in use whose construction date can be accurately determined is in Turkey. This stone arch bridge over the River Meles in Izmir dates from about 850 B.C.

The longest stone arch bridge in the world is the Rockville Bridge in Pennsylvania. The bridge has 48 spans and is 1,161 meters long. This type of bridge is no longer built in the United States because of the expense.

Early bridge builders worked with stone, which is very strong in compression but very weak when bent. So early bridges were designed so that the forces of the load could be transferred to compression forces in the stone. Bridges, buildings, and aqueducts were all built by the Romans using arches, because arches take advantage of the high compression strength of stone.

Science

2 Facilitate

- Have volunteers each read one paragraph aloud. As they are reading, direct students' attention to the diagrams.
- Point out that traffic does not necessarily refer to vehicles. Traffic can also mean people and animals.
- Challenge interested students to make a list of the different types of bridges. Then have students illustrate them with pictures or sketches and make a bulletin board display for the class.
- Invite a volunteer to find a diagram of the parts of a bridge in an encyclopedia or visual dictionary. In particular, have the student find illustrations of abutments to share with the class.
- Point out that bridges are too expensive and it would be too dangerous for builders to find out by trial and error how many supports a bridge needs. Ask students: **How do builders know how many supports a bridge needs?** *(Answers will vary. Samples: they calculate the forces mathematically; they build scale models and test them; they use computer simulations)*
- Model a beam bridge by laying a meter stick between two desks. Show how the meter stick bends as you add weight to the center of the stick.
- If there is a bridge in or near your town, encourage students to find out more about the bridge. Ask students to research when the bridge was built, why it was needed, how much it cost, why the design was chosen, and how people got around or across the obstacle before the bridge was built.
- Point out that this page is titled "The Balance of Forces." Ask: **What does this mean?** *(The force of the load on the bridge is balanced by upward forces.)* Ask: **What might happen if the forces were not balanced?** *(The bridge could move or collapse.)*

Science

2 Facilitate

- Ask: **Why do trains need flat bridges?** *(Trains are very heavy. A train needs a huge amount of power to go uphill so railroads are built as flat as possible.)*
- Ask: **Why would builders prefer working with steel than iron?** *(Answers may vary. Sample: A bridge of a given strength can be built with lighter materials.)*
- As the class reads the text, direct students' attention to the bridge diagrams.
- Challenge an interested student to find a drawing or photograph of a tropical woven bridge. Have students compare the designs of the bridges. Ask: **Woven bridges sway in the wind. What does that tell you about suspension bridges?** *(They probably sway in the wind also.)* Point out that suspension bridges are designed to allow for some movement in high winds. The shape of some valleys cause them to be windy so bridge designers have to include wind factors in their design.
- Clarify that the road hangs from the wires. The towers do not support the road. The towers support the giant cables from which the road hangs.
- Ask: **What does the phrase "golden age" mean?** *(a very fortunate period)* **Why were the 1800s a golden age for bridges?** *(Many bridges were built because they were needed for railroads.)*
- On the photograph of the Brooklyn Bridge, point out the span while you explain that a span is one section of a bridge. A bridge may have several spans.

Science

The Golden Age of Bridges

In the 1800s in the United States, the invention of the steam locomotive and the expansion of railroads increased the demand for bridges. Trains pulling heavy freight needed strong, flat bridges. Builders began to use cast iron instead of stone and wood. By the late 1800s, they were using steel, which was strong and relatively lightweight.

The use of new building materials was not the only change. Engineers began designing different types of bridges as well. They found that they could build longer, larger bridges by using a suspension structure.

Suspension bridges are modern versions of long, narrow woven bridges found in tropical regions. These simple, woven suspension bridges can span long distances. Crossing one of these natural structures is like walking a tightrope. The weight of people and animals traveling over the bridge pushes down on the ropes, stretching them and creating tension forces.

Modern suspension bridges follow the same principles of tension as do woven bridges. A suspension bridge is strong in tension. In suspension bridges, parallel cables are stretched the entire length of the bridge—over giant towers. The cables are anchored at each end of the bridge. The roadway hangs from the cables, attached by wire suspenders. The weight of the bridge and the load on it act to pull apart or stretch the cables. This pulling apart creates tension force.

The towers act as supports for the bridge. The abutments that anchor the cables exert reaction forces as well. So forces in balance keep a suspension bridge from collapsing.

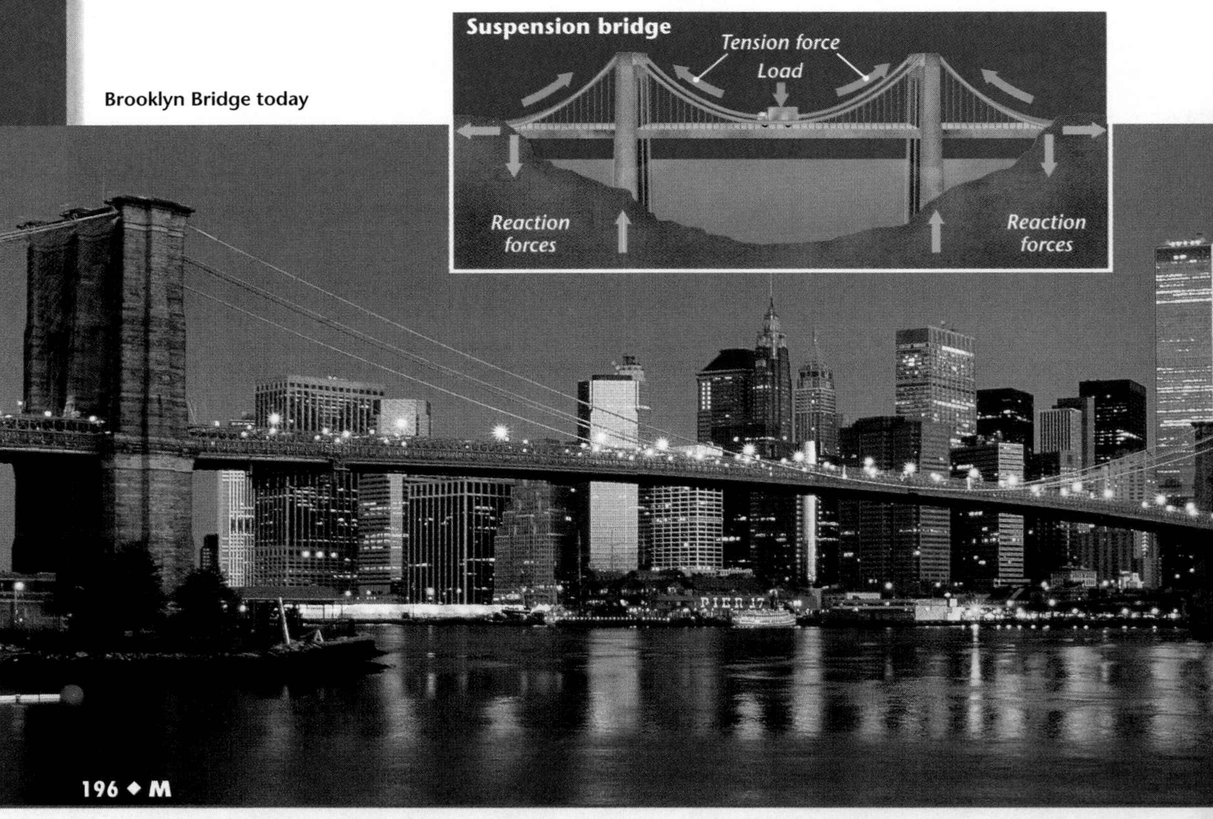

Brooklyn Bridge today

Background

Facts and Figures Iron, steel, and other metals are more flexible than stone but they are also very strong in tension. So it is possible to design a bridge that takes advantage of the strength of wire in tension to build higher and longer bridges than would be practical with stone (or the modern equivalent of stone, concrete). Suspension bridges can span greater distances than beam or arch bridges because the strong steel cables transfer force to the tall towers. The towers can be built high enough to allow huge ocean liners to sail underneath. The tallest masted ships could still sail beneath the Brooklyn Bridge.

Each of the smaller cables that hang from the four main cables of the Brooklyn Bridge is made up of seven bundles of seven steel wires.

A Great Engineering Feat

When it opened in 1883, the Brooklyn Bridge was the longest suspension bridge in the world—one half span longer than any other. It united New York City by joining Brooklyn and Manhattan. Yet when the idea was first proposed, people said it couldn't done.

In the mid-1800s, many people from Brooklyn had jobs across the East River in Manhattan. But the only way to get there was by ferry. Fierce ocean tides, stormy weather, and ice chunks in winter could make the journey risky. In 1868 John Augustus Roebling, a German immigrant engineer, was hired to build a bridge.

An engineering genius, Roebling designed a suspension bridge using four cables stretched over two giant granite towers. Roebling was the first engineer to design bridge cables of strong, flexible steel instead of cast iron.

Each cable, about 16 inches in diameter, would contain nearly 5,300 wires. After the cables were in place, 1,500 smaller suspension cables would be attached to the main cables to support the roadway. It's not surprising that people didn't believe that it could be done.

It was impossible to lift heavy cables over the towers. So for each cable, builders had to reel wire back and forth across the East River—3,515 miles of wire for each cable! To "spin the cables" John Roebling invented a traveling wheel that could carry the wire in a continuous loop, from one side of the river over the towers to the other side and back. It's an invention that is still used today.

Science Activity

Work in groups to make a suspension bridge, using 2 chairs, a wooden plank, rope, and some books.

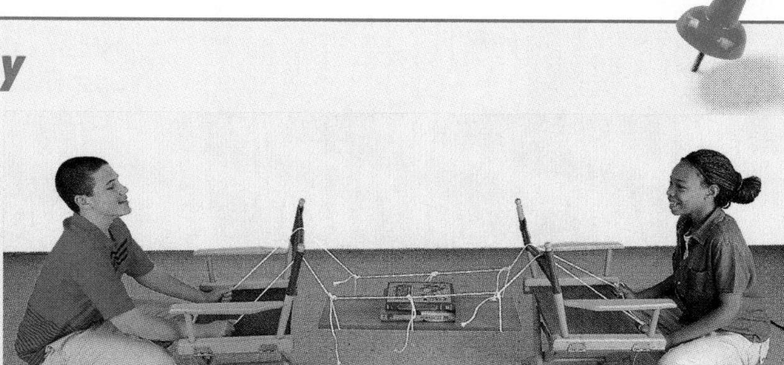

- Place 2 chairs back to back and stretch 2 ropes over the backs of the chairs. Hold the ropes at both ends.
- Tie 3 pieces of rope to the longer ropes. Place the plank through the loops.
- Have students hold the ropes tightly at each end. Load books on top of the plank to see how much it will hold.

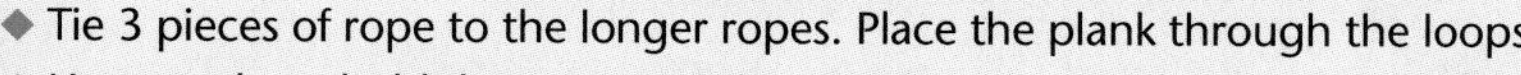

Why is it important to anchor the ropes tightly at each end?

Background

History John Roebling never lived to see his bridge reach completion. On June 28, 1869, he was inspecting the site of a bridge tower while standing on a ferry slip. Pilings on the slip shifted, and Roebling's foot was crushed between two pilings. Tetanus developed and Roebling was dead within a month. Washington Roebling, his son, took over the construction.

Some years later, Washington Roebling became disabled by caisson disease ("the bends"). In those days, the cause of the disease was not understood. Partly paralyzed, Washington supervised construction by telescope from his bedroom window in Brooklyn Heights.

- Ask: **In the 1990s, the record for the world's longest suspension bridge span has been exceeded several times. Do you think the record will continue to be broken?** *(Answers may vary. Sample: No; there must be some limit to how much weight a single span can support.)* If possible, find a civil engineer to discuss bridge design with the class.
- Point out that the Brooklyn Bridge was successfully built even though many people believed it was impossible. Ask students to suggest inventions or achievements that some people today feel are impossible but that are likely to be achieved in the future.
- Point out that the cranes you see on construction sites today did not exist when the Brooklyn Bridge was being built.

Science Activity

ACTIVITY

Materials *2 chairs, thin rope, wooden plank about 50 cm × 20 cm × 1 cm, several books for load*
Time 20 minutes

Have two students in each group hold the ends of the ropes while the other group members attach the vertical ropes and place the plank. Since the load is transferred to tension in the ropes, they must be anchored or held securely.

To extend this activity, invite students to experiment with changing the distance between the chairs or changing where students attach the vertical ropes.

Have students demonstrate for themselves that their suspension bridge can sway slightly in wind without damage.

Teaching Resources The following worksheets correlate with this page: Build an Arch Bridge, page 174; Move That Bridge!, page 175; and How Rainbow Bridge was Formed, page 176.

3 Assess

Activity Assessment

Ask students what to describe the function of each part of their "chair bridge" and what structure in the Brooklyn Bridge performs the same function.

Social Studies

2 Facilitate

- Ask students: **How might bridge workers die?** *(Answers may vary. Sample: falling from the bridge)* Explain that several bridge workers suffered from caisson disease ('the bends"), which is usually associated with divers. The caissons had to be pressurized to prevent water from flowing in. When workers ascended to the surface too quickly, bubbles of nitrogen gas sometimes formed in the blood stream, causing excruciating pain or permanent paralysis.
- Ask students: **Why did Roebling have workers twist the wires together?** *(Twisting the strands of wire together gave them the strength of a single thick wire while still remaining flexible.)*

Social Studies Activity

Assign each group a different kind of famous bridge to research (for example, suspension, arch, beam). Tell students to begin by planning what questions each student will be responsible for researching. Suggest that students locate information about the bridge they are researching by reading about the city in which it is located.

Events connected to the bridge may be famous accidents, annual celebrations, or significant historical dates. Schedule time for students to make their presentations to the class.

Teaching Resources The following worksheets correlate with this page: Pros and Cons, page 177; Comparing Bridges, page 178; and Find the Bridges, page 179.

3 Assess

Activity Assessment

Evaluate students' research procedures, particularly note-taking. Make sure students' presentations include the points on the student page.

Social Studies

Against All Odds

The dedication of the Roebling family—John (left), Washington (center), and Emily (right)—ensured the success of the Brooklyn Bridge.

When John Roebling was hired in 1868 to build the Brooklyn Bridge, he was already an experienced suspension bridge engineer. He had plans for the bridge that he'd been working on since 1855.

But before bridge construction even began in 1869, John Roebling died in a bridge-related accident. Fortunately, he had worked out his bridge design to the last detail. His son, Colonel Washington Roebling, who was also a skilled engineer, dedicated himself to carrying out his father's plans.

The construction dragged on for 14 years and cost nearly 30 lives. Colonel Roebling himself became so disabled that he was forced to direct construction from his home. Using binoculars, Colonel Roebling followed every detail. His remarkable, energetic wife, Emily Warren Roebling, learned enough engineering principles to deliver and explain his orders to the workers.

Workers building the Brooklyn Bridge

As soon as the giant towers were up, workers unrolled the steel wire back and forth across the towers to weave the cables. The next step was to twist the wires together. But the workmen were terrified of hanging so high on the bridge and refused to work. Finally, Frank Farrington, the chief mechanic, crossed the river on a small chair dangling from a wheel that ran across an overhead line. Farrington completed his journey to the roar of the crowd. This feat was billed as the greatest trapeze act of all time. Somewhat reassured, the builders returned to work. But it took two more years to string the cables. The bridge was one of the greatest engineering achievements of its time.

In the end, the Brooklyn Bridge project succeeded only because of the determination and sacrifices of the Roebling family. It became the model for hundreds of other suspension bridges.

Social Studies Activity

How do you think the Brooklyn Bridge changed the lives of New Yorkers? In groups, research the history of another famous bridge. Present your findings to your class along with drawings and photos. Find out

- when and why the bridge was built
- the type of bridge
- how peoples' lives changed after it was built—include effects on trade, travel, and population
- how landforms affected the bridge building
- events connected to the bridge

Background

Integrating Science and Technology
Roebling designed his bridge using steel wire instead of the iron wire that had traditionally been used. Steel wire was a relatively new material then and had not yet proven itself. The wire for the Brooklyn Bridge was supplied by a contractor. After the workers had begun reeling the wire to make cables, they discovered that the wire did not match the bid specifications. The contractor had committed fraud by substituting cheaper and weaker wire. Fortunately, Roebling initially designed the bridge using steel wire that would be six times stronger than necessary. The cheaper wire that had been substituted was still five times stronger than necessary so the weaker wire remained in the bridge.

The New York Times *May 25, 1883*

Two Great Cities United

This historic painting shows fireworks at the opening of the Brooklyn Bridge in 1883.

The Brooklyn bridge was successfully opened yesterday. The pleasant weather brought visitors by the thousands from all around. Spectators were packed in masses through which it was almost impossible to pass, and those who had tickets to attend the ceremonies had hard work to reach the bridge. Every available house-top and window was filled, and an adventurous party occupied a tall telegraph pole. It required the utmost efforts of the police to keep clear the necessary space.

After the exercises at the bridge were completed the Brooklyn procession was immediately re-formed and the march was taken up to Col. Roebling's residence. From the back study on the second floor of his house Col. Roebling had watched through his telescope the procession as it proceeded along from the New-York side until the Brooklyn tower was reached. Mrs. Roebling received at her husband's side and accepted her share of the honors of the bridge.

For blocks and blocks on either side of the bridge there was scarcely a foot of room to spare. Many persons crossed and re-crossed the river on the ferry boats, and in that way watched the display. Almost every ship along the river front was converted into a grand stand.

The final ceremonies of the opening of the great bridge began at eight o'clock, when the first rocket was sent from the center of the great structure, and ended at 9 o'clock, when a flight of 500 rockets illuminated the sky. The river-front was one blaze of light, and on the yachts and smaller vessels blue fires were burning and illuminating dark waters around them.

Language Arts Activity

A reporter's goal is to inform and entertain the reader. Using a catchy opening line draws interest. Then the reader wants to know the facts—what, who, where, when, why, and how (5 Ws and H).

You are a school reporter. Write about the opening of a bridge in your area. It could be a highway overpass or a bridge over water, a valley, or railroad tracks.

- Include some of the 5 Ws and H.
- Add interesting details and descriptions.

Background

Integrating Science and Technology In the summer of 1940, a new bridge was built over the narrows of Puget Sound, uniting two other cities, Tacoma and Seattle. Four months later, on November 7, 1940, the bridge collapsed. The aerodynamic forces of wind on bridges was not well understood in 1940. The bridge was simply too flexible. It was also built with plate girders, which provided a flat, eight foot high wall of steel on which the wind could blow. The combination proved disastrous when a 42 mile an hour wind set up torsional vibrations of the bridge that eventually tore the suspenders, causing the bridge to collapse.

When the bridge was rebuilt, open trusses were used instead of plate girders. The trusses are stiffer than girders and the wind can blow through the trusses, thus reducing the force exerted by the wind on the bridge.

Language Arts

2 Facilitate

- Ask: **Why was every house-top and window filled?** *(People wanted to see the procession and the fireworks.)* **Why was the bridge opening such a huge event?** *(Answers may vary. Samples: the bridge had taken years to build; many people believed it could never be built)*
- Clarify that the word party in the first paragraph can mean one person. Students may imagine that a whole group of people climbed to the top of a telegraph pole.
- To extend this exploration, have students think about where in or near your town they think a bridge would be useful. Have students consider what type of bridge would be most suitable for the location.

Language Arts Activity

Students were probably not present when a bridge was opened, so have them think of a bridge in or near your town. Then have them imagine how the town was different before the bridge was built. Students could talk to long-term residents to find out what public opinion was during the construction and how town life changed as a result. Or you may wish to have students write about another civic event. Have pairs of students check each other's work to ensure that the main facts are included in the article.

Teaching Resources The following worksheets correlate with this page: Letter to the Editor, page 180; Many Kinds of Bridges, page 181; and A Poem Written on a Bridge, page 182.

3 Assess

Activity Assessment

Make sure students' writing is in the form of a newspaper article. Check that the major facts (5 Ws and H) are included. Students' stories should be informative but also interesting.

Mathematics

2 Facilitate

- To extend this exploration, cut four 10-cm × 1-cm strips of heavy cardboard. Punch a hole 0.5-cm from the end of each strip. Attach the strips end-to-end with brads to form a closed figure. Show the students how the shape of the figure can be altered. Now remove one of the strips so that a triangle is formed. Show the students how the triangle has a fixed shape. Ask students which shape would be better to use in bridge supports. *(The triangle, because of its fixed shape.)*

Math Activity

Urge students to record their answers slowly and carefully. They can easily write down the wrong letters if they work too hastily.

Teaching Resources The following worksheets correlate with this page: Graphing Bridge Data, page 183; and Konigsberg Bridge Problem, pages 184-185.

3 Assess

Activity Assessment

1. AE and IF are parallel. AI, BH, CG, and DF are parallel to each other. BG and CF are parallel. CH, DG, and EF are parallel.
2. All pairs of lines that are not parallel intersect.
3. rectangle
4. triangle
5. obtuse
6. acute
7. right triangle; It has a 90° angle.
8. A square does not have a rigid shape.

Mathematics

Bridge Geometry

As railroad traffic increased in the 1800s, truss bridges became popular. Designed with thin vertical and diagonal supports to add strength, truss bridges were really reinforced beam bridge structures. Many of the early wood truss bridges couldn't support the trains that rumbled over them. Cast iron and steel trusses soon replaced wood trusses.

Using basic triangular structures, engineers went to work on more scientific truss bridge designs. The accuracy of the design is crucial to handling the stress from heavy train loads and constant vibrations. As in all bridge structures, each steel piece has to be measured and fitted accurately—including widths, lengths, angles, and points of intersection and attachment.

Forces Acting on Geometric Shapes

A **basic triangle** in a truss bridge is strong because its shape cannot be distorted.

A **triangle in a truss bridge** can support a heavy load with its relatively small weight.

A **square or rectangle** is not as strong as a triangle.

It can collapse into a **parallelogram** under a heavy load.

Look closely at the truss patterns. In drawing bridge plans, engineers use geometric shapes.

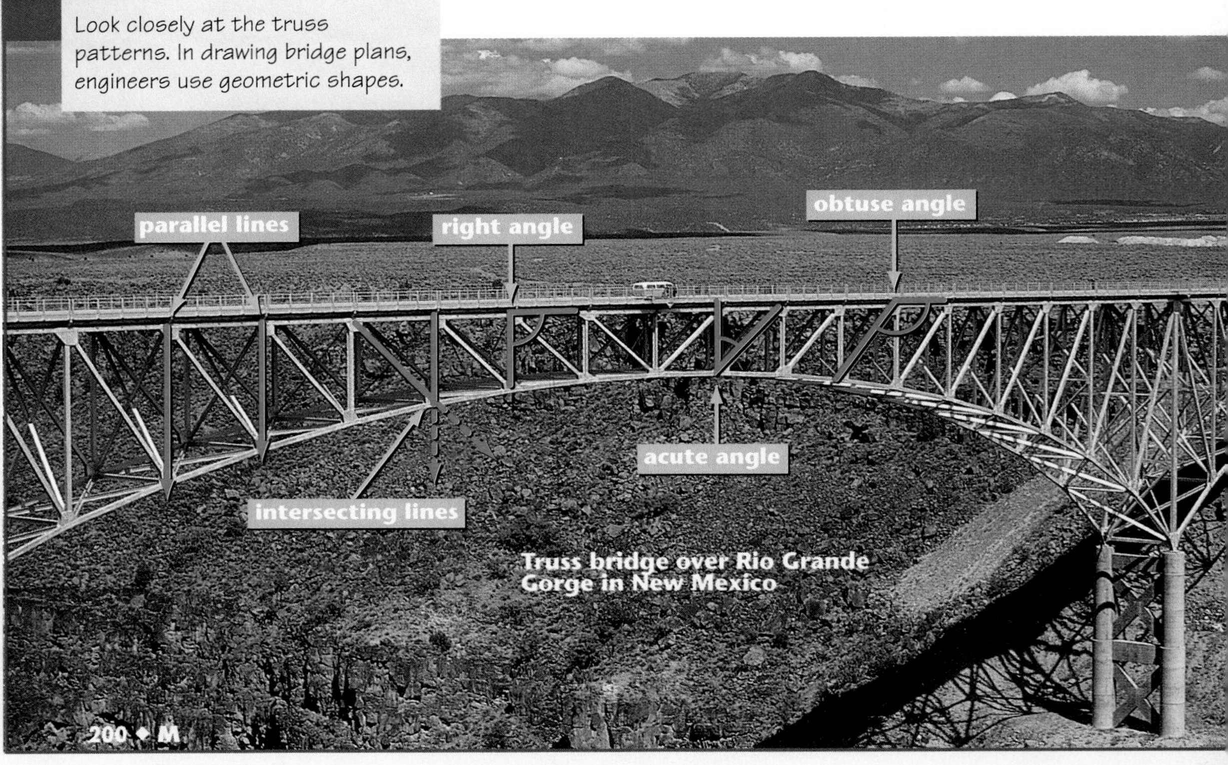

Truss bridge over Rio Grande Gorge in New Mexico

Background

Integrating Science and Technology When engineers have distances to measure that cannot be measured directly, they use trigonometry. Trigonometry is a branch of mathematics that deals with relationships between the sides and angles of triangles. A distance can be measured by representing it with one side of a triangle, measuring other sides or angles in the triangle, and then using trigonometric formulas to calculate the length of the side to be measured. Trigonometry has many applications in engineering, for example, studying vibrations in a building or a bridge.

Math Activity

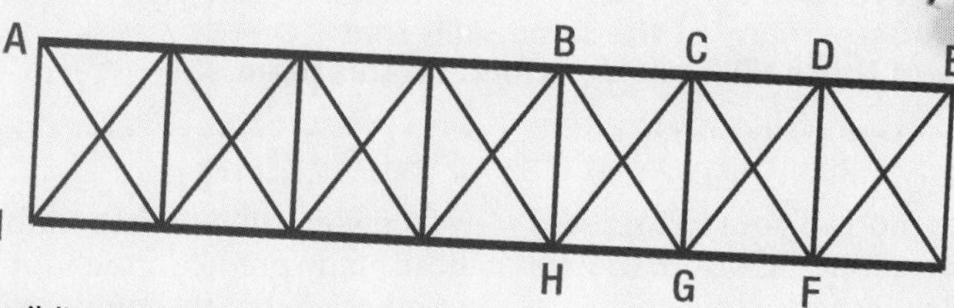

The chief building engineer has asked you to draw up exact plans for a new truss bridge. How well will you do as an assistant? You will soon find out by answering these questions:

1. Which lines are parallel?
2. Which lines intersect?
3. What kind of figure is formed by ABHI?
4. What kind of figure is formed by HCF?
5. What kind of angle is BGF—obtuse or right?
6. What kind of angle is CHG?
7. What kind of triangle is BHG? What makes it this kind of triangle?
8. Why is a triangle stronger than a square?

Tie It Together

Bridge the Gap

Work in small groups to build a model of a bridge out of a box of spaghetti and a roll of masking tape. Meet as a group to choose the type of bridge you will build. Each bridge should be strong enough to hold a brick. You can build—

- a beam bridge
- a truss bridge
- an arch bridge
- a suspension bridge (This one is challenging.)

After drawing a sketch of the bridge design, assign jobs for each team member. Then

- decide how long the bridge span will be
- measure and cut the materials
- build the roadway first for beam, truss, and suspension bridges
- build the arch first in an arch bridge

When your bridge is complete, display it in the classroom. Test the strength of each bridge by placing a brick on the roadway. Discuss the difference in bridge structures. Determine which bridge design is the strongest.

Tie It Together

Time 2 class periods (1 period for planning and building; 1 period for finishing building, testing the design, examining other groups' work, and cleaning up) You may want to add an extra day so students can test whether their bridges could stay standing overnight.

Tips Divide the class into four groups. Assign each group a type of bridge.

- Make sure students understand that because their bridges are different designs, some groups will take longer than others. Students should not try to race.
- Have students spend 15 minutes planning their designs before you hand out the building materials. Urge students to plan first, not begin building by trial and error.
- You may wish to line each work area with newspaper to make cleanup easier.
- If the bridges will be sitting overnight, have students work in parts of the room where their constructions may be left.
- To discourage groups from using excessive amounts of masking tape to reinforce the spaghetti, you may wish to give each group a limited amount of tape rather than an entire roll.
- Groups making suspension bridges may need the most help. Suggest that they make the towers from spaghetti and the cables from rolled lengths of tape.

Extend As an alternative to building four different types of bridges, have all groups build the same type of bridge. To encourage them to use their materials as efficiently as possible, assign costs to all materials (such as \$1 million for each length of spaghetti and \$5 million for each meter of masking tape). Assign a volunteer to "sell" materials and keep track of how much money each group spends on materials.

READING STRATEGIES

Further Reading Oxlade, Chris, *Bridges*, Raintree/Steck Vaughn, 1997.
Mann, Elizabeth B. and Alan Witschonke, *The Brooklyn Bridge: A Wonders of the World Book*, Mikaya Press, 1996.

Developing scientific thinking in students is important for a solid science education. To learn how to think scientifically, students need frequent opportunities to practice science process skills, critical thinking skills, as well as other skills that support scientific inquiry. The *Science Explorer* Skills Handbook introduces the following key science skills:

- Science Process Skills
- SI Measuring Skills
- Skills for Conducting a Scientific Investigation
- Critical Thinking Skills
- Information Organizing Skills
- Data Table and Graphing Skills

The Skills Handbook is designed as a reference for students to use whenever they need to review a science skill. You can use the activities provided in the Skills Handbook to teach or reinforce the skills.

Think Like a Scientist

Observing

Before students look at the photograph, remind them that an observation is only what they can see, hear, smell, taste, or feel. Ask: **Which senses will you use to make observations from this photograph?** *(Sight is the only sense that can be used to make observations from the photograph.)* **What are some observations you can make from the photograph?** *(Answers may vary. Sample answers: The boy is wearing sneakers, sport socks, shorts, and a tee shirt; the boy is sitting in the grass holding something blue against his knee; the boy is looking at his knee; there is a soccer ball laying beside the boy.)* List the observations on the chalkboard. If students make any inferences or predictions about the boy at this point, ask: **Can you be sure your statement is factual and accurate from just observing the photograph?** Help students understand how observations differ from inferences and predictions.

Inferring

Review students' observations from the photograph. Then ask: **What inferences can you make from your observations?** *(Students may say that the boy hurt his knee playing soccer and is holding a coldpack against his injured knee.)* **What experience or knowledge helped you make this inference?** *(Students may have experienced knee injuries from playing soccer, and they may be familiar with coldpacks like the one the boy is using.)* **Can anyone suggest another possible explanation for these observations?** *(Answers may vary. Sample answer: The boy hurt his knee jogging, and he just happened to sit beside a soccer ball his sister left in the yard.)* **How can you find out whether an inference is correct?** *(by further investigation)*

Predicting

After coming to some consensus about the inference that the boy hurt his knee, encourage students to make predictions about what will happen next. *(Students' predictions may vary. Sample answers: The boy will go to the doctor. A friend will help the boy home. The boy will get up and continue playing soccer.)*

Think Like a Scientist

Although you may not know it, you think like a scientist every day. Whenever you ask a question and explore possible answers, you use many of the same skills that scientists do. Some of these skills are described on this page.

Observing

When you use one or more of your five senses to gather information about the world, you are **observing.** Hearing a dog bark, counting twelve green seeds, and smelling smoke are all observations. To increase the power of their senses, scientists sometimes use microscopes, telescopes, or other instruments that help them make more detailed observations.

An observation must be factual and accurate—an exact report of what your senses detect. It is important to keep careful records of your observations in science class by writing or drawing in a notebook. The information collected through observations is called evidence, or data.

Inferring

When you explain or interpret an observation, you are **inferring,** or making an inference. For example, if you hear your dog barking, you may infer that someone is at your front door. To make this inference, you combine the evidence—the barking dog—and your experience or knowledge—you know that your dog barks when strangers approach—to reach a logical conclusion.

Notice that an inference is not a fact; it is only one of many possible explanations for an observation. For example, your dog may be barking because it wants to go for a walk. An inference may turn out to be incorrect even if it is based on accurate observations and logical reasoning. The only way to find out if an inference is correct is to investigate further.

Predicting

When you listen to the weather forecast, you hear many predictions about the next day's weather—what the temperature will be, whether it will rain, and how windy it will be. Weather forecasters use observations and knowledge of weather patterns to predict the weather. The skill of **predicting** involves making an inference about a future event based on current evidence or past experience.

Because a prediction is an inference, it may prove to be false. In science class, you can test some of your predictions by doing experiments. For example, suppose you predict that larger paper airplanes can fly farther than smaller airplanes. How could you test your prediction?

Use the photograph to answer the questions below.

Observing Look closely at the photograph. List at least three observations.

Inferring Use your observations to make an inference about what has happened. What experience or knowledge did you use to make the inference?

Predicting Predict what will happen next. On what evidence or experience do you base your prediction?

Classifying

Could you imagine searching for a book in the library if the books were shelved in no particular order? Your trip to the library would be an all-day event! Luckily, librarians group together books on similar topics or by the same author. Grouping together items that are alike in some way is called **classifying.** You can classify items in many ways: by size, by shape, by use, and by other important characteristics.

Like librarians, scientists use the skill of classifying to organize information and objects. When things are sorted into groups, the relationships among them become easier to understand.

ACTIVITY

Classify the objects in the photograph into two groups based on any characteristic you choose. Then use another characteristic to classify the objects into three groups.

SKILLS HANDBOOK

ACTIVITY

This student is using a model to demonstrate what causes day and night on Earth. What do the flashlight and the tennis ball in the model represent?

Making Models

Have you ever drawn a picture to help someone understand what you were saying? Such a drawing is one type of model. A model is a picture, diagram, computer image, or other representation of a complex object or process. **Making models** helps people understand things that they cannot observe directly.

Scientists often use models to represent things that are either very large or very small, such as the planets in the solar system, or the parts of a cell. Such models are physical models—drawings or three-dimensional structures that look like the real thing. Other models are mental models—mathematical equations or words that describe how something works.

Communicating

Whenever you talk on the phone, write a letter, or listen to your teacher at school, you are communicating. **Communicating** is the process of sharing ideas and information with other people. Communicating effectively requires many skills, including writing, reading, speaking, listening, and making models.

Scientists communicate to share results, information, and opinions. Scientists often communicate about their work in journals, over the telephone, in letters, and on the Internet. They also attend scientific meetings where they share their ideas with one another in person.

ACTIVITY

On a sheet of paper, write out clear, detailed directions for tying your shoe. Then exchange directions with a partner. Follow your partner's directions exactly. How successful were you at tying your shoe? How could your partner have communicated more clearly?

On what did you base your prediction? *(Scientific predictions are based on knowledge and experience.)* Point out that in science, predictions can often be tested with experiments.

Classifying

ACTIVITY

Encourage students to think of other common things that are classified. Then ask: **What things at home are classified?** *(Clothing might be classified by placing it in different dresser drawers; glasses, plates, and silverware are grouped in different parts of the kitchen; screws, nuts, bolts, washers, and nails might be separated into small containers.)* **What are some things that scientists classify?** *(Scientists classify many things they study, including organisms, geological features and processes, and kinds of machines.)* After students have classified the different fruits in the photograph, have them share their criteria for classifying them. *(Some characteristics students might use include shape, color, size, and where they are grown.)*

Making Models

ACTIVITY

Ask students: **What are some models you have used to study science?** *(Students may have used human anatomical models, solar system models, maps, stream tables.)* **How did these models help you?** *(Models can help you learn about things that are difficult to study, either because they are too big, too small, or complex.)* Be sure students understand that a model does not have to be three-dimensional. For example, a map in a textbook is a model. Ask: **What do the flashlight and tennis ball represent?** *(The flashlight represents the sun, and the ball represents Earth.)* **What quality of each item makes this a good model?** *(The flashlight gives off light, and the ball is round and can be rotated by the student.)*

Communicating

ACTIVITY

Challenge students to identify the methods of communication they've used today. Then ask: **How is the way you communicate with a friend similar to and different from the way scientists communicate about their work to other scientists?** *(Both may communicate using various methods, but scientists must be very detailed and precise, whereas communication between friends may be less detailed and precise.)* Encourage students to communicate like a scientist as they carry out the activity. *(Students' directions should be detailed and precise enough for another person to successfully follow.)*

Making Measurements

Measuring in SI

Review SI units in class with students. Begin by providing metric rulers, graduated cylinders, balances, and Celsius thermometers. Use these tools to reinforce that the meter is the unit of length, the liter is the unit of volume, the gram is the unit of mass, and the degree Celsius is the unit for temperature. Ask: **If you want to measure the length and width of your classroom, which SI unit would you use?** *(meter)* **Which unit would you use to measure the amount of matter in your textbook?** *(gram)* **Which would you use to measure how much water a drinking glass holds?** *(liter)* **When would you use the Celsius scale?** *(To measure the temperature of something)* Then use the measuring equipment to review SI prefixes. For example, ask: **What are the smallest units on the metric ruler?** *(millimeters)* **How many millimeters are there in 1 cm?** *(10 mm)* **How many in 10 cm?** *(100 mm)* **How many centimeters are there in 1 m?** *(100 cm)* **What does 1,000 m equal?** *(1 km)*

Length ACTIVITY *(Students should state that the shell is 4.6 centimeters, or 46 millimeters, long.)* If students need more practice measuring length, have them use meter sticks and metric rulers to measure various objects in the classroom.

Liquid Volume ACTIVITY *(Students should state that the volume of water in the graduated cylinder is 62 milliliters.)* If students need more practice measuring liquid volume, have them use a graduated cylinder to measure different volumes of water.

Making Measurements

When scientists make observations, it is not sufficient to say that something is "big" or "heavy." Instead, scientists use instruments to measure just how big or heavy an object is. By measuring, scientists can express their observations more precisely and communicate more information about what they observe.

Measuring in SI

The standard system of measurement used by scientists around the world is known as the International System of Units, which is abbreviated as SI (in French, *Système International d'Unités*). SI units are easy to use because they are based on multiples of 10. Each unit is ten times larger than the next smallest unit and one tenth the size of the next largest unit. The table lists the prefixes used to name the most common SI units.

Common SI Prefixes

Prefix	Symbol	Meaning
kilo-	k	1,000
hecto-	h	100
deka-	da	10
deci-	d	0.1 (one tenth)
centi-	c	0.01 (one hundredth)
milli-	m	0.001 (one thousandth)

Length To measure length, or the distance between two points, the unit of measure is the **meter (m).** One meter is the approximate distance from the floor to a doorknob. Long distances, such as the distance between two cities, are measured in kilometers (km). Small lengths are measured in centimeters (cm) or millimeters (mm). Scientists use metric rulers and meter sticks to measure length.

Common Conversions

1 km = 1,000 m
1 m = 100 cm
1 m = 1,000 mm
1 cm = 10 mm

ACTIVITY

The larger lines on the metric ruler in the picture show centimeter divisions, while the smaller, unnumbered lines show millimeter divisions. How many centimeters long is the shell? How many millimeters long is it?

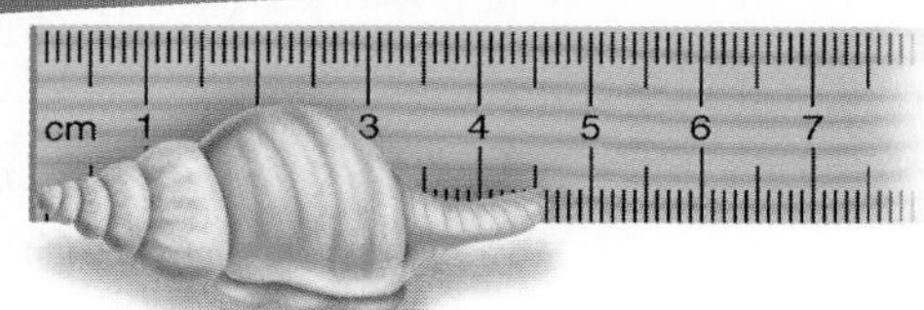

Liquid Volume To measure the volume of a liquid, or the amount of space it takes up, you will use a unit of measure known as the **liter (L).** One liter is the approximate volume of a medium-sized carton of milk. Smaller volumes are measured in milliliters (mL). Scientists use graduated cylinders to measure liquid volume.

Common Conversion

1 L = 1,000 mL

ACTIVITY

The graduated cylinder in the picture is marked in milliliter divisions. Notice that the water in the cylinder has a curved surface. This curved surface is called the *meniscus*. To measure the volume, you must read the level at the lowest point of the meniscus. What is the volume of water in this graduated cylinder?

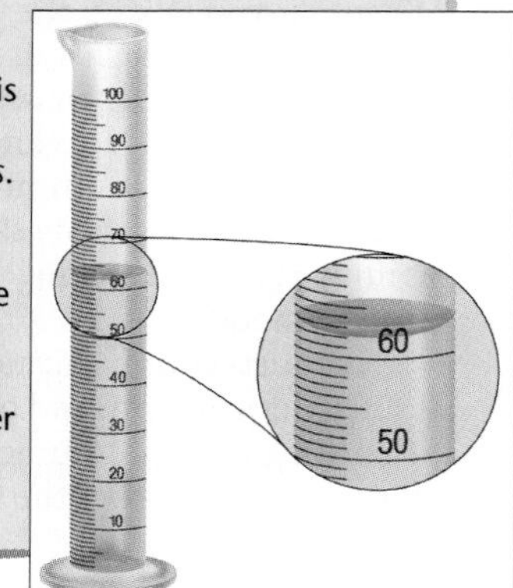

Mass To measure mass, or the amount of matter in an object, you will use a unit of measure known as the **gram (g)**. One gram is approximately the mass of a paper clip. Larger masses are measured in kilograms (kg). Scientists use a balance to find the mass of an object.

Common Conversion
1 kg = 1,000 g

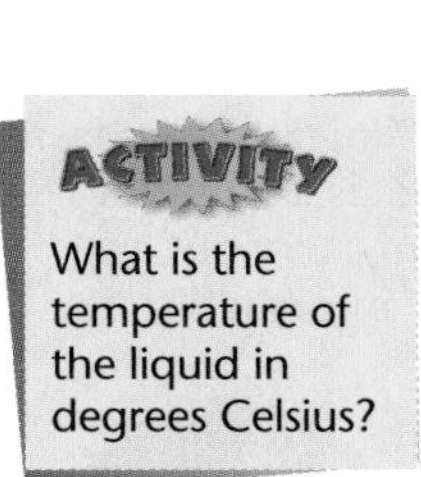

ACTIVITY

The electronic balance displays the mass of an apple in kilograms. What is the mass of the apple? Suppose a recipe for applesauce called for one kilogram of apples. About how many apples would you need?

Temperature
To measure the temperature of a substance, you will use the **Celsius scale**. Temperature is measured in degrees Celsius (°C) using a Celsius thermometer. Water freezes at 0°C and boils at 100°C.

ACTIVITY

What is the temperature of the liquid in degrees Celsius?

Converting SI Units

To use the SI system, you must know how to convert between units. Converting from one unit to another involves the skill of **calculating**, or using mathematical operations. Converting between SI units is similar to converting between dollars and dimes because both systems are based on multiples of ten.

Suppose you want to convert a length of 80 centimeters to meters. Follow these steps to convert between units.

1. Begin by writing down the measurement you want to convert—in this example, 80 centimeters.
2. Write a conversion factor that represents the relationship between the two units you are converting. In this example, the relationship is *1 meter = 100 centimeters.* Write this conversion factor as a fraction, making sure to place the units you are converting from (centimeters, in this example) in the denominator.
3. Multiply the measurement you want to convert by the fraction. When you do this, the units in the first measurement will cancel out with the units in the denominator. Your answer will be in the units you are converting to (meters, in this example).

Example

80 centimeters = __?__ meters

$$80 \text{ cent\cancel{im}eters} \times \frac{1 \text{ meter}}{100 \text{ cent\cancel{im}eters}} = \frac{80 \text{ meters}}{100}$$

$$= 0.8 \text{ meters}$$

ACTIVITY

Convert between the following units.

1. 600 millimeters = _?_ meters
2. 0.35 liters = _?_ milliliters
3. 1,050 grams = _?_ kilograms

SKILLS HANDBOOK

Mass *(Students should state that the mass of the apple is 0.1 kilograms. They would need 10 apples to make 1 kilogram.)* If students need practice determining mass, have them use a balance to determine the mass of various common objects, such as coins, paper clips, and books.

Temperature *(Students should state that the temperature of the liquid is 35°C.)* If students need practice measuring temperature, have them use a Celsius thermometer to measure the temperature of various water samples.

Converting SI Units

ACTIVITY

Review the steps for converting SI units and work through the example with students. Then ask: **How many millimeters are in 80 centimeters?** *(Students should follow the steps to calculate that 80 centimeters is equal to 800 millimeters.)*

Have students do the conversion problems in the activity. *(**1.** 600 millimeters = 0.6 meters; **2.** 0.35 liters = 350 milliliters; **3.** 1,050 grams = 1.05 kilograms)* If students need more practice converting SI units, have students make up conversion problems and trade with a partner.

Conducting a Scientific Investigation

Posing Questions

Before students do the activity on the next page, walk them through the steps of a typical scientific investigation. Begin by asking: **Why is a scientific question important to a scientific investigation?** *(It is the reason for conducting a scientific investigation and how every investigation begins.)* **What is the scientific question in the activity at the bottom of the next page?** *(Is a ball's bounce affected by the height from which it is dropped?)*

Developing a Hypothesis

Emphasize that a hypothesis is a prediction about the outcome of a scientific investigation, but it is *not* a guess. Ask: **On what information do scientists base their hypotheses?** *(Their observations and previous knowledge or experience)* Point out that a hypothesis does not always turn out to be correct. Ask: **In that case, do you think the scientist wasted his or her time? Explain your answer.** *(No, because the scientist probably learned from the investigation and maybe could develop another hypothesis that could be supported.)*

Designing an Experiment

Have a volunteer read the Experimental Procedure in the box. Then call on students to identify the manipulated variable *(amount of salt added to water)*, the variables that are kept constant *(amount and starting temperature of water, placing containers in freezer)*, the responding variable *(time it takes water to freeze)*, and the control *(Container 3)*.

Ask: **How might the experiment be affected if Container 1 had only 100 mL of water?** *(It wouldn't be a fair comparison with the containers that have more water.)* **What if Container 3 was not included in the experiment?** *(You wouldn't have anything to compare the other two containers to know if their freezing times were faster or slower than normal.)* Help students understand the importance of keeping all variables constant except the manipulated variable. Also be sure they understand the role of the control. Then ask: **What operational definition is used in this experiment?** *("Frozen" means the time at which a wooden stick can no longer move in a container.)*

Conducting a Scientific Investigation

In some ways, scientists are like detectives, piecing together clues to learn about a process or event. One way that scientists gather clues is by carrying out experiments. An experiment tests an idea in a careful, orderly manner. Although all experiments do not follow the same steps in the same order, many follow a pattern similar to the one described here.

Posing Questions

Experiments begin by asking a scientific question. A scientific question is one that can be answered by gathering evidence. For example, the question "Which freezes faster—fresh water or salt water?" is a scientific question because you can carry out an investigation and gather information to answer the question.

Developing a Hypothesis

The next step is to form a hypothesis. A **hypothesis** is a prediction about the outcome of the experiment. Like all predictions, hypotheses are based on your observations and previous knowledge or experience. But, unlike many predictions, a hypothesis must be something that can be tested. A properly worded hypothesis should take the form of an *If*... *then*... statement. For example, a hypothesis might be *"If I add salt to fresh water, then the water will take longer to freeze."* A hypothesis worded this way serves as a rough outline of the experiment you should perform.

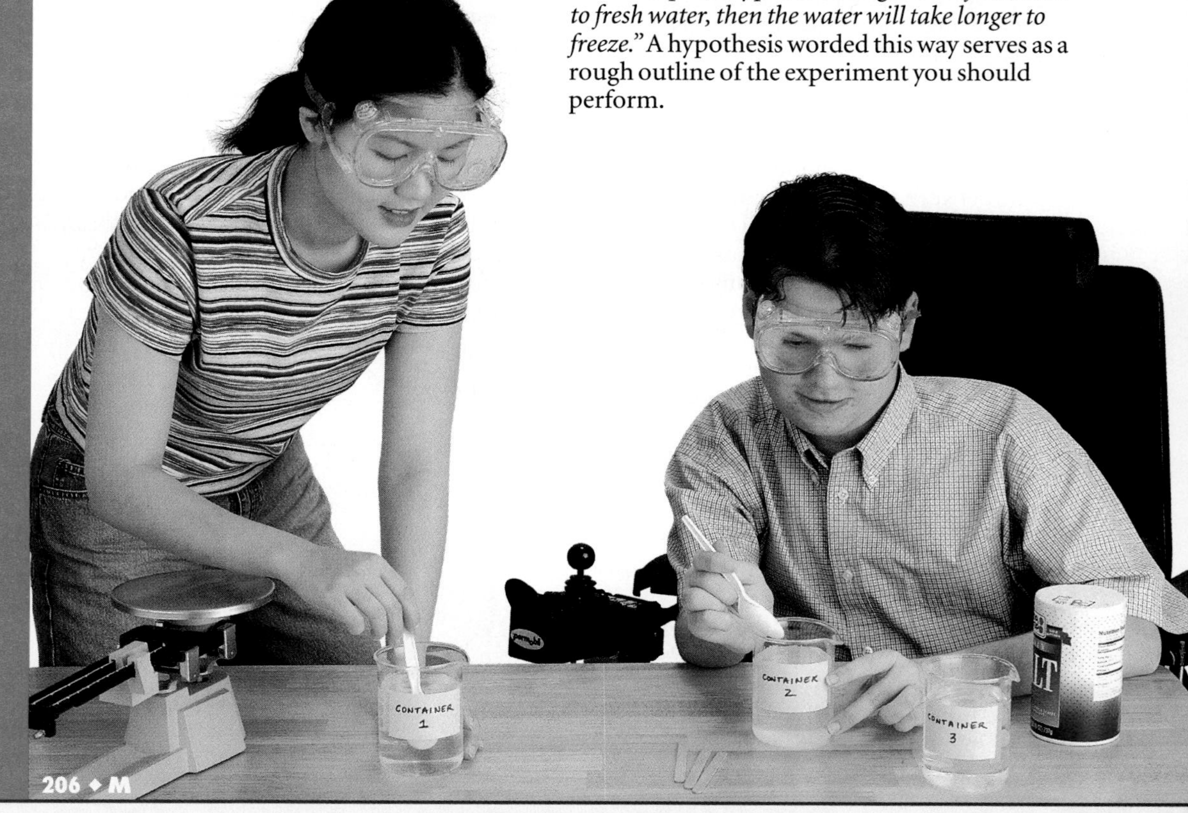

Designing an Experiment

Next you need to plan a way to test your hypothesis. Your plan should be written out as a step-by-step procedure and should describe the observations or measurements you will make.

Two important steps involved in designing an experiment are controlling variables and forming operational definitions.

Controlling Variables In a well-designed experiment, you need to keep all variables the same except for one. A **variable** is any factor that can change in an experiment. The factor that you change is called the **manipulated variable.** In this experiment, the manipulated variable is the amount of salt added to the water. Other factors, such as the amount of water or the starting temperature, are kept constant.

The factor that changes as a result of the manipulated variable is called the responding variable. The **responding variable** is what you measure or observe to obtain your results. In this experiment, the responding variable is how long the water takes to freeze.

An experiment in which all factors except one are kept constant is a **controlled experiment.** Most controlled experiments include a test called the control. In this experiment, Container 3 is the control. Because no salt is added to Container 3, you can compare the results from the other containers to it. Any difference in results must be due to the addition of salt alone.

Forming Operational Definitions
Another important aspect of a well-designed experiment is having clear operational definitions. An **operational definition** is a statement that describes how a particular variable is to be measured or how a term is to be defined. For example, in this experiment, how will you determine if the water has frozen? You might decide to insert a stick in each container at the start of the experiment. Your operational definition of "frozen" would be the time at which the stick can no longer move.

EXPERIMENTAL PROCEDURE

1. *Fill 3 containers with 300 milliliters of cold tap water.*
2. *Add 10 grams of salt to Container 1; stir. Add 20 grams of salt to Container 2; stir. Add no salt to Container 3.*
3. *Place the 3 containers in a freezer.*
4. *Check the containers every 15 minutes. Record your observations.*

Interpreting Data

The observations and measurements you make in an experiment are called data. At the end of an experiment, you need to analyze the data to look for any patterns or trends. Patterns often become clear if you organize your data in a data table or graph. Then think through what the data reveal. Do they support your hypothesis? Do they point out a flaw in your experiment? Do you need to collect more data?

Drawing Conclusions

A conclusion is a statement that sums up what you have learned from an experiment. When you draw a conclusion, you need to decide whether the data you collected support your hypothesis or not. You may need to repeat an experiment several times before you can draw any conclusions from it. Conclusions often lead you to pose new questions and plan new experiments to answer them.

ACTIVITY

Is a ball's bounce affected by the height from which it is dropped? Using the steps just described, plan a controlled experiment to investigate this problem.

SKILLS HANDBOOK

Interpreting Data

Emphasize the importance of collecting accurate and detailed data in a scientific investigation. Ask: **What if the students forgot to record the times that they made their observations in the experiment?** *(They wouldn't be able to completely analyze their data to draw valid conclusions.)* Then ask: **Why are data tables and graphs a good way to organize data?** *(They often make it easier to compare and analyze data.)* You may wish to have students review the Skills Handbook pages on Creating Data Tables and Graphs at this point.

Drawing Conclusions

Help students understand that a conclusion is not necessarily the end of a scientific investigation. A conclusion about one experiment may lead right into another experiment. Point out that in scientific investigations, a conclusion is a summary and explanation of the results of an experiment.

Tell students to suppose that for the Experimental Procedure described on this page, they obtained the following results: Container 1 froze in 45 minutes, Container 2 in 80 minutes, and Container 3 in 25 minutes. Ask: **What conclusions can you draw about this experiment?** *(Students might conclude that the more salt that is added to fresh water, the longer it takes the water to freeze. The hypothesis is supported, and the question of which freezes faster is answered—fresh water.)*

ACTIVITY You might wish to have students work in pairs to plan the controlled experiment. *(Students should develop a hypothesis, such as "If I increase the height from which a ball is dropped, then the height of its bounce will increase." They can test the hypothesis by dropping balls from varying heights (the manipulated variable). All trials should be done with the same kind of ball and on the same surface (constant variables). For each trial, they should measure the height of the bounce (responding variable).)* After students have designed the experiment, provide rubber balls and invite them to carry out the experiment so they can collect and interpret data and draw conclusions.

Thinking Critically

Comparing and Contrasting

Emphasize that the skill of comparing and contrasting often relies on good observation skills, as in this activity. *(Students' answers may vary. Sample answer: Similarities—both are dogs and have four legs, two eyes, two ears, brown and white fur, black noses, pink tongues; Differences—smooth coat vs. rough coat, more white fur vs. more brown fur, shorter vs. taller, long ears vs. short ears.)*

Applying Concepts

Point out to students that they apply concepts that they learn in school in their daily lives. For example, they learn to add, subtract, multiply, and divide in school. If they get a paper route or some other part-time job, they can apply those concepts. Challenge students to practice applying concepts by doing the activity. *(Antifreeze lowers the temperature at which the solution will freeze, and thus keeps the water in the radiator from freezing.)*

Interpreting Illustrations

ACTIVITY

Again, point out the need for good observation skills. Ask: **What is the difference between "interpreting illustrations" and "looking at the pictures"?** *("Interpreting illustrations" requires thorough examination of the illustration, caption, and labels, while "looking at the pictures" implies less thorough examination.)* Encourage students to thoroughly examine the diagram as they do the activity. *(Students' paragraphs may vary, but should describe the internal anatomy of an earthworm, including some of the organs in the earthworm.)*

Thinking Critically

Has a friend ever asked for your advice about a problem? If so, you may have helped your friend think through the problem in a logical way. Without knowing it, you used critical-thinking skills to help your friend. Critical thinking involves the use of reasoning and logic to solve problems or make decisions. Some critical-thinking skills are described below.

Comparing and Contrasting

When you examine two objects for similarities and differences, you are using the skill of **comparing and contrasting.** Comparing involves identifying similarities, or common characteristics. Contrasting involves identifying differences. Analyzing objects in this way can help you discover details that you might otherwise overlook.

ACTIVITY: Compare and contrast the two animals in the photo. First list all the similarities that you see. Then list all the differences.

Applying Concepts

When you use your knowledge about one situation to make sense of a similar situation, you are using the skill of **applying concepts.** Being able to transfer your knowledge from one situation to another shows that you truly understand a concept. You may use this skill in answering test questions that present different problems from the ones you've reviewed in class.

ACTIVITY: You have just learned that water takes longer to freeze when other substances are mixed into it. Use this knowledge to explain why people need a substance called antifreeze in their car's radiator in the winter.

Interpreting Illustrations

Diagrams, photographs, and maps are included in textbooks to help clarify what you read. These illustrations show processes, places, and ideas in a visual manner. The skill called **interpreting illustrations** can help you learn from these visual elements. To understand an illustration, take the time to study the illustration along with all the written information that accompanies it. Captions identify the key concepts shown in the illustration. Labels point out the important parts of a diagram or map, while keys identify the symbols used in a map.

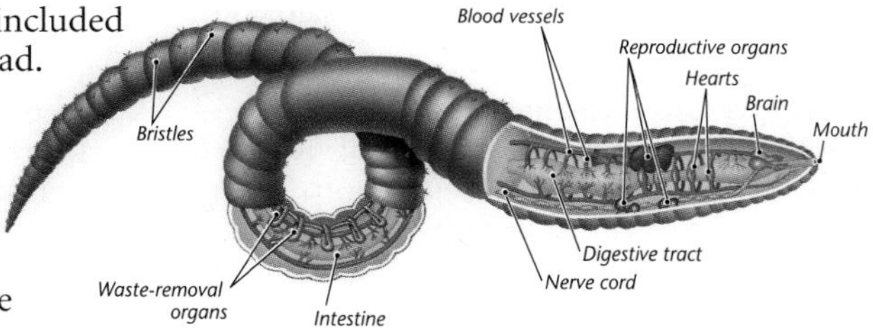

▲ Internal anatomy of an earthworm

ACTIVITY: Study the diagram above. Then write a short paragraph explaining what you have learned.

Relating Cause and Effect

If one event causes another event to occur, the two events are said to have a cause-and-effect relationship. When you determine that such a relationship exists between two events, you use a skill called **relating cause and effect.** For example, if you notice an itchy, red bump on your skin, you might infer that a mosquito bit you. The mosquito bite is the cause, and the bump is the effect.

It is important to note that two events do not necessarily have a cause-and-effect relationship just because they occur together. Scientists carry out experiments or use past experience to determine whether a cause-and-effect relationship exists.

ACTIVITY You are on a camping trip and your flashlight has stopped working. List some possible causes for the flashlight malfunction. How could you determine which cause-and-effect relationship has left you in the dark?

Making Generalizations

When you draw a conclusion about an entire group based on information about only some of the group's members, you are using a skill called **making generalizations.** For a generalization to be valid, the sample you choose must be large enough and representative of the entire group. You might, for example, put this skill to work at a farm stand if you see a sign that says, "Sample some grapes before you buy." If you sample a few sweet grapes, you may conclude that all the grapes are sweet—and purchase a large bunch.

ACTIVITY A team of scientists needs to determine whether the water in a large reservoir is safe to drink. How could they use the skill of making generalizations to help them? What should they do?

Making Judgments

When you evaluate something to decide whether it is good or bad, or right or wrong, you are using a skill called **making judgments.** For example, you make judgments when you decide to eat healthful foods or to pick up litter in a park. Before you make a judgment, you need to think through the pros and cons of a situation, and identify the values or standards that you hold.

ACTIVITY Should children and teens be required to wear helmets when bicycling? Explain why you feel the way you do.

Problem Solving

When you use critical-thinking skills to resolve an issue or decide on a course of action, you are using a skill called **problem solving.** Some problems, such as how to convert a fraction into a decimal, are straightforward. Other problems, such as figuring out why your computer has stopped working, are complex. Some complex problems can be solved using the trial and error method—try out one solution first, and if that doesn't work, try another. Other useful problem-solving strategies include making models and brainstorming possible solutions with a partner.

SKILLS HANDBOOK

Relating Cause and Effect

Emphasize that not all events that occur together have a cause-and-effect relationship. For example, tell students that you went to the grocery and your car stalled. Ask: **Is there a cause-and-effect relationship in this situation? Explain your answer.** *(No, because going to the grocery could not cause a car to stall. There must be another cause to make the car stall.)* Have students do the activity to practice relating cause and effect. *(Students should identify that the flashlight not working is the effect. Some possible causes include dead batteries, a burned-out light bulb, or a loose part.)*

Making Generalizations

Point out the importance of having a large, representative sample before making a generalization. Ask: **If you went fishing at a lake and caught three catfish, could you make the generalization that all fish in the lake are catfish? Why or why not?** *(No, because there might be other kinds of fish you didn't catch because they didn't like the bait or they may be in other parts of the lake.)* **How could you make a generalization about the kinds of fish in the lake?** *(By having a larger sample)* Have students do the activity to practice making generalizations. *(The scientists should collect and test water samples from a number of different parts of the reservoir.)*

Making Judgments

Remind students that they make a judgment almost every time they make a decision. Ask: **What steps should you follow to make a judgment?** *(Gather information, list pros and cons, analyze values, make judgment)* Invite students to do the activity, and then to share and discuss the judgments they made. *(Students' judgments will vary, but should be supported by valid reasoning. Sample answer: Children and teens should be required to wear helmets when bicycling because helmets have been proven to save lives and reduce head injuries.)*

Problem Solving

ACTIVITY

Challenge student pairs to solve a problem about a soapbox derby. Explain that their younger brother is building a car to enter in the race. The brother wants to know how to make his soapbox car go faster. After student pairs have considered the problem, have them share their ideas about solutions with the class. *(Most will probably suggest using trial and error by making small changes to the car and testing the car after each change. Some students may suggest making and manipulating a model.)*

Organizing Information

Concept Maps

ACTIVITY

Challenge students to make a concept map with at least three levels of concepts to organize information about types of transportation. All students should start with the phrase *types of transportation* at the top of the concept map. After that point, their concept maps may vary. *(For example, some students might place* private transportation *and* public transportation *at the next level, while other students might have* human-powered *and* gas-powered. *Make sure students connect the concepts with linking words. Challenge students to include cross-linkages as well.)*

Compare/ Contrast Tables

Have students make their own compare/contrast tables using two or more different sports or other activities, such as playing musical instruments. Emphasize that students should select characteristics that highlight the similarities and differences between the activities. *(Students' compare/contrast tables should include several appropriate characteristics and list information about each activity for every characteristic.)*

Organizing Information

As you read this textbook, how can you make sense of all the information it contains? Some useful tools to help you organize information are shown on this page. These tools are called *graphic organizers* because they give you a visual picture of a topic, showing at a glance how key concepts are related.

Concept Maps

Concept maps are useful tools for organizing information on broad topics. A concept map begins with a general concept and shows how it can be broken down into more specific concepts. In that way, relationships between concepts become easier to understand.

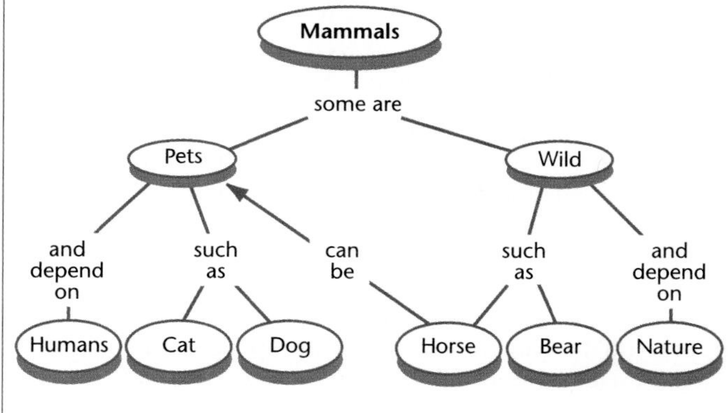

A concept map is constructed by placing concept words (usually nouns) in ovals and connecting them with linking words. Often, the most general concept word is placed at the top, and the words become more specific as you move downward. Often the linking words, which are written on a line extending between two ovals, describe the relationship between the two concepts they connect. If you follow any string of concepts and linking words down the map, it should read like a sentence.

Some concept maps include linking words that connect a concept on one branch of the map to a concept on another branch. These linking words, called cross-linkages, show more complex interrelationships among concepts.

Compare/Contrast Tables

Compare/contrast tables are useful tools for sorting out the similarities and differences between two or more items. A table provides an organized framework in which to compare items based on specific characteristics that you identify.

To create a compare/contrast table, list the items to be compared across the top of a table. Then list the characteristics that will form the basis of your comparison in the left-hand column. Complete the table by filling in information about each characteristic, first for one item and then for the other.

Characteristic	Baseball	Basketball
Number of Players	9	5
Playing Field	Baseball diamond	Basketball court
Equipment	Bat, baseball, mitts	Basket, basketball

Venn Diagrams

Another way to show similarities and differences between items is with a Venn diagram. A Venn diagram consists of two or more circles that partially overlap. Each circle represents a particular concept or idea. Common characteristics, or similarities, are written within the area of overlap between the two circles. Unique characteristics, or differences, are written in the parts of the circles outside the area of overlap.

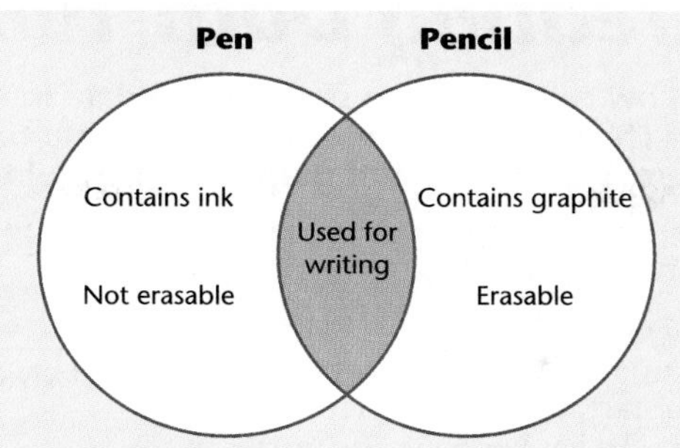

To create a Venn diagram, draw two overlapping circles. Label the circles with the names of the items being compared. Write the unique characteristics in each circle outside the area of overlap. Then write the shared characteristics within the area of overlap.

Flowcharts

A flowchart can help you understand the order in which certain events have occurred or should occur. Flowcharts are useful for outlining the stages in a process or the steps in a procedure.

To make a flowchart, write a brief description of each event in a box. Place the first event at the top of the page, followed by the second event, the third event, and so on. Then draw an arrow to connect each event to the one that occurs next.

Preparing Pasta

Boil water → Cook pasta → Drain water → Add sauce

Cycle Diagrams

A cycle diagram can be used to show a sequence of events that is continuous, or cyclical. A continuous sequence does not have an end because, when the final event is over, the first event begins again. Like a flowchart, a cycle diagram can help you understand the order of events.

To create a cycle diagram, write a brief description of each event in a box. Place one event at the top of the page in the center. Then, moving in a clockwise direction around an imaginary circle, write each event in its proper sequence. Draw arrows that connect each event to the one that occurs next, forming a continuous circle.

Steps in a Science Experiment

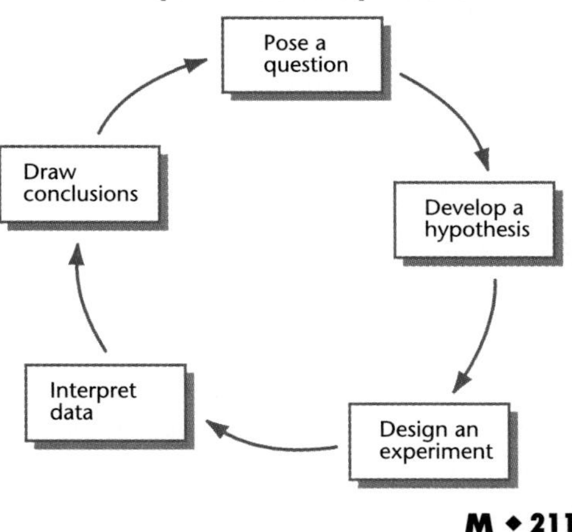

SKILLS HANDBOOK

Venn Diagrams — ACTIVITY

Students can use the same information from their compare/contrast tables to create a Venn diagram. Make sure students understand that the overlapping area of the circles is used to list similarities and the parts of the circles outside the overlap area are used to show differences. If students want to list similarities and differences among three activities, show them how to add a third circle that overlaps each of the other two circles and has an area of overlap for all three circles. *(Students' Venn diagrams will vary. Make sure they have accurately listed similarities in the overlap area and differences in the parts of the circles that do not overlap.)*

Flowcharts — ACTIVITY

Encourage students to create a flowchart to show the things they did this morning as they got ready for school. Remind students that a flowchart should show the correct order in which events occurred or should occur. *(Students' flowcharts will vary somewhat. A typical flowchart might include: got up → ate breakfast → took a shower → brushed teeth → got dressed → gathered books and homework → put on jacket.)*

Cycle Diagrams — ACTIVITY

Review that a cycle diagram shows a sequence of events that is continuous. Then challenge students to create a cycle diagram that shows how the weather changes with the seasons where they live. *(Students' cycle diagrams may vary, though most will include four steps, one for each season.)*

Creating Data Tables and Graphs

Data Tables

Have students create a data table to show how much time they spend on different activities during one week. Suggest that students first list the main activities they do every week. Then they should determine the amount of time they spend on each activity each day. Remind students to give this data table a title. *(Students' data tables will vary. A sample data table is shown below.)*

Bar Graphs

Students can use the data from their data table above to make a bar graph showing how much time they spend on different activities during a week. The vertical axis should be divided into units of time, such as hours. Remind students to label both axes and give their graph a title. *(Students' bar graphs will vary. A sample bar graph is shown below.)*

Creating Data Tables and Graphs

How can you make sense of the data in a science experiment? The first step is to organize the data to help you understand them. Data tables and graphs are helpful tools for organizing data.

Data Tables

You have gathered your materials and set up your experiment. But before you start, you need to plan a way to record what happens during the experiment. By creating a data table, you can record your observations and measurements in an orderly way.

Suppose, for example, that a scientist conducted an experiment to find out how many Calories people of different body masses burn while doing various activities. The data table shows the results.

CALORIES BURNED IN 30 MINUTES OF ACTIVITY

Body Mass	Experiment 1 Bicycling	Experiment 2 Playing Basketball	Experiment 3 Watching Television
30 kg	60 Calories	120 Calories	21 Calories
40 kg	77 Calories	164 Calories	27 Calories
50 kg	95 Calories	206 Calories	33 Calories
60 kg	114 Calories	248 Calories	38 Calories

Notice in this data table that the manipulated variable (body mass) is the heading of one column. The responding variable (for Experiment 1, the number of Calories burned while bicycling) is the heading of the next column. Additional columns were added for related experiments.

Bar Graphs

To compare how many Calories a person burns doing various activities, you could create a bar graph. A bar graph is used to display data in a number of separate, or distinct, categories. In this example, bicycling, playing basketball, and watching television are three separate categories.

To create a bar graph, follow these steps.

1. On graph paper, draw a horizontal, or *x*-, axis and a vertical, or *y*-, axis.
2. Write the names of the categories to be graphed along the horizontal axis. Include an overall label for the axis as well.
3. Label the vertical axis with the name of the responding variable. Include units of measurement. Then create a scale along the axis by marking off equally spaced numbers that cover the range of the data collected.
4. For each category, draw a solid bar using the scale on the vertical axis to determine the appropriate height. For example, for bicycling, draw the bar as high as the 60 mark on the vertical axis. Make all the bars the same width and leave equal spaces between them.
5. Add a title that describes the graph.

Calories Burned by a 30-kilogram Person in Various Activities

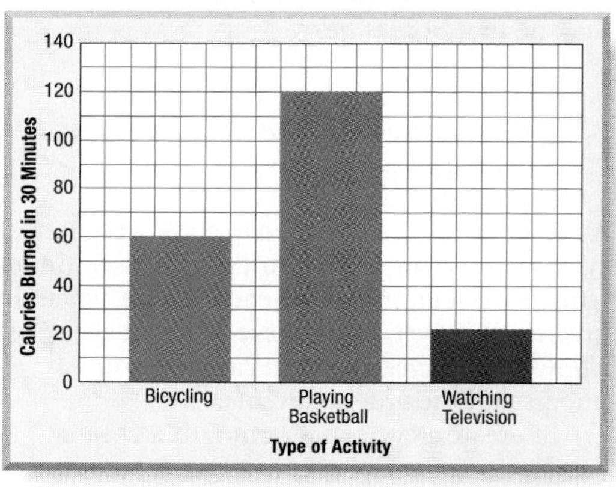

Time Spent on Different Activities in a Week

	Going to Classes	Eating Meals	Playing Soccer	Watching Television
Monday	6	2	2	0.5
Tuesday	6	1.5	1.5	1.5
Wednesday	6	2	1	2
Thursday	6	2	2	1.5
Friday	6	2	2	0.5
Saturday	0	2.5	2.5	1
Sunday	0	3	1	2

Time Spent on Different Activities in a Week

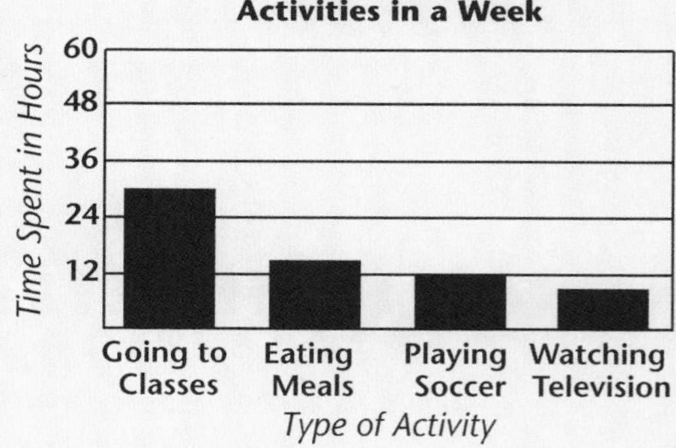

Line Graphs

To see whether a relationship exists between body mass and the number of Calories burned while bicycling, you could create a line graph. A line graph is used to display data that show how one variable (the responding variable) changes in response to another variable (the manipulated variable). You can use a line graph when your manipulated variable is *continuous,* that is, when there are other points between the ones that you tested. In this example, body mass is a continuous variable because there are other body masses between 30 and 40 kilograms (for example, 31 kilograms). Time is another example of a continuous variable.

Effect of Body Mass on Calories Burned While Bicycling

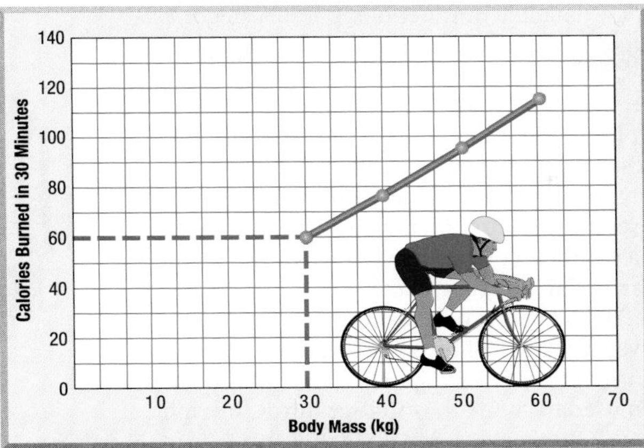

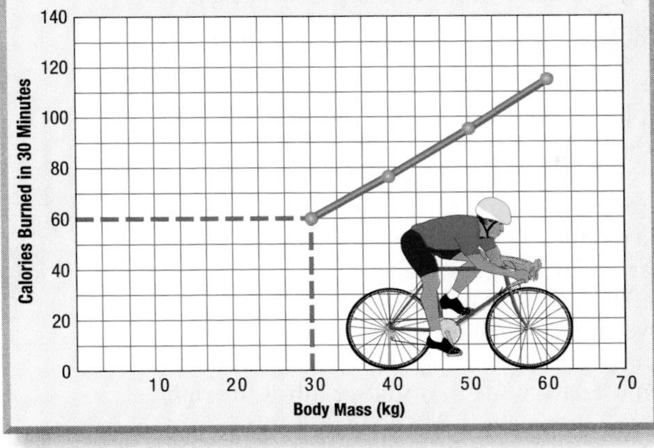

Line graphs are powerful tools because they allow you to estimate values for conditions that you did not test in the experiment. For example, you can use the line graph to estimate that a 35-kilogram person would burn 68 Calories while bicycling.

To create a line graph, follow these steps.

1. On graph paper, draw a horizontal, or *x*-, axis and a vertical, or *y*-, axis.
2. Label the horizontal axis with the name of the manipulated variable. Label the vertical axis with the name of the responding variable. Include units of measurement.
3. Create a scale on each axis by marking off equally spaced numbers that cover the range of the data collected.
4. Plot a point on the graph for each piece of data. In the line graph above, the dotted lines show how to plot the first data point (30 kilograms and 60 Calories). Draw an imaginary vertical line extending up from the horizontal axis at the 30-kilogram mark. Then draw an imaginary horizontal line extending across from the vertical axis at the 60-Calorie mark. Plot the point where the two lines intersect.
5. Connect the plotted points with a solid line. (In some cases, it may be more appropriate to draw a line that shows the general trend of the plotted points. In those cases, some of the points may fall above or below the line.)
6. Add a title that identifies the variables or relationship in the graph.

ACTIVITY

Create line graphs to display the data from Experiment 2 and Experiment 3 in the data table.

ACTIVITY

You read in the newspaper that a total of 4 centimeters of rain fell in your area in June, 2.5 centimeters fell in July, and 1.5 centimeters fell in August. What type of graph would you use to display these data? Use graph paper to create the graph.

SKILLS HANDBOOK

Line Graphs

Walk students through the steps involved in creating a line graph using the example illustrated on the page. For example, ask: **What is the label on the horizontal axis? On the vertical axis?** *(Body Mass (kg); Calories Burned in 30 Minutes)* **What scales are used on each axis?** *(3 squares per 10 kg on the x-axis and 2 squares per 20 calories on the y-axis)* **What does the second data point represent?** *(77 Calories burned for a body mass of 40 kg)* **What trend or pattern does the graph show?** *(The number of Calories burned in 30 minutes of cycling increases with body mass.)*

ACTIVITY Have students follow the steps to carry out the first activity. *(Students should make a different graph for each experiment with different y-axis scales to practice making scales appropriate for data. See sample graphs below.)*

ACTIVITY Have students carry out the second activity. *(Students should conclude that a bar graph would be best to display the data. A sample bar graph for these data is shown below.)*

Rainfall in June, July, and August

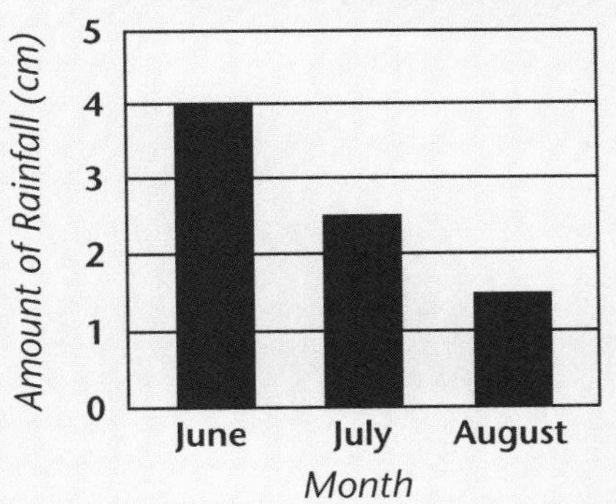

Effect of Body Mass on Calories Burned While Playing Basketball

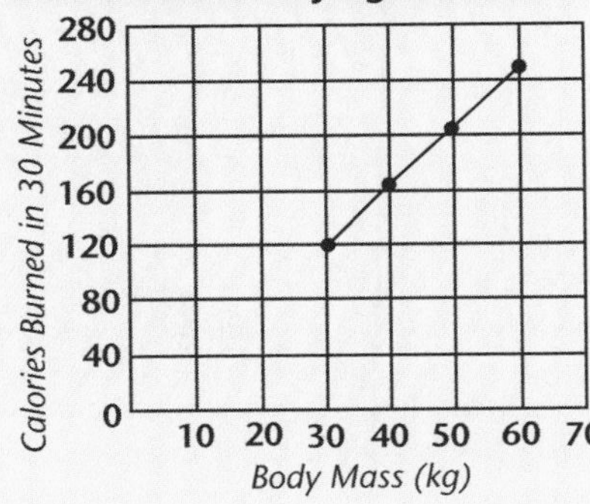

Effect of Body Mass on Calories Burned While Watching Television

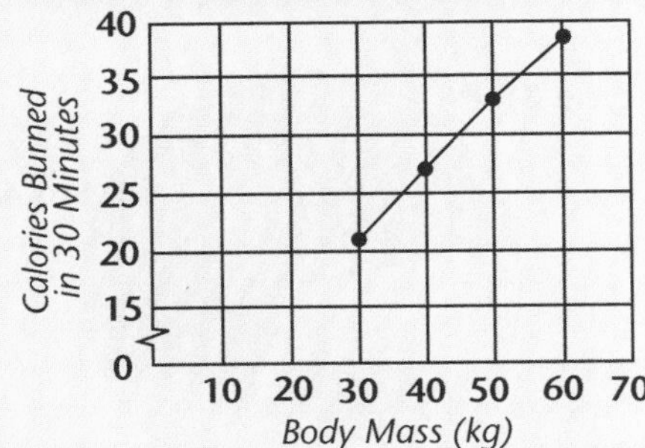

Circle Graphs

Emphasize that a circle graph has to include 100 percent of the categories for the topic being graphed. For example, ask: **Could the data in the bar graph titled "Calories Burned by a 30-kilogram Person in Various Activities" (on the previous page) be shown in a circle graph? Why or why not?** *(No, because it does not include all the possible ways a 30-kilogram person can burn Calories.)* Then walk students through the steps for making a circle graph. Help students to use a compass and a protractor. Use the protractor to illustrate that a circle has 360 degrees. Make sure students understand the mathematical calculations involved in making a circle graph.

ACTIVITY You might wish to have students work in pairs to complete the activity. *(Students' circle graphs should look like the graph below.)*

Circle Graphs

Like bar graphs, circle graphs can be used to display data in a number of separate categories. Unlike bar graphs, however, circle graphs can only be used when you have data for *all* the categories that make up a given topic. A circle graph is sometimes called a pie chart because it resembles a pie cut into slices. The pie represents the entire topic, while the slices represent the individual categories. The size of a slice indicates what percentage of the whole a particular category makes up.

The data table below shows the results of a survey in which 24 teenagers were asked to identify their favorite sport. The data were then used to create the circle graph at the right.

FAVORITE SPORTS

Sport	Number of Students
Soccer	8
Basketball	6
Bicycling	6
Swimming	4

To create a circle graph, follow these steps.

1. Use a compass to draw a circle. Mark the center of the circle with a point. Then draw a line from the center point to the top of the circle.
2. Determine the size of each "slice" by setting up a proportion where x equals the number of degrees in a slice. (NOTE: A circle contains 360 degrees.) For example, to find the number of degrees in the "soccer" slice, set up the following proportion:

$$\frac{\text{students who prefer soccer}}{\text{total number of students}} = \frac{x}{\text{total number of degrees in a circle}}$$

$$\frac{8}{24} = \frac{x}{360}$$

Cross-multiply and solve for x.

$$24x = 8 \times 360$$
$$x = 120$$

The "soccer" slice should contain 120 degrees.

Sports That Teens Prefer

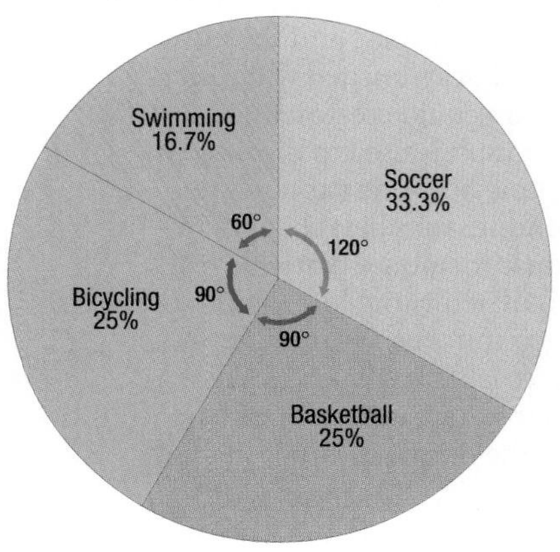

3. Use a protractor to measure the angle of the first slice, using the line you drew to the top of the circle as the 0° line. Draw a line from the center of the circle to the edge for the angle you measured.
4. Continue around the circle by measuring the size of each slice with the protractor. Start measuring from the edge of the previous slice so the wedges do not overlap. When you are done, the entire circle should be filled in.
5. Determine the percentage of the whole circle that each slice represents. To do this, divide the number of degrees in a slice by the total number of degrees in a circle (360), and multiply by 100%. For the "soccer" slice, you can find the percentage as follows:

$$\frac{120}{360} \times 100\% = 33.3\%$$

6. Use a different color to shade in each slice. Label each slice with the name of the category and with the percentage of the whole it represents.
7. Add a title to the circle graph.

ACTIVITY In a class of 28 students, 12 students take the bus to school, 10 students walk, and 6 students ride their bicycles. Create a circle graph to display these data.

Ways Students Get to School

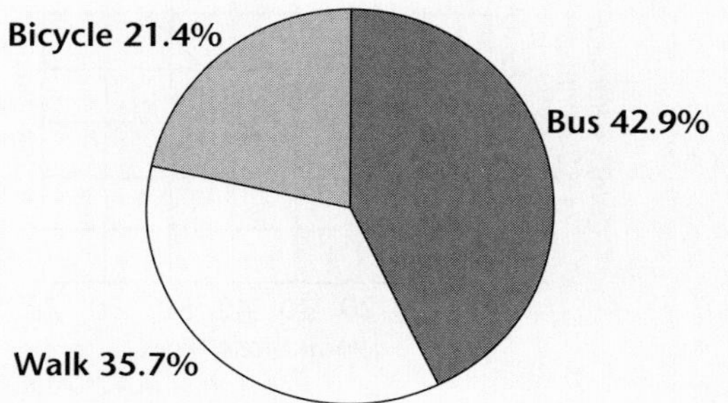

Laboratory Safety

Safety Symbols

These symbols alert you to possible dangers in the laboratory and remind you to work carefully.

Safety Goggles Always wear safety goggles to protect your eyes in any activity involving chemicals, flames or heating, or the possibility of broken glassware.

Lab Apron Wear a laboratory apron to protect your skin and clothing from damage.

Breakage You are working with materials that may be breakable, such as glass containers, glass tubing, thermometers, or funnels. Handle breakable materials with care. Do not touch broken glassware.

Heat-resistant Gloves Use an oven mitt or other hand protection when handling hot materials. Hot plates, hot glassware, or hot water can cause burns. Do not touch hot objects with your bare hands.

Heating Use a clamp or tongs to pick up hot glassware. Do not touch hot objects with your bare hands.

Sharp Object Pointed-tip scissors, scalpels, knives, needles, pins, or tacks are sharp. They can cut or puncture your skin. Always direct a sharp edge or point away from yourself and others. Use sharp instruments only as instructed.

Electric Shock Avoid the possibility of electric shock. Never use electrical equipment around water, or when the equipment is wet or your hands are wet. Be sure cords are untangled and cannot trip anyone. Disconnect the equipment when it is not in use.

Corrosive Chemical You are working with an acid or another corrosive chemical. Avoid getting it on your skin or clothing, or in your eyes. Do not inhale the vapors. Wash your hands when you are finished with the activity.

Poison Do not let any poisonous chemical come in contact with your skin, and do not inhale its vapors. Wash your hands when you are finished with the activity.

Physical Safety When an experiment involves physical activity, take precautions to avoid injuring yourself or others. Follow instructions from your teacher. Alert your teacher if there is any reason you should not participate in the activity.

Animal Safety Treat live animals with care to avoid harming the animals or yourself. Working with animal parts or preserved animals also may require caution. Wash your hands when you are finished with the activity.

Plant Safety Handle plants in the laboratory or during field work only as directed by your teacher. If you are allergic to certain plants, tell your teacher before doing an activity in which those plants are used. Avoid touching harmful plants such as poison ivy, poison oak, or poison sumac, or plants with thorns. Wash your hands when you are finished with the activity.

Flames You may be working with flames from a lab burner, candle, or matches. Tie back loose hair and clothing. Follow instructions from your teacher about lighting and extinguishing flames.

No Flames Flammable materials may be present. Make sure there are no flames, sparks, or other exposed heat sources present.

Fumes When poisonous or unpleasant vapors may be involved, work in a ventilated area. Avoid inhaling vapors directly. Only test an odor when directed to do so by your teacher, and use a wafting motion to direct the vapor toward your nose.

Disposal Chemicals and other laboratory materials used in the activity must be disposed of safely. Follow the instructions from your teacher.

Hand Washing Wash your hands thoroughly when finished with the activity. Use antibacterial soap and warm water. Lather both sides of your hands and between your fingers. Rinse well.

General Safety Awareness You may see this symbol when none of the symbols described earlier appears. In this case, follow the specific instructions provided. You may also see this symbol when you are asked to develop your own procedure in a lab. Have your teacher approve your plan before you go further.

Laboratory Safety

Laboratory safety is an essential element of a successful science class. It is important for you to emphasize laboratory safety to students. Students need to understand exactly what is safe and unsafe behavior, and what the rationale is behind each safety rule.

Review with students the Safety Symbols and Science Safety Rules listed on this and the next two pages. Then follow the safety guidelines below to ensure that your classroom will be a safe place for students to learn science.

- Post safety rules in the classroom and review them regularly with students.
- Familiarize yourself with the safety procedures for each activity before introducing it to your students.
- Review specific safety precautions with students before beginning every science activity.
- Always act as an exemplary role model by displaying safe behavior.
- Know how to use safety equipment, such as fire extinguishers and fire blankets, and always have it accessible.
- Have students practice leaving the classroom quickly and orderly to prepare them for emergencies.
- Explain to students how to use the intercom or other available means of communication to get help during an emergency.
- Never leave students unattended while they are engaged in science activities.
- Provide enough space for students to safely carry out science activities.
- Keep your classroom and all science materials in proper condition. Replace worn or broken items.
- Instruct students to report all accidents and injuries to you immediately.

Laboratory Safety

Additional tips are listed below for the Science Safety Rules discussed on these two pages. Please keep these tips in mind when you carry out science activities in your classroom.

General Precautions

- For open-ended activities like Chapter Projects, go over general safety guidelines with students. Have students submit their procedures or design plans in writing and check them for safety considerations.
- In an activity where students are directed to taste something, be sure to store the material in clean, *nonscience* containers. Distribute the material to students in *new* plastic or paper dispensables, which should be discarded after the tasting. Tasting or eating should never be done in a lab classroom.
- During physical activity, make sure students do not overexert themselves.
- Remind students to handle microscopes and telescopes with care to avoid breakage.

Heating and Fire Safety

- No flammable substances should be in use around hot plates, light bulbs, or open flames.
- Test tubes should be heated only in water baths.
- Students should be permitted to strike matches to light candles or burners *only* with strict supervision. When possible, you should light the flames, especially when working with sixth graders.
- Be sure to have proper ventilation when fumes are produced during a procedure.
- All electrical equipment used in the lab should have GFI switches.

Science Safety Rules

To prepare yourself to work safely in the laboratory, read over the following safety rules. Then read them a second time. Make sure you understand and follow each rule. Ask your teacher to explain any rules you do not understand.

Dress Code

1. To protect yourself from injuring your eyes, wear safety goggles whenever you work with chemicals, burners, glassware, or any substance that might get into your eyes. If you wear contact lenses, notify your teacher.
2. Wear a lab apron or coat whenever you work with corrosive chemicals or substances that can stain.
3. Tie back long hair to keep it away from any chemicals, flames, or equipment.
4. Remove or tie back any article of clothing or jewelry that can hang down and touch chemicals, flames, or equipment. Roll up or secure long sleeves.
5. Never wear open shoes or sandals.

General Precautions

6. Read all directions for an experiment several times before beginning the activity. Carefully follow all written and oral instructions. If you are in doubt about any part of the experiment, ask your teacher for assistance.
7. Never perform activities that are not assigned or authorized by your teacher. Obtain permission before "experimenting" on your own. Never handle any equipment unless you have specific permission.
8. Never perform lab activities without direct supervision.
9. Never eat or drink in the laboratory.
10. Keep work areas clean and tidy at all times. Bring only notebooks and lab manuals or written lab procedures to the work area. All other items, such as purses and backpacks, should be left in a designated area.
11. Do not engage in horseplay.

First Aid

12. Always report all accidents or injuries to your teacher, no matter how minor. Notify your teacher immediately about any fires.
13. Learn what to do in case of specific accidents, such as getting acid in your eyes or on your skin. (Rinse acids from your body with lots of water.)
14. Be aware of the location of the first-aid kit, but do not use it unless instructed by your teacher. In case of injury, your teacher should administer first aid. Your teacher may also send you to the school nurse or call a physician.
15. Know the location of emergency equipment, such as the fire extinguisher and fire blanket, and know how to use it.
16. Know the location of the nearest telephone and whom to contact in an emergency.

Heating and Fire Safety

17. Never use a heat source, such as a candle, burner, or hot plate, without wearing safety goggles.
18. Never heat anything unless instructed to do so. A chemical that is harmless when cool may be dangerous when heated.
19. Keep all combustible materials away from flames. Never use a flame or spark near a combustible chemical.
20. Never reach across a flame.
21. Before using a laboratory burner, make sure you know proper procedures for lighting and adjusting the burner, as demonstrated by your teacher. Do not touch the burner. It may be hot. And never leave a lighted burner unattended!
22. Chemicals can splash or boil out of a heated test tube. When heating a substance in a test tube, make sure that the mouth of the tube is not pointed at you or anyone else.
23. Never heat a liquid in a closed container. The expanding gases produced may blow the container apart.
24. Before picking up a container that has been heated, hold the back of your hand near it. If you can feel heat on the back of your hand, the container is too hot to handle. Use an oven mitt to pick up a container that has been heated.

Using Chemicals Safely

- When students use both chemicals and microscopes in one activity, microscopes should be in a separate part of the room from the chemicals so that when students remove their goggles to use the microscopes, their eyes are not at risk.

Using Glassware Safely

- Use plastic containers, graduated cylinders, and beakers whenever possible. If using glass, students should wear safety goggles.
- Use only nonmercury thermometers with anti-roll protectors.
- Check all glassware periodically for chips and scratches, which can cause cuts and breakage.

216 ◆ M

Using Chemicals Safely

25. Never mix chemicals "for the fun of it." You might produce a dangerous, possibly explosive substance.
26. Never put your face near the mouth of a container that holds chemicals. Never touch, taste, or smell a chemical unless you are instructed by your teacher to do so. Many chemicals are poisonous.
27. Use only those chemicals needed in the activity. Read and double-check labels on supply bottles before removing any chemicals. Take only as much as you need. Keep all containers closed when chemicals are not being used.
28. Dispose of all chemicals as instructed by your teacher. To avoid contamination, never return chemicals to their original containers. Never simply pour chemicals or other substances into the sink or trash containers.
29. Be extra careful when working with acids or bases. Pour all chemicals over the sink or a container, not over your work surface.
30. If you are instructed to test for odors, use a wafting motion to direct the odors to your nose. Do not inhale the fumes directly from the container.
31. When mixing an acid and water, always pour the water into the container first and then add the acid to the water. Never pour water into an acid.
32. Take extreme care not to spill any material in the laboratory. Wash chemical spills and splashes immediately with plenty of water. Immediately begin rinsing with water any acids that get on your skin or clothing, and notify your teacher of any acid spill at the same time.

Using Glassware Safely

33. Never force glass tubing or thermometers into a rubber stopper or rubber tubing. Have your teacher insert the glass tubing or thermometer if required for an activity.
34. If you are using a laboratory burner, use a wire screen to protect glassware from any flame. Never heat glassware that is not thoroughly dry on the outside.
35. Keep in mind that hot glassware looks cool. Never pick up glassware without first checking to see if it is hot. Use an oven mitt. See rule 24.
36. Never use broken or chipped glassware. If glassware breaks, notify your teacher and dispose of the glassware in the proper broken-glassware container. Never handle broken glass with your bare hands.
37. Never eat or drink from lab glassware.
38. Thoroughly clean glassware before putting it away.

Using Sharp Instruments

39. Handle scalpels or other sharp instruments with extreme care. Never cut material toward you; cut away from you.
40. Immediately notify your teacher if you cut your skin when working in the laboratory.

Animal and Plant Safety

41. Never perform experiments that cause pain, discomfort, or harm to mammals, birds, reptiles, fishes, or amphibians. This rule applies at home as well as in the classroom.
42. Animals should be handled only if absolutely necessary. Your teacher will instruct you as to how to handle each animal species brought into the classroom.
43. If you know that you are allergic to certain plants, molds, or animals, tell your teacher before doing an activity in which these are used.
44. During field work, protect your skin by wearing long pants, long sleeves, socks, and closed shoes. Know how to recognize the poisonous plants and fungi in your area, as well as plants with thorns, and avoid contact with them.
45. Never eat any part of an unidentified plant or fungus.
46. Wash your hands thoroughly after handling animals or the cage containing animals. Wash your hands when you are finished with any activity involving animal parts, plants, or soil.

End-of-Experiment Rules

47. After an experiment has been completed, clean up your work area and return all equipment to its proper place.
48. Dispose of waste materials as instructed by your teacher.
49. Wash your hands after every experiment.
50. Always turn off all burners or hot plates when they are not in use. Unplug hot plates and other electrical equipment. If you used a burner, check that the gas-line valve to the burner is off as well.

Using Sharp Instruments

- Always use blunt-tip safety scissors, except when pointed-tip scissors are required.

Animal and Plant Safety

- When working with live animals or plants, check ahead of time for students who may have allergies to the specimens.
- When growing bacteria cultures, use only disposable petri dishes. After streaking, the dishes should be sealed and not opened again by students. After the lab, students should return the unopened dishes to you. Students should wash their hands with antibacterial soap.
- Two methods are recommended for the safe disposal of bacteria cultures. *First method:* Autoclave the petri dishes and discard without opening. *Second method*: If no autoclave is available, carefully open the dishes (never have a student do this) and pour full-strength bleach into the dishes and let stand for a day. Then pour the bleach from the petri dishes down a drain and flush the drain with lots of water. Tape the petri dishes back together and place in a sealed plastic bag. Wrap the plastic bag with a brown paper bag or newspaper and tape securely. Throw the sealed package in the trash. Thoroughly disinfect the work area with bleach.
- To grow mold, use a new, sealable plastic bag that is two to three times larger than the material to be placed inside. Seal the bag and tape it shut. After the bag is sealed, students should not open it. To dispose of the bag and mold culture, make a small cut near an edge of the bag and cook in a microwave oven on high setting for at least 1 minute. Discard the bag according to local ordinance, usually in the trash.
- Students should wear disposable nitrile, latex, or food-handling gloves when handling live animals or nonliving specimens.

End-of Experiment Rules

- Always have students use antibacterial soap for washing their hands.

Glossary

absolute zero The temperature at which no more energy can be removed from matter. (p. 170)

acceleration The rate at which velocity changes. (p. 34)

actual mechanical advantage The mechanical advantage that a machine provides in a real situation. (p. 115)

air resistance The fluid friction experienced by objects falling through the air. (p. 59)

Archimedes' principle The rule that the buoyant force on an object is equal to the weight of the fluid displaced by that object. (p. 91)

balanced forces Equal forces acting on an object in opposite directions. (p. 46)

Bernoulli's principle The rule that a stream of fast-moving fluid exerts less pressure than the surrounding fluid. (p. 98)

bimetallic strip A strip made of two different metals that expand at different rates. (p. 186)

boiling Vaporization that occurs on and below the surface of a liquid. (p. 184)

boiling point The temperature at which a liquid substance boils. (p. 184)

buoyant force The upward force exerted by a fluid on a submerged object. (p. 91)

Celsius scale The temperature scale on which zero and 100 are the temperatures at which water freezes and boils. (p. 169)

centripetal force A force that causes an object to move in a circle. (p. 71)

change of state The physical change of matter from one state to another. (p. 182)

chemical energy The potential energy stored in chemical bonds. (p. 144)

combustion The process of burning a fuel to produce thermal energy. (p. 187)

compound machine A device that combines two or more simple machines. (p. 128)

condensation The change from the gaseous to the liquid form of matter. (p. 185)

conduction The transfer of heat between particles within a substance. (p. 172)

conductor A material that easily transfers heat between its particles. (p. 175)

controlled experiment An experiment in which all factors except one are kept constant. (p. 207)

convection The transfer of heat by the movement of currents within a fluid. (p. 173)

convection current A current caused by the rising of heated fluid and sinking of cooled fluid. (p. 173)

density The mass of a substance contained in a unit of volume. (p. 94)

efficiency The percentage of the input work that is converted to output work. (p. 114)

elastic potential energy The energy of stretched or compressed objects. (p. 143)

electrical energy The energy of moving electric charges. (p. 145)

electromagnetic energy The energy of light and other forms of radiation. (p. 145)

energy The ability to do work or cause change. (p. 140)

energy conversion The process of changing one form of energy into another. (p. 149)

evaporation Vaporization that occurs at the surface of a liquid. (p. 184)

external combustion engine An engine powered by fuel burned outside the engine. (p. 188)

Fahrenheit scale The temperature scale on which 32 and 212 are the temperatures at which water freezes and boils. (p. 169)

fluid A substance that can easily change shape. (p. 80)

fluid friction Friction that occurs as an object moves through a fluid. (p. 57)

force A push or pull exerted on an object. (p. 44)

fossil fuels Materials such as coal that are burned to release their chemical energy. (p. 155)

free fall The motion of a falling object when the only force acting on it is gravity. (p. 58)

freezing The change from the liquid to the solid form of matter. (p. 184)

218 ◆ M

freezing point The temperature at which a substance freezes. (p. 184)

friction The force that one surface exerts on another when the two rub against each other. (p. 56)

fulcrum The fixed point around which a lever pivots. (p. 121)

G

gears Two or more wheels linked together by interlocking teeth. (p. 128)

gravitational potential energy Potential energy that depends on the height of an object. (p. 143)

gravity The force that pulls objects toward Earth. (p. 58)

H

heat Thermal energy that is transferred from one substance to another. (p. 171)

heat engine A device that converts thermal energy into mechanical energy. (p. 187)

hydraulic system A system that multiplies force by transmitting pressure from a small surface area through a confined fluid to a larger surface area. (p. 88)

hypothesis A prediction about the outcome of an experiment. (p. 206)

I

ideal mechanical advantage The mechanical advantage that a machine would have without friction. (p. 115)

inclined plane A flat surface with one end higher than the other. (p. 119)

inertia The tendency of an object to resist any change in its motion. (p. 48)

input force The force exerted on a machine. (p. 111)

insulator A material that does not easily transfer heat between its particles. (p. 175)

internal combustion engine An engine that burns fuel inside cylinders within the engine. (p. 188)

International System of Units (SI) A system of measurement based on multiples of ten and on established measures of mass, length, and time. (p. 19)

J

joule A unit of work equal to one newton-meter. (p. 109)

K

Kelvin scale The temperature scale on which zero is the temperature at which no more energy can be removed from matter. (p. 169)

kinetic energy Energy that an object has due to its motion. (p. 141)

L

law of conservation of energy The rule that energy cannot be created or destroyed. (p. 152)

law of conservation of momentum The rule that the total momentum of objects in an interaction does not change. (p. 68)

lever A rigid object that pivots about a fixed point. (p. 121)

M

machine A device that changes the amount of force exerted or the direction in which force is exerted. (p. 110)

manipulated variable The one factor that a scientist changes during an experiment. (p. 207)

mass The amount of matter in an object. (p. 49)

mechanical advantage The number of times the force exerted on a machine is multiplied by the machine. (p. 113)

mechanical energy Kinetic or potential energy associated with the motion or position of an object. (p. 144)

melting The change from the solid to the liquid form of matter. (p. 183)

melting point The temperature at which a substance melts. (p. 183)

meter The basic SI unit of length. (p. 19)

momentum The product of an object's mass and velocity. (p. 67)

motion The state in which one object's distance from another is changing. (p. 17)

N

net force The overall force on an object when all the individual forces acting on an object are added together. (p. 46)

M ◆ 219

newton A unit of measure that equals the force required to accelerate one kilogram of mass at 1 meter per second per second. (p. 53)

nuclear energy The potential energy stored in the nucleus of an atom. (p. 145)

operational definition A statement that describes how a variable is to be measured or a term is to be defined. (p. 207)

output force The force exerted on an object by a machine. (p. 111)

pascal A unit of pressure equal to one newton per square meter. (p. 79)

Pascal's principle The rule that when force is applied to a confined fluid, the increase in pressure is transmitted equally to all parts of the fluid. (p. 87)

plate One of the major pieces that make up Earth's upper layer. (p. 28)

potential energy Energy that is stored and held in readiness. (p. 142)

power The rate at which work is done. (p. 158)

pressure The force exerted on a surface divided by the total area over which the force is exerted. (p. 79)

projectile An object that is thrown. (p. 58)

pulley A grooved wheel around which is wrapped a rope, chain, or cable. (p. 126)

radiation The transfer of energy by electromagnetic waves. (p. 174)

reference point A place or object used for comparison to determine if an object is in motion. (p. 18)

responding variable The factor that changes as a result of changes to the manipulated variable in an experiment. (p. 207)

rolling friction Friction that occurs when an object rolls over a surface. (p. 57)

S

satellite Any object that travels around another object in space. (p. 71)

screw An inclined plane wrapped around a central cylinder to form a spiral. (p. 121)

sliding friction Friction that occurs when one solid surface slides over another. (p. 57)

specific heat The amount of heat required to raise the temperature of one kilogram of a substance by one kelvin. (p. 176)

speed The distance an object travels in one unit of time. (p. 20)

states The three forms (solid, liquid, and gas) in which matter exists. (p. 182)

temperature The measure of the average kinetic energy of the particles in a substance. (p. 168)

tendon A band of connective tissue that attaches a muscle to a bone. (p. 132)

terminal velocity The maximum velocity a falling object can achieve. (p. 59)

thermal energy The total energy of the particles in an object. (p. 144)

thermal expansion The expansion of matter when it is heated. (p. 185)

thermostat A device that regulates temperature. (p. 186)

unbalanced force A nonzero net force, which changes an object's motion. (p. 46)

vaporization The change from the liquid to the gaseous form of matter. (p. 184)

variable Any factor that can change in an experiment. (p. 207)

velocity Speed in a given direction. (p. 23)

wedge An inclined plane that moves. (p. 120)

weight The force of gravity on an object at the surface of a planet. (p. 59)

wheel and axle Two circular or cylindrical objects that are fastened together and rotate about a common axis. (p. 124)

work Force exerted on an object that causes it to move. (p. 106)

220 ◆ M

Index

M ◆ 221

222 ◆ M

M ◆ 223

Acknowledgments

Illustration

John Edwards & Associates: 68–69, 72, 81, 88 t, 142, 149, 188, 189
GeoSystems Global Corporation: 29
Andrea Golden: 10, 194
Martucci Design: 24, 38, 79, 96
Matt Mayerchak: 40, 102, 164, 192
Morgan Cain & Associates: 60, 71, 75, 80, 84, 87, 88 b, 91, 94, 100, 103, 111, 120, 121, 126, 127, 137, 168, 169, 173, 176, 182, 183, 186, 190, 193, 195, 196
Ortelius Design Inc.: 30–31, 124–125
Matthew Pippin: 156
Rob Schuster: 99
J/B Woolsey Associates: 11, 13, 41, 59, 65, 89, 99 insets

Photography

Photo Research Sue McDermott

Cover Image Judy White/Picture Perfect

Nature of Science
Page 10, Brian Smale/Discover Magazine; **11,** Stephen G. Maka/DRK Photo; **12,** Brian Smale/Discover Magazine; **12 inset,** Helen Ghiradella/Discover Magazine.

Chapter 1
Pages 14–15, Frans Lanting/Minden Pictures; **16 t,** Richard Haynes; **16 bl,** Bob Abraham/The Stock Market; **16 br,** Roy Morsch/The Stock Market; **17 t,** D. Roundtree/The Image Bank; **17 b,** Steve Maslowshi/Photo Researchers; **18,** NASA; **19 l,** Chuck Zsymanski/International Stock; **19 r,** Robert Maier/Animals Animals; **20,** Mike Agliolo/International Stock; **21,** John Kelly/The Image Bank; **22,** National Motor Museum, Beaulieu, England; **23 t,** Topham/The Image Works; **23 b,** David Barnes/The Stock Market; **24,** Marc Romanelli/The Image Bank; **25,** A.T. Willet/The Image Bank; **27,** Richard Haynes; **28 t,** Russ Lappa; **28 b,** Image Makers/The Image Bank; **31,** Richard Haynes; **32,** Richard Haynes; **33,** Lou Jones/The Image Bank; **34 t,** Richard Haynes; **34 b,** Mike Hewitt/Allsport; **35 l,** Tracy Frankel/The Image Bank; **35 m,** Tim DeFrisco/Allsport; **35 r,** Yann Guichaoua/Agence Vandystadt/ Allsport; **36 t,** Addison Geary/Stock Boston; **36 inset,** Corel Corp.; **37,** Corel Corp.; **39 t,** Robert Maier/Animals Animals; **39 b,** Mike Agliolo/International Stock.

Chapter 2
Pages 42–43, David Stoecklein/The Stock Market; **44 t,** Russ Lappa; **44 bl,** Calimberti/Liaison International; **44 br,** Alain Ernoult/The Image Bank; **45,** Richard Thom/Visuals Unlimited; **46,** Elisabeth Weiland/Photo Researchers; **47 all,** Richard Haynes; **48,** Bilderberg/The Stock Market; **49 t,** Russ Lappa; **49 b, 51, 52,** Richard Haynes; **54,** Richard Haynes; **55,** Russ Lappa; **56 t,** Jan Hinsch/Science Photo Library/Photo Researchers; **56 b,** B & C Alexander/Photo Researchers; **57 tl,** The Photo Works/Photo Researchers; **57 tr,** Welzenbach/The Stock Market; **57 b,** Russ Lappa; **58 t,** Jack Novak/Superstock; **58 bl,** Megna/Peticolas/Fundamental Photographs; **58br,** Richard Megna/ Fundamental Photographs; **61,** NASA; **62,** Richard Haynes; **63,** Ken O'Donaghue; **64 t,** Richard Haynes; **64 b,** Ed Young/Science Photo Library/Photo Researchers; **65,** Bob Woodward/The Stock Market; **66 l,** Syracuse/Dick Blume/The Image Works; **66 r,** Michael Devin Daly/The Stock Market; **68,** Russ Lappa; **70 t,** Richard Haynes; **70 b,** Corel Corp.; **71,** Jeff Hunter/The Image Bank; **73,** Superstock.

Chapter 3
Pages 76–77, Rana Clamitans/Visuals Unlimited; **78 t,** Richard Haynes; **78 bl,** Chlaus Lotscher/ Stock Boston; **78 br,** Milton Feinberg/Stock Boston; **82 l, 82 r,** Richard Megna/Fundamental Photographs; **83,** Russ Lappa; **84,** Benn Mitchell/The Image Bank; **85,** Russ Lappa; **86 t,** Richard Haynes; **86 b,** Chris Sheridan/ Monkmeyer; **89 l,** Stuart Westmorland/Photo Researchers; **89 inset,** Andrew Mertiner/Photo Researchers; **90 t,** Russ Lappa; **90 b,** Ken Marshall/Madison Press Limited; **91,** Russ Lappa; **93,** Richard Haynes; **94,** Russ Lappa; **95,** Runk/Schoenberger/Grant Heilman Photography, Inc.; **97 t,** Richard Haynes; **97 b,** Mercury Archives/The Image Bank; **98 t,** Richard Haynes; **98 b,** Patti McConville/The Image Bank; **100 t,** Russ Lappa; **100 b,** Richard Haynes; **101 tl,** Chlaus Lotscher/ Stock Boston; **101 tr,** Milton Feinberg/Stock Boston; **101 b,** Mercury Archives/The Image Bank.

Chapter 4
Pages 104–105, Belinda Banks/Tony Stone Images; **106 all,** Richard Haynes; **107 t,** David A. Jentz/Photo Network; **107 b,** Fotopic/Omni-Photo Communications; **109,** Stephen McBrady/Photo Edit; **110 t,** Richard Haynes; **110 b,** Skjold/Photo Edit; **111,** Skjold/Photo Edit; **112,** Siegfried Tauquer/Leo De Wys; **113 t,** David Young-Wolff/Photo Edit; **113 b,** Richard Haynes; **114,** Russ Lappa; **117,** Richard Haynes; **118 t,** Richard Haynes; **118 b,** Russ Lappa; **119,** John Akhtar/Vivid Images Phtg., Inc.; **120 t,** Tony Freeman/Photo Edit; **120 b, 121,** Russ Lappa; **122 t,** Museum of Modern Art, New York/©FPG International 1991; **123 t,** Russ Lappa; **123 l,** Jerry Wachter/Photo Researchers; **123 r,** Elliot Smith/International Stock; **124 t,** Sylvain Grandadam/Tony Stone Images; **124 b,** Gerard Champion/The Image Bank; **125 t,** Jeffrey Aaronson/Network Aspen; **125 r,** G.B. Archives/Sygma; **126,** John Elk/Stock Boston; **128 t,** David R. Frazier; **128 b,** Tony Freeman/Photo Edit; **129,** Jeff Smith/The Image Bank; **130,** Cleo Freelance Photo/New England Stock; **131,** Richard Haynes; **132,** Russ Lappa; **133 all,** Richard Haynes; **134 t,** Ken Karp; **134 m, b,** Richard Haynes; **135,** Tony Freeman/Photo Edit.

Chapter 5
Pages 138–139, Chris Rogers/The Stock Market; **140 t,** Richard Haynes; **140 b,** Charles Doswell III/Tony Stone Images; **141,** Zigy Kaluzny/Tony Stone Images; **143,** J. MacPherson/The Stock Market; **144 l,** John Shaw/Tom Stack & Associates; **144 m,** Paul Silverman/Fundamental Photographs; **144 r,** Daniel Cox/Allstock/PNI; **144–145,** James Balog/Tony Stone Images; **145 t,** William L. Wantland/Tom Stack & Associates; **145 b,** Howard Sochurek/The Stock Market; **146, 147, 148 t,** Richard Haynes; **148 b,** Ken Straiton/The Stock Market; **150 t,** Dr, Harold E. Edgerton/The Harold E. Edgerton 1992 Trust; **150 b,** Jon Chomitz; **151 l,** Richard Megna/Fundamental Photographs; **151 r,** Russ Lappa; **152,** "Waterfall" by M. C. Escher, ©1998, Cordon Art-Baarn-Holland, All Rights Reserved; **153,** Courtesy of the Archives, California Institute of Technology; **154 t,** Russ Lappa; **154 b,** Ludek Pesek/Photo Researchers; **155,** Bryan Peterson/The Stock Market; **158,** Russ Lappa; **159,** Bill Bachmann/Photo Researchers; **161,** Richard Haynes; **162,** The Granger Collection, NY; **163 t,** J. MacPherson/The Stock Market; **163 b,** Dr, Harold E. Edgerton/The Harold E. Edgerton 1992 Trust; **165,** Globus, Holway & Lobel/The Stock Market.

Chapter 6
Pages 166–167, Alfred Pasieka/Peter Arnold; **168, 170, 171 t,** Russ Lappa; **171 b,** Michael Mancuso/Omni-Photo Communications; **172,** Stephen L. Saks/Photo Researchers; **173,** Ken O'Donaghue; **174 t,** Tom Campbell/Gamma-Liaison; **174 b,** Richard Haynes; **175 l,** Wayne Lynch/DRK Photo; **175 r,** Gay Bumgarner/TSI; **177,** Mike Mazzaschi/Stock Boston; **179,** Richard Haynes; **180,** Andy Sacks/TSI; **181 t,** Richard Haynes; **181 b,** Wayne Eastep/TSI; **182 tl,** Runk/Schoenberger/Grant Heilman Photography; **182 tr,** Jack Reznicki/The Stock Market; **182 bl,** Jan Halaska/Photo Researchers; **184,** R. Knolan Benfield, Jr./Visuals Unlimited; **185,** Richard Choy/Peter Arnold, Inc.; **187 t,** Richard Haynes; **187 b,** Larry Ulrich/DRK Photo; **189,** Xenophon A. Beake/The Stock Market; **191,** Wayne Lynch/DRK Photo.

Interdisciplinary Exploration
Page 194 t, IFA/Peter Arnold; **194–195 m,** John Higginson/TSI; **194–195 b** Chris Warren /International Stock; **196–197,** Bob Kramer/Stock Boston; **197 t,** Joseph Pobereskin/TSI; **197 b,** Richard Haynes; **198 tl, 198 b,** Corbis-Bettmann; **198 tm, 198 tr,** The Granger Collection, NY; **199,** Corbis-Bettmann; **200–201,** Richard Weiss/Peter Arnold.

Skills Handbook
Page 202, Mike Moreland/Photo Network; **203 t,** Foodpix; **203 m,** Richard Haynes; **203 b,** Russ Lappa; **206,** Richard Haynes; **208,** Ron Kimball; **209,** Renee Lynn/Photo Researchers.

224 ◆ M